The SLL Lighting Handbook

Corrigenda

Page 344: Table 26.5: row 1, column 3: class P1 value for minimum maintained horizontal illuminance has been amended to 3 lx in line with BS EN 13201-2: 2015.

The Society of
Light and Lighting

222 Balham High Road, London SW12 9BS
+44 (0)20 8675 5211
www.cibse.org

© November 2018 The Society of Light and Lighting

PDF amended to incorporate correction to Table 26.5 (page 344)
Reprinted January 2020 incorporating correction to Table 26.5 (page 344)

The Society is part of CIBSE, which is a registered charity, number 278104.

ISBN 978-1-912034-41-3 (book)
ISBN 978-1-912034-42-0 (PDF)

Design, layout and typesetting by CIBSE Publications

Printed in England on FSC paper by Page Bros. (Norwich) Ltd., Norwich, Norfolk NR6 6SA

Note from the publisher

This publication is primarily intended to give guidance. It is not intended to be exhaustive or definitive and it will be necessary for users of the guidance given to exercise their own professional judgement when deciding whether to abide by or depart from it.

Any commercial products depicted, mentioned or described within this publication are included for the purposes of illustration only and their inclusion does not constitute endorsement or recommendation by the Society.

Foreword by the CIBSE President

Lighting forms a vital part of our built environment, allowing us to work well, to see the buildings and spaces around us at night and to escape safely from buildings when the need arises. Today as part of the Chartered Institution of Building Services Engineers, the Society of Light and Lighting offers the strength of a chartered professional institution with the freedom to serve the world of light and lighting without being restricted solely to engineering.

The interdependency of disciplines such as daylighting, façade design, lighting technology and digital engineering mean that knowledge must be connected and transferred seamlessly, whether it be from the CIBSE Knowledge Portal, the latest research insight from our internationally acclaimed journal *Lighting Research and Technology*, or the *SLL Lighting Handbook*, the first-stop for anyone seeking information on lighting.

The Chartered Institution of Building Services Engineers (CIBSE) has its origins in the final years of the Victorian era when technical solutions to building comfort were emerging. Its origins were from two learned institutions: the Institution of Heating and Ventilating Engineers, founded in 1897, and the Illuminating Engineering Society, founded 1909. By Royal Charter, these two institutions were amalgamated in 1976.

The Society of Light and Lighting's *Handbook* provides a strong emphasis on lighting's role in the built environment as an integral part of a low-energy and sustainable future.

Stephen Lisk FCIBSE FSLL
CIBSE President

Foreword by the president of the Society of Light and Lighting

As president of the Society of Light and Lighting (SLL) it gives me great pleasure to introduce you to this brand-new edition of the *SLL Lighting Handbook*. This new edition has been completely rewritten and expanded giving even further information on lighting design, technology and the application of light in various situations both interior and exterior.

The *SLL Lighting Handbook* gives a thorough overview of all the items you may need to consider in the application of lighting, bridging links with the *SLL Code for Lighting* and the various detailed Lighting Guides published by the Society.

Since its release in 2009, the original edition of the *Handbook* has been in easy reach of my desk, acting as a first point of reference in my day-to-day work, and I look forward to using this revised edition to the same extent.

So be you a practitioner of light, student or working in a related field, I am certain this all new edition of the *SLL Lighting Handbook* will be useful in any lighting activities you undertake.

Iain Carlile MSLL
SLL President

Preface

The first edition of the *SLL Lighting Handbook* was produced in 2009 to celebrate the centenary of the Society of Light and Lighting. It was well received by our members and the wider international lighting community and so it was decided to create an expanded edition to build on its success.

Where the first edition consisted of twenty-three chapters, this edition has thirty-four, plus four appendices, making it some 50% bigger. The old chapters on light and on vision have been removed, as it was felt they would sit better amongst the fundamentals of lighting covered in the *SLL Code for Lighting*, which is also being revised.

This new edition has its chapters grouped in three sections. The first covers various design aspects of lighting, the second covers important areas of lighting technology and the third a big section covering specific applications in the field of interior and exterior lighting. With this range it is hoped that the *Handbook* will guide the reader from initial design decisions, through selection of appropriate technical solutions, and then on to detail design and finally commissioning and handover of a successful lighting scheme.

I give a great deal of thanks and appreciation to the large number of the Society's Members and their employers listed below, who generously contributed their time to write, review and variously contribute to this *Handbook*.

Paul Ruffles BSc CEng HonFSLL FCIBSE
Project Manager and Editor-in-Chief

Chapter authors and principal contributors

Lou Bedocs (Thorn Lighting)
Richard Beesley (Chief Technology Officer, Mackwell)
Nicholas Bukorović (Head of M&E Engineering, FBW Group)
Benedict Cadbury (Lampholder Lighting Design)
Richard Caple (Thorlux Lighting)
Gerard Harbers (Xicato)
Dan Hodgson (Lighting Applications Director, ACDC)
David Holmes (Consultant)
Andy Hughes (Senior Manager, Zumtobel Group)
Reinhard Lecheler (Senior Director, R&D Lighting Electronics, Osram GmbH)
Paul Littlefair (BRE)
Iain Macrae (Consultant)
Dominic Mayrick (Partner, Hoare Lea)
Keith Miller (Director, GIA Equation)
Nigel Monaghan (Chief Lighting Engineer, ASD Lighting)
Sophie Parry (Key Account Manager, Zumtobel Group)
Simon Robinson (Technical Director, WSP)
Paul Ruffles (Lighting Design & Technology)
Jonathan Rush (Partner, Hoare Lea)
Iain Ruxton (Design Associate, Spiers and Major)
Mike Simpson (Design Lead — Lighting Design, Philips Lighting)
Peter Thorns (Thorn Lighting Ltd.)

Cosmin Ticleanu (BRE)
Alan Tulla (Alan Tulla Lighting)
Ruth Kelly Waskett (Principal Daylight Designer, Hoare Lea)

Contributors and reviewers
Pavlina Akritas (Associate, Arup)
Panos Andrikopoulos (Senior Lighting Scientist, ACT Lighting Design)
John Aston (Consultant)
Michael Attard (Managing Director, Ridi Lighting)
Lawrence Barling (Senior Technical Manager, Lighting Industry Association)
Harry Barnitt (whilst with Sill Lighting)
Andrew Bissell (Director, Light4)
Tim Bowes (Whitecroft Lighting)
David Burton (Principal Engineering Leader — Building Services, Rail for London)
Iain Carlile (Associate, dpa lighting consultants)
Arfon Davies (Director, Arup)
Densel Davy (Nottinghamshire County Council)
Jason Ford (Technical Manager, Osram Ltd.)
Steve Fotios (Professor of Lighting and Visual Perception, University of Sheffield)
Allan Howard (WSP)
Kevin Kelly (Emeritus Researcher, Technological University Dublin)
Fabien Le Dem (Arup)
Peter Le Manquais (WILA Lighting Ltd.)
Mark Lissauer (Projects Director, Franklite Ltd.)
Helen Loomes (Business Development Director, TRILUX Lighting)
Nick MacLiammoir (Arup)
David Mooney (Associate, Atkins)
Saba Napoletano (Marketing Services Manager, iGuzzini Middle East)
Rachael Nicholls (Senior Designer, dpa lighting consultants)
Walter Parmiani (Principal Engineer for International Standards, UL International Ltd.)
Liz Peck (LPA Lighting)
Peter Phillipson (Principal, Future Group Lighting Design)
Tony Price (Vanguardia Ltd.)
Peter Raynham (UCL Institute for Environmental Design and Engineering)
Roger Sexton (VP Specifier Service, Xicato)
Jeff Shaw (Associate Director, Arup)
Jim Shove (Fagerhult)
Mike Smith (Director, BSRIA)
Manny Stone (MID Lighting)
Chris Tiernan (ERCO Lighting)
Karen van Creveld (Karen van Creveld Lighting Design)
Mark Sutton Vane (Director, Sutton Vane Associates)
Chris Watts (Safety Consultant)
Barrie Wilde (Lighting Designer, The Light Studio)

Acknowledgements
The Society gratefully acknowledges any contributors that have been inadvertently omitted
from the above lists and the many individuals and organisations that have provided photographs
and/or permission to reproduce photographs.

Project Manager and Editor-in-Chief

Paul Ruffles (Lighting Design and Technology)

Technical Secretary

John Fitzpatrick

Editor

Ken Butcher

SLL Secretary

Brendan Keely

CIBSE Editorial Manager

Ken Butcher

CIBSE Head of Knowledge

Nicholas Peake

Contents

Part 1: Fundamentals

Chapter 1: Lighting design process

1.1	Objectives		1
1.2	People		1
	1.2.1	Activity	1
	1.2.2	Experience	1
	1.2.3	Wellbeing	2
1.3	Issues		2
	1.3.1	Amenity (function)	2
	1.3.2	Ambience (experience)	3
	1.3.3	Legibility (understanding)	3
	1.3.4	Image (identity)	3
	1.3.5	Accessibility (inclusive design)	4
	1.3.6	Safety	4
	1.3.7	Security	4
	1.3.8	Cost (value)	4
	1.3.9	'Buildability'	4
	1.3.10	Maintenance	4
	1.3.11	Technology	5
	1.3.12	Sustainability	5
1.4	Constraints		6
	1.4.1	Legislation	6
	1.4.2	Standards	7
	1.4.3	Accreditations and assessments	8
1.5	Process		8
	1.5.1	Brief	8
	1.5.2	Analysis	9
	1.5.3	Concept design	9
	1.5.4	Technical design	10
	1.5.5	Construction	14
	1.5.6	Handover and post-occupancy	14
References			15

Chapter 2: Daylighting

2.1	The benefits of daylight		16
	2.1.1	Energy use	16
	2.1.2	Aesthetics	16
	2.1.3	Occupant health and wellbeing	16
	2.1.4	View out	17
2.2	The need to control daylight		17
	2.2.1	Glare from windows	17
	2.2.2	Overheating	18
	2.2.3	Privacy and security	18
2.3	Shading		19
	2.3.1	Solar shading	19
	2.3.2	Glare control	20
	2.3.3	Glazing-based shading solutions	21
2.4	Assessment of daylight quantity		21
	2.4.1	Daylight availability	21
	2.4.2	Predicting daylight quantity	22

	2.4.3	No sky line	23
	2.4.4	Limitations of daylight factor	24
	2.4.5	Estimation of annual electrical lighting requirements	24
2.5	**Daylighting solutions**		**24**
	2.5.1	Windows	24
	2.5.2	Rooflights	26
	2.5.3	Glazed streets, courtyards and atria	26
	2.5.4	Remote distribution	27
2.6	**Maintenance considerations**		**28**
2.7	**Conclusion**		**28**
2.8	**Further reading**		**28**
References			**29**

Chapter 3: Emergency lighting

3.1	**Legislation and standards**		**30**
3.2	**Types of emergency lighting**		**31**
	3.2.1	Emergency escape lighting	32
	3.2.2	Emergency safety lighting	36
	3.2.3	Standby lighting	36
3.3	**Design approaches**		**36**
3.4	**Emergency lighting equipment**		**37**
	3.4.1	Power sources	37
	3.4.2	Circuits	38
	3.4.3	Luminaires	40
	3.4.4	Luminaire classification	41
	3.4.5	Light sources	41
	3.4.6	Unpowered light sources	42
3.5	**Scheme planning**		**42**
	3.5.1	Risk assessment	42
	3.5.2	Planning sequence	43
3.6	**Installation, testing and maintenance**		**46**
	3.6.1	Installation	47
	3.6.2	Maintenance and inspection	47
	3.6.3	Documentation	48
	3.6.4	Commissioning and certification	48
	3.6.5	Completion certificate	49
References			**50**

Chapter 4: Design ethos

4.1	**Introduction**		**53**
4.2	**The CIBSE Code of Conduct**		**54**
4.3	**Professional standards and the Bribery Act**		**55**
	4.3.1	The Act	56
	4.3.2	Conduct during tendering or negotiations	56
4.4	**Professional standards and tendering procedures**		**56**
	4.4.1	Principles	57
	4.4.2	Expectations	57
4.5	**The use of, responsibilities for, and assessing of 'equal and approved' products**		**58**
	4.5.1	Who reviews any alternative products submitted?	58
	4.5.2	What must be checked?	58
4.6	**Sustainability**		**60**
	4.6.1	Avoiding over-lighting	60
	4.6.2	Maintenance factor	60

4.6.3	Achieving correct control	61
4.6.4	Achieving a ranking in BREAM, LEED or similar energy rating systems	61
4.6.5	Embodied energy	61
4.6.6	End of life recycling	62
References		62

Chapter 5: Coordination with other services

5.1	Introduction	63
5.2	Hierarchy of services in ceiling voids	63
5.2.1	Drainage systems	64
5.2.2	Ventilation ducts and grills	64
5.2.3	Sprinkler systems	64
5.2.4	Fire alarm equipment	64
5.2.5	Power and data wiring	65
5.3	Coordinating the ceiling void	65
5.4	Integration with air conditioning systems	66
5.4.1	Cooling methods	66
5.4.2	Centralised cooling systems	66
5.4.3	Fan coil units	67
5.4.4	The natural cycle	67
5.4.5	Chilled beams	67
5.4.6	Air handling luminaires	68
5.4.7	Integrated chilled beams	68
5.4.8	Impact on lighting	69
References		70

Part 2: Technology

Chapter 6: Light sources

6.1	Electric lamp characteristics	71
6.1.1	Luminous flux	71
6.1.2	Power demand	71
6.1.3	Luminous efficacy	71
6.1.4	Lumen maintenance	72
6.1.5	Life	72
6.1.6	Colour properties	73
6.1.7	Run-up time	73
6.1.8	Restrike time	74
6.1.9	Other factors	74
6.2	Electric light	75
6.2.1	Light emitting diodes	75
6.2.2	Tungsten	78
6.2.3	Tungsten halogen	79
6.2.4	Fluorescent	80
6.2.5	Metal halide	83
6.2.6	Low-pressure sodium	86
6.2.7	High-pressure sodium	87
6.2.8	Induction	90
6.2.9	Electroluminescent	91
6.2.10	Summary of lamp characteristics	91
6.3	Gas lighting	93
6.4	Production of radiation	93
6.4.1	Incandescence	93
6.4.2	Electric discharges	94

	6.4.3	Electroluminescence	96
	6.4.4	Luminescence	96
	6.4.5	Radioluminescence	97
	6.4.6	Cathodoluminescence	97
	6.4.7	Chemiluminescence	97
	6.4.8	Thermoluminescence	97
6.5	Daylight		97
References			98

Chapter 7: Control gear

7.1	Control gear terminology		99
7.2	Transformers for low voltage Incandescent lamps		103
7.3	Electronic control gear for high frequency fluorescent light sources		103
7.4	Control gear for discharge lamps		104
7.5	Control gear for LED/OLED light sources		105
	7.5.1	Cable length from remote drivers	106
	7.5.2	Amplitude modulation drivers	106
	7.5.3	Constant current drivers	106
	7.5.4	Constant voltage drivers	107
	7.5.5	DMX drivers (digital multiplexing)	108
	7.5.6	Phase-cut dimmers	108
	7.5.7	Galvanic insulated 'SELV' drivers and non-insulated drivers	109
	7.5.8	Outdoor drivers	110
7.6	Control gear for emergency lighting applications		110
	7.6.1	Emergency lighting: self-contained batteries	110
	7.6.2	Emergency lighting: central battery systems	111
7.7	Control gear for circadian lighting luminaires		112
7.8	Inrush current		112
References			113

Chapter 8: Luminaires

8.1	Interior luminaire types		114
	8.1.1	Direct luminaires	114
	8.1.2	Indirect luminaires	114
	8.1.3	Direct/indirect luminaires	115
	8.1.4	Downlights	115
	8.1.5	Spotlights	116
	8.1.6	Wall washers	116
	8.1.7	Task lights	117
	8.1.8	Use for emergency lighting	117
8.2	Exterior luminaire types		117
	8.2.1	Road lighting luminaires	117
	8.2.2	Post-tops	118
	8.2.3	Secondary reflectors	119
	8.2.4	Floodlights	119
	8.2.5	Wallpacks	120
	8.2.6	Bollards and ground recessed luminaires	121
8.3	Certification and classification		121
	8.3.1	Certification	121
	8.3.2	Classification	122
References			125

Chapter 9: Power to lighting systems

| 9.1 | Introduction | | 126 |

9.2	Design process	126
9.3	Final circuit distribution	127
9.4	Conventional cabling systems	128
9.5	Modular cabling systems	128
9.6	Connection methods	129
	9.6.1 Single point connectors	129
	9.6.2 Busbar systems	130
	9.6.3 Lighting track systems	131
9.7	Distributed power and control systems	131
9.8	Direct current power supplies	131
9.9	Power over Ethernet (PoE)	132
References		133

Chapter 10: Controls

10.1	Introduction	134
10.2	Common terminology	134
	10.2.1 Manual control	134
	10.2.2 Occupancy detection: presence detection	135
	10.2.3 Occupancy detection: absence detection	136
	10.2.4 Photocells	136
10.3	Application examples	137
	10.3.1 Daylight linking	137
	10.3.2 Constant illuminance adjustment	137
10.4	Dimming and regulation	138
	10.4.1 Dimming	138
	10.4.2 Regulation	139
10.5	Basis of lighting control design	139
10.6	Lighting control for visual effects	141
10.7	Control of circadian lighting	142
10.8	Lighting control for energy efficiency	142
	10.8.1 Predicting lighting energy where lighting controls are incorporated	143
	10.8.2 Lighting Energy Numeric Indicator (LENI)	143
	10.8.3 Typical step by step LENI calculation based on the Quick Method	146
10.9	Automatic testing and monitoring of emergency lighting	147
10.10	Commissioning and handover	148
References		149

Part 3: Applications

Chapter 11: Common building areas

11.1	Introduction	151
11.2	Entrance halls	151
11.3	Reception desk	152
11.4	Atria	152
11.5	Corridors	153
11.6	Waiting areas	155
11.7	Ramps	155
11.8	Lift lobbies	156
11.9	Staircases	156
11.10	Emergency lighting of staircases	157
11.11	Escalators	158
11.12	Toilets	158

11.13	Staff changing rooms	159
11.14	Staff showers	160
11.15	Tea points and refreshment areas	160
11.16	Sick bay/first aid room	160
11.17	Cleaners' rooms	161
11.18	Store rooms	161
11.19	Loading bays	161
11.20	Plant rooms, electrical risers and service spaces	162
References		162

Chapter 12: Offices

12.1	Functions of lighting in offices	163
12.2	Factors to be considered	163
	12.2.1 Type of work done	163
	12.2.2 Screen type	164
	12.2.3 Daylight availability	165
	12.2.4 Ceiling height	165
	12.2.5 Obstruction	166
	12.2.6 Surface finishes	166
12.3	Lighting recommendations	168
	12.3.1 Illuminances	168
	12.3.2 Light distribution	169
	12.3.3 Maximum luminance	169
	12.3.4 Discomfort glare control	170
	12.3.5 Light source colour properties	170
	12.3.6 Wellness	171
12.4	Approaches to office lighting	171
	12.4.1 Direct lighting	171
	12.4.2 Indirect lighting	172
	12.4.3 Direct/indirect lighting	173
	12.4.4 Localized lighting	174
	12.4.5 Supplementary task lighting	175
	12.4.6 Cove lighting	175
	12.4.7 Luminous ceilings	175
	12.4.8 Daylight	176
References		176

Chapter 13: Industrial premises

13.1	Functions of lighting in industrial premises	177
13.2	Factors to be considered	177
	13.2.1 Legislation and guidance	177
	13.2.2 The environment	178
	13.2.3 Daylight availability	178
	13.2.4 Need for good colour vision	179
	13.2.5 Obstruction	179
	13.2.6 Directions of view	180
	13.2.7 Access	181
	13.2.8 Rotating or reciprocating machinery	181
	13.2.9 Safety and emergency egress	182
13.3	Lighting recommendations	182
	13.3.1 Control rooms	182
	13.3.2 Storage	184
	13.3.3 Ancillary areas	186
	13.3.4 Speculative factory units	186

13.4	Approaches to industrial lighting	187
	13.4.1 General lighting	187
	13.4.2 Localized lighting	187
	13.4.3 Local lighting	187
	13.4.4 Visual inspection	188
	13.4.5 Visual aids	188
References		188

Chapter 14: Educational premises

14.1	Functions of lighting for educational premises	190
14.2	Factors to be considered	190
	14.2.1 Students' capabilities	190
	14.2.2 Daylight or electric light	191
	14.2.3 Lines of sight	191
	14.2.4 Flat or racked floor	192
	14.2.5 Suspended or open ceiling	192
	14.2.6 Presence of visual aids	192
	14.2.7 Surface finishes	192
14.3	Lighting recommendations	192
	14.3.1 Illuminance	192
	14.3.2 Illuminance uniformity	193
	14.3.3 Glare control	193
	14.3.4 Light source colour properties	194
	14.3.5 Flicker	194
	14.3.6 Control systems	195
14.4	Approaches to lighting educational premises	195
	14.4.1 Classrooms and lecture halls	195
	14.4.2 IT room	196
	14.4.3 Arts studio	197
	14.4.4 Science laboratories	197
	14.4.5 School street or atrium	197
	14.4.5 Seminar room	198
	14.4.6 Library	198
	14.4.7 Assembly hall	198
	14.4.8 Music room	199
	14.4.9 Drama studio	199
References		199

Chapter 15: Retail premises

15.1	Functions of lighting in retail premises	200
15.2	Factors to be considered	200
	15.2.1 Shop profile	200
	15.2.2 Daylight or electric light?	201
	15.2.3 Nature of merchandise	202
	15.2.4 Obstructions	202
	15.2.5 Integration with the interior design	202
	15.2.6 Self-pay terminals	203
	15.2.7 Energy	203
15.3	Lighting recommendations	203
	15.3.1 Illuminances	203
	15.3.2 Illuminance uniformity	203
	15.3.3 Luminance	204
	15.3.4 Light source colour properties	204

15.4	Approaches to retail lighting	204
	15.4.1 General lighting	204
	15.4.2 Store entrances, shop fronts and displays	205
	15.4.3 Accent lighting	206
	15.4.4 Display lighting	207
Reference		209

Chapter 16: Museums and art galleries

16.1	Functions of lighting in museums and art galleries	210
16.2	Factors to be considered	210
	16.2.1 Daylight and windows	210
	16.2.2 Conservation of exhibits	211
	16.2.4 Adaptation	212
	16.2.5 Balance	212
	16.2.6 Shadows and modelling	213
	16.2.7 Glare	213
	16.2.8 Veiling reflections and highlights	214
	16.2.9 Out of hours activities	214
	16.2.10 Security and emergency	214
	16.2.11 Maintenance	215
	16.2.12 Flexibility	215
16.3	Lighting approaches for museums and art galleries	215
	16.3.1 Wall mounted displays	215
	16.3.2 Three-dimensional displays	215
	16.3.3 Showcase lighting	216
References		217

Chapter 17: Hospitals and healthcare buildings

17.1	Functions of lighting in hospitals and healthcare facilities	218
17.2	Factors to be considered	218
	17.2.1 Daylight	218
	17.2.2 Lines of sight	218
	17.2.3 Colour rendering requirements	218
	17.2.4 Observation without disturbance to sleep	219
	17.2.5 Emergency lighting	219
	17.2.6 Luminaire safety	219
	17.2.7 Cleanliness	220
	17.2.8 Electromagnetic compatibility (EMC)	220
17.3	Approaches for the lighting of different areas in hospitals	221
	17.3.1 Entrance halls, waiting areas and lift halls	221
	17.3.2 Reception and enquiry desks	221
	17.3.3 Hospital streets and general corridors	222
	17.3.4 Changing rooms, cubicles, toilets, bath, wash and shower rooms	223
	17.3.5 Wards	223
	17.3.6 Reading lighting	227
	17.3.7 Night lighting	227
	17.3.8 Night observation lighting (watch lighting)	227
	17.3.9 Clinical areas and operating departments	227
	17.3.10 Operating theatres	228
References		229

Chapter 18: Places of worship

| 18.1 | Functions of lighting in places of worship | 230 |
| 18.2 | Factors to be considered | 230 |

	18.2.1	The illuminance of the task	230
	18.2.2	Modelling	231
	18.2.3	Daylight availability	231
	18.2.4	Lighting for people with disabilities	233
	18.2.5	Listed buildings	234
18.3		Lighting recommendations	235
	18.3.1	Areas for prayer and service	235
	18.3.2	Ancillary areas	236
	18.3.3	Multi-purpose rooms	236
18.4		Approaches to lighting for places of worship	237
	18.4.1	General lighting	237
	18.4.2	Lighting of the general surround	238
	18.4.3	Task lighting	238
	18.4.4	Architectural considerations	239
References			240

Chapter 19: Communal residential buildings

19.1		Introduction	241
19.2		Factors to be considered	241
	19.2.1	Occupants' capabilities	241
	19.2.2	Daylight	241
	19.2.3	Colour rendering and colour temperature of light sources	242
	19.2.4	Energy efficiency	242
	19.2.5	Safety	242
	19.2.6	Security	243
19.3		Lighting recommendations	244
19.4		General aspects of lighting in communal residential buildings	244
	19.4.1	Entrances	245
	19.4.2	Corridors	245
	19.4.3	Stairs	245
	19.4.4	Study bedrooms and bed-sitting rooms	246
	19.4.5	Kitchens	247
	19.4.6	Lounges	247
	19.4.7	Recreation areas	248
	19.4.8	Bathrooms	248
	19.4.9	Exterior lighting	248
	19.4.10	Lighting controls	248
19.5		Nursing and care homes	249
References			249

Chapter 20: Places of entertainment

20.1		Introduction	251
20.2		Principles of lighting	251
	20.2.1	Character and atmosphere	251
	20.2.2	Lighting and decoration	252
	20.2.3	Daylight	253
	20.2.4	Colour rendering and colour temperature	253
	20.2.5	Modelling, glare and sparkle	253
	20.2.6	Energy-efficient lamps	254
	20.2.7	Lighting controls	254
20.3		Lighting design: interior	256
	20.3.1	General design considerations	256
	20.3.2	Bars and pubs	256
20.4		Lighting design: exterior	259

	20.4.1	General considerations	259
	20.4.2	Location of luminaires	259
	20.4.3	Control	260
	20.4.4	Gardens and terraces	260
	20.4.5	External smoking areas	261
	20.4.6	Façades	261
	20.4.7	Car parks	261
20.5		**Emergency lighting**	262
20.6		**Specific types of premises**	262
	20.6.1	Restaurants	262
	20.6.2	Clubs	264
	20.6.3	Theatres and concert halls	265
References			268

Chapter 21: Courts and custodial buildings

21.1		**Courts**	269
	21.1.1	Courtrooms (Crown, Magistrates' and County)	269
	21.1.2	Defendant and witness areas	270
	21.1.3	Child witness waiting suite	270
	21.1.4	Jurors' areas	271
	21.1.5	Judges' accommodation	271
	21.1.6	Associated circulation areas	271
	21.1.7	Lighting recommendations	272
	21.1.8	Lighting control and energy efficiency	272
	21.1.9	Emergency lighting	273
21.2		**Custodial lighting**	273
	21.2.1	Prison standard cell and 'safer cell' lighting requirements	273
	21.2.2	Police cell lighting requirements	275
	21.2.3	Security and inspection areas in prisons	275
	21.2.4	Circulation and association areas in prisons	276
	21.2.5	Daylight	276
	21.2.6	Lighting recommendations	276
	21.2.7	Lighting control and energy efficiency	277
	21.2.8	Light source colour properties	277
	21.2.9	Emergency lighting	278
References			278

Chapter 22: Transport buildings

22.1		**Introduction**	279
22.2		**Identification of tasks**	279
22.3		**Design priorities and strategies**	280
	22.3.1	Orientation and safe movement	280
	22.3.2	Hazard identification	280
	22.3.3	Wayfinding	280
	22.3.4	Safety and security	280
	22.3.5	Visual adaptation	281
22.4		**Accessible design considerations**	281
22.5		**Access, installation and maintenance**	282
22.6		**Risk assessment and emergency lighting**	283
22.7		**Typical transport building areas**	284
	22.7.1	Concourses	284
	22.7.2	Check-Ins/counters/information desks	284
	22.7.3	Escalators and moving walkways	285
	22.7.4	Boarding and alighting points	286

22.8	Specific lighting requirements by transport mode	287
	22.8.1 Railways	287
	22.8.2 Airports	287
	22.8.3 Ports and harbours	289
	22.8.4 Trams and street running systems	290
	22.8.5 Bus and coach stations	291
	22.8.6 Routes and structures for bicycles	292
References		292

Chapter 23: Extreme environments

23.1	Introduction	294
23.2	Environments	294
	23.2.1 Cold and freezing environments	294
	23.2.2 Hot and humid environments	296
	23.2.3 Dusty environments	297
	23.2.4 Chemicals and chemical vapours	299
	23.2.5 Submersion: pools, ponds and water features	302
	23.2.6 Wash-down/clean rooms	305
	22.2.7 Marine (onshore, offshore and submersion)	307
	23.2.8 Vibration, impact and vandalism	308
	23.2.9 Explosive environments	311
23.3	Emergency lighting	313
23.4	Remote lighting techniques	314
	23.4.1 Projector lighting	314
	24.4.2 Panel lighting	314
	24.4.3 Light guides	314
23.5	Lamp performance charts	314
References		315

Chapter 24: Exterior workplaces

24.1	Introduction	317
24.2	Factors to be considered	317
	24.2.1 Scale	317
	24.2.2 Nature of work	317
	24.2.3 Need for good colour vision	318
	24.2.4 Obstruction	318
	24.2.5 Interference with complementary activities	318
	24.2.6 Hours of operation	319
	24.2.7 Impact on the surrounding area	319
	24.2.8 Atmospheric conditions	319
24.3	Lighting recommendations	319
	24.3.1 Illuminance and illuminance uniformity	319
	24.3.2 Glare control	319
	24.3.3 Light source colour properties	319
	24.3.4 Loading areas	320
	24.3.5 Chemical and fuel industries	321
	24.3.6 Sidings, marshalling yards and goods yards	322
24.4	Approaches to exterior workplace lighting	323
	24.4.1 High mast floodlighting	323
	24.4.2 Integrated lighting	324
	24.4.3 Localised lighting	324
References		324

Contents

Chapter 25: Exterior architectural lighting

25.1	Overview: key aspects	325
25.2	Context	325
25.3	Colour and materials	326
25.4	Contrast	328
25.5	Control	329
25.6	Global applications	330
25.7	People	331
25.8	Type of luminaire	331
	25.8.1 Position	331
	25.8.2 Shape	332
	25.8.3 Optic	332
	25.8.4 Output	332
	25.8.5 Controls	332
25.9	Type of application	333
	25.9.1 Surface mount (building)	333
	25.9.2 Recessed mount	334
	25.9.3 Surface mount (ground)	335
	25.9.4 Pole mount	336
	25.9.5 Backlit façades	336
	25.9.6 Delineation	338
References		339

Chapter 26: Roads and urban spaces

26.1	Introduction	340
26.2	Traffic routes	340
26.3	Conflict areas	342
26.4	Pedestrian crossings	343
26.5	Coordination	343
26.6	Areas adjacent to the carriageway, residential or minor roads or pedestrian streets	343
26.7	Road lighting design	344
	26.7.1 Fundamentals	344
	26.7.2 Calculation of design spacing	346
	26.7.3 Bends in the road	347
	26.7.4 Plotting of luminaire positions	348
	26.7.5 Lighting design for subsidiary roads	348
	26.7.6 Calculation of design spacing	349
	26.7.7 Plotting of luminaire positions	349
26.8	Lighting for urban centres and public amenity areas	349
26.9	Tunnel lighting	350
26.10	Lighting controls	351
26.11	Smart cities	352
References		352

Chapter 27: Security lighting

27.1	Functions of security lighting	354
27.2	Factors to be considered	354
	27.2.1 Type of site	354
	27.2.2 Site features	354
	27.2.3 Ambient light levels	355
	27.2.4 Crime risk	355

	27.2.5	CCTV surveillance	355
	27.2.6	Impact on the surrounding area	356
27.3		**Lighting recommendations**	**356**
	27.3.1	Illuminance and illuminance uniformity	356
	27.3.2	Glare control	357
	27.3.3	Light source colour properties	357
27.4		**Approaches to security lighting**	**358**
	27.4.1	Secure areas	358
	27.4.2	Public spaces	360
	27.4.3	Private areas	361
27.5		**Lighting equipment**	**362**
	27.5.1	Luminaires	362
	27.5.2	Lighting columns	362
	27.5.3	Lighting controls	363
	27.5.4	Maintenance	363
References			**364**

Chapter 28: Sports

28.1		**Functions of lighting for sports**	**365**
28.2		**Factors to be considered**	**365**
	28.2.1	Standard of play and viewing distance	365
	28.2.2	Playing area	366
	28.2.3	Luminaires	366
	28.2.4	Television	367
	28.2.5	Coping with power failures	368
	28.2.6	Obtrusive light	368
28.3		**Lighting recommendations**	**369**
	28.3.1	Athletics	370
	28.3.2	Bowls	370
	28.3.3	Cricket	371
	28.3.4	Five-a-side football (indoor)	372
	28.3.5	Fitness training	373
	28.3.6	Football	373
	28.3.7	Lawn tennis	373
	28.3.8	Rugby (union and league)	374
	28.3.9	Swimming	374
28.4		**Lighting in large facilities**	**375**
	28.4.1	Multi-use sports halls	375
	28.4.2	Small sports stadia	376
	28.4.3	Indoor arenas	376
	28.4.4	Swimming pools	377
References			**378**

Chapter 29: Historic buildings and spaces

29.1		**Introduction**	**379**
29.2		**Historic building being converted to a new use**	**379**
29.3		**Re-use of historic buildings and interiors**	**379**
29.4		**Historic Building preserved 'as is'**	**380**
	29.4.1	Daylight control	381
	29.4.2	Lighting equipment	382
	29.4.3	Emergency lighting in historic interiors	384
29.5		**Historic or sensitive exterior spaces**	**385**
	29.5.1	Lighting equipment	385

| | 29.5.2 | Emergency lighting in sensitive exterior spaces | 386 |
| Reference | | | 386 |

Chapter 30: Commissioning of lighting installations

30.1	Context		387
	30.1.1	Luminaires	387
	30.1.2	Emergency lighting	387
	30.1.3	Lighting controls	388
	30.1.4	Documentation, training and handover	388
	30.1.5	Energy efficiency	388
	30.1.6	Competence	389
	30.1.7	Safety	389
30.2	Forming a commissioning management team		389
	30.2.1	Commissioning activities	390
	30.2.2	Commissioning method statements	390
	30.2.3	Commissioning programme of works	390
30.3	Pre-commissioning checks		391
	30.3.1	General considerations	391
	30.3.2	Status of the lighting installation	391
	30.3.3	Pre-commissioning certificate	393
30.4	Functional commissioning		393
	30.4.1	Interior lighting	393
	30.4.2	Emergency lighting	394
	30.4.3	Exterior lighting	394
	30.4.4	Lighting controls	394
	30.4.5	Relationship between lighting and automatic solar shading	398
	30.4.6	Measurement of illuminance	398
	30.4.7	Proving interfacing to other services	398
	30.4.8	Visual inspection	398
	30.4.9	Functional commissioning certification	398
30.5	Lighting installation handover		399
	30.5.1	O&M media	399
	30.5.2	Witness testing	400
	30.5.3	Operator training	401
	30.5.4	Commissioning completion certificate	403
30.6	Post-completion checks and adjustments		404
	30.6.1	Category A or B projects	404
	30.6.2	Seasonal checks	404
References			404

Chapter 31: Performance verification

31.1	The need for performance verification		406
31.2	Competency of those undertaking measurements		406
31.3	Preparing for the survey		407
	31.3.1	Equipment	407
	31.3.2	Site	407
31.4	Instrumentation		408
	31.4.1	Illuminance meters	408
	31.4.2	Luminance meters	409
31.5	Methods of measurement		410
	31.5.1	Open-plan areas	410
	31.5.2	Defined task areas	412
	31.5.3	Exterior lighting	413
31.6	Measurement of illuminance variation		414

31.6.1	Illuminance diversity	414
31.6.2	Illuminance uniformity	415
31.7	**Luminance measurements**	**415**
31.8	**Measurement of reflectance**	**415**
References		**416**

Chapter 32: Maintenance

32.1	**The need for lighting maintenance for both traditional and LED light sources**	**417**
32.2	**Maintained illuminance**	**417**
32.3	**Determination of maintenance factor for interior lighting**	**417**
32.3.1	Designing for lighting maintenance	418
32.3.2	Maintenance factors for LEDs	419
32.3.3	Lamp/light source replacement: traditional and LED light sources	421
32.3.4	Lamp lumen maintenance factor (LLMF)	422
32.3.5	Lamp survival factor (LSF)	422
32.3.6	Luminaire maintenance factor (LMF)	422
32.3.7	Room surface maintenance factor (RSMF)	423
32.4	**Cleaning luminaires**	**423**
32.5	**Room surface cleaning**	**424**
32.6	**Determination of maintenance factor for exterior lighting**	**424**
References		**425**

Appendix 1: Reflectance and colour

A1.1	**Introduction**	**426**
A1.2	**Light reflecting properties**	**427**
A1.2.1	Specular reflection	427
A1.2.2	Diffuse reflection	428
A1.2.3	Glossy and semi-matte reflection	429
A1.2.4	Transmission	429
A1.3	**Illumination and colour**	**430**
A1.3.1	Colour constancy and chromatic adaptation	430
A1.3.2	Colour rendering	431
A1.3.3	Colour preference: IES TM-30-15 Colour Gamut Index (R_g)	436
A1.4	**Lighting properties of building materials**	**439**
A1.4.1	Reflectance of building materials	440
A1.4.2	Colour of building materials	441
A1.4.3	Surface finish of building materials	442
A1.4.4	Surface deterioration and maintenance	442
A1.5	**Colour contrast and adaptation**	**443**
References		**443**

Appendix 2: Circadian lighting

A2.1	**Background**	**445**
A2.2	**Circadian lighting solutions**	**446**
A2.3	**Risks of early adoption**	**449**
A2.4	**Conclusion**	**450**
References		**450**

Appendix 3: Building Regulations and environmental labelling schemes

A3.1	**Building Regulations**	**452**
A3.2	**BREEAM**	**453**
A3.3	**LEED**	**454**

A3.4	WELL Building Standard	455
	A3.4.1 WELL version v1	456
	A3.4.2 WELL version v2	457
A3.5	Enhanced Capital Allowances	459
References		459

Appendix 4: Glossary of terms

A4.1	Introduction	461
A4.2	Glossary	461
References		479

Index 481

Part 1: Fundamentals

Chapter 1: Lighting design process

1.1   Objectives

All artificial lighting is installed because of the needs of people. Whether those needs relate to work, rest or play, people must be at the heart of lighting design.

We need light so that we can see where we are going, so we can avoid trip hazards, so that we feel safe, so that we can see to read, write, draw, build, analyse. We need light to eat, to drink, to socialise, to pursue our vocations, interests, passions. We need light to be human.

Between dawn and dusk, daylight can provide much of what we need, but our requirements for a sheltered and controllable environment means that we spend a lot of our time inside buildings, where daylight is often insufficient and needs to be supplemented. Once daylight has faded, artificial light is required if we are to carry on our lives into the hours of darkness.

Lighting design is all about people.

The objectives of lighting design are to allow people to carry out their lives indoors and after dark, and to enhance their experience of doing so.

1.2   People

1.2.1   Activity

People need to carry out various activities in artificially lit spaces, and different types of activity create different drivers for lighting design.

Many workplace tasks, for example, require certain levels of light to enable adequate comfortable perception, varying from the relatively straightforward requirements of a typical desk-based worker, to the more demanding needs of someone inspecting printing or other industrial processes, where very accurate colour rendition and the ability to examine very fine detail are critical. The lighting needs of a professional kitchen are different again to those of a warehouse. The variety of lighting requirements is as wide as the variety of employment.

Various standards and guidance documents give extensive quantitative guidance on appropriate lighting for various tasks, these form a solid starting point for many lighting design exercises.

Other human activities have lighting requirements which are less easy to define in numerical guidance, because they are more focussed on the experience than on the task — a restaurant or hotel lobby, for example, or certain types of retail — whereas standards-based guidance is appropriate for a supermarket, a high-end fashion store or jeweller's shop is likely to strive to create a more dramatic environment in the pursuit of luxury. A gym operator may prefer a higher level of light than is technically needed to enable customers to work out, so as to boost their energy levels. In these cases, a different approach to lighting is required.

1.2.2   Experience

Whatever activity is being carried out, the experience of being in a space affects people — lighting is a significant element in creating and managing this experience. This is where lighting design becomes much more creative and demanding than the delivery of quantitative criteria with an engineered solution based on a simple standard.

A certain light level can be achieved in any number of ways — for example, 300 lux on a desk could be achieved with downlights, indirect lighting, desk lights, Chinese paper lanterns or Christmas tree lights. Some of these possibilities are of course more practical than others, but all would produce a very different experience.

Lighting design creates an experience by combining different lighting elements, and controlling them together. Whilst downlighting, for example, might be the most efficient way to deliver the technical requirement of light in a workplace, elements such as the lighting of key vertical surfaces, the decorative pendant over the reception desk and the lit coves in the meeting rooms all add layers of quality to the experience, which makes it a pleasant place in which to work.

1.2.3 Wellbeing

It has long been clear that lighting quality affects human wellbeing, and in recent years there has been a great deal of debate and research concerning the potential benefits of changing colour temperatures and intensity of the light so as to complement or support natural circadian rhythms.

Whether 'circadian lighting' is relevant to a particular project or not, the quality of experience created by lighting, together with how well it facilitates the relevant activity, is undoubtedly reflected in people's levels of comfort, stress, enjoyment and productivity.

Lighting design has a direct impact on wellbeing.

1.3 Issues

Lighting design must balance a number of issues and design criteria. The balance and prioritisation of these will vary depending on the nature of a project but, as a brief overview, the following issues should always be considered.

1.3.1 Amenity (function)

The major function of lighting is to enable people to see clearly in the absence of sufficient daylight. This is both a quantitative and a qualitative issue. The ability to see sufficiently well to carry out a given task depends on the amount of light present, but also on its qualities.

The nature of surfaces and their corresponding reflectance and visual brightness, the colour of the light and the manner in which it renders the colour of these surfaces and materials are major considerations. In areas where any form of recognition is important, lighting with good colour rendering should be provided.

The degree of contrast, or light and shade, within an area is governed by the nature of the space and the activity taking place within it. Too much contrast can create problems with certain visual tasks, whilst lack of contrast can result in a poor-quality environment.

The healthy eye can see in very low lighting conditions (less than 1 lux) and very bright lighting conditions (in excess of 100 000 lux). However, when the eye moves from high levels of light to low levels of light it can often take some time to adapt to the change. The appropriate lighting of spaces is therefore not only about the amount of light used in a specific space but also about managing the contrast with surrounding areas to facilitate any necessary visual adaptation.

Providing the appropriate quantitative level of light for amenity is, of course, essential but good lighting design achieves this whilst also creating an appropriate quality of experience.

1.3.2 Ambience (experience)

As well as providing the means to see, light also plays a key role in how people experience a space.

The psychological importance of light is often disregarded or underestimated. Lighting plays a major part not only in the way that people perceive a space but also in how they understand and use it. Light is part of various visual messages. It reveals and conceals elements within a space, supports way-finding, and in general creates an appropriate atmosphere.

Like colour and texture, light can influence the success or failure of a space irrespective of its functional properties. The effect light has on the perceived quality of a space and on the psychology of a user is not to be underestimated.

1.3.3 Legibility (understanding)

Lighting can help to make spaces legible after dark, on both macro and micro scales, from large urban areas to small interior volumes. Spaces and forms must be revealed in a visually intelligible manner.

Daylight has direction, intensity and quality, which allow us to clearly and intuitively understand the environment we are in. Artificial lighting provides different ways in which form and volume can be revealed and lighting design should consider how people understand spaces and should light them accordingly.

The legibility of any large or complex space after dark can be enhanced or ruined dependent upon a hierarchical approach to illuminating the surfaces and objects within it. These elements support intuitive wayfinding, becoming part of the 'mental map' people form, which makes an environment intelligible and navigable.

1.3.4 Image (identity)

By day, people look at whatever they like. Memorable buildings and places form a variety of lasting impressions.

After dark, lighting can 'curate' the visual experience of architecture, landscape and city. Surfaces and objects which are not lit are less visible, or even completely concealed, and the image which people remember is a version of the space with lighting applied.

The lighting designer works with the physical environment to create this after-dark image, carefully managing hierarchies of illumination to achieve a considered composition of elements.

Lighting contributes not only to the experience but to the memory, the 'postcard image', and the marketable brand.

1.3.5   Accessibility (inclusive design)

Lighting must be designed to ensure that users with varying visual and physical needs are properly considered. The effect of lighting on those with sensory or physical disabilities, including the elderly, should be carefully taken into account. This includes the avoidance of excessive contrast and glare, the avoidance of confusion through the use of excessively shiny surfaces, the control of shadow, and the careful use of upward light such that it does not cause confusion.

1.3.6   Safety

Lighting can assist in creating a safer environment by drawing attention to and lighting potential hazards.

In exterior areas where there is a mix of pedestrians and vehicles it is essential that lighting enables drivers to clearly identify pedestrians. This is not a function of the quantity of light alone but rather its quality. Steps, changes of level, junctions and crossing points and proximity to water edges are all potential hazards. Lighting to these areas should become an integral part of any safety and access solution.

Interior spaces also have potential hazards — steps, ramps, and escalators, for example — which lighting can help building users to negotiate. In industrial facilities, there may also be risks in the form of machinery, vehicles, etc; again, well-designed lighting can help to make it easy for people to stay safe.

1.3.7   Security

After dark, light helps people to feel secure. This issue predominantly relates to exterior public spaces. A legible streetscape and the ability to see others promotes feelings of safety and helps to deter crime. The technical requirements of CCTV systems should be taken into account — whilst camera technology has progressed to the point where cameras function well in comparatively low light levels, any need for facial recognition will affect the choice of lighting solutions.

1.3.8   Cost (value)

Lighting must be designed to optimise value with respect to both capital and running costs. Whole-life costs should be considered in relationship to project life, energy costs, hours of use, labour rates and maintenance/replacement periods. Lighting value should be carefully considered so that the greatest benefit is gained from the spend.

1.3.9   'Buildability'

The design must ensure that the lighting can be successfully installed. This should be achieved through consideration of the selection of materials and equipment, installation processes and procurement methods. Action should be taken to manage the number of differing types of equipment and accessories across a project. Where possible, luminaires should be located so as to facilitate easy access for installation as well as maintenance.

1.3.10   Maintenance

Lighting should generally be cost-effective and easy to run. Future maintenance of the installation must be considered at all stages of design. Considerations include a clear and consistent strategy for the replacement and cleaning of luminaires, lamps (where applicable), drive electronics, accessories, and other components. The ability to access equipment with ease is critical — where equipment locations are hard to reach, adequate access strategies should be put in place. Remember that the long service life of LED lighting does not mean lights can be installed as a 'fit-and-forget' exercise — premature failures are possible, focusing requirements for adjustable lights may change, and all lights still require periodic cleaning if their output is not to be diminished by the built-up of dirt. The lighting designer will often not be able to resolve access issues alone, but must work closely with architects, engineers and clients to identify and mitigate any problems.

1.3.11   Technology

The last decade or so has seen the most dramatic changes in lighting technology since the invention of the tubular fluorescent lamp and, arguably, since the advent of electric light with the work of Edison and Swan. The LED revolution has had a significant effect on the technical work of the lighting designer, but it is important to remember that the principles of good lighting design remain the same.

The lighting designer must be able to select the most appropriate technology for any given situation, which means keeping up to date with a rapidly changing market, as well as having a thorough understanding of lighting's recent past.

Whilst designers should look to take advantage of the latest technology where the benefits represent good value, it is also important to understand when simpler devices may provide the right solution, generally at lower cost. We should always consider not only what the current state of the art is, but what already exists within a building or within a client's estate.

1.3.12   Sustainability

The design and management of buildings is under ever-increasing pressure to be as sustainable as possible. As far as lighting is concerned, there are a number of sustainability agendas.

The most obvious is energy consumption. Lighting is traditionally one of the big energy consumers in a building; it is also the most visible user of energy. Technological advances have helped in this respect — LED lighting has generally reduced the energy consumption of most types of lighting installation when compared with older technologies. However, it is important to remember that luminaire efficiency is not the be-all and end-all when it comes to efficiency — lighting control is just as important.

The luminaire that consumes the least power is of course the luminaire that is switched off or, more usefully put, the luminaire that is switched off when it is not required. This is not to say that every luminaire should be ruthlessly controlled by presence sensing so that it is only on when absolutely needed by a person in order to carry out a task. As explained above, lighting is for experience as well as amenity. Intelligent use of lighting control will enable significant energy savings and also allow for the management of experience, whilst presence detection and daylight monitoring provide automated switching and dimming of lights as required, scene-setting control allows for the experience of a space to be changed to best suit the activity being carried out, the time of day, or the whim of occupants.

The other side of the energy story for lighting involves the embedded energy (and carbon) in the manufacture of lighting equipment, in transporting it and storing it. Whilst there is little the lighting designer can do to affect these hidden energy costs for any given product, care should be taken in specification with the aim of using the most sustainable equipment available for any given task. Lights which can easily be refurbished with replacement LED modules, circuit boards and drivers, for example, deliver better value for embedded energy than those which must be replaced entirely at the end of LED life.

The big picture of sustainability also has direct environmental aspects — light pollution, light trespass, and the effect of light on habitat. A wide variety of flora and fauna can have their natural lifecycles disrupted by artificial lighting, as indeed can human beings.
Lighting must be designed to manage the environmental impact on residents, visitors, the wider area, wildlife and their habitats. Measures to reduce environmental impact may include the reduction of light spill that may directly contribute to sky glow or light trespass outside of the site, the use of lighting control to reduce lighting when appropriate, and the reduction of overall light levels. Design should also minimise environmental impact through the careful selection, use and disposal of lamps, luminaires and supporting infrastructure.

The Institution of Lighting Professionals' *Guidance Notes for the Reduction of Obtrusive Light* (ILP, 2011) give a solid starting point for assessing light trespass and light pollution.

Finally, the agenda which is often forgotten is lighting's positive contribution to social and economic sustainability — well designed and well managed lighting extends our day, enabling us to work and play after the sun goes down. As our towns and cities tend increasingly towards the 24-hour economy, lighting is a key factor in making them viable.

1.4 Constraints

1.4.1 Legislation

It is important to understand that there are various legal requirements relating to lighting in buildings and in the public realm, which should be considered as possible constraints to a design. It is, however, also important to realise that these are generally quite limited, and that a great deal of confusion exists between mandatory requirements and good practice, recommendations, guidance and other 'official' documentation.

It is, of course, essential that the lighting designer, client and other members of the design team are aware of the relevant legal requirements.

Legal requirements vary in different countries, but the UK represents a fairly typical situation. The mandatory legislation relevant to lighting breaks down into four main areas:

- *Emergency lighting*: BS 5266-1: *Emergency lighting. Code of practice for the emergency lighting of premises* (BSI, 2016) sets out the requirements for emergency lighting in most non-domestic premises. This is essentially mandatory — Building Control authorities will not certify completion unless emergency lighting is demonstrated.

- Energy efficiency: in England and Wales, the Building Regulations 2010 (as amended) (TSO, 2010, 2015a, 2017) require lighting in buildings to meet certain requirements regarding energy efficiency. There are similar provisions in Scotland (the Building (Scotland) Regulations 2004 (as amended) (TSO, 2004)) and Northern Ireland (the Building Regulations (Northern Ireland) 2012 (TSO, 2012)). This is primarily expressed in terms of a minimum luminaire efficiency in lumens/watt, although recent editions have allowed designers to use the LENI ('lighting energy numeric indicator') calculation to show compliance across a whole building, expressed as lighting energy per square metre, per year (NBS, 2013, 2018; Scottish Government, 2015, 2018). This is a more in-depth metric and allows the designer to use less efficient luminaires in some applications, balanced by highly efficient units elsewhere. It also allows for the energy-saving benefits of controls. At time of writing, however, uptake of LENI is slow due perhaps to the way it has been implemented within various regulations, in the complexity involved in the calculation and the difficulty in many projects of accurately predicting building usage.

- *Health and safety*: in the UK, the Workplace (Health, Safety and Welfare) Regulations 1992 (HMSO, 1992) make very limited stipulations placing a duty on employers to ensure that every workplace must have 'suitable and sufficient' lighting, sufficient to enable people to work, use facilities and move from place to place safely and without experiencing eye-strain.

  The Regulations do not contain quantitative requirements, although compliance with the Health and Safety Executive's HSG38: *Lighting at Work* (HSE, 1997) is often regarded as the minimum to satisfy the requirements of the Regulations. At the time of writing, the most recent edition was published in 1997 and is therefore somewhat behind the curve as regards lighting technology, office display technology, energy legislation, and prevalent attitudes. There is, however, much common-sense guidance in this document and, interestingly, recommended light levels tend towards the lower end of what many standards would advise. It must be stressed again that HSG38 provides guidance only and does not represent a legal requirement.

- *Process*: in the UK, all parties involved in construction projects are legally bound to follow the Construction (Design and Management) Regulations 2015 (TSO, 2015b), which aim to manage the health, safety and welfare of construction projects, from design, through construction, into ownership and maintenance.

  The CDM Regulations do not dictate anything specific about lighting equipment, quantitative measures of light etc., but affect the process of design, installation, maintenance and ownership of lighting installations. It is incumbent upon the lighting designer to contribute to assessment and reduction of risk under these regulations. Details of the requirements of the CDM Regulations can be obtained from the Health and Safety Executive.

1.4.2   Standards

An old joke says, 'the great thing about standards is that there are so many to choose from!' There is some truth in this jocular comment. The *SLL Code for Lighting* (SLL, 2012), SLL Lighting Guides, various British Standards, European Standards (Euronorms), Building Regulations, *Secured by Design* guidance, Health and Safety Executive guidance, local authority standards, and even private companies' or institutions' own internal standards may all have relevance to particular projects. Elsewhere in the world, other similar (and dissimilar!) local and international standards exist, and all of them are irregularly updated.

Keeping track of them all is a Sisyphean task, but the vital knowledge for the lighting designer is not to have memorised every piece of guidance but to know where to look for the most appropriate reference.

As both lighting technology and lighting design have developed in recent decades, so the thinking behind lighting standards has undergone an overhaul. Editions of major standards in recent years have tended to become less prescriptive (and proscriptive), proposing various approaches, ranges rather than absolute numbers for quantitative metrics, and encouraging more thoughtful and creative design. BS EN 13201: *Road lighting* (BSI, 2015), for example, is considerably more complex than its predecessor, but allows the designer much more scope to decide what the salient aspects of any given road lighting situation are, and therefore what is the appropriate measure, before even considering the details of a solution. The upshot for designers of this shift in the thinking that goes into standards is a welcome one — standards should not be treated either as a crutch or as a ball and chain.

As noted above, very few of these standards have any legally binding status, although this does not stop all sorts of people from swearing blind that they do. They are often adopted by clients, however, as a briefing benchmark whereby adequate illumination will be provided and any future questions of liability can be satisfied.

It is important that the lighting designer has sufficient knowledge of common standards to be able to recommend relevant ones, to challenge others' selections if appropriate, and to advise where exceptions should be made.

1.4.3   Accreditations and assessments

In addition to standards and guidance documents, the lighting designer is often asked to design lighting that complies with sustainable building accreditation schemes such as the UK Building Research Establishment's BREEAM, the American LEED scheme, or others around the world. See Appendix 3, 'Building Regulations and environmental labelling schemes'.

These certification schemes typically involve a set of 'check-list' criteria whereby the design, procurement, construction and operation of buildings are evaluated. Points are scored in various categories and the final scores determine the level of certification the building receives. BREEAM awards 'pass', 'good', 'very good', 'excellent' and 'outstanding', whereas LEED has 'certified', 'silver', 'gold' and 'platinum'.

For the lighting designer, the salient parts of these and similar schemes in other countries concern energy, light quality, light pollution, controllability and commissioning, although there are other points that lighting may contribute to, such as innovation and aspects of procurement.

1.5   Process

Lighting designers working in different types of companies, and on different types of project, may have variations in their process due to differences between construction industry disciplines, contractual arrangements, and specific companies' systems.

Whatever the various stages of work may be called, and however many passes of documentation there may be, the typical process of lighting design is generally similar.

1.5.1   Brief

Before reaching for the *SLL Code for Lighting* (SLL, 2012) and firing-up a favourite calculation programme, the lighting designer must understand the brief. It may be that a clear written brief has been provided, but thorough briefs for lighting within many projects are rare. This means that lighting designers often have to effectively write their own brief. This in itself offers two important opportunities:

- Summarising a brief for lighting design allows the designer to creatively assess the objectives and constraints associated with a project, and set forth initial criteria for discussion which go beyond a purely quantitative approach.

- A brief can be agreed between all relevant parties before time and money is invested in design work, avoiding misunderstanding and disagreement later, and setting a baseline against which subsequent work can be assessed.

Defining a brief will generally include a certain amount of high-level analysis, see below. It also requires the identification of relevant stakeholders and their requirements. Stakeholders vary between projects, but might typically include the client, building users, facilities management, and tenant companies, as well as the contractors involved in construction and the rest of the design team. External bodies such as local authorities may also be stakeholders, perhaps where there is public realm within the construction site.

A good lighting brief will set out the intended use of relevant spaces, anticipated patterns of usage during day and night-time, and will identify specific requirements of any stakeholders. It should also describe the qualitative aspirations of the project. Based on this, the brief can become more detailed, proposing relevant standards (or challenging them), tabulating proposed light levels where relevant, identifying desired accreditations such as BREEAM or LEED, and perhaps discussing lighting technology.

1.5.2   Analysis

The first task in any lighting project is an element of analysis. Sometimes this may be a very simple assessment and identification of relevant standards, as in many industrial installations. Sometimes it may be an immensely complex study of stakeholders, users, circulation, tasks, function-over-time, standards, history, market, architecture, brand and aesthetics — lighting for an airport terminal, perhaps, or a large area of urban public realm have this level of complexity.

Sometimes a good brief will mean that less analysis has to be undertaken, but more often than not there is a somewhat blurred line between brief development and concept design. In either case, most of what the lighting designer needs to work out can be summarised by the apparently simple question:

'Who does what, where, when?'

Attempting to answer this question for the various spaces in a project will allow the designer to identify the objectives for lighting, be they quantitative, qualitative or both. It also gives some insight into whether spaces change in their function over the duration of the day (or week or year) — lighting requirements are not always static, but often change over time.

This analysis will often include not only the identification of activity, but will also consider views into, within, and out of spaces and the other aspects of the experience that can be affected by lighting.

1.5.3   Concept design

Concept design is the stage of a project where a lighting designer is most creative. At this stage, the brief and any relevant analysis provide the basis for ideas. What should be lit? Why? To what standards, if relevant? What about hierarchies of intensity, colour temperature, colour? How will lighting control affect the lighting over time?

The concept design stage is all about designing the human experience of light — what will this space feel like by day and night? How should this façade appear after dark? Can lighting help to make this task easier, or this stressful place more comfortable? Can light encourage work, learning, healing, pleasure?

This stage of design should result in a clearly thought out 'big picture' overview of the design. Sometimes it is relatively simple, and largely a question of relevant standards and identifying an approach that is cost-effective and will be comfortable for people. On other occasions, there may be more complexity — more layers of light to create flexible spaces with differing lighting scenes, perhaps, or the precise and sympathetic detailing that comes with lighting historic buildings. For some projects, the lighting concept may be extremely creative and ambitious: e.g. media façades, kinetic lighting, complex controls. Wherever a project lies on this spectrum, the concept design stage should result in presentation and documentation of the ideas, visually through renders, sketches, animations, demonstrations or whatever methods of communication are appropriate, and technically in terms of the principles of how different elements will be achieved, and in terms of what standards will be met (or challenged).

A client's acceptance of the lighting concept is the key milestone that enables the project to move forward into technical design and documentation.

1.5.4 Technical design

1.5.4.1 Selecting tools

At the concept design stage, the lighting designer will have presented high-level creative ideas, but will, of course, have a clear idea of how they will be achieved. In order to begin translating those ideas into a technical design, one of the first tasks is to start selecting equipment. Whilst it may be possible to think generically about some luminaires for a while, designers will begin to shortlist possible equipment and to test it, both in calculation and in real practical tests and mock-ups, so as to arrive at a specification, to be able to draw layouts, and to start thinking about and discussing details for integration.

Selecting lighting tools is always the art of compromise. Technical performance, efficiency, physical size and shape, cost, availability and compatibility must always be balanced, and the weight given to different criteria in different circumstances. The designer must decide which products represent the best solution in all respects, and which luminaires on a project are technically or aesthetically critical, and where savings can be made without significantly compromising lit effect, maintainability or architectural detail.

It is, in short, incumbent on the lighting designer to have a wide and up-to-date knowledge of the lighting marketplace, in order to be able to deliver lighting concepts with solutions that fit all design criteria.

1.5.4.2 Calculation

Calculations are a critical part of most lighting projects, but this does not mean that quantitative criteria should always lead over qualitative. Calculation is a verification tool, it is not design and it is not a substitute for knowledge and creative thinking.

This *Handbook* does not attempt to provide a thorough calculation manual, but some general caveats are worth reinforcing here.

Calculation results are an approximation at best. Although the actual maths taking place in software is highly accurate, it depends on a great many variables, many of which are generally impossible to know accurately in advance of construction and in lieu of technical measurement. The reflectance of surfaces, for example, is almost always based on a generalisation, partly because finishes may well not yet be decided. It is clear to anyone that white terrazzo will be considerably more reflective than grey carpet. Neither will have a reflectance of 0.2, but unless you set your virtual floor to have a different value, that is what the calculation software is going to use. Maintenance factors are even more of an assumption — does anyone really know at design time how often luminaires will be cleaned? And if a designer is asked to take the impact of trees into account in exterior calculations? Well, trees are notoriously non-standard and do not grow to tight tolerances. Even more inconveniently, many of them change their reflectance/transmittance substantially through the course of a year. It is clear that any attempt to calculate this scenario is going to give results that are indicative, at best.

In addition, subtle changes in parameters can change results without actually changing the design. Apart from modifications to material reflectances and other aspects of the model, changes to calculation settings, such as the density of the measuring grid, can make the difference between a scheme failing to meet a target illuminance or uniformity and it complying comfortably — without moving a single luminaire, changing its specification, or altering the quantity of luminaires involved.

In short, lighting calculations are a classic example of what computer programmers refer to as 'GIGO' — 'garbage in, garbage out'. The results are only as good as the inputs and the inputs almost always involve some major assumptions. Calculation outputs are meaningless and even dangerous if they are accepted unquestioningly. Whilst they are a useful verification tool for the lighting designer, they must be reviewed with sufficient knowledge and experience to understand what they show and what the limitations are in any particular case.

1.5.4.3   Integration and coordination

Lighting design rarely stands alone as an undertaking. Lighting designers work closely with architects, landscape architects, engineers, interior designers and other design professionals.

One of the key aspects of this collaboration is the integration of lighting into architecture, landscape, public realm or structure. This integration is an essential part of good lighting design, and the lighting design process must take into account these other contexts, and seek to achieve appropriate solutions that enhance buildings and places, rather than becoming a technical imposition upon them.

Coordinating the details of integrating luminaires requires input from various parties, and is often best resolved through holding face-to-face workshops and demonstrations.

1.5.4.4   Control

Lighting control is a widely misunderstood aspect of lighting, and is unfortunately seen as 'voodoo' by many. However, control is one of the lighting designer's most powerful tools.

Where the physical fabric of buildings and exterior space is fixed and unchanging, light can change over time. Light adds the fourth dimension to the three dimensions of most design.

It is a duty and an opportunity for the lighting designer to consider their design as it changes over time, rather than as a static snapshot. Any space which receives daylight will change in character significantly over the 24-hour cycle, and the requirements for artificial light will change accordingly. Similarly, a space which serves different purposes for people through the day may require different lighting states — the classic example might be a hotel lobby restaurant, which goes through night, early morning check-in, breakfast, coffee and meetings, lunch, afternoon tea, drinks, dinner and late-night bar. These changes are facilitated and enhanced by lighting, and control is what enables the lighting design to change between various modes of operation, creating different scenes and experiences.

Lighting control should not be an afterthought — a technology that has to be provided but is someone else's problem. It is a key aspect of designing lighting and being able to think through control and to describe performance requirements for a lighting control system are crucial skills.

1.5.4.5 Documentation

Exactly what documentation a lighting designer has to produce will vary between projects and circumstances, but always has the same function. A lighting design package must describe the lighting scheme to all other relevant parties — the rest of the design team, who have to integrate it into their work; the contractors who will eventually have to install it; the cost consultants who need to cost it accurately — the list goes on. Most importantly, lighting design documentation becomes part of a contract; it is vital that it is thorough, accurate, consistent, and professional. In order to describe the lighting scheme, the designer will produce various deliverables:

- *Drawings*: The core of any package is the drawing set. Lighting layouts show the locations in plan of luminaires, control panels and any other relevant equipment. Elevations and/or sections may be required, showing the heights at which luminaires are mounted — relevant to any wall-mounted or suspended luminaires.

  Lighting detail drawings are also vital. A layout shows the intended location, but not the detail of how a luminaire is intended to be fixed, e.g. the precise dimensions required for a slot, a cove or a hole; the bracketry, strut-work or whatever is required to support a luminaire; the space required around a luminaire in order to let it pivot for focussing; the allowance of free air so that a luminaire stays within the required operating temperatures. Detail drawings are where the designer can convey all these specific physical requirements, so that other parties can understand the requirements and integrate them into their work.

- *Specifications*: Except when creating a performance specification for a design-and-build project, the lighting equipment specification is at the heart of the lighting design package. Layouts, the calculations which verify their performance, and detail drawings are all based upon the use of particular products and accessories. Having gone to great lengths to choose the right lighting tools for the task, technically and aesthetically, the lighting designer must document these tools thoroughly so that the correct products are procured and installed.

  The designer may start with a preliminary schedule of generic equipment for purposes of a first-pass schematic or developed design, but will create a proper specification as part of the technical lighting design package.

  Specification documents should be thorough, as detailed as possible and, above all, accurate. They should provide not only a 'shopping list', but a detailed description of every item required which clearly indicates all aspects of its performance —

photometric and electrical properties, efficiency, form-factor, materials, finishes, dimensions, accessories required and other criteria, together with manufacturer information, part numbers and so on.

This depth of information is required not only to enable the correct equipment to be procured, but to protect the design should substitute products be proposed during the project.

Whilst this generally comes about in an effort to save money by proposing cheaper luminaire fittings (under the oft-misused banner of 'value engineering'), it may also be necessary due to a manufacturer discontinuing a product, a physical constraint on site, or some other circumstance. Whatever the reason, it is important that the lighting specification provides thorough and detailed data with which any proposed luminaire can be compared in order to determine whether it is genuinely 'equal and approved' and whether it will deliver the lighting scheme that the client expects.

- *Control documentation*: Whilst layouts and details explain the locations and integration principles of luminaires, and the specification describes each item in detail, a lighting designer's control documentation is vital in ensuring that an appropriate control system is procured, installed, commissioned and programmed in such a way as to deliver the design intent and operational ease that the client has been promised as part of the lighting concept.

Documentation should describe the system approach and performance requirements: e.g. the quantities and locations of button panels, touch screens, sensors and other user interfaces; requirements for interfacing with other systems; and any other relevant technical details. It should include a schedule of all the luminaires to be controlled, organised into logical groups, and identifying their power and data requirements.

Depending on the nature of a project, the lighting designer may specify an entire system as a particular set of equipment to be delivered by a particular supplier or systems integrator, or may provide a performance specification that can be put out to tender in the lighting controls market.

- *Risk assessments*: For projects in the UK, at least, the lighting designer is bound by the Construction (Design and Management) Regulations 2015 (TSO, 2015b) to design lighting systems that can be installed and maintained safely, and to contribute to safety documents maintained by another party within the project. Similar processes exist in projects elsewhere in the world, either as a requirement of local legislation, or as part of an internal system put in place by a client or contractor.

- *Reports*: It is generally the case, on projects of any size, that all design disciplines are expected to submit a report at the end of each stage. This should summarise the work done thus far, usually has some or all of the deliverable documentation appended, and often includes work such as calculations, schedules of assumptions and other justifications.

The design report acts as a 'line in the sand'. The state of the design is presented in these reports, for comment or sign-off by the client or their representatives before the project moves on to the next stage.

The report is also often considered as the evidence of work on which payment can be released to consultants and, in some cases, these reports may form 'Employers'

Requirements' — the thorough description of a design that forms the basis for a design-and-build construction contract.

Given these contractual situations, it is clear that lighting designers' reports should be clear, thorough and professional.

Smaller projects, and undertakings such as lighting-only refurbishments may not require reports.

1.5.5 Construction

The design team's responsibilities do not end when construction starts — design work continues to the end of a project. Whether due to a client's changing requirements, the demands of future tenants or circumstances on site, design often has to be revised during construction. The lighting designer may have to respond to architectural changes, co-ordination with structure or other services, client demands, or even changes in the lighting market — during the course of a long project, manufacturers may update products or even go out of business — specifications, details and layouts may have to be changed.

As luminaires are installed on site, the lighting designer will generally be expected to inspect them, witness them operating and record any issues as part of the design team's 'snagging' process.

Finally, the lighting designer generally has a part to play in the commissioning process. Adjustable luminaires must be focussed, i.e. adjusted so that they light what they were intended to light. Lighting control systems must be programmed so as to produce the desired lighting scenes, control panel functions and automation. Both these tasks may be carried out by contractors or system suppliers, but should happen under the direction of the lighting designer.

1.5.6 Handover and post-occupancy

Handover of projects is where communication can often break down. Whilst building owners and occupiers can see the luminaires that have been provided, they are often not well briefed on the operation of lighting control systems and the effects intended by the designer.

The lighting designer should try, where possible, to be involved in the handover process, so that clients and users understand what they have been provided with and reminded what the design intent was. This helps to ensure that end-users are happy that their needs have been met, and allows for final amendments to control system programming to be made with their input, if necessary.

In some cases, the lighting designer may be required to contribute to handover documentation such as sustainability certification.

Professional scopes such as the *RIBA Plan of Work* (RIBA, 2013) allow for a phase of work relating to 'post-occupancy', or 'in use'. These may include tasks such as post-occupancy evaluation, gathering user feedback, and monitoring sustainability performance, with a view to making adjustments to a building's systems (or even fabric) in order to streamline performance and satisfy users' requirements.

Although many lighting professionals believe that undertaking these activities in relation to lighting would be highly beneficial to many projects, the opportunity to do so (and to be paid for doing so) rarely occurs. Perhaps in the future some of these activities may become more common, or even mandatory under sustainability legislation.

References

BSI (2016) BS 5266-1: *Emergency lighting. Code of practice for the emergency lighting of premises* (London: British Standards Institution)

BSI (2015) BS EN 13201: *Road lighting* (London: British Standards Institution)

HMSO (1992) The Workplace (Health, Safety and Welfare) Regulations 1992 Statutory Instruments 1992 No. 3004 (London: HMSO) (available at http://www.legislation.gov.uk/uksi/1992/3004) (accessed September 2018)

HSE (1997) *Lighting at Work* HSG38 (Bootle: Health and Safety Executive) (available at http://www.hse.gov.uk/pubns/books/hsg38.htm) (accessed September 2018)

ILP (2011) *Guidance Notes for the Reduction of Obtrusive Light* (Rugby: Institution of Lighting Professionals)

NBS (2013) *Non-domestic Building Services Compliance Guide* (2013 edition for use in England) (plus addendum) (Newcastle Upon Tyne: NBS) (available at https://www.gov.uk/government/publications/conservation-of-fuel-and-power-approved-document-l) (accessed September 2018)

NBS (2018) *Domestic Building Services Compliance Guide* (2013 edition for use in England incorporating 2018 amendments) (Newcastle Upon Tyne: NBS) (available at https://www.gov.uk/government/publications/conservation-of-fuel-and-power-approved-document-l) (accessed September 2018)

RIBA (2013) *RIBA Plan of Work* (London: RIBA) (available at https://www.ribaplanofwork.com) (accessed September 2018)

Scottish Government (2015) *Domestic Building Services Compliance Guide for Scotland 2015* (Edinburgh: Scottish Government) (available at https://www.gov.scot/Topics/Built-Environment/Building/Building-standards/techbooks/techhandbooks/dbscgs) (accessed September 2018)

Scottish Government (2018) *Non-domestic Building Services Compliance Guide for Scotland 2018* (Edinburgh: Scottish Government) (available at https://www.gov.scot/Topics/Built-Environment/Building/Building-standards/techbooks/techhandbooks/ndbscg) (accessed September 2018)

SLL (2012) *SLL Code for Lighting* (London: Society of Light and Lighting)

TSO (2004) The Building (Scotland) Regulations 2004 Scottish Statutory Instruments 2004 No. 406 (as amended) (London: TSO) (available at http://www.legislation.gov.uk/ssi/2004/406) (accessed February 2018)

TSO (2010) The Building Regulations 2010 Statutory Instruments 2010 No. 2214 (as amended) (London: TSO) (available at http://www.legislation.gov.uk/uksi/2010/2214) (accessed September 2018)

TSO (2012) The Building Regulations (Northern Ireland) 2012 Statutory Instrument 2012 No. 192 (as amended) (London: TSO) (available at http://www.legislation.gov.uk/nisr/2012/192) (accessed September 2018)

TSO (2015a) The Building Regulations &c. (Amendment) Regulations 2015 Statutory Instrument 2015 No. 767 (London: TSO) (available at http://www.legislation.gov.uk/uksi/2017/856) (accessed September 2018)

TSO (2015b) The Construction (Design and Management) Regulations 2015 Statutory Instruments 2015 No. 51 (London: TSO) (available at http://www.legislation.gov.uk/uksi/2015/51) (accessed September 2018)

TSO (2017) The Building (Amendment) Regulations 2017 Statutory Instrument 2017 No. 856 (London: TSO) (available at http://www.legislation.gov.uk/uksi/2017/856) (accessed February 2018)

Chapter 2: Daylighting

The study of daylight in buildings, known as daylighting, has become a crucial aspect of sustainable building design. Using daylight in buildings has many advantages, such as a link to the natural cycle of the changes in light quality during the day, 'free' light near to windows and a view out through side windows. However, there can be disadvantages, such as solar heat gain, direct glare and reflections of the bright sky on display screens. For a full discussion on these aspects and a strategy for getting the most out of daylight refer to the SLL Lighting Guide 10: *Daylighting — a guide for designers* (SLL, 2014).

2.1 The benefits of daylight

The benefits of daylight are numerous; however, they can be described in terms of in three principal aspects: health and wellbeing, aesthetics and energy use.

2.1.1 Energy use

A building that utilises the available daylight is less reliant on electrical lighting. Good daylighting maximises a building's potential for daylight by ensuring that the quantity and distribution of daylight in the interior meets its lighting requirements for as much of the occupied time as possible, given the seasonal and diurnal availability of daylight.

2.1.2 Aesthetics

The appeal of daylit spaces is almost universal. Interiors are enlivened by the dynamic nature of sunlight and surfaces are pleasingly modelled by the flow of diffuse daylight. It is widely held that people prefer the feeling of spaciousness afforded by a well daylit space.

Figure 2.1 A view containing nature elements has many benefits
(courtesy of Ruth Kelly Waskett)

2.1.3 Occupant health and wellbeing

In the context of our evolutionary history, it is only recently that humans have come to spend most of their time inside buildings. Thus, it is no surprise that human physiology and psychology are closely linked with the 24-hour light–dark cycle of our planet. Exposure to daylight at the eye and via the skin affects a wide range of aspects, often referred to as 'non-visual effects', since they pertain to functions of the eye other than seeing. This includes the entrainment of the circadian system and its subsequent effects on sleep quality and task performance, and psychological aspects, such as short-term mood and longer-term seasonal affective conditions.

In addition to the health aspects described above, there are several wellbeing benefits associated with the ability to see outside through openings in the building envelope. The benefits of a view to outdoors have been widely documented, especially if those views contain nature elements. The presence of deciduous vegetation has the added advantage of providing shade in summer whilst allowing sunlight to enter in winter, when it may be more desirable (Figure 2.1).

2.1.4   View out

In a typical building, a view out facilitates restoration and respite from work tasks. View composition is also important, as it dictates the perceived quality of the view and thus the benefits to the wellbeing of the occupant. Typically, an outdoor scene is stratified: the top layer is sky, the middle layer may contain buildings, mountains or vegetation, and the foreground may contain smaller landscape elements, or paved areas animated by vehicles and people. This is an area of interest to which occupants most often direct their gaze. Ideally, a window view should contain all three of these layers.

Even if daylight enters a building indirectly (without the possibility of a direct view to outside), occupants will still benefit from an awareness of the time of day and localised weather conditions through changes in colour temperature and intensity.

2.2   The need to control daylight

Evidently, daylight in buildings is desirable for many reasons. However, it is not the case that more daylight leads to better daylighting, since an excess of daylight in a building can lead to problems; namely, glare and overheating. The presence of large areas of glazing can also conflict with privacy and security requirements. Therefore, good daylighting is a balance between the utilisation of available daylight at a particular site and the needs of the building occupants.

2.2.1   Glare from windows

For sources of artificial lighting, such as luminaires, the distribution and intensity of light output is often highly engineered, and thus predictable and controllable. Hence, the potential for glare from luminaires can usually be quantified for typical applications using some well-known indices, such as the unified glare rating (UGR). Glare from windows is very different, mainly because the source of glare is large and complex compared to a luminaire, and because the glare sensation elicited by light from windows varies considerably between individuals and is influenced by more numerous factors. Daylight glare can occur under cloudy or clear sky conditions, since it can arise from a bright cloudy sky as well as from direct sunlight. Glare can be caused directly, or indirectly via reflections of the primary glare source on computer screens, light-coloured surfaces (e.g. paper) or reflective surfaces within the room. Acute solar glare can also arise as a result of reflections from adjacent building façades. Currently, there is no agreed method to objectively quantify glare from windows. Therefore, the daylighting design should aim to control and reduce the likelihood of glare as much as possible, and avoid heavy reliance on shading devices, such as blinds, which, if left down for long periods, can erode the benefits of both daylight admission and view through the glazing and increase electric lighting use.

The first step in overcoming glare is to ensure that the differences in luminance between the window or rooflight and the immediate surroundings are minimized. This can be done either by decreasing the luminance of the sky or by increasing the luminance of the window surround, or both. The luminance of the sky can be reduced using shading. To increase the luminance of the window surrounds, glazing bars should be of high reflectance (i.e. a light colour), the edges of the window or rooflight aperture should be graduated or splayed, and the wall or ceiling in which the window or rooflight is installed should be of high reflectance and well illuminated (Figure 2.2).

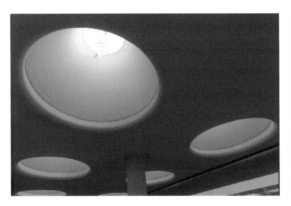 

Figure 2.2 Design features that minimize contrast between the bright view through a window and its surround: (*left*) splayed surround to a skylight at the Otaniemi Library, Finland (courtesy Hans Jan Durr); (*right*) splayed window casing/shutters with mouldings and reduction of high sky brightness by a translucent blind (courtesy Paul Ruffles)

2.2.2   Overheating

Daylight admitted to a building represents a heat gain. In winter, this may be useful, but in summer it can represent an additional cooling load. However, heat gains from electric lighting will reduce if it is switched off or dimmed in daylit spaces. Therefore, when considering the energy balance of the whole building, it is essential to bear in mind the contribution of daylighting. On a local scale, sunlight directly incident on people near a window can cause thermal discomfort. When selecting shading devices, consideration should be given to these effects, see CIBSE Guide A (CIBSE, 2015).

2.2.3   Privacy and security

Extensively glazed buildings can present privacy problems, particularly on the ground floor. Concerns about privacy can lead to blinds being closed at all times with a consequent lack of daylight and view out. There is little that can be done about the admittance of daylight but a degraded view out can be preserved without sacrificing privacy by using blinds made from perforated fabric, particularly when the outside face of the blind is of high reflectance and the inside face is of low reflectance. An alternative solution is to move workplaces away from the windows and to use this space for circulation.

Large areas of glazing, particularly if openable, may conflict with the security requirements of a building. The window specification should take account of any special security requirements. For example, consider the impact on daylighting of security screens, external security bars or explosion-proof glazing, which may have additional thickness and thus have reduced light transmittance.

2.3   Shading

The ingress of daylight into a building, and in particular direct sunlight, must be controlled in order to provide a comfortable environment for occupants. Typically, the two shading functions — glare and overheating — are addressed separately, mainly because they are often required in diametrically opposed seasonal conditions. Shading to prevent solar overheating is typically designed for conditions that arise in the summer months, i.e. high solar altitude and increased external air temperature. Shading for glare control, however, is often required most in winter, when solar altitude is low. Windows that face east or west may also require shading for glare control throughout the year since low penetrating sun at the beginning or end of the day is a possibility during all seasons.

2.3.1   Solar shading

Shading for overheating is designed to protect the façade from direct solar irradiation, before it passes through the façade and starts to heat the interior. The usual approach is to try to shade the façade at the high solar altitudes that occur during the summer months. It is important to note, however, that sun penetration may be desirable and beneficial in some interiors, especially in winter when it may provide welcome solar heating. Thus, excluding direct sun from the interior all year round is rarely a good strategy, unless there are specific functional reasons for doing so. If fixed solar shading is provided, it is usually in the form of an external element such as a structural overhang or slatted shading device. The size and shape of the louvres will be influenced by orientation of the building and its latitude. In the UK, façades with a southerly orientation are best protected with horizontal elements, whilst east and west façades are better protected by using vertical elements angled slightly to the north. Rooflights can be protected by shading elements whose dimensions are determined based on whether sunlight is to be excluded at all times.

Non-fixed solar shading elements, such as moveable awnings or external shutters, are usually manually controlled and thus reliant on occupants to use them pre-emptively, i.e. before solar irradiation starts to cause overheating. Motorised external solar shading is used less often, mainly because of the expense associated with installation and maintenance. More detail about different types of solar shading can be found in SLL Lighting Guide 10 (SLL, 2014).

Figure 2.3 External shading to reduce solar overheating
(© Denis Gilbert/VIEW Picture/age fotostock)

2.3.2 Glare control

Shading for glare control is usually provided internally, using roller blinds or Venetian blinds. However, it may also be external, incorporated within a double skin façade, or integral to the window (as in the case of inter-pane blinds). Most commonly, shades are manually controlled. One of the main disadvantages of manual shades is the well known phenomenon known as 'blinds down, lights on', whereby occupants close shades to deal with a glare condition, but do not open them again once that condition has passed. As a result, blinds are often left closed for long periods, meaning that occupants lose the benefits of both daylight exposure and view through the glazing, and that electric lighting energy use is increased. A short walk around any city will reveal numerous well-glazed office buildings where the blinds on many windows appear to be permanently closed (Figure 2.4).

Figure 2.4 A modern office building with extensive glazing and extensive use of blinds (courtesy of John Mardaljevic)

Shading can be automated so that it operates in a way that preserves the contribution of daylight as much as possible and allows a view out for occupants more of the time. However, this solution usually involves motorised façade elements that can add significantly to the complexity and cost of construction and maintenance. There are also several challenges associated with designing a control algorithm that effectively matches the shading requirements of occupants, particularly in shared open-plan spaces. The algorithm will need to adapt through the seasons and be specific for each façade of the building to cope with the different sun height and orientation relative to that façade. It can be designed to allow for manual control during the day, but to fully or partly open the blinds each morning.

Some blind materials, such as perforated fabric, allow a degraded view out to be retained while limiting daylight admission. Others, such as Venetian and vertical blinds, allow the user to adjust blind coverage and the angle of the blades to preserve a limited view out while restricting the admission of sunlight. Yet others, such as roller blinds and Venetian blinds allow the view of the sky to be restricted while preserving a view of the ground outside. Such blinds should have an internal reflectance of at least 0.5 and a high external reflectance. Where they are likely to be subject to direct sunlight, blinds should have a transmittance of less than 0.1.

2.3.3   Glazing-based shading solutions

Tinted glazing was widely used in the latter part of the 20th century and tinted solar control films are still used today as a retrofit solution to combat solar heat gain. However, glazing with a fixed tint permanently reduces the ingress of daylight to the space and can cause the exterior view to appear dull. Other glazing treatments, such as optical distortions (e.g. prismatic glazing) and fritting, can control heat gain and reduce glare. More recent innovations in glazing technology have led to the development of a number of 'smart glazing' products, such as suspended particle (SPD) glazing and electrochromic glazing (Figure 2.5). These glazing materials can vary their light transmittance in response to room conditions, such as temperature, façade illuminance or any sensor-based environmental parameter. They have the advantage of being dynamic and automatable, but without the disadvantages of moving mechanical parts. Furthermore, they are capable of controlling both solar heat gain and glare, thus removing the need for external and internal shading elements. Some do however change colour as they dim, reducing the colour rendering of the daylight entering the space.

Figure 2.5 Electrochromic glazing used in an entrance hall (courtesy of Saint Gobain S.A.)

2.4   Assessment of daylight quantity
2.4.1   Daylight availability

Daylight varies in both amount and spectrum with sun altitude and atmospheric conditions. This means that the availability of daylight varies with the time of day, time of year and weather conditions (cloud cover). Figure 2.6 below shows a typical example of how the illuminance on an unobstructed horizontal plane provided by daylight varies with the time of year and the time of day. Details on the availability of daylight can also be found in SLL Lighting Guide 10 (SLL, 2014) and Hunt (1979).

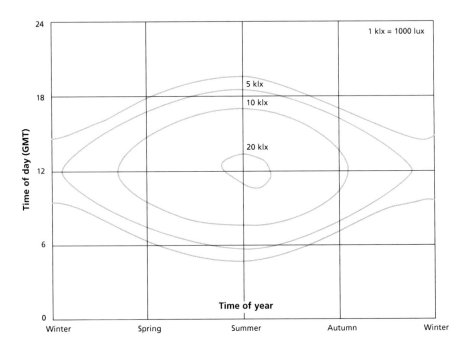

Figure 2.6 Typical example of how horizontal daylight illuminance (excluding direct sunlight) varies with time

2.4.2 Predicting daylight quantity

Inside a building, the amount of daylight available will depend on the position and size of openings. Average daylight factor is commonly used to predict the daylight potential of a room. Daylight factor should not be used to calculate absolute illuminance values, but is a very useful tool for evaluating different daylight solutions. Point daylight factors are useful at critical points (e.g. near windows and at the furthest points from a window) to determine the distribution of daylight in the room. Statistical quanta, such as maximum, minimum and median values of daylight factor, can also be informative.

Uniformity of daylight factor is often desirable, as it avoids a sharp fall in daylight levels further into the room (away from windows) and thus reduces the need for supplementary electric lighting. In some cases, patterns made by pools of light can echo architectural features and add visual interest, but this may not be appropriate for task areas.

Average and point daylight factors can be calculated manually or using simulation models. SLL Lighting Guide 10 (SLL, 2014) gives details of how to calculate average daylight factor. Manual calculation methods for point daylight factors are covered in BRE Digests 309 and 310 (BRE, 1986a/b).

For a well daylit appearance without any electric lighting for the majority of occupied hours, the average daylight factor should not be less than 5%. For a daylit appearance with some use of electric lighting during winter months, the average daylight factor should be not less than 2%. In a room where the average daylight factor is less than 2%, daylight will be noticeable only on room surfaces immediately adjacent to windows, and though the windows may still provide views out for occupants throughout the room, electric lighting will be necessary for much of the time to provide adequate task lighting.

The daylight factor is largely dependent on the angle of visible sky from the centre of the window (Figure 2.7). Similarly, inside the room, the amount of visible sky from a given point will largely determine the daylight factor at that point. Therefore, it is valuable to assess different daylight solutions in terms of how they affect the amount of sky that is visible from within a space.

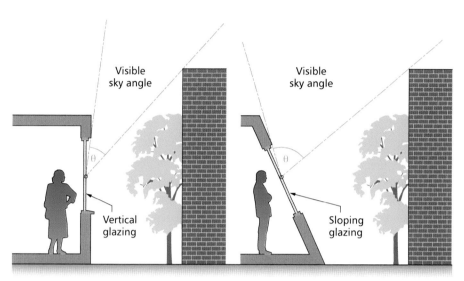

Figure 2.7 The unobstructed sky visible at the window affects the amount of daylight entering the window and reflecting around within the room

2.4.3   No sky line

The 'no sky line' is a simple analytical tool that can assist the designer when considering buildings that do not have an open view to the horizon. At the no sky line, the last visible patch of sky above the obstruction will just disappear when the window head is sighted through a point at working plane height. The no sky line divides points on the working plane which can and cannot see the sky (Figure 2.8). Supplementary electric lighting will be needed if a significant part of the working plane lies beyond the no sky line. The no sky line position can be altered by increasing the window head height or by setting the building façade back from obstructions. It must be noted that although explained using a two-dimensional diagram, the no sky line is three-dimensional in nature. Guidance on no sky lines is given in Littlefair (2011).

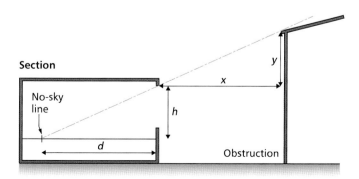

Figure 2.8 The no-sky line

2.4.4   Limitations of daylight factor

As mentioned above, daylight factor is a useful tool, particularly for evaluating multiple design schemes in terms of the relative daylight potential they offer to a space. However, it has some important limitations, which must be recognised in order to use it intelligently.

Daylight factor is based on a theoretical overcast sky condition ('CIE overcast sky'), which rarely exists in nature. Therefore, it does not take account of the effect of direct sun, nor can it be used to assess the likelihood of visual discomfort or overheating caused by solar penetration. Furthermore, daylight factor is calculated in the same way irrespective of global location, and thus does not take account of the global variation in sunlight availability. Similarly, the standard calculation methods for daylight factor do not allow for the variations in sky brightness at different façade orientations. However, an adjustment can be made for this using the orientation factors described in SLL Lighting Guide 10 (SLL, 2014).

2.4.5   Estimation of annual electrical lighting requirements

As daylight factor does not account for annual daylight availability, 'daylight autonomy' (DA) can be used to estimate the annual requirement for supplementary electric lighting, based on predicted average daylight factor. DA is a measure of how often a certain illuminance level can be maintained by the use of daylight alone and is expressed as a percentage of occupied time, either annually or on a month-by-month basis.

Climate-based daylight modelling takes full account of the annual availability of daylight and sunlight at a specific global location and given façade orientation. This computer simulation technique can be used to produce absolute illuminance values in a room and predict maximum and minimum values that are likely to be achieved throughout the year. Further guidance on the calculation of basic daylight autonomy and the use of climate-based daylight modelling is explained in SLL Lighting Guide 10 (SLL, 2014).

2.5   Daylighting solutions

Windows, rooflights and other building elements can be arranged in many different ways to achieve different daylighting solutions. Below is a brief summary of some of the most commonly used solutions.

2.5.1   Windows

Windows have the advantage of providing both daylight to the interior and a view out. Their disadvantage is that the amount of daylight delivered to the space decreases dramatically as the distance from the window increases, although the view out is preserved over a larger distance as long as there are no major internal obstructions. As a rule of thumb, daylight will penetrate to a depth of two to three times the height of the window head above the working plane, assuming no external obstruction of the sky.

Different shapes and sizes of window can be placed in a façade to achieve many different aesthetic and daylighting outcomes. For example, a clerestory, or narrow strip of windows high up on the wall (Figure 2.9) can provide deeper penetration of daylight into the space, but little by way of a view out. Clerestory windows provide a direct view of the upper parts of the sky, and are often used on northerly façades, where glare and overheating from direct sun is less likely.

Figure 2.9 Clerestory windows allow light into classroom over adjacent rooms
(© BAM PPP B.V.)

The penetration of daylight through a clerestory can be increased further into the space using prismatic refractors instead of conventional glass. The effect of these refractors is to bend the light from the upper sky onto the (light coloured) ceiling, from where it will be diffusely reflected. Good quality refractors are required if bright spots on the ceiling are to be avoided.

Another variation of the clerestory technique is a light shelf. This is usually a light reflective surface mounted internally or externally, or both, which divides a large area of glazing into a clerestory above the shelf and view window below (Figure 2.10). They are designed to provide solar shading whilst reflecting daylight and sunlight up onto the ceiling. Whilst these devices can be effective in re-distributing daylight to the back of the room, they are not often used due to expense and maintenance issues; they need to be kept clean in order to work effectively, but naturally attract a lot of dirt and dust.

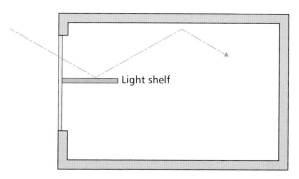

Figure 2.10 Light shelf

Glazed areas less than 15% of the window-wall area are generally undesirable, as are window shapes and layouts that break-up the view. The maximum glazed area is generally limited by thermal considerations, since glazing represents a weak point in the building envelope with respect to heat transfer. The transmittance and colour of the glazing also need to be considered. More details about the specification of glazing materials can be found in SLL Lighting Guide 10 (SLL, 2014).

2.5.2   Rooflights

Rooflights can be vertical, horizontal or sloping. Rooflights can be oriented to minimize sun penetration, as in the traditional north-facing sawtooth roof over a large space, such as a factory, (see Chapter 13, Figure 13.1) or in a single pitch roof such as that shown in Figure 2.11. The daylight penetration from rooflights can vary widely depending on the design of the rooflight and the presence of internal devices to limit sun penetration. Rooflights are a very effective way to provide daylight over a large area, single storey building.

Figure 2.11 Modern use of north light in an office environment (National Trust HQ)
(© James Winspear/VIEW Pictures/Alamy Stock Photo)

2.5.3   Glazed streets, courtyards and atria

Enclosed daylit areas in the centre of a deep-plan building can be used to increase daylight penetration throughout the building, see Figure 2.12 below. Though the quantity of daylight and depth of penetration may be relatively small, elements such as these can provide a pleasing visual experience and a degree of contact with the outside for people in the working areas deep in the plan of the building.

Figure 2.12 A glazed street/atrium (National Trust HQ)
(© Dennis Gilbert/VIEW Pictures/Alamy Stock Photo)

2.5.4   Remote distribution

It is possible to provide some daylight into spaces that have no possibility of windows or
rooflights through remote distribution devices, such as light pipes. Such systems take various
forms, but all collect daylight and sunlight in some way and transmit it through a shaft or
pipe by reflection to a distribution point in the space (Figures 2.13 and 2.14). The efficiency
of such systems is limited by the distance over which the light must be transmitted, as well as
deviations from a straight path. The efficiency of many remote distribution systems can also
vary dramatically from clear to overcast skies. Nonetheless, where there is no other possibility of
providing daylight to a space, remote distribution systems can be appreciated.

Figure 2.13 Light pipes collectors on flat roof
(courtesy of Solatube Daylighting Systems)

Figure 2.14 Light pipe tubes dropping in a grid over an office space
(courtesy of Solatube Daylighting Systems)

2.6   Maintenance considerations

The build-up of dirt on the exterior and interior surfaces of windows and rooflights will reduce the transmittance of the glass, and therefore the amount of daylight entering the building. The degree to which this occurs will depend largely on the slope of the glass and the air quality of the local environment. A busy urban environment will produce more dirt then a rural one. To minimise the problem, a regular window cleaning programme is needed, which will require easy and safe access to the windows. Without this, window cleaning will be difficult and expensive and is likely that it will not be carried out as often as necessary, if at all. Therefore, the accessibility of glazing elements should always be a key consideration in daylighting design.

2.7   Conclusion

Daylight in buildings is desirable and beneficial for many reasons, but it must be controlled in order to provide a comfortable environment for occupants and facilitate their use of the building. Good daylighting balances the need to make the best use of available daylight with aesthetic, thermal, and visual considerations, as well as practical issues such as privacy and security. A number of tools and techniques are available for the prediction of daylight quantity and quality in buildings, but these must be used with care to ensure that the correct design solution is achieved.

2.8   Further reading

This chapter provides only a brief summary of the key issues to consider when approaching daylighting design. More detailed guidance on daylighting can be found in SLL Lighting Guide 10 (SLL, 2014), as well as a number of other books, including *Daylighting Design in Architecture* (Loe and Mansfield, 1998) and *Daylighting: Architecture and Lighting Design* (Tregenza and Wilson, 2013).

References

BRE (1986a) *Estimating daylight in buildings: part 1* DG309 (Garston: BRE Electronic Publications)

BRE (1986b) *Estimating daylight in buildings: part 2* DG310 (Garston: BRE Electronic Publications)

CIE (1995) *Discomfort glare in interior lighting* CIE Technical Report 117 (Vienna, Austria: International Commission on Illumination)

Hunt DRG (1979) *Availability of daylight* (Garston: IHS BRE Press)

Littlefair PJ (2011) *Site layout planning for daylight and sunlight: a guide to good practice* BR209 (Garston: BRE Press)

Loe D and Mansfield K (1998) *Daylighting Design in Architecture* (Garston: BRECSU/BRE)

Lynes JA and Cuttle K (1988) 'Bracelet for total solar shading' *Lighting Research and Technology* **20**(3) 105–113

Tregenza P and Wilson M (2013) *Daylighting: Architecture and Lighting Design* (Abingdon: Routledge)

SLL (2014) *Daylighting — a guide for designers* SLL Lighting Guide 10 (London: Society of Light and Lighting)

Chapter 3: Emergency lighting

3.1   Legislation and standards

Emergency lighting is a legal requirement in almost all premises. Full details for the design of emergency lighting systems can be found in SLL Lighting Guide 12: *Emergency lighting* (SLL, 2015).

When the normal mains lighting fails in areas without natural light it is usually necessary to evacuate the premises, to move people to a place of safety or to allow essential processes to continue or be shut down. During this period, emergency lighting should be provided from a power source independent of that supplying the normal lighting.

The following European Union Regulation and Directives have implications for emergency lighting:

- The Construction Products Regulation (305/2011/EU) (EU, 2011)
- The Workplace Directive (89/654/EEC) (EC, 1989)
- The Signs Directive (92/58/EEC) (EC, 1992).

Requirements defined by the above Regulation and Directives have been incorporated into UK law. For emergency lighting, this has been achieved in England and Wales through the Building Regulations 2010 (TSO, 2010a) and the associated Approved Document B (NBS, 2006a/b), in Scotland through the Building (Scotland) Regulations 2004 (TSO, 2004) and associated *Technical Handbooks* (Scottish Government, 2017a/b), and in Northern Ireland through the Building Regulations (Northern Ireland) 2012 (TSO, 2012) and associated Technical Booklet E (DFPNI, 2012). The Health and Safety (Safety Signs and Signals) Regulations 1996 (HMSO, 1996) also incorporate requirements according to the EU Signs Directive (EC, 1992).

In addition, the Regulatory Reform (Fire Safety) Order 2005 (TSO, 2005) forms the primary piece of legislation in England and Wales for ensuring risk reduction and fire prevention within buildings. The order requires that an employer, owner or any person who exercises control over any part of the premises takes reasonable steps to reduce the risk of fire and to ensure that occupants can safely escape if a fire does occur. To meet these obligations, it is necessary for the designated Responsible Person (or a delegated Competent Person) to carry out a risk assessment, create and implement a plan to deal with an emergency and, where five or more persons are employed, to document the findings. BS 5266-1: *Emergency lighting. Code of practice for the emergency lighting of premises* (BSI, 2016) forms an essential reference in this respect.

Equivalent legislation to the Regulatory Reform (Fire Safety) Order 2005 (TSO, 2005) exists in Scotland under the Fire Safety (Scotland) Regulations 2006 (TSO, 2006) and in Northern Ireland under the Fire Safety Regulations (Northern Ireland) 2010 (TSO, 2010).

As well as these legal requirements for emergency lighting, various standards govern both equipment design and performance and the design of emergency lighting products and systems. BS EN 60598 is the applicable product standard for luminaires, Part 2-22 (BSI, 2014) of the standard covering the particular requirements for emergency lighting. BS 5499 (BSI, 2013a, 2014b), BS EN ISO 7010 (BSI, 2012/2016) and BS ISO 3864 (BSI, 2011a/b, 2012a) cover the location, operation, colours, design, photometric requirements and layout of emergency signs. There are numerous product standards covering lamps and individual components of luminaires. BS 5266 covers design of emergency lighting systems as well as some specific equipment and forms a key guidance document for those involved in the specification, installation and management of emergency lighting. Part 1 of BS 5266 was substantially updated in its sixth edition, principally to expand its scope to cover emergency safety lighting and standby lighting. BS 5266 consists of the following Parts:

- BS 5266-1: *Emergency lighting. Code of practice for the emergency lighting of premises* (BSI, 2016)

- BS 5266-2: *Emergency lighting. Code of practice for electrical low mounted way guidance systems for emergency use* (BSI, 1998)

- BS 5266-4: *Emergency lighting. Code of practice for design, installation, maintenance and use of optical fibre systems* (BSI, 1999a)

- BS 5266-5: *Emergency lighting. Specification for component parts of optical fibre systems* (BSI, 1999b)

- BS 5266-6: *Emergency lighting. Code of practice for non-electrical low mounted way guidance systems for emergency use. Photoluminescent systems* (BSI, 1999c).

Other standards covering the design of lighting schemes and that make reference to emergency lighting include BS EN 1838: *Lighting applications. Emergency lighting* (BSI, 2013b) (replaces BS 5266-7), BS EN 50172/BS 5266-8: *Emergency escape lighting systems* (BSI, 2004), BS EN 12464 *Lighting of workplaces* (BSI, 2011c, 2014c) and BS EN 12193: *Sports lighting* (BSI, 2007).

3.2   Types of emergency lighting

Emergency lighting can take several different forms depending on its purpose, as shown by Figure 3.1. The main classifications are 'emergency escape lighting', 'emergency safety lighting' and 'standby lighting'. Emergency escape lighting is further subdivided into the lighting of the escape route, the lighting of open areas where there is no defined escape route, and the lighting of high-risk task areas where a hazardous activity takes place and needs to be made safe before evacuation.

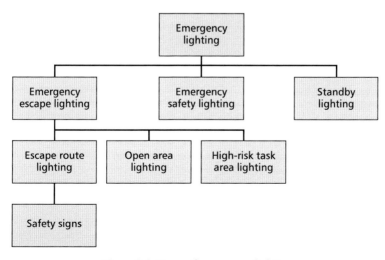

Figure 3.1 Types of emergency lighting

3.2.1   Emergency escape lighting

Emergency escape lighting provides illumination of escape routes, signs and points of emphasis to assist occupants in evacuating a building in a safe manner.

3.2.1.1   Escape route lighting

An escape route is a clearly defined route provided for the safe evacuation of occupants in an emergency to a place of safety. The lighting of such routes is specified in terms of minimum illuminances on the floor, illuminance diversity, glare limits, response times, duration and light source colour rendering. The specific criteria are as follows:

- *Minimum illuminance*: 1 lux along the centre line for escape routes up to 2 m in width; 0.5 lux along the centre band of the route, consisting of at least 50% of the route width. For wider escape routes, these may be considered as a number of 2 m wide strips or are treated as open area lighting.

- *Illuminance diversity*: maximum/minimum illuminance on the centre line < 40.

- *Maximum luminaire luminous intensity for level routes*: see values in Table 3.1 below; these apply in all directions for angles between 60 and 90 degrees from the downward vertical.

- *Maximum luminaire luminous intensity for non-level routes*: see values in Table 3.1 below; these apply for all directions and angles.

- *Maximum response time*: 50% of required illuminance within 5 s of supply failing and 100% of required illuminance within 60 s.

- *Minimum duration*: 1 hour if premises are evacuated immediately upon supply failure and not reoccupied until batteries are fully recharged, otherwise 3 hours.

- *Minimum light source general colour rendering index*: CRI > 40.

3.2.1.2   Open area lighting

An open area is defined as a room with a floor area greater than 60 m^2 or a room that has been deemed as requiring emergency lighting via risk assessment; for example, an inner room that forms part of the escape route or an underground or windowless room. Signage defining access to escape routes should be visible from all points within an open area.

The lighting requirements for open areas are as follows:

- *Minimum illuminance*: on the empty floor, excluding a 0.5 m wide perimeter band: 0.5 lx.

- *Illuminance diversity*: maximum/minimum illuminance on the empty floor < 40.

- *Maximum luminaire luminous intensity*: see values in Table 3.1 below. These values apply in all directions for angles in the zone 60 to 90 degrees from downward vertical.

- *Maximum response time*: 50% of required illuminance within 5 s of supply failing and 100% of required illuminance within 60 s.

- *Minimum duration*: 1 hour if premises are evacuated immediately upon supply failure and not reoccupied until batteries are fully recharged, otherwise 3 hours.

- *Minimum light source general colour rendering index*: CRI > 40.

3.2.1.3 High-risk task area lighting

A high-risk task area is defined as one where a hazardous activity occurs that has to be made safe or terminated before leaving or where people passing by may be exposed to the hazard, e.g. cooking, moving machinery. The presence of a high-risk task area should be revealed by the mandatory risk assessment required by the applicable fire safety regulations. The lighting requirements for high-risk task areas are as follows:

- *Minimum illuminance*: 10% of the required maintained illuminance on the reference plane for the task or the illuminance level determined by risk assessment if higher, but at least 15 lx and free from any stroboscopic effects that could create a hazard.

- *Minimum/average illuminance uniformity*: on the reference plane for the task > 0.1.

- *Maximum luminaire luminous intensity*: see values in Table 3.1. These values apply in the zone 60 to 90 degrees from downward vertical.

- *Maximum response time*: 100% of minimum illuminance within 0.5 s of supply failing.

- *Minimum duration*: period for which the risk exists to people.

- *Minimum light source general colour rendering index*: CRI > 40.

Table 3.1 Disability glare limits

Mounting height above floor (m)	Maximum luminous intensity for escape route and open area lighting (cd)	Maximum luminous intensity for high-risk task area lighting (cd)
$h < 2.5$	500	1000
$2.5 \leq h < 3.0$	900	1800
$3.0 \leq h < 3.5$	1600	3200
$3.5 \leq h < 4.0$	2500	5000
$4.0 \leq h < 4.5$	3500	7000
$h \geq 4.5$	5000	10 000

3.2.1.4 Safety signs

It should be noted that safety signs must be visible at all times when the premises are occupied to indicate safety equipment locations and safe routes to leave a building, whether the main lighting is working or not. Safety signs include escape route and exit signs, fire safety notices and any other safety-related signs identified by risk assessment and that need to be conspicuous and legible whenever the premises are occupied.

For escape route and exit signs, BS 5499-4 (BSI, 2013a) provides recommendations and guidance on their selection, location and use. Escape route pictograms are required to adhere to the format defined within BS EN ISO 7010 (BSI, 2012/2016) (Figure 3.2), although European format pictograms (Figure 3.3) also remain acceptable for some situations; for example, where refurbishments are taking place and the additional requirement to ensure that only one pictogram format is used throughout the building is being observed. For other safety signs, BS 5499-10 (BSI, 2014b) provides guidance on their location and use.

Figure 3.2 Examples of BS EN ISO 7010 exit sign pictograms

Figure 3.3 Example of European format exit sign pictogram

In addition to design aspects, all safety signs must conform to BS ISO 3864-4 (BSI, 2011b) in terms of their colorimetric and photometric properties as well as meeting geometric, response time and duration requirements. For internally illuminated safety signs, these must also meet the requirements of ISO 30061 (ISO, 2007) with the luminance measurement method for contrast being according to BS EN 60598-2-22 (BSI, 2014a). The requirements for safety signs can be summarised as follows.

Internally illuminated safety signs, when powered:

- *Colour*: according to BS ISO 3864-4 Table 2 chromaticity coordinates.
- *Minimum luminance of safety colour*: 2 cd/m^2.
- *Luminance contrast*: luminance ratio of contrast colour white between 5 and 15 of that of the safety colour.
- *Luminance diversity*: ratio of maximum to minimum luminance within either white or safety colour < 10:1.
- *Maximum response time*: 50% of required luminance within 5 s of supply failing and 100% of required luminance within 60 s.
- *Minimum duration*: 1 hour if premises are evacuated immediately upon supply failure and not reoccupied until batteries are fully recharged, otherwise 3 hours.

Internally illuminated safety signs, when unpowered:

- *Colorimetric and photometric requirements*: BS ISO 3864-4 Table 1 for externally illuminated signs applies.

Externally illuminated safety signs:

- *Colorimetric and photometric requirements*: BS ISO 3864-4 Table 1 applies.

- *Minimum illuminance during emergency lighting conditions*: 5 lx.

Viewing distances for escape route signs:

- *Maximum viewing distance*: $l = z_0$ (distance factor) $\times h$ (sign height), where z_0 is according to BS ISO 5499-4 Table 3 for powered internally illuminated escape route signs or BS ISO 5499-4 Table 2 for externally illuminated escape route signs.

- *Viewing angle not perpendicular to the sign face*: the distance factor z_0 is reduced by a multiplying factor of the cosine of viewing angle to the normal of the sign face.

Viewing distance for other safety signs:

- *Maximum viewing distance*: $l = z_0$ (distance factor) $\times h$ (sign height), where z_0 is according to BS ISO 5499-10 Table 1 for externally illuminated safety signs or distance factor of 60 for powered internally illuminated safety signs.

- *Viewing angle not perpendicular to the sign face*: distance factor z_0 is reduced by a multiplying factor of the cosine of viewing angle to the normal of the sign face.

3.2.1.5   Points of emphasis

In addition to providing illumination and signage for escape routes, open areas and high-risk task areas, emergency escape lighting luminaires should also be positioned at or within a 2-metre horizontal distance of any points that present an increased hazard on the escape route or that require particular highlighting.

Points of emphasis are defined as follows:

- any exit door intended to be used in an emergency

- stairs or any other changes in level

- changes in direction

- any safety signs including escape route signs that need to be externally illuminated

- intersections of corridors

- final exits, including the route outside the building to a place of safety

- firefighting equipment and first aid points

- areas where escape equipment is provided for disabled people

- refuges and call points, including two-way communication systems and disabled toilet alarm call points

- manual release points for electronically locked doors.

3.2.1.6   Non-residential premises used for recreation

For premises such as theatres, cinemas and restaurants, the recommendations for emergency escape lighting are modified to allow for typical use of the building.

It is often necessary for such premises that the normal lighting be dimmed or turned off, and in these circumstances a maintained system should be installed. For cinema and theatre auditoria, where the recommended maintained illuminance level could affect normal working, a reduced maintained level of 0.02 lx is acceptable provided required emergency illuminance levels are restored within 5 s of a failure in supply to the normal lighting.

For areas with *fixed* seating, these are treated as for the recommendations for open areas except that the acceptable minimum illuminance for the emergency lighting level is reduced to 0.1 lx on a plane 1 m above the floor, this taking into account the fact that seating rows tend to direct people to adjacent gangways for which the recommendations for escape routes apply.

3.2.2   Emergency safety lighting

If the risk assessment of the premises allows occupants to remain in the building in the event of a failure of the normal lighting supply, then additional measures to those specified for emergency escape lighting, and according to the guidance for emergency safety lighting provided by BS 5266-1 (BSI, 2016), may be applied. Minimum illuminance within any areas that occupants remain or move in this case is 1 lx. However, a risk assessment should consider whether higher illuminance levels may be necessary, for example, to ensure the safe movement of people within the building or to allow for people with visual impairments.

Where the emergency plan defines a 'stay put' strategy, procedures should then make clear any consequent or subsequent actions to maintain safety, for example, to impose an eventual evacuation procedure should a supply failure continue to the point where only one hour emergency duration remains in batteries.

3.2.3   Standby lighting

In areas or places where continued normal occupancy and operation of the premises during a failure of the normal lighting supply is required, standby lighting may be installed. An example of such a location would be an operating theatre in a hospital. The system should provide adequate illumination for the visual tasks as recommended in the 'Schedule of lighting requirements' (section 2.2) of the *SLL Code for Lighting* (SLL, 2012). If standby lighting is used for escape lighting, then the escape lighting part should be segregated from the rest of the system and should conform to the rules applied to emergency lighting systems.

3.3   Design approaches

Emergency lighting should be considered as an integrated part of the building lighting. Unless this is done, there is a risk that the normal lighting and the emergency lighting will clash in function and appearance to the detriment of the whole scheme.

Emergency lighting can be provided either by self-contained units or a centrally powered system using batteries or a motor-generator set. A self-contained unit contains its own power source and can be a stand-alone luminaire or an emergency version of the normal lighting luminaires. Central systems provide power to the emergency light source via separate, protected wiring to slave luminaires.

For small buildings, the most economical solution has historically been self-contained units, with centrally supplied systems tending to be specified for larger buildings such as office blocks, factories and shopping centres. The balance of costs between the two types of system is related to the equipment cost, installation cost and maintenance costs, with recent advancements in the technologies associated with emergency lighting tending to even out the cost differences between the two types of system regardless of installation size. The technology factors influencing this trend include:

- widespread adoption of LED, allowing improved reliability and system efficiencies with consequent reduction in battery capacities

- improved reliability and operating lifetime of batteries

- increased adoption of automatic testing as recommended by BS 5266-1

- utilisation of standardised communication protocols (e.g. DALI), allowing the remote monitoring of automatically tested self-contained luminaires

- greater availability of cost-effective LED luminaires suitable for use with centrally powered inverter systems (e.g. DALI-dimmable LED drivers).

Together, these factors have provided significant improvements in the overall safety and reliability of emergency lighting systems whilst allowing reductions in system component and maintenance costs.

3.4 Emergency lighting equipment

3.4.1 Power sources

3.4.1.1 Self-contained luminaires

Self-contained luminaires have a secondary sealed battery, a charger (control unit), circuitry (which monitors the mains supply) and a light source. In the mains-healthy condition, the battery is charged. In the event of a failure of the mains supply, the battery supplies the light source via an inverter or drive circuit. The battery is commonly a sealed rechargeable nickel-cadmium or nickel-metal hydride type conforming to its respective performance requirements of BS EN 61951-1 (BSI, 2014d) and BS EN 61951-2 (BSI, 2017a) and the safety requirements of BS EN 62133 (BSI, 2017b/c). Other battery types may also be used provided they conform to their relevant performance and safety standards as well as the specific requirements of Annex A of BS EN 60598-2-22 (BSI, 2014a), which includes standardised temperature classifications, charge and discharge current limits, and a requirement that the battery allows the luminaire to meet its rated duration for a minimum service life of four years. Where lithium–ion batteries are used, these are generally limited to the more stable chemistry types such as lithium–ion phosphate (LiFePO$_4$). Precautions must also be applied in the transport and disposal of batteries, for which significant differences in associated costs between the various battery chemistries can also apply (see Chapter 4, 'Design ethos').

3.4.1.2 Central battery systems

Central battery systems consist of a remotely located power source connected by protected wiring to slave luminaires. The batteries consist of either vented or sealed lead-acid or nickel cadmium alkaline cells. These have high storage capacity, long life and a wide operating voltage range. Batteries used for central battery systems must conform to BS EN 50171 (BSI, 2001). In addition to the battery, the system includes sub-circuit monitoring of the supply to normal lighting, and an automatic change-over device to connect the slave luminaires to the power supply when the mains supply fails. There are three main types of systems:

- *AC/DC battery powered systems*: these systems supply direct current from the battery to the emergency slave luminaires, normally at 24, 50 or 110 V. If a maintained system is required, this is normally achieved by using a transformer to provide the appropriate output voltage in the supply healthy condition. Special or modified luminaires have to be used to be compatible with both AC and DC supplies over the range of output voltages and the effects of supply-cable voltage drop. These luminaires normally provide higher light outputs than are available from self-contained luminaires.

- *AC/AC battery powered systems*: these modify the output from the battery by using an inverter to create 230/240 V AC. These systems can operate any suitable normal luminaires, which do not need to be modified, and so they can provide full light output in the emergency condition. The power unit has to be matched to the emergency load and be capable of supplying both the total wattage and VA rating of the load and also of providing the full starting surge of the luminaires. Static inverters designed for the application should be compatible with the luminaire characteristics but caution should be exercised if a system using a general-purpose uninterruptible power supply unit (see below) is being designed. BS EN 50171 (BSI, 2001) sets out some important points that need to be checked.

- *Uninterruptible power supplies (UPS)*: these are a form of AC inverter that continue to provide their output without a break during a supply failure, enabling them to be used with discharge lamps that otherwise would have unacceptably long re-strike times. Because these inverters are normally used for computer back-up, care must be taken to ensure they are correctly engineered for emergency lighting use. The UPS must comply with the requirements of the various Parts of BS EN 62040: *Uninterruptible power systems (UPS)* (BSI, 2006–2017), as well as BS EN 50171 (BSI, 2001). The charger must be capable of recharging the battery to 80% of capacity within 12 hours. The battery must be designed for a 10-year design life (lower life batteries exhibit a sudden failure mode, which will not be picked up by the emergency lighting testing procedures). The output must be capable in the emergency condition of clearing all distribution protection devices and fuses (normally a UPS unit drops to zero voltage when sensing a distribution short circuit). It is important to clear the protection device and re-supply those parts of the building that do not have a fault. The inverter must be capable of starting the load from the battery in an emergency. The system monitors, as defined in BS EN 50171, should be supplied.

3.4.1.3   Generators

The main components of a generator system are a prime mover driving an alternator, fuel tanks, operating controls, and starter batteries or flywheel drive. The generator has to be able to start automatically and to provide the power for the load within 5 s as detailed in BS 5266-1 (BSI, 2016). As with all central systems, the distribution wiring must be fire protected and the final normal lighting circuit must be monitored such that emergency luminaires are automatically activated if the local circuit fails. As compliance with the safety requirements for the whole generator system may be arduous, it may be preferable to provide one-hour-duration battery-powered luminaires in addition to the generator set. Testing of generators should be in accordance with the manufacturer's instructions.

3.4.2   Circuits

3.4.2.1   Cabling

For self-contained systems, all the wiring is internal to the luminaire. The luminaire should conform to BS EN 60598-2-22 (BSI, 2014a) and be CE-marked.

For central systems, the integrity of the system is the paramount design consideration as the failure of a single part could render the entire emergency lighting installation ineffective. Where possible, the power supply should incorporate some redundancy, for example more than one battery room and multiple distribution circuits can be provided. To enhance integrity further, the distribution circuits should be divided and segregated such that the risk of a total loss of emergency lighting in any one area is minimized. Precautions should include the use of fire survival cables such as mineral-insulated copper conductor (MICC) cables, armoured power cables to BS 7846 (BSI, 2015b) or low-smoke-and-fume (LSF) cables in protected routes. Examples of methods of protection include metal trunking and conduit. Cables run in ceiling voids that do not form part of a fire-rated zone should not be run on open trays unless they are of the MICC type, armoured cable to BS 7846 or conform to cable performance standards BS 6387 (BSI, 2013c) or IEC 60364-5-52 (IEC, 2009). Particular attention should be paid to the most vulnerable parts of the distribution system, for example where cabling enters and leaves enclosures and luminaires. Suitable glands should be provided that maintain the same level of integrity as the cabling being used. Where slave luminaires are spurred off a main circuit, the final cabling should be to the same standard as the rest of the system. Cabling provided solely for emergency lighting purposes should be clearly identified as such and labelled accordingly. It is desirable to include some form of sensing to prove the integrity of the emergency lighting circuits.

3.4.2.2 Electromagnetic compatibility (EMC)

It is important that the overall design of emergency lighting systems are EMC-compliant, as many of the components used in these systems, although individually suitable, may interact in such a way as to generate electrical interference. Verification should be sought from the equipment manufacturers and systems integrators that EMC issues have been considered properly. This is particularly important when attempting to convert conventional luminaires to emergency lighting luminaires with an 'emergency pack'.

3.4.2.3 Protection

Cabling, changeover relays and luminaires should be resistant to interference from transient over-voltages caused by supply surges and by switching (changeover). Protection should be provided that ensures safe operation of the emergency lighting under transient conditions, as well as protecting the equipment itself from damage.

Surge-protection devices should be self-resetting and not render the emergency lighting inoperative.

3.4.2.4 Interactions

Where a building management system (BMS) is employed, it is essential that any failure of this does not adversely affect the emergency lighting, for example by incorrectly switching maintained luminaires. A BMS-system failure should not be seen by the emergency lighting system hold-off relays as a general lighting power-supply failure.

The increased use of lighting controls has seen a greater integration of emergency lighting monitoring and testing as part of overall lighting control and management systems. Depending on the type of emergency system selected, additional care must be taken to ensure the emergency lighting is capable of operating independently from the control system, thus in the event of a power failure allowing the emergency lighting to default to emergency operation condition. Systems utilising a communication interface such as DALI ('digital addressable lighting interface') must be configured such that emergency luminaires default to a safe 'system failure level' upon a power failure, including where supply may be lost to system controls. Luminaires used on central systems must also default to a defined output, and it must be ensured that any dimming system is overridden under alarm conditions.

3.4.2.5 Special circuits

In addition to these general considerations, there are some special circuits required for maintenance work or testing. For details, see SLL Lighting Guide 12: *Emergency lighting* (SLL, 2012).

3.4.3 Luminaires

There are two basic types of emergency lighting luminaires: self-contained and slave. These should both conform to BS EN 60598-2-22 (BSI, 2014a).

3.4.3.1 Self-contained luminaires

Self-contained emergency luminaires contain a battery to provide power and may be of three main types: maintained, non-maintained or combined. A maintained luminaire is one in which all the emergency lighting light sources are operating when the normal lighting is on and when there is a failure of the mains electricity supply. A non-maintained luminaire is one in which all the emergency lighting light sources are in operation only when the electricity supply to the normal lighting fails. A combined (or sustained) luminaire is one containing at least two light sources, one of which is energized from the normal lighting supply and the other from the emergency lighting supply.

Self-contained luminaires may be dedicated or may be converted from normal luminaires by adding an emergency conversion unit. When carrying out a conversion, it is essential that the modified luminaire complies with all relevant standards; for example, to ensure that the temperature limits of components, particularly batteries, are not exceeded. If the work is not carried out by the original equipment manufacturer, the person who does it must have relevant training and experience. More detailed guidance can be found in ICEL Publication 1004: *The requirements for the re-engineering of luminaires for emergency lighting use* (ICEL, 2014). The product must be retested for compliance with CE Mark requirements and conform to BS EN 60598-2-22 (BSI, 2014a).

3.4.3.2 Slave luminaires

Slave luminaires are normal luminaires that have mains-voltage operating components or have components intended only for emergency use, and have a power feed from a central emergency power source. Special care must be taken over the loop-in and loop-out of supply wiring using joint glands so that fire will not damage the feed cables in the luminaire. Alternatively, the luminaires may be fed by means of a spur off a protected ring. Slave luminaires may be designed to operate from either AC or DC power supplies. For an AC supply, the luminaire is normally AC, but may be DC with internal rectifiers. Supply voltage in emergency mode may not be the same as that in mains mode — if the luminaires are maintained, a changeover relay will be needed. For a DC supply, the luminaires may be DC or fitted with an inverter to operate on AC. Again, if they are maintained, a changeover relay will be required. In both cases, the designer must be clear as to the lumen output available from the luminaires in emergency mode.

3.4.4 Luminaire classification

Table 3.2 below shows the emergency lighting luminaire classification system defined by BS EN 60598-2-22 (BSI, 2014a). Emergency luminaires must be marked with the resulting code, which identifies the type of system, mode of operation, facilities and, for self-contained luminaires, the rated duration. Figure 3.4 below shows an example classification marking, which informs that the luminaire is of self-contained type with non-maintained mode of operation; that it includes remote rest mode, inhibit mode and automatic testing facilities; and that it has a rated emergency duration of three hours.

Table 3.2 Emergency lighting luminaire classification

Type	Mode of operation	Facilities	Duration for self-contained luminaires
x = self-contained	0 = non-maintained	A = including test device	10 = 10 minutes
z = central system	1 = maintained	B = including remote rest mode	60 = 1 hour
	2 = combined non-maintained	C = including inhibit mode	120 = 2 hours
	3 = combined maintained	D = high-risk task-area luminaire (0.5 s to 100% output)	180 = 3 hours
	4 = compound non-maintained	E = with non-replaceable lamp(s) and/or battery	
	5 = compound maintained	F = automatic test gear (denoted EL-T)	
	6 = satellite	G = internally illuminated safety sign	

Figure 3.4 Example luminaire classification marking

3.4.5 Light sources

To be suitable for use in emergency lighting luminaires, light sources need to have fast run-up and restrike times, and preferably a long life. Tungsten and tungsten halogen lamps are infrequently used because of their low efficiency and short life, except in low-temperature applications, because in such conditions their light output is not affected.

Light emitting diodes (LEDs) are now the most widely used light source in emergency lighting. Their small footprint, high efficacy and long life have revolutionised the way emergency lighting is designed and operated. Small form factors coupled with the availability of high-lumen packages provide a highly efficient and reliable light source suited to the requirements of emergency lighting, particularly when combined with appropriate optics.

Fluorescent lamps, in either linear or compact form, continue to be used in many emergency lighting schemes. Lamps may be run with hot or cold cathodes, hot cathode providing advantages in cycle life and starting reliability. Lamps with internal starters should not be used and care must be exercised when using amalgam versions of fluorescent lamps because these have slow run-up characteristics. Care should also be taken when replacing fluorescent lamps as wide tolerances can affect performance. High-pressure discharge lamps are not normally suitable for emergency lighting because of their extended run-up and re-strike times.

An important consideration in the selection of light sources for use in emergency lighting is the likelihood of their failure, as any dark area around a failed light in an emergency lighting installation can be dangerous. Chapter 6, 'Light sources', gives general information on this but, for accurate information, the emergency luminaire or lamp manufacturer's data should be used for all actual designs of emergency lighting. The manufacturer's data are based on light sources running on conventional control gear in normal ambient conditions. This gives values of lamp survival factor (LSF) that may be expected for maintained emergency lighting installations. LSF in non-maintained installations is harder to predict. Although the number of hours that lamps are running in non-maintained installations is low, regular inspections are necessary to ensure all units are working. Lamps used in climates, or spaces, with high temperatures or low temperatures need special consideration. See Chapter 23, 'Extreme environments'.

3.4.6 Unpowered light sources

There are two forms of safety sign that do not require any power to be delivered.

One uses radioactive tritium as a light source. Tritium powered signs give a low light output but can be useful in locations where flammable or explosive atmosphere is present. A risk assessment should be undertaken to ensure that their output is adequate at the location where they are intended to be used. Special care must be taken during disposal of these devices as they are radioactive and there are legal obligations for their safe handling and storage.

The other uses the phenomenon of photo-luminescence to provide light (see section 3.2.1.4). For this to work, the sign has to be well illuminated prior to the emergency. In the event of mains failure, a chemical reaction, created by the previous illumination, causes the sign to emit light at a low level, considerably less than the signage requirements of BS EN 1838 (BSI, 2013b); however, they are useful to provide additional information and are required for emergency lighting on ships.

Low-mounted way guidance systems may be used in addition to the required emergency lighting. Such systems should conform to BS 5266-6.

3.5 Scheme planning

3.5.1 Risk assessment

The first step in planning an emergency lighting installation is to carry out a fire risk assessment according to the type of premises. In workplaces where five or more people are employed, such an assessment is a legal requirement. A fire risk assessment requires working through the following steps:

- *Identify potential fire hazards in the workplace*: sources of ignition, fuels, work processes.

- *Identify the location of people at significant risk in case of fire*: who might be in danger (employees, visitors) and why?

- *Evaluate the risks*: are safety measures adequate or does more need to be done — fire detection, warning, means of fighting fire, means of escape, fire safety training of employees, maintenance and testing of fire precautions?

- *Carry out improvements.*

- *Record findings and actions taken*: prepare emergency plans, inform, instruct and train employees.

● *Keep assessment under review*: revise it when situation changes.

3.5.2 Planning sequence

Given that the risk assessment reveals a need for emergency lighting, it is then necessary to identify the lighting requirements that have to be met, the type of system to be used, mode of operation and aspects such as duration and photometric performance.

3.5.2.1 Mode of operation

Maintained luminaires should be specified in the following circumstances:

● for exit signs where occupants may be unfamiliar with the premises

● in areas where failure of an individual luminaire affecting the normal lighting could lead to a hazardous situation

● for non-residential premises used for recreation (e.g. cinemas, theatres) where the normal lighting might be dimmed or turned off.

Where emergency illumination only needs to be provided upon failure of the mains supply, non-maintained luminaires may be specified.

3.5.2.2 Duration

The minimum duration for emergency escape lighting stipulated by BS EN 1838 (BSI, 2013b) is one hour, although for most applications a longer duration is required. BS 5266-1 (BSI, 2016) considers the factors to be taken into account when specifying the duration of the system, such as the size and complexity of the premises, its intended use, and whether occupants may be unfamiliar with its layout (see Table 3.3 below).

For premises that are not expected to be evacuated immediately upon a supply failure, such as sleeping accommodation or places of entertainment, or where reoccupation is expected to take place as soon as the supply is restored, a minimum duration of three hours should be specified. A minimum duration of three hours should also be specified where occupants might be unfamiliar with the building layout or where emergency safety lighting is being deployed.

A minimum duration of one hour should only be specified if the premises are evacuated immediately in the event of a supply failure and are not reoccupied until the batteries have fully recharged following re-establishment of the supply. Owing to these restrictions, the application of 1-hour rated systems is uncommon in practice.

3.5.2.3 Photometric compliance

BS EN 60598-2-22 (BSI, 2014a) requires manufacturers of emergency luminaires to make available intensity distribution data to enable system designers to calculate the photometric parameters of the emergency lighting installation.

When authenticated, these data can be used to confirm photometric compliance of the system according to the requirements of BS EN 1838 (BSI, 2013b) and the design procedures defined within BS 5266-1 (BSI, 2016), thereby reducing the need for on-site photometric measurements, which historically have been shown to be complex to set up, time consuming and prone to error.

Table 3.3 Recommended duration

Application class	Example premises	Occupants expected to be familiar with layout?	System considerations	Recommended minimum duration (hours)
Premises used as sleeping accommodation	Hotels, hospitals, care homes, guest houses, boarding schools	No	Premises may not be evacuated immediately upon supply failure Occupants may be disabled Requirement for early reoccupation upon restoration of supply likely Higher likelihood of standby or emergency safety lighting being required	3
Non-residential premises used for treatment or care	Clinics, dental practices, special schools	No	Premises may not be evacuated immediately upon supply failure Evacuation times may be extended Requirement for early reoccupation upon restoration of supply likely	3
Non-residential premises used for recreation	Theatres, cinemas, concert halls, exhibition halls, sports halls, public houses, restaurants	No	Premises may not be evacuated immediately upon supply failure Requirement for early reoccupation upon restoration of supply likely	3
Non-residential premises used for teaching, training and research, and offices	Schools, colleges, technical institutes, laboratories	Yes	Timely and orderly evacuation can be expected for this class of premises	1 (if no requirement for early reoccupation is specified) 3 (if early reoccupation is required or premises are occupied outside of normal weekday office hours)
Non-residential public premises	Shops, shopping malls, libraries, town halls, art galleries, museums	No	Evacuation times may be extended owing to the possibility of large numbers of occupants Requirement for early reoccupation upon restoration of supply likely	3

Table continues

Table 3.3 Recommended duration — *continued*

Application class	Example premises	Occupants expected to be familiar with layout?	System considerations	Recommended minimum duration (hours)
Industrial premises	Factories, workshops, warehouses	Yes	Timely and orderly evacuation can be expected for this class of premises	1 (if no requirement for early reoccupation is specified) 3 (if early reoccupation is required)
Common access routes within residential accommodation	Flats, maisonettes	Yes	Timely and orderly evacuation can be expected for this class of premises Escape routes will generally be leading from premises used as sleeping accommodation	3
Covered car parks	Single level or multi-storey car parks	No	Risk assessment should identify the extent and location of the pedestrian escape route Impact resistant luminaires may be required	3
Sports stadia	Football grounds, athletics stadia, velodromes	No	Evacuation times may be extended owing to the possibility of large numbers of occupants Requirement for early reoccupation upon supply restoration likely Impact resistant luminaires may be required	3

3.5.2.4   Considerations for specific locations

Certain locations within the premises may not fall under the criteria to be designated as an escape route, open area or high-risk task area, although they may be deemed by risk assessment as requiring emergency lighting. BS 5266-1 (BSI, 2016) provides specific guidance for the following locations:

- *External areas in the immediate vicinity of exits*: to be illuminated in accordance with the requirements for escape routes. Reliance cannot be placed on the presence of street lighting to provide illumination unless it can be demonstrated that the street lighting will be on at all times the premises is in use.

- *Evacuation lift cars*: emergency illumination to be provided in accordance with BS EN 81-20 (BSI, 2014e).

- *Moving stairways and walkways*: to be illuminated in accordance with the requirements for escape routes.

- *Toilet facilities and changing rooms*: multi-closet and disabled facilities without borrowed light should have emergency illumination from at least one luminaire. All facilities exceeding a floor area of 8 m^2 to be illuminated in accordance with requirements for open areas.

- *Motor–generator, control, plant and switch rooms*: emergency lighting to be provided according to a minimum illuminance level of 15 lx in the plane of the visual task.

- *Covered car parks*: areas identified as pedestrian escape routes should be provided with emergency lighting meeting the requirements for escape routes.

In addition, there may be locations within the premises where activities take place that require controlled shutdown procedures or that support functions to ensure the safety of occupants during a supply failure. Risk assessment may identify that these locations require a higher light level and/or faster response time and BS 5266-1 provides examples of such locations together with recommended illuminance levels, response times, minimum duration and applicable working plane (see Table 3.4). Guidance is also provided for the calculation of specified illuminances at the various heights and orientations of the considered working planes.

Table 3.4 Recommended illuminance for specific locations

Location	Response time (s)	Illuminance (lux)	Duration (minutes)	Reference plane
Kitchens	0.5	15	30	Horizontal on working plane, switches and cut-outs visible
First aid rooms	5	15	30	Horizontal on working plane
Treatment rooms	0.5	50	30	Horizontal on working plane
Refuges	5	5	Full rated*	Horizontal on floor, vertical at wall-mounted communication devices and signs
Plant rooms including emergency operation controls for lifts	5	15	Full rated*	In plane(s) of visual task
Fire alarm panel	5	15	Full rated*	In plane of visual task
Reception areas	5	15	Full rated*	In plane of visual task
Panic bars and security devices	5	5	Full rated*	In plane(s) of visual task
Swimming pool surrounds, swimming areas and diving areas	0.5	5	Full rated*	Horizontal on floor and treads

* Rated duration of the emergency lighting for the associated area or building

Further information on the emergency lighting design procedure can be found in SLL Lighting Guide 12: *Emergency lighting* (SLL, 2015).

3.6   Installation, testing and maintenance

The success of an emergency lighting system depends not only on the design, planning and selection of the right equipment but also on the satisfactory installation and maintenance of the equipment throughout its service life. Systems should be installed with appropriate test facilities for the application and testing must be able to be conducted without risk to occupants of the premises either at the time of the test or during the recharge period afterwards.

3.6.1   Installation

The emergency lighting system should be installed as instructed by the designer of the scheme and in accordance with the equipment manufacturer's instructions. The designer usually provides a schedule of installation, including scheme plans and wiring/piping drawings in which the location of equipment, placing of protection devices and the choice and routing of wiring/piping are set out. The schedule or drawings may also give the sequence of fixing and connections, particularly of complex systems. All such schedules and drawings should be added to the log book on completion of the installation. These should be updated with information of all scheme modifications made during the life of the installation.

3.6.2   Maintenance and inspection

Maintenance and inspection of the installation should be done regularly. The designer should provide a maintenance schedule that should list and give details of replacement components such as lamp type, battery, fuses, cleaning and topping-up fluids.

Caution should be exercised while carrying out maintenance as unenergised circuits may suddenly become energised automatically. Prime movers and generators will almost always be started without warning in an emergency or auto test since a sensor remote from the plant enclosure initiates the sequence of operations.

Batteries should be maintained in accordance with manufacturers' recommendations. Sealed batteries used in self-contained luminaires require no maintenance. Self-contained batteries are required to have a minimum operational life of four years, although typically may not need to be replaced for a significantly longer time beyond this depending on operating factors such as operating temperature and frequency of interruptions to the supply. It is required that batteries are periodically checked via testing and replaced with a type specified by the manufacturer if required. Sealed batteries, used in central systems, generally have a longer operating life than self-contained batteries. In addition to periodic testing of duration, specific maintenance may also need to be carried out on central batteries, for example checking and tightening of connections, and cleaning and greasing of terminals.

Luminaires and safety signs should be cleaned at regular intervals that may coincide with the time of inspection. Any defects noted should be recorded in a log book and rectified as soon as possible with the responsible person being notified in case any short-term protection procedures for the premises are necessary until repairs are effected. The cleaning interval is dependent on the environment around the installation. Serviceable components should be replaced at the end of the recommended component service life by an approved part.

Inspection and testing of various aspects of emergency lighting should be carried out daily, monthly and yearly.

The charging supply to central battery systems should be checked daily as should progress on rectifying any faults entered in the log book.

A short functional test should be performed at least monthly, by simulating a failure of the normal lighting power supply, to verify that all emergency luminaires are operating. This applies to both self-contained and centrally supplied systems. The duration of the function test should be sufficient to verify changeover operation and to check correct function of the emergency light source, but otherwise should be kept short so as not to discharge batteries unduly or to cause damage or unnecessary wear to certain types of light source. Generators should be checked for automatic starting and to ensure that they energise the emergency lighting system correctly.

A full duration test of all systems should be performed at least yearly to verify that the emergency lighting provides its design output for the full design duration. The duration test should be arranged to occur at a point in time where the time needed to recharge batteries has the least impact on the occupation of the building.

Records should be kept of all the tests made and of the results obtained. Where self-testing or remote testing features are being used, those responsible for emergency lighting systems should verify that the tests have been conducted on schedule and have given satisfactory results. Details of routine testing are given in BS EN 50172/BS 5266-8 (BSI, 2004).

An increasing trend is for emergency lighting to incorporate some form of automatic testing facility, or for the luminaires to incorporate a remote monitoring feature. This is particularly the case where occupants may be expected to remain in the building during a supply failure, for which BS 5266-1 strongly recommends that an automatic test system is used. The electrical test should verify that any automatic testing system performs as intended, without impairing the integrity of the lighting design. Where self-testing or remote monitoring systems are used as the basis of compliance with BS 5266-1 (BSI, 2016), a visual inspection of the installed equipment should be carried out at least annually to verify that it is in good condition. BS EN 62034 (BSI, 2012c) gives details of automatic test systems for battery powered emergency escape lighting.

3.6.3   Documentation

Given the extensive regulatory framework associated with emergency lighting, good documentation of the installation is essential. The documentation should include the completion certificate, initial inspection certificate and periodic test and inspection log based on the model certificates provided in BS 5266-1 (BSI, 2016).

3.6.4   Commissioning and certification

3.6.4.1   Electrical testing

A full electrical test in accordance with BS 7671 (BSI, 2018) is required when commissioning an emergency lighting installation.

For self-contained systems, an electrical test should be carried out to ascertain that all luminaires are working in the correct manner, i.e. maintained, non-maintained and, where appropriate, combined. It should be verified that the battery-charging supply is present and indicated, and that the luminaires operate in emergency mode on simulation of a general supply failure. After initial commissioning, and allowing for a full charge of all batteries, a duration test should be performed to confirm that the system will perform for the designed duration. It should be confirmed that all luminaires reset to normal or standby mode as appropriate after the restoration of the normal supply.

Where additional controls such as switched–maintained, inhibiting or rest mode facilities are fitted, it shall be verified that these operate in the correct manner.

For central battery or generator systems, the system should be tested in normal and emergency modes to determine the correct changeover of luminaires and full functionality in emergency mode. With central systems, it is essential that a duration test is carried out. It should be confirmed that all luminaires and off-line battery units reset to normal or standby mode, as appropriate, after the restoration of the normal supply.

Where self-testing and remote testing systems are included, the system should be set up and tested for functioning in accordance with the supplier's instructions. A copy of these instructions should be placed with the log book.

3.6.4.2   Photometric measurements

Where authenticated photometric data are not available to allow confirmation of illuminance levels by calculation, on-site photometric measurements may be made in accordance with Annex D of BS 5266-1 (BSI, 2016).

On-site performance testing of emergency lighting installations can be very difficult. The testing requires good instrumentation and well laid out plans for the measurement conditions.

Any illuminance meter used should have a photocell with good cosine incident light correction. An illuminated-dial or digital-display type meter should be used so that readings may be visible at low illuminances. The light meter should have an operating range of 0.01 lx to 100 lx with a sensitivity of 0.01 lx for escape routes and areas, and a range of 10 lx to 1000 lx with a sensitivity of 1.0 lx for high-risk areas. The accuracy of the instrument should conform to BS 667 Type F. The photocell should preferably be on a remote lead to avoid shadowing.

The illuminance measurements should be made on a horizontal plane on the escape route area or task area. In most cases it is advisable to select a number of specific areas or points for test that represent the worst conditions. See SLL Lighting Guide 12: *Emergency lighting* (SLL, 2015) for suggested measurement locations.

The results of these illuminance measurements can be checked against design data. Measurements should be taken during the hours of darkness. If there is steady extraneous light from street lighting or moonlight the contribution of the emergency lighting can be estimated by taking the difference between measurements of the same point, with and without emergency lighting.

The illuminances provided by the emergency lighting system will vary with time, so the tests should be completed as quickly as is possible within the rated duration. This will minimize the charge losses from the batteries. This is particularly relevant in an occupied building because, with fully discharged batteries, the building may have reduced emergency lighting cover for up to 24 hours. It is valuable to have data that relate the lumen output of the luminaire at any time to the lamp/battery life cycle

3.6.5   Completion certificate

On completion of design, installation and commissioning of the emergency lighting system, a completion certificate should be prepared and supplied to the occupier/owner of the premises as part of the handover. An example of a completion certificate is given in SLL Lighting Guide 12: *Emergency lighting* (SLL, 2015). All sections of the completion certificate should be signed by the specified competent persons.

References

BSI (1998) BS 5266-2: *Emergency lighting. Code of practice for electrical low mounted way guidance systems for emergency use* (London: British Standards Institution)

BSI (1999a) BS 5266-4: *Emergency lighting. Code of practice for design, installation, maintenance and use of optical fibre systems* (London: British Standards Institution)

BSI (1999b) BS 5266-5: *Emergency lighting. Specification for component parts of optical fibre systems* (London: British Standards Institution)

BSI (1999c) BS 5266-6: *Emergency lighting. Code of practice for non-electrical low mounted way guidance systems for emergency use. Photoluminescent systems* (London: British Standards Institution)

BSI (2001) BS EN 50171: 2001: *Central power supply systems* (London: British Standards Institution)

BSI (2004) BS EN 50172: 2004/BS 5266-8: 2004: *Emergency escape lighting systems* (London: British Standards Institution)

BSI (2006–2017) BS EN 62040: *Uninterruptible power systems* (5 Parts) (London: British Standards Institution)

BSI (2007) BS EN 12193: 2007: *Light and lighting. Sports lighting* (London: British Standards Institution)

BSI (2011a) BS ISO 3864-1: 2011: *Graphical symbols. Safety colours and safety signs. Design principles for safety signs and safety markings* (London: British Standards Institution)

BSI (2011b) BS ISO 3864-4: 2011: *Graphical symbols. Safety colours and safety signs. Colorimetric and photometric properties of safety sign materials* (London: British Standards Institution)

BSI (2011c) BS EN 12464-1: 2011: *Light and lighting. Lighting of work places. Indoor work places* (London: British Standards Institution)

BSI (2012a) BS ISO 3864-3: 2012: *Graphical symbols. Safety colours and safety signs. Design principles for graphical symbols for use in safety signs* (London: British Standards Institution)

BSI (2012b) BS EN 61056-1: 2012: *General purpose lead-acid batteries (valve-regulated types). General requirements, functional characteristics. Methods of test* (London: British Standards Institution)

BSI (2012c) BS EN 62034: 2012: *Automatic test systems for battery powered emergency escape lighting* (London: British Standards Institution)

BSI (2012/2016) BS EN ISO 7010: 2012 + A6: 2016: *Graphical symbols. Safety colours and safety signs. Registered safety signs* (London: British Standards Institution)

BSI (2013a) BS 5499-4: 2013: *Safety signs. Code of practice for escape route signing* (London: British Standards Institution)

BSI (2013b) BS EN 1838: 2013: *Lighting applications. Emergency lighting* (London: British Standards Institution)

BSI (2013c) BS 6387: 2013: *Test method for resistance to fire of cables required to maintain circuit integrity under fire conditions* (London: British Standards Institution)

BSI (2014a) BS EN 60598-2-22: 2014: *Luminaires. Particular requirements. Luminaires for emergency lighting* (London: British Standards Institution)

BSI (2014b) BS 5499-10: 2014: *Guidance for the selection and use of safety signs and fire safety notices* (London: British Standards Institution)

BSI (2014c) BS EN 12464-2: 2014: *Light and lighting. Lighting of work places. Outdoor work places* (London: British Standards Institution)

BSI (2014d) BS EN 61951-1: 2014: *Secondary cells and batteries containing alkaline or other non-acid electrolytes. Portable sealed rechargeable single cells. Nickel-cadmium* (London: British Standards Institution)

BSI (2014e) BS EN 81-20: 2014: *Safety rules for the construction and installation of lifts. Lifts for the transport of persons and goods. Passenger and goods passenger lifts* (London: British Standards Institution)

BSI (2015) BS 7846: 2015: *Electric cables. Thermosetting insulated, armoured, fire-resistant cables of rated voltage 600/1000 V for fixed installations, having low emission of smoke and corrosive gases when affected by fire. Specification* (London: British Standards Institution)

BSI (2016) BS 5266-1: *Emergency lighting. Code of practice for the emergency lighting of premises* (London: British Standards Institution)

BSI (2017a) BS EN 61951-2: 2017: *Secondary cells and batteries containing alkaline or other non acid electrolytes. Secondary sealed cells and batteries for portable applications. Nickel-metal hydride* (London: British Standards Institution)

BSI (2017b) BS EN 62133-1: 2017: *Secondary cells and batteries containing alkaline or other non-acid electrolytes. Safety requirements for portable sealed secondary cells, and for batteries made from them, for use in portable applications. Part 1: Nickel systems* (London: British Standards Institution)

BSI (2017c) BS EN 62133-2: 2017: *Secondary cells and batteries containing alkaline or other non-acid electrolytes. Safety requirements for portable sealed secondary lithium cells, and for batteries made from them, for use in portable applications. Part 2: Lithium systems* (London: British Standards Institution)

BSI (2018) BS 7671: 2018: *Requirements for Electrical Installations. IET Wiring Regulations* (London: British Standards Institution)

DFPNI (2012) *Fire safety* Technical Booklet E (Belfast: Northern Ireland Department of Finance and Personnel) (available at https://www.finance-ni.gov.uk/publications/technical-booklet-e) (accessed September 2018)

EC (1989) 'Council Directive 89/654/EEC of 30 November 1989 concerning the minimum safety and health requirements for the workplace (first individual directive within the meaning of Article 16 (1) of Directive 89/391/EEC)' ('the Workplace Directive') *Official Journal of the European Communities* **L393** (30.12.1989) 1–12 (available at http://eur-lex.europa.eu/legal-content/EN/TXT/?uri=CELEX%3A31989L0654) (accessed September 2018)

EC (1992) 'Council Directive 92/58/EEC of 24 June 1992 on the minimum requirements for the provision of safety and/or health signs at work (ninth individual Directive within the meaning of Article 16 (1) of Directive 89/391/EEC)' (the 'Signs Directive') *Official Journal of the European Communities* **L245** (26.8.1992) 23–42 (available at http://eur-lex.europa.eu/legal-content/EN/TXT/?uri=celex:31992L0058) (accessed September 2018)

EU (2011) 'Regulation (EU) No 305/2011 of the European Parliament and of the Council of 9 March 2011 laying down harmonised conditions for the marketing of construction products and repealing Council Directive 89/106/EEC Text with EEA relevance' (the 'Construction Products Regulation') *Official Journal of the European Union* **L88** (4.4.2011) 5–43 (available at http://eur-lex.europa.eu/legal-content/EN/TXT/?uri=celex%3A32011R0305) (accessed September 2018)

HMSO (1996) Health and Safety (Safety Signs and Signals) Regulations 1996 Statutory Instrument 1996 No. 341 (London: Her Majesty's Stationery Office) (available at https://www.legislation.gov.uk/uksi/1996/341) (accessed September 2018)

ISO (2007) ISO 30061: 2007 (CIE S 020/E:2007): *Emergency lighting* (Geneva: International Organization for Standardisation)

ICEL (2014) *Requirements for the Re-engineering of Luminaires for Emergency Lighting Use* ICEL Publication 1004 (Telford: Lighting Industry Association/Industry Committee for Emergency Lighting) (available at https://www.thelia.org.uk/knowledge/icel-1004-requirements-re-engineering-luminaires-emergency-lighting-use) (accessed September 2018)

IEC (2009) IEC 60364-5-52: 2009: *Low-voltage electrical installations. Part 5-52: Selection and erection of electrical equipment. Wiring systems* (Geneva, Switzerland: International Electrotechnical Commission)

NBS (2006a) *Fire safety* Approved Document B: Volume 1: Dwellinghouses (2006 edition incorporating 2010 and 2013 amendments) (Newcastle upon Tyne: NBS) (available at https://www.gov.uk/government/publications/fire-safety-approved-document-b) (accessed September 2018)

NBS (2006b) *Fire safety* Approved Document B: Volume 2: Buildings other than dwellinghouses (2006 edition incorporating 2007, 2010 and 2013 amendments) (Newcastle upon Tyne: NBS) (available at https://www.gov.uk/government/publications/fire-safety-approved-document-b) (accessed September 2018)

Scottish Government (2017a) *Technical Handbook 2017 Domestic* (Edinburgh: The Scottish Government) (available at http://www.gov.scot/Topics/Built-Environment/Building/Building-standards/techbooks/techhandbooks) (accessed September 2018)

Scottish Government (2017b) *Technical Handbook 2017 Non-Domestic* (Edinburgh: The Scottish Government) (available at http://www.gov.scot/Topics/Built-Environment/Building/Building-standards/techbooks/techhandbooks) (accessed September 2018)

SLL (2012) *SLL Code for Lighting* (London: Society of Light and Lighting)

SLL (2015) *Emergency lighting* SLL Lighting Guide 12 (London: Society of Light and Lighting)

TSO (2004) Building (Scotland) Regulations 2004 Scottish Statutory Instrument 2004 No. 406 (as amended) (London: TSO) (available at http://www.legislation.gov.uk/ssi/2004/406) (accessed September 2018)

TSO (2005) Regulatory Reform (Fire Safety) Order 2005 Statutory Instrument 2005 No. 1541 (London: TSO) (available at http://www.legislation.gov.uk/uksi/2005/1541e) (accessed September 2018)

TSO (2006) The Fire Safety (Scotland) Regulations 2006 Scottish Statutory Instruments 2006 No. 456 (London: TSO) (available at http://www.legislation.gov.uk/ssi/2006/456) (accessed September 2018)

TSO (2010) The Fire Safety Regulations (Northern Ireland) 2010 Statutory Rules of Northern Ireland 2010 No. 325 (London: TSO) (available at http://www.legislation.gov.uk/nisr/2010/325) (accessed September 2018)

TSO (2010) The Building Regulations 2010 SI 2010 No. 2214 (as amended) (London: TSO) (available at http://www.legislation.gov.uk/uksi/2010/2214) (accessed September 2018)

TSO (2012) The Building Regulations (Northern Ireland) 2012 Statutory Rules of Northern Ireland 2012 No. 192 (as amended) (London: TSO) (available at http://www.legislation.gov.uk/nisr/2012/192) (accessed September 2018)

Chapter 4: Design ethos

4.1   Introduction

The previous chapters considered the design process to create lit spaces and environments that provide good lighting for those who use them. This chapter covers more of the ethics and ethos of a professional involved in lighting, be that as a designer, supplier or installer.

Members of the Society of Light and Lighting are required to abide by a Code of Conduct. Other professional organisations have similar codes of conduct. This is to ensure that members of such bodies conduct themselves in a way that will not bring the Society (or any other professional body) or the individual member into disrepute. For instance, a professional needing to specify or recommend a product should look impartially at alternatives and obtain comparative technical details and costs so that they can select the product that best meets the constraints of the project and is in the long-term interests of their client. If instead, they consistently pick the same familiar products or favourite supplier, it is likely to be viewed as not meeting professional expectations. Similarly, constantly picking the same few contractors to quote for projects without, from time to time, considering reasonable alternatives, may also be viewed as unprofessional and lead to suspicions of impropriety. Section 4.2 outlines the requirements of the CIBSE Code of Conduct in more detail.

In the UK, the Bribery Act 2010 (TSO, 2010) covers the giving and receiving of money, goods or favours in exchange for doing something known to be wrong, or omitting to do something known to be correct. Similar laws exist in many other countries. Of course, suppliers, specifiers and installers need to cooperate and understand each other's viewpoints and needs. Some social interaction can help improve relationships and ease communications. Visits to factories or recent projects, where products being considered have been installed, are sensible professional acts, but only where necessary and where other competing products are given similar consideration. However, undue frequency or lavishness of entertainment or gifts, especially during negotiations or tendering actions, leaves both parties open to accusations of bribery. Section 4.3 covers the requirements of the Bribery Act in more detail.

A major area of concern around bribery and propriety is during tendering exercises where the need for confidentiality and impartiality are particularly important. There are many professional and legal pitfalls to be avoided. Section 4.4 outlines tendering procedures.

Sometimes a contractor will suggest an alternative product to those specified. It may be that the lighting designer and client have had a long process of product review, on-site trials and clear product costing, and do not want to consider alternatives. However, on many projects there is an option built into the contract for the installer to suggest 'equal and approved' products. Section 4.5 discusses how this process should be handled so that the products that are finally selected and installed meet the requirements of the project and the design responsibility for them is clearly defined.

Finally, there is the important issue of ensuring that products and designs are sustainable. Products need to use the minimum materials and energy necessary to fulfil their purpose and designs need to use the minimum through-life energy to provide the correct lighting levels and visual environment for the users and spaces being designed for. Section 4.6 addresses these issues and some of the design methodologies, such as BREEAM, and product recycling schemes.

4.2 The CIBSE Code of Conduct

Members of the Society of Light and Lighting are bound by the CIBSE Code of Conduct. This was drafted by the multi-disciplinary Professional Conduct Committee, which included a Fellow of the Society. This Code is described below, although similar codes cover other professionals, such as architects and members of other chartered bodies.

Members of the Society, of all grades, are required to maintain the highest standards of professional conduct. All members must order their conduct in accordance with the Code.

Members engaged in work outside the United Kingdom shall comply as far as is possible with the Code and with any established standards of conduct that exist in that country.

In detail, the Code of Conduct requires that Members shall:

- At all times so order their conduct as to uphold the dignity and reputation of their profession and to safeguard the public interest in matters relevant to the art, science and practice of building services engineering.

- Exercise professional skill, care and diligence to the best of their ability and discharge their duties and responsibilities with fidelity, and with proper regard for professional standards.

- Actively maintain, and where possible encourage others to maintain, their professional competence through systematic improvement and broadening of their knowledge and skill in accordance with Institution guidelines on Continuing Professional Development as published from time to time.

- Reject bribery and all forms of corrupt behaviour, and make positive efforts to ensure others do likewise.

- Avoid, where possible, real or perceived conflict of interest and disclose to their employer or client any significant interest in another company, firm or person carrying on any business which may benefit directly or indirectly from their work.

- When acting on behalf of the Institution declare their position if faced with a conflict of interest, accurately represent the views of the Institution, and refrain from promoting their own or their employer's interest.

- Take all reasonable steps to prevent avoidable danger to the health, safety and welfare of themselves, colleagues and the general public.

- Raise a concern, either within the workplace or externally, including a danger, risk, malpractice or wrongdoing, which affects others.

- Promote the principles of sustainability and seek to prevent the avoidable adverse impact on the environment and society.

- Only undertake work for which they have sufficient professional and technical competence and adequate resources to meet their obligations. They should also disclose relevant limitations of competence.

- Treat all persons fairly and with respect and embrace equality of opportunity, diversity and the elimination of discrimination.

- Cooperate and integrate proactively and with other professionals in the built environment.

- Observe the proper duties of confidentiality owed to appropriate parties.

- Notify the Institution if convicted of a criminal offence or disqualified as a company director.

- Assess relevant liability, and if appropriate hold professional indemnity insurance.

- Notify the Institution of any significant violation of the Institution's Code of Conduct by another member.

A specifying engineer/designer is expected to give clear professional consideration to the selections and specification of products for any given system in a building and to contractors who may install it. An engineer/designer who considers alternatives and obtains comparative technical details and costs so that they can select the most appropriate product that meets the constraints of the project and is in the long terms interests of the client, is carrying out their duties correctly.

An engineer who consistently picks the 'old faithful' product or merely contacts their favourite supplier for details of a product that will fulfils the role envisaged, is likely to be viewed as not meeting professional expectations.

4.3   Professional standards and the Bribery Act

In the UK, the Bribery Act 2010 (TSO, 2010) received Royal Assent on 8 April 2010 and came into force on 1 July 2011. There are similar Acts or regulations in place in other countries. A full copy of the Act and its Explanatory Notes can be accessed on the gov.uk website (http://www.legislation.gov.uk/ukpga/2010/23).

The Act covers those who give or receive hospitality to people from other companies that they have a professional relationship with, as well as the direct payment in cash or kind for doing or omitting to do something that is required of them. Whilst the employer may have issued guidance to professional staff on the standards expected within the company, this section addresses the individual professional standards that the Society expects members to uphold. This is to ensure that members do not bring the Society into disrepute nor expose themselves to legal proceedings over claims that they have offered or received bribes or inducements that have influenced their professional impartiality.

The giving and receiving of gifts and hospitality is often acceptable and improves the relationships and understanding between members within the industry. Such gifts may range from a cheap pen to a case of vintage wine and from a seat at an industry dinner to a weekend at a luxury hotel. It is important that both the giver and receiver are certain that the balance between the cost of the gift or hospitality and the mutual professional benefit that is accrued from the exchange can be justified.

At the acceptable end of this spectrum are the minor logo-covered gifts that sit on members' desks, an invitation to an industry-related dinner or the normal meals and perhaps hotel stay during a factory visit. At the other extreme are those who give or receive lavish gifts or hospitality at or around the time that their companies are in negotiations over a supply contract. Those involved in such transactions may perceive them to be a hidden method of giving or receiving an inducement — much more subtle than cash in a brown envelope. However, the courts are likely to perceive such lavishness to be exactly what it is intended to be.

4.3.1   The Act

The offences under the Bribery Act 2010 are:

(1)   offering a bribe

(2)   receiving a bribe

(3)   bribing a foreign public official, and

(4)   failing to prevent bribery.

The Act covers situations where a person intends for the 'bribe' to bring about, or reward, the improper performance by another person of a relevant function or activity. For a Society member, this might be where someone 'turns a blind eye' to some defect on site.

It also covers the case where, say, the regular use of one lighting or component supplier results in regular invites from that supplier to prestige events or overseas visits

Members should note offence 4 — failing to prevent bribery. If a member becomes aware of an action by others that could amount to bribery, even within their own company, they must make their opinion clear to those involved.

Guidance from the Ministry of Justice (MoJ, 2012a) states that corporate hospitality can be bribery, for example if it is disproportionate or lavish. Corporate hospitality will need to be for an obvious and legitimate commercial purpose. What will be lavish will be a question of degree. What might be acceptable for one customer is likely to be different for another.

It is essential that members or their companies ensure total transparency by maintaining proper records about gifts or corporate hospitality given or received and by whom. Many companies keep a register where employees can record gifts, events and hospitality received.
To quote from the Ministry of Justice's guidance document (MoJ, 2012b):

> 'The Government does not intend for the Act to prohibit reasonable and proportionate hospitality and promotional or other similar business expenditure intended for these purposes. It is, however, clear that hospitality and promotional or other similar business expenditure can be employed as bribes.'

4.3.2   Conduct during tendering or negotiations

During periods where companies are tendering for work or are in negotiations about the details of supply, ordering or contract, members should avoid giving or receiving gifts or entertainment with the other party. Members must also be careful in the time before or after such periods of tendering or negotiation in their relationship with these other parties. An invitation to a dinner at the Ritz a few weeks after awarding a contract to the host is likely to be regarded with suspicion.

4.4   Professional standards and tendering procedures

Whilst the employer may have issued guidance to professional staff on the standards expected within the company for tender conduct, this section addresses the individual professional standards that the Society expects its members to uphold. This is to ensure that members do not bring the Society into disrepute nor expose themselves to legal proceedings over claims that they have not acted fairly or equitably in their involvement in tender actions.

4.4.1 Principles

There are three issues to consider when going out to tender: proportionality, equity and prior involvement.

4.4.1.1 Proportionality

Proportionality refers to the issue of how many companies to invite to tender. Preparing and submitting a tender return takes staff time and money. These costs have to be recovered in some way by the tendering companies and are reflected in a company's future tenders. A single client would naturally want to go out to as many companies as possible to obtain tenders in the hope of finding a slightly lower cost. However, their professional advisors need to ensure that the number of companies approached is proportionate to the value and complexity of the project or portion being tendered. For the industry as a whole the larger the number of tenders — most of which will be unsuccessful — that a company has to respond to, the higher their overheads and the higher the overall tender return costs will eventually become. There is also the worry that the greater the number of tenders a company has to deal with the poorer their response will be to each individual tender. This may result in mis-pricing and subsequent attempts to claw back costs.

4.4.1.2 Equity

Equity refers to ensuring that all companies invited to tender have an equal opportunity to succeed in the tender and will have their tender submissions considered equally. Companies or individuals must not be added to tender lists to 'make up the numbers' or just to give an impression of geographic or ethnic equality.

4.4.1.3 Prior involvement

Prior involvement refers to those projects where one of the parties being invited to tender has had some prior involvement with the tendering body relating to the tendered package. Such cases may be where one contractor has been advising the design team on buildability up to tender and, because of their deep understanding of that work, will be sensibly included on the tender list for the actual work. Or it could be a supplier who has produced a prototype of a product to prove its practicality or to demonstrate to a client. Where there has been prior involvement by one of the tenderers, this information must be conveyed to the other tenderers.

4.4.2 Expectations

The Society expects that its members will not be party to invitations to tender where there is clear evidence that the tender process will not adhere to the above principles. In other words, where there is an intent to go out to a disproportionate number of tenders; or where there is one or more 'favoured' parties being invited and the other names are there to 'make up the numbers'; or where the prior involvement of one of the tenderers is not revealed to the other tenderers.

Many SLL members are part of design teams where discussions about companies or individuals to be invited to tender for work or supply of goods take place. Where such discussions contravene the above principles then the member should withdraw from the discussion and make their reasons known to the other participants.

4.5 The use of, responsibilities for, and assessing of 'equal and approved' products

Those responsible for a lighting scheme need to ensure that any luminaire or lighting element submitted as an alternative to the one specified meets the same standards as the one specified, achieves the same results, and has the same standard of review by members of the design team.

On many projects a client will seek, or a contractor will offer, an alternative to the lighting equipment specified. The reasons for this can be to save cost, to ease installation or to save time on the contract. Whatever the reason for the proposed change, this should be declared with the submission and request for change of the specified item. Whilst there are often good reasons for the proposed change it can cause problems for the original designer, as the specified product would have been selected for reasons of technical performance, appearance or compatibility with other parts of the lighting system of related building services.

Products offered as alternatives are most often a luminaire, but can also be part or all of a lighting control system or something as simple as a movement detector. In the descriptions below all these possible pieces of lighting equipment are referred to as 'elements'.

4.5.1 Who reviews any alternative products submitted?

In all cases the intent to substitute an element should trigger a design compliance review to ensure the substitution does not result in failure of the overall scheme to meet the design intent, Building Regulations, energy scheme benchmarks or standards.

The designer of the lighting scheme shall carry out the review if such reviews were part of their original professional agreement, or he/she has been given additional fees to carry out such a review.

If no such arrangements have been made then the designer will not be able to comment on any alternatives to their original design put forward for consideration. It is possible that the contractor/manufacturer may commission the designer to carry out the assessment of any suggested alternative. In these circumstances, clear professional separation between the designer's original commission and the new commission must be maintained, i.e. the designer must analyse and comment on the suggested alternatives in a neutral and objective manner. The person carrying out this work is referred to below as the 'reviewer'.

4.5.2 What must be checked?

The reviewer should request the submission of the full photometric characteristics for all alternative luminaires being offered, including the necessary polar curves or equivalent, as well as detailed lighting calculations. Such data and calculation should be reviewed to ensure that the alternative luminaires still meet or exceed the scheme parameters and criteria such as lighting levels and uniformity. Any calculations must be made using the same parameters, such as room reflectance and maintenance factors, as the original calculations. Submission of such calculations must be considered as a legal undertaking by the submitting party, and should be covered by suitable professional indemnity.

4.5.2.1 Lighting energy consumption

The energy consumption of the submitted luminaire must be checked against that of the specified luminaire. If the energy consumption is higher a re-calculation of the overall energy consumption of the luminaires in the building may be required to confirm that the installation still meets the energy consumption requirements of the Building Regulations, BREAM or LEED (as appropriate). In the case of external public lighting that is un-metered, the energy consumption of the luminaires should be checked to ensure that they comply with the requirements of BSCP 520 (Elexon, 2016).

4.5.2.2   Construction and robustness

The reviewer must be satisfied that the elements being offered as alternatives are of equal quality, durability and robustness as those specified. This may require submission of samples for both specified and alternative elements and any components forming or supporting them. This is not to say that an element with lesser construction and robustness properties will not be acceptable, but this does give a measure and yardstick against any declared 'benefits'.

4.5.2.3   Design intent

Any alternative proposals should enable the original design intent to be achieved. This relates to where light is incident on surface and brightness ratios within given spaces or areas. Where a proposed element's performance in any way differs from the specified element a case should be submitted to support the alternative design intent and deal with the differences specifically.

4.5.2.4   Aesthetic acceptance

Alternative luminaires must be considered both individually and in relation to other luminaires on the project to ensure aesthetic acceptability. This exercise should be carried out in conjunction with the architects, designers, client and other interested parties who were involved in the selection of the original luminaires. In the case of exterior lighting this assessment should be carried out in conjunction with any fixing system, for instance in road lighting, the bracket and where applicable the lighting column. It is not equitable to subject any alternative luminaire to greater review than the original luminaire.

4.5.2.5   Electrical equality

If the project circumstances had dictated special characteristics for the element that are not covered by normal product or installation standards or directives then the assessment process should assess whether the proposed element meets these special characteristics. Compatibility of components and systems should be checked to ensure safety and performance of the original design is maintained, e.g. any change from the specified control gear may adversely affect the projected lamp life.

4.5.2.6   Equality of other technical properties

Elements should only be specified that meet and comply with British Standards or European Standards. Any alternative elements should be submitted with full specification and technical detail sheets to show that they meet the same or equivalent standards. Where a proposed element's performance in any way differs from the specified element, a case should be submitted to support the alternative product and deal with the differences specifically.

4.5.2.7   Controls

The level of control, monitoring and reporting properties of any control system alternatives should be identified. Where a proposed element's performance in any way differs from the specified element a case should be submitted to support the alternative proposal and deal with the differences specifically.

The ease and simplicity of maintenance should be considered as part of any assessment of any alternative element submitted. Any alternative luminaires should meet any specific maintenance factor and IP rating for the installation.

4.6   Sustainability

There are many aspects to ensuring that lighting products and lighting designs have a positive impact on society and on the environment. Trying to minimise energy use and material use helps everyone in the long run.

4.6.1   Avoiding over-lighting

One of the most important factors affecting energy use in lighting is choosing the correct lighting level for the space or task. If the lighting designer specifies 500 lux where 300 lux is sufficient, then 66% too much energy is consumed; being clever with energy efficient lamps or controls will not recover this substantial over-use of energy.

Similarly, if an illuminance of 300 lux is aimed for, but the actual illuminance is 380 lux in order to make a neat arrangement on the ceiling with an initial luminaire choice, then again energy is being wasted and a slightly different luminaire or spacing arrangement should be considered. Some over-lighting is inevitable with fixed arrangements of luminaires, but this should be minimised.

It is of course possible to consider under-lighting slightly. If the choice is between one scheme producing 286 lux and another producing 312 lux, then this small degree of over-lighting is acceptable. If it is a choice between 286 lux and, say, 366 lux then this can be raised with the client and the implications of going for the slight under-lighting discussed and agreed.

4.6.2   Maintenance factor

The other important issue in this age of LED lighting is the maintenance factor and the long life of LEDs. The task lighting levels given in this *Handbook* and the *SLL Code for Lighting* are all maintained values — in other words the level that will exist at the worst moment in the maintenance cycle of the space. The maintenance factor takes into account the slow build-up of dirt on room surfaces and luminaires, as well as the reduction in light output of the lamps or LEDs up to the planned point of maintenance and/or replacement. The assumed maintenance regime can be discussed with the client as it is possible to reduce initial capital expenditure if the chosen lamps offer a better maintenance regime for the future. See Chapter 32, 'Maintenance' for full coverage of this issue.

For instance, in an area being lit to 500 lux, the difference between a maintenance regime that would result in a maintenance factor of 0.74, compared to one that results in a better maintenance factor of 0.82, is a reduction in the initial ighting level from 676 lux to 610 lux — roughly a 10% reduction in initial capital cost and in lifetime energy use.

With traditional lamp types, the light loss to failure or replacement was well known and easily used in maintenance factor calculations. However with the long-lived LEDs there is a potential problem. If the client has been informed that LEDs will last for decades and LEDs with a quoted characteristic of 50 000 hours to the L70 point are chosen, then the lighting is being designed for the point where the light output of the LEDs will be 70% of that when new. Therefore the maintenance factor calculation begins with a lamp lumen depreciation factor of 0.7. When this is multiplied by a room surface maintenance factor of, say, 0.9 and a luminaire light loss factor of again, say, 0.9 the maintenance factor is reduced to 0.57. This means that to achieve a design maintained lighting level of 300 lux, the initial lighting level will need to be 530 lux — that is 75% more light and 75% more energy use than needed. It can be worse. For a reasonably clean warehouse, with a room surface maintenance factor of 0.8 and a luminaire light loss factor of 0.75, the a maintenance factor is 0.42 requiring an initial lighting level of over 700 lux — more than twice the maintained 300 lux needed.

To overcome this problem one of two courses may be taken. The first is to explain this issue to the client, informing them that if they are happy to replace the LED luminaires sooner than 50 000 hours, then a higher lamp lumen depreciation factor may be used in the calculation thus reducing the number of luminaires installed, giving a lower initial light level. So, for instance, if this approach is agreed to, a different point on the depreciation curve of the LEDs would be chosen, such as the point where it reaches 80% of its initial light output. In other words, use a lamp lumen depreciation factor of 0.8 for a point where the quoted LED life might be, say, 42 000 hours. Of course, the client could choose to let the LEDs continue their gentle decline in light output past this point, but that is up to them and their staff representatives to sort out at that future time. The second, and better way to deal with initial over-lighting, is to use a control system or self-regulating luminaires to reduce the initial light output of the luminaires so as to achieve the correct task lighting level from the start. The system would initially start life with the luminaires dimmed and then slowly, over the years, ramp-up the light output from the luminaires to maintain the desired lighting level as the LEDs gently fade. This not only reduces energy use and over-lighting, but increases the life of most LEDs.

4.6.3   Achieving correct control

Once an acceptable design that provides roughly the required lighting level has been achieved, consideration should be given to controls that will minimise wasted light when areas are unoccupied. The easiest areas to treat in this way are infrequently visited rooms such as stores. The next set of areas are those not always occupied, such as meeting rooms and toilets. More complex systems can be installed to allow lights near windows to dim when there is adequate daylight available and/or for areas of an office or factory that are unoccupied in the early morning or late afternoon to have the lights dimmed or turned off. For more guidance on this topic, refer to Chapter 10, 'Controls'.

4.6.4   Achieving a ranking in BREAM, LEED or similar energy rating systems

There are a number of schemes for achieving a quality mark for buildings that achieve good energy use and for sustainable construction. Even if a client is not interested in achieving one of these marks, it is good to aim to achieve as many of the targets as possible during a design, as they represent good practice. These schemes and their various targets are described in Appendix 3.

Most countries have Building Regulations that require new schemes or significant refurbishments to achieve set energy targets and/or require the use of products that meet set performance targets. Again, see Appendix 3 for more details on the criteria and impact of such regulations.

4.6.5   Embodied energy

One area that manufacturers need to consider is the energy used in the raw materials and in making and shipping of parts and finished products. Different materials, such as aluminium, plastic and glass, require different amounts of energy for their mining or refining and different amount of energy used in their moulding and production. This is a complex subject and whilst it would be difficult for a manufacturer to calculate all the energy expenditure used in the components supplied to them, it is at least worth them asking their suppliers — if only to make them think through the issue.

Even the packaging materials make an impact on our environment. Expanded polystyrene packaging is non-biodegradable and takes up space in landfill where it sits for centuries. It is also a problem for contractors who have to fill-up skips with it on site and have to pay for its disposal.

4.6.6   End of life recycling

In the UK, the Waste Electrical and Electronic Equipment Regulations 2013 (TSO, 2013) (the 'WEEE Regulations') require that:

> 'Producers of electrical and electronic equipment (EEE) are responsible for financing and ensuring the disposal of end-of-life products in an environmentally sound way arising from both household and non-household users.'

There are Producer Compliance Schemes in the UK such as Lumicom (http://www.lumicom. co.uk) and Recolight (https://www.recolight.co.uk) that provide a route for compliance for manufacturers. These take responsibility for financing the safe disposal of each member's share of products at end-of-life.

Companies are classed as a producer if they put a product in scope of the WEEE Regulations onto the UK market. This applies to all companies who:

- manufacture and sell electrical and electronic equipment under their own brand

- resell, under their own brand, equipment produced by other suppliers

- import electrical and electronic equipment on a professional basis into an EU Member State.

References

Elexon (2016) *Unmetered Supplies Registered in SMRS* Balancing and Settlement Code BSCP 520 (London: Elexon Ltd.) (available at https://www.elexon.co.uk/wp-content/uploads/2016/06/BSCP520_v25.0.pdf) (accessed October 2017)

MoJ (2011a) *The Bribery Act 2010 — Quick start guide* (London: Ministry of Justice) (available at https://assets.publishing.service.gov.uk/government/uploads/system/uploads/attachment_data/file/181764/bribery-act-2010-quick-start-guide.pdf) (accessed June 2018)

MoJ (2011b) *The Bribery Act 2010 — Guidance* (London: Ministry of Justice) (available at https://assets.publishing.service.gov.uk/government/uploads/system/uploads/attachment_data/file/181762/bribery-act-2010-guidance.pdf) (accessed June 2018)

TSO (2010) The Bribery Act 2010 2010 c.23 (London: The Stationery Office) (available at https://www.legislation.gov.uk/ukpga/2010/23) (accessed October 2013)

TSO (2013) The Waste Electrical and Electronic Equipment Regulations 2013 Statutory Instrument 2013 No. 3113 (London: The Stationery Office) (available at http://www.legislation.gov.uk/uksi/2013/3113) (accessed October 2013)

Chapter 5: Coordination with other services

5.1   Introduction

The built environment, be it within buildings or external to them, is becoming ever more complex. Space for services is being reduced to make buildings more efficient and once distinctly separate components are being integrated in a single enclosure or component. The lighting designer and designers of other building services need to consider the impact on each other of combining their systems in one space or structure.

Lighting has become increasingly integrated into components and fabric of buildings and the built environment with the small size and versatility of LEDs. Items where integration can occur include handrails, doors, floor coverings and mechanical plant amongst many more. The lighting designer and the installers need to consider the impact on each other of combining built environment elements, which previously may not have been considered.

Lamps and LED arrays are designed to give their optimum output and stated colour temperature at a given ambient temperature. If lamps are cooled below this temperature, their colour will shift and their efficiency will fall. This can result in the lighting installation delivering below its design intentions. This means that the interaction between mechanical building services systems, in particular cooling systems and lighting, is very important.

In much the same way as lighting has to be carefully placed in a ceiling to optimise the use of luminaires, components associated with the supply and extract of air from a space also require careful placement. This can often lead to the preferred location of luminaires and supply diffusers being situated in the same location.

When additional services such as fire alarm smoke detectors, public address speakers, sprinkler heads and movement detectors are added into the equation, it is easy to see how a ceiling can become congested, with the inevitable need for compromise.

The need for mechanical services and luminaires to optimally be in the same locations within ceilings, along with the architectural preference for minimal ceiling congestion, has led to the development of integrated cooling and lighting solutions.

5.2   Hierarchy of services in ceiling voids

Ceiling voids in buildings can present some of the most complex coordination elements of a project. Ventilation ducts, pipework for hot and cold water, sprinkler systems, drainage systems, electrical installations and data installations all compete for space. However, some are more difficult to make compromises with, so a hierarchy of importance to coordination should be considered. Some services are more flexible than others when it comes to coordination and so can be moved to suit ceiling and ceiling void layouts. Designers should consider a hierarchy of services when planning service void layouts and reflected ceiling plans. Figure 5.1 shows a 3D model of a typical corridor ceiling void with the lighting zone shown in olive green at the lowest level.

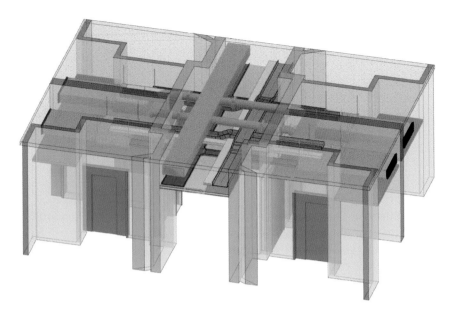

Figure 5.1 3D model showing ceiling void coordination (© Chris Clark/WSP)

5.2.1　Drainage systems

It may seem odd to suggest that lighting designers need to consider drainage systems first. However, as space for services in ceiling voids reduces, careful consideration needs to be given to drainage runs through ceiling voids. Drainage, due to its need to use long, straight pipes with slow falls to remove waste by gravity, cannot really be significantly altered spatially within ceiling voids.

5.2.2　Ventilation ducts and grills

The mechanical services usually take up the most space within ceiling voids. Supply and extract ducts distribute air through the ceiling void in a branching pattern of ducts. The ducts that enter or leave the ceiling voids into the service risers will be the largest, with the sizes slowly diminishing as the ducts split and distribute to grilles over the ceiling.

5.2.3　Sprinkler systems

If sprinklers are to be installed, then, as a life safety system, sprinkler head positions are the most important element to be located on ceilings. As sprinkler heads need to be distributed in a grid over the space they are protecting, an early discussion with the designer of the sprinkler system should reveal the parts of the ceiling where luminaires cannot be installed.

5.2.4　Fire alarm equipment

Fire alarm equipment, particularly ceiling mounted smoke detectors, needs to be considered with regard to the position of luminaires and how they might affect air flow around them. Smoke detectors need unrestricted air flow within 500 mm of their location, so any luminaire that sits below ceiling level should not be positioned any closer than this to a smoke detector. Heat detectors do not require the same free space around them but care should be taken when positioning luminaires that radiate a significant amount of heat. Where aspirating smoke detectors are being used, they need to be sited carefully so that fresh air from supply grills does not blow smoke away from them.

5.2.5   Power and data wiring

Electrical wiring, including data, security and fire alarm cables are normally contained in trunking or fixed to cable tray. This distributes through the ceiling void from riser locations and whilst reasonably flexible in installed height, does need to be accessible for adding or changing wiring.

5.3   Coordinating the ceiling void

Early discussion with the building services designers and architect is important in order to understand the limitations on ceiling void space.

Whilst coordination of ceiling void spaces should be planned with priority over routing going to larger and less flexible systems such as drainage and ventilation, it may be possible to identify a clear 'zone' immediately above the ceiling for luminaires that are intended to be recessed into the ceiling. If such a zone can be identified early in the design process, it will allow the lighting designers greater flexibility in placing luminaires, even if they have to be repositioned later in the design process. Figure 5.2 shows a section through the corridor of the 3D model shown in Figure 5.1.

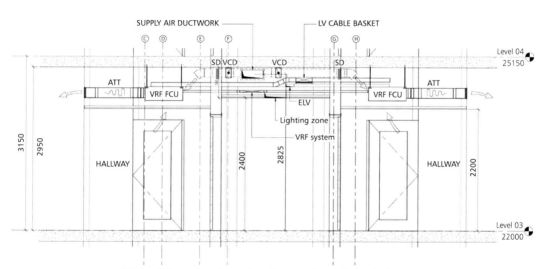

Figure 5.2 Section through ceiling void (© Chris Clark/WSP)

Figure 5.3 Typical ceiling void in a commercial building

5.4 Integration with air conditioning systems

5.4.1 Cooling methods

Traditionally, mechanical cooling in office spaces has been dealt with by either cooling air before it is supplied into a room or by using local cooling units that employ a fan to force air across a cool surface. Either method can result in differing temperatures across an office ceiling.

5.4.2 Centralised cooling systems

In large buildings, the air supplied to its office spaces can be chilled centrally and supplied via insulated ductwork to where the cool air is needed. This method will result in supply diffusers being positioned within the ceiling and air supplied via them at typically 6 to 8 °C below the ambient temperature of the space being cooled. Extract from these spaces can be via dedicated extract grilles, via a plenum ceiling incorporating perforated ceiling tiles, or via the luminaires themselves.

Whilst such a system has no obvious connection to the lighting within the space, care should be taken to not position luminaires too close to supply diffusers due to the Coanda effect. This phenomenon results in air which leaves a confinement, such as through a supply diffuser, tracking a surface close to its exit point, such as a ceiling, and entraining and mixing with the room air as the jet travels across the ceiling. As long as the surface remains smooth, the effect can carry air across a ceiling for some distance depending on its discharge rate. Where a luminaire is recessed into a ceiling and has a smooth curving reflector, it is possible for air to flow into the luminaire and across the lamp. See CIBSE Guide B2, section 2.4.3.5, page 2-61 for an explanation of the Coanda effect (CIBSE, 2016a).

Where air is extracted via a ceiling plenum, the rate of any airflow through the ceiling will depend on the location of the extract ductwork above it. For example, a space 20 metres long and 7 metres wide with an extract point above the ceiling at one end of the room will see a higher extract air flow close to that end. The end of the room farthest away will have a consequently lower level of extract.

Again, this may not appear to be related to the lighting installation. However higher extract airflow at one end of a room can result in the luminaires, particularly if they are open, being subject to different ambient conditions across the space. This leads to slight changes in light output and possibly colour from the lamps in these luminaires.

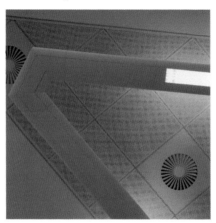

Figure 5.4 Supply diffuser and suspended luminaire (courtesy of Simon Robinson)

5.4.3   Fan coil units

The principal of operation is to run a cooling medium such as chilled water through a series of finned pipes, similar in look to a car radiator and known as a cooling coil. A fan is then used to push air across that cooling coil and into the space to be cooled.

These units are usually referred to as fan coil units (FCU) and whilst they can be wall or floor mounted, they are usually hidden away in ceiling voids with only their supply diffusers, and sometimes extract grilles, readily visible. Often, the system will supply air to a space via supply diffusers and extract it to ceiling voids through perforated ceiling tiles in the same way as for centralised systems. This latter method can give a more balanced flow of air across the luminaires in a space than can be achieved through specific extract grilles, and differs from the possible problems with single point extract in central systems because each FCU deals with a proportion of the air.

5.4.4   The natural cycle

By its very nature, cool air will fall to the ground and displace warm air, which will rise. If the supply of cool air is maintained, then a cycle will develop. It is not simply a case, however, of providing a space with cool air at any given point and expecting such a cycle to begin and be effective at providing cooling to the whole space. Inevitably such an approach would lead to localised stagnation and the cooling effect would not be uniform. In addition, any pipe or duct carrying a cooling medium such as chilled water or air, would find condensation building up on its outer surface if the coolant temperature were too low and inadequately insulated and vapour barriered. Any condensation finding its way into luminaires could lead to component failure in addition to the associated safety concerns.

Figure 5.5 Example of lighting and mechanical services
coordination (courtesy of Simon Robinson)

5.4.5   Chilled beams

In order to gain the benefit of not running fans constantly within fan coil units, and to take advantage of the natural cycle created by falling cool air, the chilled beam concept is becoming more popular in office developments.

Essentially, a chilled beam is a cooling coil that is stretched into a linear section of flow and return pipework, each with a series of radiating fins attached. Because the cooling surface is spread over a much greater area, uniformity in the cooling effect can be achieved without the need to use energy by running fans. However, the risk of condensation on the cool pipework still exists and, to ensure it does not form, the cooling medium cannot run at temperatures as low as those used in fan coil units.

In addition, the humidity within the space has to be carefully controlled to make sure any potential water source for condensation formation is limited.

For more information about the mechanical aspects of office cooling solutions, see CIBSE Guide B3 (CIBSE, 2016b) and BSRIA's *Illustrated Guide to Mechanical Building Services* (BSRIA, 2017).

5.4.6   Air handling luminaires

Where cool air is provided from a fan coil unit, it is sometimes possible for the air return path to pass through a recessed modular luminaire. This combination of extract point and luminaire has the advantage of reducing ceiling congestion and placing both luminaire and extract point at preferred positions.

Care should be taken, however, when selecting such luminaires and consideration should be given to a number of factors as poor design can lead to lamps running below their optimum temperatures when air flows across them. These include:

- *the type of lamp used and its operating temperature*: T5 lamps for example, operate efficiently at a higher temperature than T8 lamps; LED arrays operate more efficiently at typical office temperatures

- *the air path through the luminaire*: air should ideally pass through the sides of the luminaire and not over the lamps.

Figure 5.6 Example of integrated chilled beams
(courtesy of Dominic Meyrick/Hoare Lea)

5.4.7   Integrated chilled beams

The nature of chilled beams means that they occupy a large proportion of ceiling space and so integrating lighting into them is sometimes the only option.

A number of manufacturers offer chilled beams with integrated lighting and presence/absence control.

The issues of integrating lighting are similar to those of air handling luminaires, the difference being that lamps may be subject to cold air falling from the chilled pipework within the beam rather than the return air temperature.

5.4.8 Impact on lighting

Light sources, be they fluorescent, LED or any of the high pressure lamp types, are designed to operate optimally within a specific temperature range. Moving outside of these ranges will affect the efficiency of the lamp, resulting in a lower output and a change in the colour of light emitted (colour temperature).

The effect of temperature on lamps is well known and can be accounted for at the installation design stage provided the interaction of the various design elements is understood.

Differences in ambient temperature across a ceiling can be caused by either pre-determined control of mechanical systems or by unplanned interaction such as unbalanced extract from an office space.

Where a number of similar luminaires are installed in a common space and are subject to overall control, then drifts in colour temperature and output will not be readily noticeable. However, with the advent of better and more precise localised control of heating and cooling systems over small areas in large open plan spaces, the effect on lighting can be quite pronounced.

Integrated chilled beams are usually controlled independently of each other, which allows the temperature around any integrated lamps to differ depending on whether the chilled beam is operating or not. Because the lamps are so close to the chilled water circuit within the beams and may be subject to falling cold air passing over them, they are likely to suffer a change in colour temperature. In relatively small spaces, this may not be noticeable. However, in large open plan spaces, particularly where several beams can be viewed simultaneously, differences in colour temperature will be noticeable.

When designing or advising on the use or installation of systems that integrate lighting with mechanical chilled services, the location of lamps within the air handling luminaire or chilled beam and the air path should be carefully considered.

Whilst not directly related to lighting design, the control of the mechanical systems should be clarified and where fluctuations in temperature of adjacent chilled beams is likely to occur, careful selection of integrated chilled beams should be made.

Table 5.1 Typical operating temperatures of cooling systems

Technology	Typical operating temperatures
Fan coil unit air supply	6 °C to 8 °C below the ambient temperature in the space to be cooled.
Chilled beam surface temperature	14 °C to 18 °C

Table 5.2 Optimal operating temperatures of lamps

Lamp type	Optimal operating temperature
T5 lamp optimum operating temperature	35 °C around the lamp
T8 lamp optimum operating temperature	25 °C around the lamp
LED optimum operating temperature	25 °C

Typical performance curves for T8, T5 and LED drivers are shown in Figure 5.7.

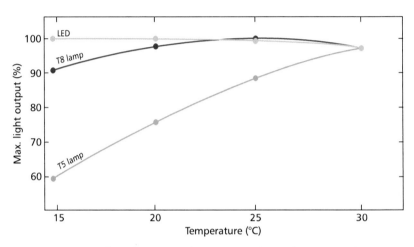

Figure 5.7 Typical performance curves for T5 and T8 linear fluorescent plus LED arrays over the ambient temperature range that is likely to be encountered in a cooled office space

It can be seen that the output of T5 lamps is affected to a greater extent than T8 or LED as the temperature around the lamp falls. If integrated cooling/lighting solutions are not properly designed, there could be a noticeable difference in illumination levels depending on whether the mechanical systems are cooling the space at any given time.

For detailed information and specific lamps characteristics, consultation with the lamp manufacturer should be made.

References

BSRIA (2017) *Illustrated Guide to Mechanical Building Services* BG31/2017 (Bracknell: BSRIA)

CIBSE (2016a) *Ventilation and ductwork* CIBSE Guide B2 (London: Chartered Institution of Building Services Engineers)

CIBSE (2016b) *Air conditioning and refrigeration* CIBSE Guide B3 (London: Chartered Institution of Building Services Engineers)

Part 2: Technology

Chapter 6: Light sources

There are many types of light source from daylight to candles, from LEDs to tungsten filament lamps. Each type has its own characteristics such as efficiency, colour, lumen output and an ability to dim or not. This chapter will start by describing these characteristics in detail before going on to describe each main type of light source. The end section will provide more technical information about the actual mechanisms they use to create light.

6.1 Electric lamp characteristics

There are a number of key properties of lamps that need to be considered when choosing which light source is right for a particular application. The following sections list these properties.

6.1.1 Luminous flux

In any lighting application, the amount of light that is needed is a key decision that has to be made. From this it is then possible to work out how many lamps of given rating are needed. There are lamps with lumen outputs less than 1 lumen through to lamps with outputs in excess of 200 000 lumens. In most applications, it is the average maintained illuminance that is important, so it is important to consider the lumen maintenance through life at the same time as the initial luminous flux.

6.1.2 Power demand

It is important in any lighting scheme to know what the total power demand is going to be so that the electrical infrastructure can be correctly designed. The power consumed by the lamp is important. However, with many lamp types it is important also to consider the impact of the control gear as well. In most cases it will be the total circuit watts that is important rather than the lamp wattage.

One further complication with some lamp types is that the voltage and current waveforms are not exactly in phase with one another. Thus, the volts multiplied by the amps in the circuit may be higher than the watts. The power factor of the circuit is defined by the following equation:

$$\text{Power factor} = \frac{\text{watts}}{\text{volts} \times \text{amps}}$$

Most lamp circuits are designed to have a power factor greater than 0.85.

The other factor that may affect the sizing of the cables that supply a lighting installation is the current required during the run-up of the lamps. With some types of lamp this can be more than double the nominal running current.

When using lighting controls, the power demand is more difficult to predict as the power consumed may be reduced at the time when full output is not required from the lamp.

6.1.3 Luminous efficacy

Luminous efficacy is usually expressed in terms of lumens per watt. Many lamp manufacturers produce lumens per watt figures for their lamps. However, for discharge lamps and other lamps requiring some form of control gear, these figures may be misleading as they refer to the power consumed in the lamp only and do not consider the power lost in the control gear. All the values quoted in this chapter for efficacy are based on total circuit watts.

Efficacy is a primary concern when selecting a lamp. In general, if a range of lamps is suitable for a particular installation then it is the most efficient that should be used.

6.1.4 Lumen maintenance

The light output of most lamps decreases as the lamps get older. With some relatively short-life lamps this is not a problem as they fail before the light output has fallen significantly. Table 6.1 gives some typical values for the lamp lumen maintenance factor (LLMF) for some lamps types.

Table 6.1 Typical values of lamp lumen maintenance factor (LLMF)

Lamp type	Lamp lumen maintenance factor for stated operation time (hours)										
	100	500	1000	1500	2000	4000	6000	8000	10 k	12 k	14 k
Linear fluorescent	1	0.99	0.98	0.97	0.96	0.95	0.94	0.93	0.92	0.92	0.91
Compact fluorescent	1	0.98	0.97	0.95	0.93	0.86	0.83	0.89	0.78	—	—
High pressure mercury	1	0.99	0.97	0.95	0.93	0.87	0.80	0.76	0.72	0.68	0.64
High pressure sodium	1	0.99	0.98	0.97	0.96	0.93	0.92	0.91	0.90	0.89	0.88
High pressure sodium, improved colour	1	0.99	0.98	0.97	0.96	0.93	0.90	0.89	0.88	0.88	—

LED lamp type	Lamp lumen maintenance factor for stated operation time (hours)										
	1000	5000	10 k	15 k	20 k	25 k	30 k	35 k	40 k	45 k	50 k
L80B50@50000 h	1	0.98	0.96	0.94	0.92	0.90	0.88	0.86	0.84	0.82	0.80
L70B50@50000 h	0.99	0.97	0.94	0.91	0.88	0.85	0.82	0.79	0.76	0.73	0.70

These values are provided as rough guidance only and for any particular scheme it is important to obtain accurate figures from the lamp manufacturer for the particular lamp being used.

As the lumen output of a lamp falls through its life it may reach a point at which it no longer provides enough light for a particular requirement and thus it is usually worth considering replacing lamps before they have failed.

For LEDs the lumen depreciation (e.g. L80) is for a batch where on average the batch will achieve 80% of the initial output. Individual LEDs may be above or below this percentage.

6.1.5 Life

It is normal when considering the life of a lamp to talk about the percentage of lamps that will survive after a certain number of hours of operation. This value is known as the lamp survival factor (LSF). Table 6.2 list typical lamp survival factor for some lamp types.

Table 6.2 Typical values of lamp survival factor (LSF)

Lamp type	Lamp survival factor for stated operation time (hours)										
	100	500	1000	1500	2000	4000	6000	8000	10 k	12 k	14 k
Linear fluorescent	1	1	1	1	1	1	0.99	0.95	0.85	0.75	0.64
Compact fluorescent	1	1	1	1	1	1	0.99	0.95	0.85	0.75	0.64
High pressure mercury	1	1	1	1	0.99	0.98	0.97	0.95	0.92	0.88	0.84
High pressure sodium	1	1	1	1	0.99	0.98	0.96	0.94	0.92	0.89	0.85
High pressure sodium, improved colour	1	1	1	0.99	0.98	0.96	0.90	0.79	0.65	0.50	—

The values in Table 6.2 are intended only as a guide and the lamp manufacturer should be consulted for accurate information for any particular lamp type. Other factors in a particular installation may affect the life of the lamp used. These factors include the switching frequency, the supply voltage, the ambient temperature and the presence of vibration.

Traditional lamps use physical failures to determine life. LEDs use lumen depreciation to determine life. This can be confusing but means the lumen depreciation for LEDs is also a life metric.

Generally the loss of light through depreciation can be accounted for in the design of an installation. The cost of replacing physical failures will determine when lamps are replaced in bulk. See Chapter 32, 'Maintenance', for a full discussion on this issue.

6.1.6 Colour properties

The colour of the light produced by a lamp is generally described by two parameters: the correlated colour temperature and the colour rendering index. The colour temperature describes how warm or cool the light from a lamp is — warm from tungsten lamps, cool from blue skies. The colour rendering is the ability of the light to accurately render colours. A high colour rendering allows the viewer to discern the shades and subtlety of colour in a painting or choose accurately clothes that match. Poor colour rendering makes it more difficult to tell colours apart such as, say, dark green and blue. Colour temperature and colour rendering are fully described in the *SLL Code for Lighting* (SLL, 2012).

For most applications, there is a minimum requirement for the colour rendering properties of the lamps used and the correlated colour temperature of the source is generally chosen for the appearance and atmosphere that the lighting is designed to create.

6.1.7 Run-up time

When a lamp is switched on it takes a certain amount of time to reach full light output. The usual measure used to assess the run-up time is the time that it takes for a lamp to reach 80% of its full output. For an LED lamp this might be a fraction of a second, while for high-pressure sodium it could be as much as five minutes. For some applications, such as road lighting, the run-up time is not important. However, for occasionally used rooms in a home it is very important.

Although LEDs appear to switch on instantly, the light output is strongly linked to temperature. As temperature rises so light output falls. Depending on the heat control of the luminaire the steady state light output may be less than that at switch-on.

6.1.8   Restrike time

When some gas discharge lamps extinguish due to an interruption in the mains supply it is not possible to restart them until the lamp has cooled down. This may take several minutes. The use of lamps with a long restrike time may cause problems in some installations due to the possibility of a small power outage causing a long blackout.

6.1.9   Other factors

There are also many other factors that impact upon the use of lamps in a particular application. These factors include:

- *Lamp size*: some lamps are too large for certain applications, whilst some small lamps may produce too high a luminance for others.

- *Operating position*: not all lamps may be used in all orientations, some discharge lamp manufacturers produce diagrams similar to Figure 6.1 to show which operating positions are permitted. The figure shows that the lamp in question must only be used in the horizontal position ±20°.

- *Dimming*: it is not possible to dim all lamp types and some types may be only dimmed down to a given percentage of their output. Dimming for some lamps may require the use of special control gear.

- *Ambient temperature*: not all lamps will run at a given temperature. For example, some compact fluorescent lamps are not suitable for outdoor use as they will not start if they are too cold.

- *Disposal of lamps*: lamps may contain hazardous substances such as lead, sodium and mercury. This may mean with particular lamps that formal procedures have to be followed when disposing of the lamps. Under the European WEEE Directive (EU, 2012) it is the responsibility of the lamp manufacturer to provide the means of recycling used lamps. For more information about the recycling of lamps in the UK, see the Recolight website (https://www.recolight.co.uk).

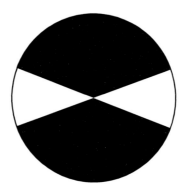

Figure 6.1 Typical restricted operating position symbol

6.2 Electric light

6.2.1 Light emitting diodes

The basic operating principle behind light emitting diodes (LEDs) is shown in Figure 6.2. LEDs are available in a wide variety of sizes, colours and power ratings and development continues at a rapid rate (see the CIBSE's *A guide to the specification of LED lighting products* (CIBSE, 2012) and the licht.de website (https://www.licht.de/en/service/publications-and-downloads/lichtwissen-series-of-publications)).

The chip of semiconductor material in the centre of the lamp comprises a wide variety of materials. Different materials result in a different colour of light being produced. Table 6.3 lists some of the more commonly used materials.

Table 6.3 Materials used in LEDs and the colour of the radiation produced

Materials	Colour of radiation
Aluminium gallium arsenide (AlGaAs)	Red and infrared
Aluminium gallium phosphide (AlGaP)	Green
Aluminium gallium indium phosphide (AlGaInP)	Orange-red, orange, yellow and green
Gallium arsenide phosphide (GaAsP)	Red, orange-red, orange and yellow
Gallium phosphide (GaP)	Red, yellow and green
Gallium nitride (GaN)	Green, pure green (or emerald green) and blue
Indium gallium nitride (InGaN)	Near ultraviolet, bluish-green and blue
Zinc selenide (ZnSe)	Blue
Aluminium nitride (AlN), aluminium gallium nitride (AlGaN)	Near to far ultraviolet
Diamond (C)	Ultraviolet

The chip is mounted onto one of the lead-in wires. In high power LEDs the mounting is designed in such a way as to conduct heat away from the chip. The other lead wire is bonded to the chip and generally connected to a very small area close to the actual semiconductor junction. The whole device is then potted in a plastic resin, usually epoxy.

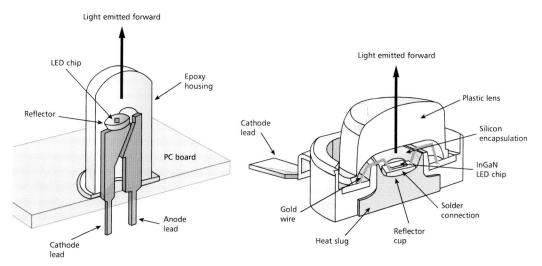

Figure 6.2 The construction of low power (left) and high power (right) LEDs

As mentioned the mounting for the LED is designed to conduct heat away from the LED chip. Unlike most traditional light sources LEDs do not naturally emit heat and therefore control of heat within the LED chip is critical. This is commonly performed by using heat sinks that are designed to conduct the heat away from the LED chip and dissipate it in free air. This has implications on the design of LED products as heat-sinks can have a significant impact on the weight of LED luminaires and many heat-sinks are composed of materials that need correct disposal at end-of-life to minimise environmental impact. However, careful control of the junction temperature of the LED is essential to optimise light output and also prolong the life of the LED chip.

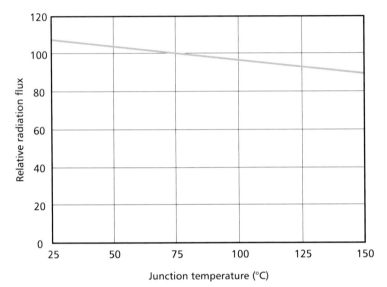

Figure 6.3 Typical variation in light output with varying junction temperature (Source: *US DOE Solid-State Lighting R&D Plan* (USDOE, 2016))

LEDs generally have a long life and may last up to 100 000 hours. This creates problems when describing the LED lifetime when compared to established discharge technologies. Established practice is that lamp life is dictated by the time to physical failure of the lamp; that is the point where the lamp fails completely and emits no light. With LED technology, the LED light source could continue to emit light throughout its stated lifetime (50 000+ hours) without total failure. However, as the LED light source ages the amount of light emitted will decrease until it ceases to emit enough light to be functionally effective. This means that the life of an LED product is effectively defined by the lighting design.

Generally, an LED product will have a defined 'Lx@N hours' value, where x denotes the loss in lumen output after N burning hours. For example, L70@50 000 hours shows that after 50 000 operating hours the lumen output will have fallen to 70% of the initial lumens. This does not mean that the LED product will have failed, but it does indicate that a space would have to be considerably over-lit at the start of the lighting system's life to counteract the loss of light as the operating hours increase. In practice, the 'x' value is the input into the maintenance factor calculation for the lamp lumen maintenance factor (see section 6.1.4).

An additional value may be defined to complement the Lx value. All values quoted for the performance of a light source, be they lifetime or lumen output, are based upon the performance of a sample of the product over a test period. The lifetime value quoted for traditional discharge lamps is the time at which 50% of the test sample have failed and obviously 50% are still operational. For LED technologies, this would be given as a B50 value, where 50 indicates that 50% of the test sample will be above x (in Lx) and 50% will be below x. But the total batch achieves x% depreciation after 50 000 hours. This is termed the *median useful life* for the LED product. Statistically, a different 'By' value could be chosen, for example L80B10@50 000 hours. This indicates that 90% of the test sample (i.e. 100% – 10%) are predicted to achieve 80% of the initial lumens (or greater) after 50 000 hours and is termed the *useful life* for the LED product. At face value this seems significantly better. However in practice this is not necessarily the case. As manufacturing processes have improved, resulting in much tighter tolerances in products, the real difference between B50 and B10 has shrunk as the variability of product has decreased, clustering product performance more tightly around the mid-point. The result is that the difference in lumen output between a B50 and a B10 quality LED product may only be 2% in terms of actual lumen output. This is shown in Figure 6.4 below.

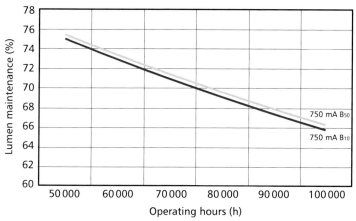

Figure 6.4 Typical B50 and B10 lumen maintenance through life for a good quality white LED module

The third lifetime criterion that may be quoted is the *time to abrupt failure* of an LED product, denoted as 'Cz'. For any given quantity of LED product there will be a percentage of product that fail catastrophically, that is cease to emit light. This is indicated by the Cz parameter. Typically, z is a very small fraction and within the context of a lighting installation will have a negligible effect. For installations with difficult to access luminaires or where the loss of a lighting fixture could be critical this parameter may require consideration.

LEDs generally emit light in a relatively narrow frequency band, so that most LEDs produce light that is a saturated colour. It is possible to make white LEDs by using a blue or ultraviolet chip and putting a phosphor coat around it. White can also be achieved by combining a mixture of red, green and blue chips.

LEDs have many applications associated with signals and signage. The use of saturated colours in these applications is a real advantage. This coupled with the ease of producing light in a number of small units means that LEDs are replacing other light sources in these applications. It is also possible to make lamps that are a cluster of LEDs of different colours. By controlling the outputs of the different colours, it is possible to make a lamp that can produce light in a wide variety of colours.

LEDs were first available as practical light sources in 2003 for saturated colours and 2008 for white light. Since then they have seen a rapid development in performance and now represent the most common light source for all applications. The following sections will describe traditional lamps, which have now mainly been superseded by alternative LED solutions. In many cases there are LED alternatives that are a direct replacement for these lamps.

6.2.2   Tungsten

The tungsten lamp is operated by heating a filament in the lamp to a high temperature, so that it emits light. The basic principle of the lamp may be simple, but the technology required to maintain a filament at a high enough temperature to give a significant amount of light whilst ensuring the lamp has a reasonable life is highly complex. The basic and most popular form of the lamp is the 'general lighting service' (GLS) lamp.

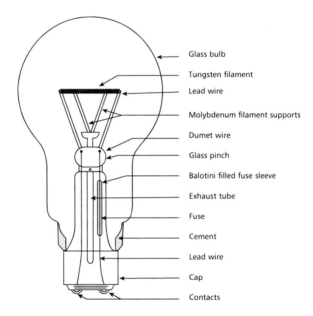

Glass bulb
Tungsten filament
Lead wire
Molybdenum filament supports
Dumet wire
Glass pinch
Balotini filled fuse sleeve
Exhaust tube
Fuse
Cement
Lead wire
Cap
Contacts

Figure 6.5 Construction of a GLS lamp

The filament design is critical in setting up the operating characteristics of the lamp. The length of the filament wire is largely determined by the supply voltage, whilst the thickness of the wire is determined by the operating current of the lamp. The filament is coiled to reduce heat convection to the filling gas. There are various forms of filament coiling with the coiled coil being one of the most common (see Figure 6.6).

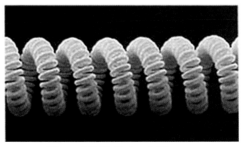

Figure 6.6 Coiled coil filament

The filament must be robust enough to withstand the shocks and vibration that the lamp receives during its life and at the same time be rigid enough so that it does not droop. Support wires can help prevent the filament from drooping but they conduct heat away from the filament and thus reduce the efficiency of the lamp. Therefore, normal service lamps are made with hard brittle filaments that only need a few support wires. Lamps for rough service (vibration) are made with a softer more malleable filament but have several support wires.

There are many variations on this basic lamp type. They are designed to run on voltages between 1.5 and 415 volts at wattages between 0.5 and 2000 watts. There is also a wide variety of bulb shapes including lamps with built-in reflectors.

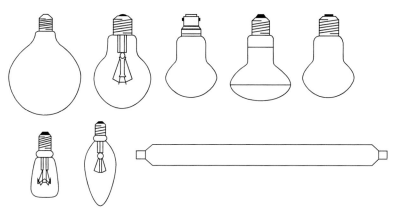

Figure 6.7 Varieties of lamp shapes

Recent legislation on the minimum efficacy of light sources has meant the tungsten lamp has now largely been replaced by other lamp types.

6.2.3   Tungsten halogen

The applications of conventional tungsten lamps are limited by their physical size and luminous efficacy. Raising the filament temperature to increase the luminous output has the effect of increasing the rate of blackening of the glass envelope, which is a result of the evaporation of tungsten from the filament. By adding a halogen to the gas fill a chemical transport cycle involving the reaction of tungsten reduces the amount of blackening of the envelope. To ensure this transport cycle can occur a smaller envelope size is needed which has a higher wall temperature. It is then possible to reduce the size of lamp, increase the pressure of the filling gas and thereby limit the loss of the tungsten from the filament.

The chemistry of the tungsten halogen cycle is highly complex. However the key stages are:

- the halogen combining with the tungsten on the wall of the lamp (zone 3)

- the tungsten halide vapour mixing with the fill gas of the lamp (zone 2)

- the tungsten halide dissociating close to the filament of the lamp, leaving the halogen free to migrate though the fill gas to the lamp wall again and the tungsten being deposited on the filament (zone 1).

The cycle is illustrated in Figure 6.8 below.

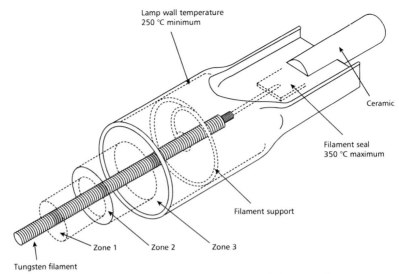

Figure 6.8 Illustration of the tungsten halogen cycle

To enable an efficient cycle, it is necessary for the wall of the lamp to run at a temperature above 250 °C; this means that the bulb has to be made from quartz or hard glass.

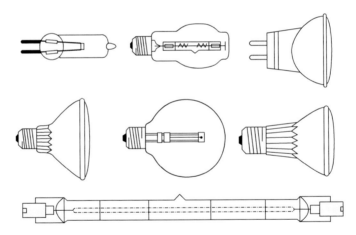

Figure 6.9 Forms of tungsten halogen light sources

Tungsten halogen lamps are more efficient and have longer lives compared with standard tungsten lamps. Also, they are more compact than standard lamps. However, they are more expensive as it is difficult to make the quartz outer bulb and it is harder to introduce the gas fill into the lamp due to the high filling pressure.

6.2.4   Fluorescent

Fluorescent lamps are the most commonly used form of discharge lamp. They come in a variety of shapes and sizes and are available in a wide range of colours. The original form of the lamp was a long straight tube. Newer forms of the lamp, known as compact fluorescent lamps, have been developed where the lamp tube is bent or folded to produce a smaller light source.

Fluorescent lamps work by generating ultraviolet radiation in a discharge in low pressure mercury vapour. This is then converted into visible light by a phosphor coating on the inside of the tube. The electric current supplied to the discharge has to be limited by control gear to maintain stable operation of the lamp. Traditionally this was done with magnetic chokes, but most circuits now use high frequency electronic control gear. Electronic control gear has a number of advantages. First, driving the lamp at high frequency maintains the ions in the gas and thus makes the lamp run more efficiently; secondly, it reduces the amount of flicker in the lamp and, finally, the electronic gear consumes less power than a magnetic choke.

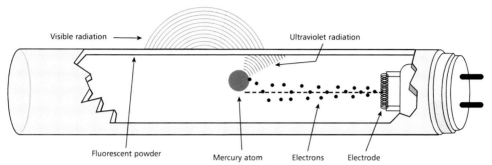

Figure 6.10 Working principle of a fluorescent lamp

The lamps are made from the following main components:

- *Tube*: this is made from a glass with a high iron content so that any short-wave ultraviolet (UV) radiation that gets through the phosphor coating is absorbed by the glass

- *Phosphor coating*: there are a wide variety of phosphors available. Each produces a different spectrum of light and by careful blending of the various phosphors lamp makers can tailor a wide range of lamp colours. The lumen output of the lamp also depends on the choice of phosphor mix. It is also important to control the particle size of the phosphor powders and the thickness of the coating.

  There are two main types of phosphor mixes currently used in fluorescent lamps:

  — *Tri-phosphors*: mixes of three narrow band phosphors. They generally achieve colour rendering values greater than R_a80 and have a high efficacy and good lumen maintenance.

  — *Multi-phosphors*: mixes of a number (usually five) phosphors. These mixes usually give a colour rendering higher than R_a90; however, the efficacy is normally lower than a tri-phosphor mix.

- *Electrodes*: generally coils of tungsten wire coated in a material that, when heated, will give off electrons readily (see Figure 6.11). To start the lamp a current is passed through the coil to heat the emissive coating. However, once the lamp is running the ionised gas atoms hitting the electrode provide enough energy to keep the cathode hot. The electrodes are generally surrounded by a shield as some of the material used to coat the electrode evaporates during the life of the lamp. If the shield were not present the material would be deposited on the wall of the lamp, causing a black ring and reducing the light output.

- *Gas fill*: the lamp fill is made up of two components: a noble gas mixture and mercury vapour. The noble gas in the lamp has three main functions. Firstly, it reduces the mobility of the free electrons in the lamp and, by careful control of the pressure, optimises the number of electrons with the appropriate amount of energy to excite the mercury atoms. Secondly, the gas reduces the rate at which the coatings on the electrodes evaporate and thus prolongs the life of the lamp. Finally, it lowers the breakdown voltage of the lamp and thus makes starting easier. Most lamps use either a mixture of argon and krypton or argon and neon. The use of the heaver krypton gas makes the lamps slightly more efficient but it is significantly more expensive. The vapour pressure of mercury in the lamp is significantly lower than the pressure of the noble gas mixture and it is controlled by the temperature of the coolest part of the lamp. At the cold spot of the lamp the mercury condenses to form liquid mercury. At this point the liquid and gaseous mercury are in equilibrium and the vapour pressure is determined by the temperature. As the vapour pressure of mercury is critical to the operation of the lamp, the light output of the lamp varies with temperature, see Figure 6.12. Most lamps are optimised to run in an environment with an ambient temperature of 25 °C. However, some are set up to run at an ambient temperature of 35 °C. In some lamp types, the mercury dose is mixed with other metals such as bismuth or indium. These metals form an amalgam with the mercury and this reduces the vapour pressure of the mercury at any given temperature. This enables the lamp to operate at higher temperatures but has the drawback that the lamp takes a long time to reach full output.

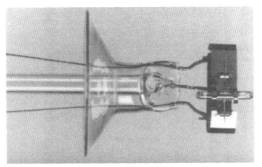

Figure 6.11 The electrode assembly

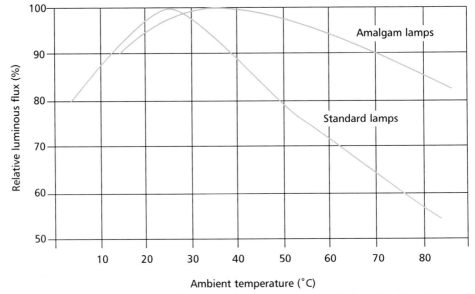

Figure 6.12 Luminous flux as a function of temperature for standard and amalgam lamps

There are two main types of fluorescent lamps: traditional linear lamps and compact fluorescent lamps.

Linear lamps come in variety of diameters and lengths. The main diameters of lamp are the T8 lamps, which are 25 mm in diameter, and the T5 types, which are 16 mm. These families of lamps come in a variety of lengths and wattages. Linear fluorescent lamps are generally efficient light sources with some of the lamps exceeding 100 lumens per watt. They also come in a wide variety of colours with a range of colour rendering properties.

There are a large variety of compact fluorescent lamp types; Figure 6.13 illustrates some of the range.

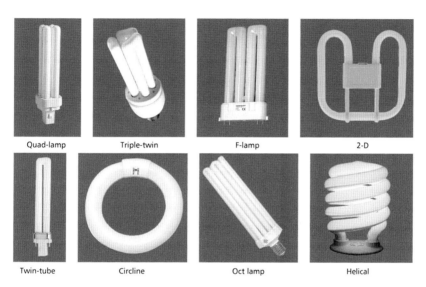

| Quad-lamp | Triple-twin | F-lamp | 2-D |
| Twin-tube | Circline | Oct lamp | Helical |

Figure 6.13 Types of compact fluorescent lamp

In general compact fluorescent lamps are less efficient than linear lamps but, because of their small size, they are suited to many applications where a smaller lamp is needed. Some of the lamps have the control gear built into them and can be retro-fitted into GLS lamp sockets.

6.2.5 Metal halide

Mercury lamps consist of a discharge in a quartz discharge tube containing mercury vapour at high pressure (2 to 10 atmospheres). Some of the radiation from the discharge occurs in the visible spectrum but part of the radiation is emitted in the ultraviolet. The outer bulb of the lamp is coated internally with a phosphor that converts this UV into visible light. Because of their poor performance and the fact that better lamp types are available for almost all of the applications these lamps are being phased out and are no longer available in Europe due to the European Energy-related Products Directive (ErP) (EU, 2013, 2017).

Metal halide lamps were developed as a way of improving the performance of high pressure mercury lamps in terms of their colour appearance and light output. They work by introducing the salts of other metals into the arc tube. As each element has its own characteristic spectral line, by adding a mixture of different elements into the discharge it is possible to create a light source with good colour rendering in a variety of colours.

There are many problems with introducing new elements into a discharge. Firstly the element must be volatile and secondly it should not chemically attack the arc tube. To avoid these problems it has become common practice to introduce metals into the lamp as metal halides. Metal halides are generally more volatile than the metals themselves and the metal halides do not attack the arc tube. The metal halide compound breaks up into the metal and halogen ions at the high temperatures in the centre of the discharge and reforms at the lower temperatures near the wall of the tube.

Many different combinations of elements have been used to make metal halide lamps, Table 6.3 lists some of the more common combinations of elements together with the spectral output they create.

Table 6.3 Spectral power distributions of metal halide lamps (the lithium (Li) line is due to impurities in quartz of the tube wall)

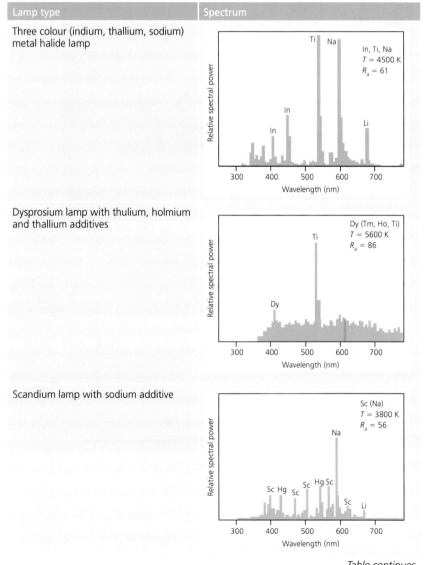

Lamp type	Spectrum
Three colour (indium, thallium, sodium) metal halide lamp	
Dysprosium lamp with thulium, holmium and thallium additives	
Scandium lamp with sodium additive	

Table continues

Table 6.3 Spectral power distributions of metal halide lamps — *continued*

Lamp type	Spectrum
Thulium lamp with a range of additives	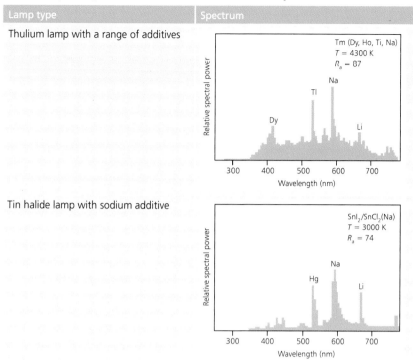
Tin halide lamp with sodium additive	

Because of the differing lamp chemistry there is a wide range of lamps that vary in terms of their efficacy, colour and electrical properties.

One of the main problems with metal halide lamps that use quartz discharge tubes is colour stability. As the colour of the light output is a function of the ions present in the discharge tube, any changes to the gas composition due to some metals being absorbed by the quartz tube or changes in temperature in the tube can cause significant colour shifts. These colour shifts are particularly a problem for the lower wattage lamps. This problem has largely been solved by the introduction of ceramic or sintered alumina tubes, which are much more resistant to chemical attack than quartz tubes and can operate at higher temperatures. Lamps with these tubes are now very popular for low wattage (up to 250 W) metal halide lamps.

The construction of a metal halide lamp is similar to that of a high-pressure mercury lamp. The key differences are that it is unusual to use an auxiliary electrode in the lamp, lamp ignition being achieved using a high voltage pulse from the control gear. Also, there is no phosphor coating on the outer bulb.

There are a wide variety of shapes of lamp. Figure 6.14 shows some of them.

There is a vast range of metal halide lamps ranging in power from 20 W to over 2 kW. The lamps have good colour rendering between R_a60 and R_a95 and they have reasonably high efficacies, in the range 60 to 95 lumens per watt. For these reasons, this lamp type has many applications where a compact light source with good colour rendering is needed.

Most metal halide lamps should be used with protective covers to protect against UV radiation and lamp failure. It is important with these lamps to ensure that the luminaire in which they are used is suitable.

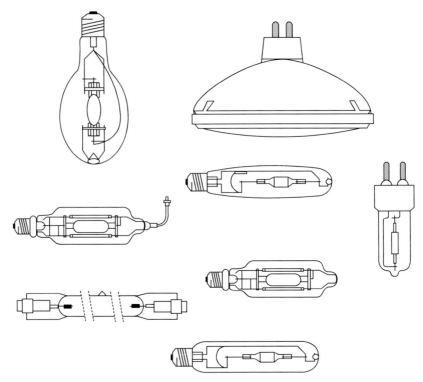

Figure 6.14 Forms of metal halide lamps

6.2.6 Low-pressure sodium

Low-pressure sodium lamps are similar in many ways to fluorescent lamps as they are both low-pressure discharge lamps. The differences in characteristics stem from the use of sodium in the discharge tube rather than mercury. The key differences are the need to run the lamp hotter to maintain the vapour pressure of sodium, the need to contain the very reactive sodium metal and the fact that sodium emits its light in the visible rather than the UV spectrum, so there is no need for a phosphor layer.

A typical lamp of this design is shown in Figure 6.15.

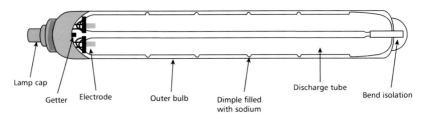

Figure 6.15 Construction of a low-pressure sodium lamp

The main components of a low-pressure sodium lamp are:

- *Discharge tube*: this is made of normal soda lime glass with a coating on the inside of a special sodium resistant aluminoborate glass. Making this 'ply-glass' tube is technically difficult as great care is needed to ensure that there are no thermal stresses in the final tube that might lead to cracking during the life of the lamp. Some lamp types have dimples in the side of the tube to act as reservoirs of sodium.

- *Fill gas*: neon with about 1% of argon at a pressure of approximately 1000 Pa. This mixture is used as it has a much lower breakdown voltage than neon on its own and thus makes starting the lamp much easier. Sodium metal is also put into the tube. The sodium vapour pressure in the tube when it is at its operating temperature of 260 °C is about 0.7 Pa.

- *Outer bulb*: made of soda lime glass, the inside is coated with a layer of indium oxide. This layer reflects the bulk of the infrared radiation from the arc tube and thus keeps it warm. Between the outer bulb and the arc tube the gas pressure is very low, below 0.01 Pa. To maintain the vacuum a barium 'getter' is used.

A relatively high voltage is needed to start an arc in the neon fill gas. The arc then slowly warms up the lamp and the discharge tube and the vapour pressure of the sodium starts to rise until the lamp reaches thermal stability after about 15 minutes.

The wavelength of the light emitted from a low-pressure sodium lamp is 589 nm, close to the peak of the photopic sensitivity curve and, as the lamp is relatively efficient at converting electricity into visible radiation, the lamp is one of the most efficient light sources in terms of lumens per watt. The best of the range can achieve in excess of 180 lumens per watt. The problems with the lamp are large size, long run-up time and monochromatic light that does not render colours. This type of lamp has mainly been used for street lighting but recently the importance of some colour rendering on roads has been recognised and the lamp is rarely used in new installations.

6.2.7   High-pressure sodium

The high-pressure sodium lamp generates light in a discharge through sodium vapour at high pressure. As the vapour pressure of sodium in a lamp rises the spectrum at first broadens and then it splits in two with a gap appearing at about 586 nm. Table 6.4 below shows the spectra from sodium lamps with different vapour pressures.

As the vapour pressure rises the colour rendering of the lamp increases. However, this is at the expense of efficacy in terms of lumen per watt. Figure 6.16 shows the construction of a high-pressure sodium lamp.

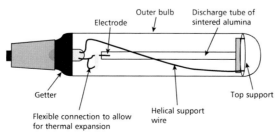

Figure 6.16 Construction of a high-pressure sodium lamp

Table 6.4 The spectra of sodium lamps at different vapour pressures of sodium

Lamp type	Spectrum
Low-pressure sodium lamp; sodium vapour pressure = 0.7 Pa	
Standard high-pressure sodium lamp; sodium vapour pressure = 10 kPa	
Colour improved high-pressure sodium lamp; sodium vapour pressure = 40 kPa	
White high-pressure sodium lamp; sodium vapour pressure = 95 kPa	

The main components used in the construction of the lamp are as follows:

- *Discharge tube*: made of polycrystalline alumina (PCA). This material is ceramic rather than a glass, which makes it very hard to work as it is not possible to soften it, and it is hard to cut. PCA is used because it is resistant to chemical attack by hot sodium; it is stable at high temperatures and transparent. Because it is not possible to work the PCA, the tube is cut to length and fitted with end caps. The discharge tube is mounted into a support frame and sealed into an outer bulb.

- *End caps*: the use of niobium metal as part of the end cap assembly is common as it expands with temperature at the same rate as the PCA tube and thus does not cause stresses in the lamp as it heats up.

- *Electrodes*: made with tungsten rods with a tungsten wire wound around them, with emitter material made from oxides of metals such as barium, calcium and yttrium.

- *Fill gas*: usually xenon at a cold pressure of 3 kPa, which corresponds to an operating pressure of about 20 kPa. A higher xenon pressure would improve lamp efficacy but make starting harder as it needs a high voltage to break down. Some types of lamp use high pressure xenon and have an ignition wire held close to the tube to help starting. There are also some lamps that use argon as a fill gas; these are much easier to start but are less efficient in terms of lumens per watt. A dose of sodium mercury amalgam is used in most high-pressure sodium lamps. Mercury is used because its vapour acts as a buffer gas and helps improve the efficiency of the lamp. However, the mercury contributes very little to the output spectrum of the lamp. Some lamps are now made without mercury in them. The absence of mercury makes the disposal of the lamp at the end of life easier as there are no environmentally damaging substances in the lamp. The metal dose in the lamp is never fully vaporised in the lamp and so the pressure of the sodium and mercury vapours in the lamp is dependent on the temperature of the coolest part of the discharge tube. This makes the output of the lamp temperature dependent and can also give problems associated with the voltage across the tube rising if the lamp gets too hot. The cold spot on most discharge tubes is in the area behind the electrode. As this area of the tube is blackened through the life of the lamp, the cold spot temperature tends to rise through life. This can give rise to problems in old lamps where the pressure in the discharge tube rises to the point where it is no longer possible for voltage available from the supply to sustain an arc in the lamp.

- *Outer bulb*: generally made of a borosilicate glass and may be in a number of different shapes. Figure 6.17 shows some of the more common shapes

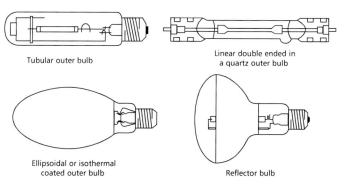

Tubular outer bulb

Linear double ended in a quartz outer bulb

Ellipsoidal or isothermal coated outer bulb

Reflector bulb

Figure 6.17 Outer bulb shapes for high-pressure sodium lamps

The high-pressure sodium lamp is an efficient source of light (efficacies up to 140 lumens per watt), it has a long life with reasonable lumen maintenance. However the colour rendering on the standard lamp is poor (R_a20), which is now considered unacceptable for many applications. The white high-pressure sodium lamp has a spectrum with minimal output in the yellow. This has the property of making a large number of colours appear more vivid and so this lamp has a number of applications in retail lighting.

6.2.8   Induction

Induction lamps are essentially gas discharge lamps that do not have electrodes. Instead the electric field in the lamp is induced by an induction coil that is operating at a high frequency. The only types of induction lamps that are currently in production are based on fluorescent lamp technology. Figure 6.18 shows the layout of a cavity-type lamp.

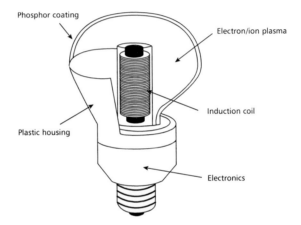

Figure 6.18 A cavity type induction lamp

The lamp consists of a glass bottle with a cavity into which the induction coil is placed. The glass vessel has a gas filling similar to a conventional fluorescent lamp. The phosphor coating on the inside of the lamp is similar as well. The induction coil in the centre of the lamp is fed from a high frequency generator.

An alternative architecture for this type of lamp is to have the induction coil wrapped around a toroidal lamp. Figure 6.19 shows a lamp of this type.

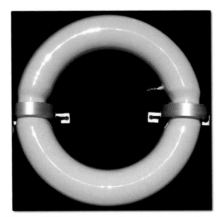

Figure 6.19 An external coil induction lamp

Induction lamps have many of the same properties as fluorescent lamps. However, they are slightly less efficient. The main advantage with this type of lamp is a long life. This is because there are no electrodes to fail and the inside of the lamp does not get coated with material that has been vaporised away from the electrodes. A number of lamps of this type have rated lives of 100 000 hours. They are more expensive than conventional fluorescent lamps so tend to be used in places where it is difficult to change lamps and thus long life is an important feature of the lamp.

6.2.9   Electroluminescent

The basic principle of electroluminescent (EL) light sources is discussed in section 6.4.3.

Generally, the light sources are made up as panels with a construction similar to that shown in Figure 6.20.

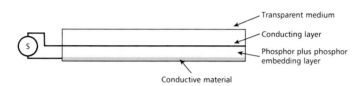

Figure 6.20 Section through an electroluminescent panel

An electroluminescent (EL) panel is made up of the following components:

- *Lower conductor layer*: which carries one side of the electrical supply into the light source. In older types of panel this conductor would be a sheet of metal but in the newer flexible panels it is generally some type of foil.

- *Phosphor layer*: this contains the phosphor used to generate the light together with a medium, usually some form of plastic resin, used to keep the grains of phosphor separate from one another.

- *Top conductor*: comprises a transparent material that conducts electricity to the top surface of the phosphor layer.

- *Transparent medium*: forming the top layer of the device. In older devices, this layer is usually made of glass, but in more modern units it is likely to be a flexible transparent film.

EL panels are not a particularly efficient light source. Typically, they have efficacies of a few lumens per watt. The light output of an EL panel is not that great, typically less than 300 lumens per square meter. There are many applications for EL panels as it is relatively easy to cut them to shape and size so they can be used for signage and to back-light displays in electronic equipment.

6.2.10 Summary of lamp characteristics

Table 6.5 below gives a summary of the key characteristics of the main lamp families.

Table 6.5 Summary of lamp characteristics

Lamp type	Output range (lm)	Power range (W)	Efficacy (lm·W⁻¹)	Control gear	Colour temp. (K)	Colour rendering (R_a)	Run-up time	Dimming	Life (h)[1]	Comments
Incandescent										
GLS	5–12000	1–1000	8–14	No	2500–2700	100	Instant	Easy to 0%	1000	Large variety of shapes and sizes of lamp
TH	40–40000	4–2000	15–25	No[2]	3000–3200	100[3]	Instant	Easy to 0%	1500–4000	
Fluorescent										
T8	650–6200	13–80	50–96	Yes	2700–8000	50–95	30 s	Easy to 2%	8000–16000[5]	
T5	120–6550	6–85	20–93[4]	Yes	2700–8000	82–95	30 s	Easy to 2%	8000–20000[5]	
Compact (CFL)	250–6500	5–85	30–82	Yes[5]	2700–6000	85	15–90 s	Some types to 5%	Up to 10000[5]	
Metal halide lamps										
Quartz tube	5200–220000	85–2050	60–98	Yes	3000–6000	60–90	1–8 min	No	2000–7000	
Ceramic tube	1600–26000	20–250	65–97	Yes	3000–4400	78–93	2 min	Limited[6]	6000–10000	The lamp range is increasing rapidly
Low-pressure sodium										
SOX SOX-E	1800–32000	26–180	70–200	Yes	N/A	N/A	10–20 min	No	15000–20000	Good lumen maintenance, but power consumption goes up through life
High-pressure sodium										
Std. SON	4300–130000	50–1000	53–142	Yes	1900–2100	19–25	3–7 min	Limited to 25%	10000–20000	
Delux SON	12500–37000	165–430	75–86	Yes	2150	65	5 min	Limited to 25%	10000–14000	
White SON	1800–5000	45–115	40–44	Yes	2500	83	2 min	No	6000–9000	
Induction										
	2600–12000	55–165	47–93	Yes	2550–4000	80–89	1 min	No	60000+	
LED										
White LED	1–120 typical	0.1–7	30–200	Yes	2700–6500	20–90	<1 min	Yes	Up to 100000	

Notes to Table 6.5

[1] Economic life may be limited by lumen depreciation.

[2] Many TH types are designed to run on low voltages and thus need a transformer or other device to supply the necessary voltage.

[3] Some lamps with dichroic reflectors have part of the red end of the spectrum missing and thus do not give a colour rendering index of 100, information from lamp makers on this topic is hard to find.

[4] Most T5 lamps are optimised to give maximum light output at 35 °C. The figures in this table are based upon their output at 25 °C. As in most luminaires the lamp operates at a temperature close to 35 °C then the apparent light output ratio (LOR) of the luminaire appears to be higher than normal.

[5] Some types have control gear built-in.

[6] Most manufacturers are working on dimming control gear for this sort of lamp, but most products released onto the market so far have had major problems.

6.3   Gas lighting

Historically flames were the first form of artificial lighting. They are occasionally still used to create a particular atmosphere, but they are not considered as major sources of artificial light. Gas lighting only became possible during the industrial revolution. During the 1780s several inventors had been working with the flammable gas that is produced when coal is made into coke and they realised that it could be used for lighting. The problem was that it became necessary to set up a whole infrastructure of pipes to supply the gas to where it was needed. In 1813 a company was set up in London to supply gas and by 1815 there were 26 miles of gas pipe installed.

The first gaslight burners were little more than small openings at the end of a gas pipe. Over a period of time the shape of the burners evolved so that each unit would produce more light. However, a major improvement in performance was achieved in 1887 with the invention of the gas mantle. The gas mantle is a tube of fabric, impregnated with thorium and cerium oxides. When the lamp is lit the fabric burns away leaving a brittle mesh of oxides. The cerium oxide is a thermoluminescent material, see section 6.4.8.

6.4   Production of radiation

6.4.1   Incandescence

When an object is heated to a high temperature, the atoms within the material become excited by the many interactions between them and energy is radiated in a continuous spectrum. The exact nature of the radiation produced by an idealized radiator, known as a black body, was studied by Max Planck at the end of the 19th century and he developed the following formula that predicts the radiation produced:

$$M_{c\lambda}^{th} = \frac{c_1}{\lambda^5 \left(\exp(c_2/\lambda T) - 1\right)}$$

where $M_{c\lambda}^{th}$ is the spectral radiant exitance, c_1 and c_2 are constants, with values of 3.742×10^{-16} W·m^{-2} and 1.439×10^{-2} m·K respectively, λ is the wavelength and T is the temperature (K). The values of the spectral radiant exitance are plotted for different values of T in Figure 6.21.

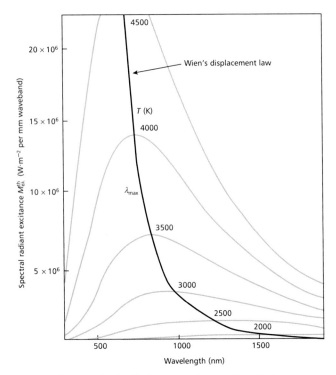

Figure 6.21 Radiation according to Planck's law

The wavelength for maximum power (λ_{max}) is inversely proportional to the temperature (T). The following formula was developed by Planck's co-worker at the University of Berlin and is known as Wien's displacement law:

$$\lambda_{max} = \frac{c_3}{T}$$

where c_3 has a value of 2.90×10^{-3} m·K.

The result of the application of this formula is that if an object is heated to a high enough temperature (in excess of 2000 °C) it will produce a reasonable amount of light. This provides the basic operating principle of the incandescent lamp.

In practice, many materials when heated radiate energy at slightly different rates to that predicted by Planck. This property can be exploited by light source makers. For example, tungsten emits about a third more energy as light than would be predicted by Planck's formula.

6.4.2   Electric discharges

An electric discharge is an electric current that flows through a gas. These discharges generally take a high voltage to start but once started they can carry considerable currents with very little voltage drop. A good example of such a discharge is the natural phenomenon of lightning.

In an electric discharge, the electric current is carried by electrons that have been removed from the gas atoms and ions that are gas atoms with one or more electrons removed. This is shown in Figure 6.22.

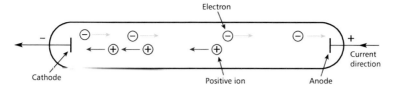

Figure 6.22 Electric discharge through an ionized gas

The negatively charged electrons tend to drift towards the anode whilst the positively charged ions drift towards the cathode. As the ions are several thousand times heavier than the electrons they tend to be less mobile.

When an electron collides with an atom, one of three things may happen:

- the electron rebounds with only a small change in energy: *elastic collision*
- the impact excites the atom and the electron loses energy: *excitation*
- the impact removes an electron from the atom: *ionization*.

Elastic collisions simply heat the gas. Excitation raises the energy state of the atom so that it may radiate light. Ionization generates more free electrons so that the discharge is maintained.

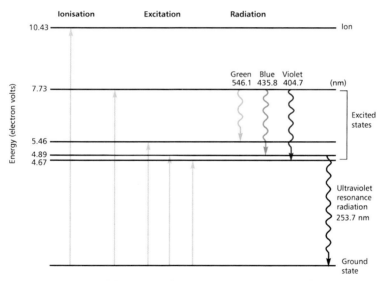

Figure 6.23 Simplified energy level and transition diagram for mercury

The result of any collision between an electron and an atom is largely dependent on the energy of the electron. If the energy of the electron is less than that necessary to raise the atom to the first excited state then the collision will be elastic.

The most common transition is between the ground state of the atom and the first excited state. Radiation from the atom returning to ground state tends to dominate the output of the discharge; this radiation is known as resonance radiation.

In low-pressure discharges, such as low-pressure sodium, the light output tends to be at a series of discrete wavelengths, each corresponding to a particular energy transition in the atoms of the gas. In high-pressure discharges the atoms of the gas interact with one another and this coupled with the higher electric and magnetic fields in the discharge cause the individual wavelengths found in the low-pressure discharge to broaden into wider bands of radiation output. In developing lamps the selection of atoms or molecules that have energy transitions that correspond to radiation in visible or ultraviolet is important.

Starting a discharge can be difficult because if there are no ions and free electrons present, the gas will not conduct a current. Most lamps use either a high voltage pulse or heated electrodes covered in special powders to get started.

The electrical properties of the discharge are unusual and in general discharges do not obey Ohm's law. This is because the current in a discharge is carried by electrons and ions and their number is generally a function of the current, thus at higher currents it is easier for the charge to pass through the discharge and the voltage drops. In order to maintain a steady current through a lamp most discharge lamps require control gear.

6.4.3   Electroluminescence

Some materials will convert electricity into light directly. Two major physical processes account for the majority of the various electroluminescence phenomena. They are the recombination of current carriers in certain semiconductors and via the excitation of luminescent centres in certain phosphors.

Pure semiconductors intrinsically have a very high resistivity and it is only when they are doped with other materials that it is possible to pass electricity through them. Some materials induce conduction by negatively charged carriers (n-type) and some by positively charged carriers (p-type). When charged carriers of different types recombine the energy released may be emitted as light. See section 6.2.1 for more information on light emitting diodes.

Some phosphors can be excited by electrical fields (usually an alternating field) to produce light. The most common material used is zinc sulphide generally doped with another metal such as copper. The process by which the radiation is created is not fully understood. However, this has not stopped the process being used to make self-luminous signs. For more information on electroluminescent light sources see section 6.2.9.

6.4.4   Luminescence

The term luminescence is sometimes also known as fluorescence, or photoluminescence. The process involves a material absorbing radiation and then re-emitting light. The energy may be re-radiated almost immediately or it may take several hours. There are a number of ways that the material can hold the energy and this impacts on the length of the time the energy is stored and the amount of energy that is re-radiated.

In Figure 6.24, image (a) represents simple luminescence where the material absorbs the energy and the next transition is to re-radiate the energy. In (b) some of the energy is lost in the material via another process before re-radiation takes place. In (c) some of the energy is dissipated and the material falls into a state where it cannot re-radiate until it is restored to the higher energy level. This process can lock energy into materials and is the basis of some 'glow in the dark' materials.

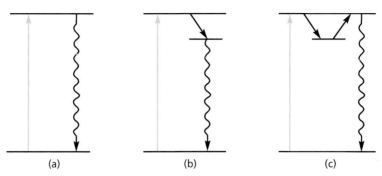

Figure 6.24 Simplified representations of energy level schemes in luminescence

6.4.5 Radioluminescence

This occurs in a similar manner to luminescence, but the primary source of the activation energy is particles or gamma rays emitted by a decaying nucleus of a radioactive atom.

6.4.6 Cathodoluminescence

In cathodoluminescence the energy driving the phosphor is an electron that has been accelerated away from a cathode. This process is the means by which light is generated in a cathode ray tube.

6.4.7 Chemiluminescence

Some chemical reactions can produce light directly, not via the heat the reaction creates. The process is used by some living organisms to generate light, the best-known example being the glow-worm.

6.4.8 Thermoluminescence

This is exhibited by some materials when they are heated. The materials give out much more light than would be expected due to blackbody radiation. The best known practical use of the method of light production is the mantle used in some types of gas lamps.

6.5 Daylight

The sun is a large cloud of high temperature hydrogen gas. It is held together by its own gravitational force. As the atoms of hydrogen are held together at such pressure and high temperature it is possible for nuclear fusion to take place and the hydrogen is converted into heavier elements, mainly helium. This process releases a lot of energy which keeps the sun hot; the sun is so hot it radiates energy by incandescence.

The sun is the biggest source of light on earth. Light from the sun not only gives us light so that we can see, it also powers the whole ecosystem on earth. Light from the sun can reach the earth in two ways: directly as sunlight, and, after it has been modified and redistributed, by the atmosphere as skylight.

Considerations of the use and control of daylighting within buildings are covered in Chapter 2, 'Daylighting' and also SLL Lighting Guide 10: *Daylighting — a guide for designers* (SLL, 2014).

References

CIBSE (2012) *A guide to the specification of LED lighting products* (London: Chartered Institution of Building Services Engineers/Society of Light and Lighting) (available at https://www.cibse.org/knowledge/knowledge-items/detail?id=a0q20000008I71aAAC) (accessed September 2018) (registration required)

EU (2010) 'Directive 2010/30/EU of the European Parliament and of the Council of 19 May 2010 on the indication by labelling and standard product information of the consumption of energy and other resources by energy-related products (Text with EEA relevance)' *Official Journal of the European Union* **L153** (18.6.2010) 1–12 (available at http://eur-lex.europa.eu/legal-content/EN/ALL/?uri=CELEX:32010L0030) (accessed September 2018) [no longer in force; replaced by Regulation 2017/1369 (EU, 2017)]

EU (2012) 'Directive 2012/19/EU of the European Parliament and of the Council of 4 July 2012 on waste electrical and electronic equipment (WEEE) Text with EEA relevance' *Official Journal of the European Union* **L197** (24.7.2012) 38–71 (available at http://eur-lex.europa.eu/legal-content/EN/TXT/?uri=celex%3A32012L0019) (accessed September 2018)

EU (2017) 'Regulation (EU) 2017/1369 of the European Parliament and of the Council of 4 July 2017 setting a framework for energy labelling and repealing Directive 2010/30/EU' *Official Journal of the European Union* **L198** 1–23 (28.7.2017) (available at http://eur-lex.europa.eu/legal-content/EN/TXT/?uri=CELEX:32017R1369) (accessed September 2018)

SLL (2012) *SLL Code for Lighting* (London: Society of Light and Lighting)

SLL (2014) *Daylighting — a guide for designers* SLL Lighting Guide 10 (London: Chartered Institution of Building /Services Engineers/Society of Light and Lighting)

USDOE (2016) *US DOE Solid-State Lighting R&D Plan* (Washington DC: US Department of Energy) (available at https://energy.gov/sites/prod/files/2016/06/f32/ssl_rd-plan_%20jun2016_0.pdf) (accessed September 2018)

Chapter 7: Control gear

Many lamps and light sources require some form of control gear (often referred to as ballasts, chokes, drivers, igniter or inductive/electronic transformers) to enable the correct start-up, control and operation of the lamp or light source. These forms of control gear should be selected by lighting application and also need to be compatible with the lamp or light source.

Some control gear types also incorporate a connection for a form of communication to enable the lamp or light source to be controlled remotely and/or provide luminaire status feedback.

The control gear can be incorporated within the luminaire but often the control gear is separate or even remote to the luminaire and may also supply multiple luminaires.

Lamps and light sources requiring control gear can be generally categorised as follows:

- incandescent lamps other than mains electricity rated
- fluorescent lamps
- high intensity discharge lamps
- other discharge lamps
- LED/OLED light sources
- emergency luminaires.

7.1   Control gear terminology

1-10 volt interface

This is an analogue control interface for control gear, which has the function of current source for a control device. The output power of the control gear is controlled between minimum/off and maximum values by the control voltage applied to the control terminals of the control gear. Details are specified in draft International Standard IEC 63128 (IEC, 2018a).

Amplitude dimming

This is a dimming method used in some LED drivers where the amplitude of the current supplied to the LEDs is reduced to a level that provides the desired light output. This reduced LED current has no significant modulation and thus avoids or limits visual stroboscopic effects or interference with digital cameras.

The downside of this method is that there can be undesired colour shifts or uneven light distribution along extended LED modules at low dimming levels. A complementary dimming method is the pulse width modulation (PWM) dimming method, see definition below. Some drivers use a combination of amplitude and PWM dimming.

Ambient temperature

Control gear is designed to operate in a defined maximum and minimum ambient temperature environment. It is therefore important to ensure that the selected control gear is not operating outside the specified rating, otherwise the control gear may not perform as expected and/or could fail prematurely. In addition, product certifications for safety and/or performance are only valid within the specified temperature range. As the ambient temperatures may not be easily determined (e.g. within a luminaire) the better reference for a control gear is the case temperature (t_c) at an indicated position on its outer surface.

Audible noise

Audible noise can be created by control gear, especially if the control gear is dimmed by phase-cut dimmers. It is important to check with the manufacturer regarding any audible noise levels when control gear/luminaires are installed in areas such as hospital wards, libraries and study rooms but also homes and some offices, as the low background noise may cause some users of the space to become distracted.

DALI/DALI-2 protocol control gear

DALI (digital addressable lighting interface) is an open control interface for lighting systems as defined by IEC 62386-101 (IEC, 2014). Compared to analogue control interfaces, DALI provides multiple functions such as scene settings, group commands, light regulation and colour control. Control commands are distributed via a two-wire galvanic insulated low voltage cable. DALI-based lighting systems may also be integrated in other building management systems such as KNX.

Version 2 of the IEC 62386 family of standards allows certification of DALI-2 compliant control gear and control devices by the Digital Illumination Interface Alliance (DiiA). Certified products are eligible to carry the DALI-2 logo and are listed on the DiiA website (https://www.digitalilluminationinterface.org).

Dimming and regulation

Dimming can mean two modes of operation in relation to control gear. Care should be taken when selecting control gear that is to be used when the luminaire light output needs to be dimmed.

- *Mains dimming*: the input power is reduced to compatible control gear by using a phase-cut dimmer ahead of the control gear.

- *Regulation*: the dimming effect of the luminaire output is achieved by a separate analogue (1–10 V) or digital signal (e.g. DALI) that is separately connected to the control gear and electronically regulates the output power of the driver to the lamp/LED array from within the control gear internal circuit, whilst the power input available to the control gear remains constant.

DMX (digital multiplexing)

Some control gear can accept DMX protocol communications. This protocol is commonly used to control luminaire brightness and colour changes for façade and theatrical/stage lighting and is used to communicate with RGB/RGBW (red/green/blue/white) or similar multi-channel control gear.

Electromagnetic interference (EMI) and electromagnetic compatibility (EMC)

Control gear has the potential to create electrical interference either via its supply cables or as electromagnetic radiation. Both forms of interference can have an adverse effect on nearby electrical/electronic equipment so it is important that the control gear is suitably designed to ensure little or no electrical interference is generated.

Additionally, there is also the potential for control gear to be adversely affected by electrical interference and/or static electricity created by other electrical circuits and devices. Therefore, the control gear will also require an acceptable level of immunity from such external sources.

Within the European Union manufacturers and importers of control gear are obliged to prove that their products comply with the EMC Directive of the European Union (EU, 2014). Compliance can be assumed if relevant harmonized standards are being met and corresponding tests have been performed and documented.

There may be unusual situations in which electromagnetic interference in a building or area is higher than the acceptable limits contained within the EMC standards. Such projects could include hospital MRI scanner rooms, radar installations, electricity substations, high voltage laboratories or buildings in close proximity to radio transmitters.

In outdoor and street lighting applications high immunity capabilities against mains surge voltages up to 6 kV may be required.

Special applications may require dedicated specified and designed control gear or additional screening and, if possible, on-site trials of proposed luminaires/control gear prior to specification and installation.

Flicker

Flicker is one example of the phenomena known by the more general term 'temporal light artefacts' (TLAs), which describe the visual effects induced by light sources whose intensity or spectral distribution change over time.

Flicker means that part of the TLA that can be perceived directly by humans and where the modulation frequencies of the light source range up to about 80 Hz. Flicker can be objectively measured by using the PstLM metric described in IEC/TR 61547-1 (IEC, 2017).

The control gear may contribute to perceived flicker in the lit area. Often flicker is due to low quality control gear or poor quality lamps/light sources. The specifier should ensure that the specified luminaires, both individually and collectively in the lit space, do not introduce flicker that could be a distraction or problem for the space users. Applications where flicker can be a problem include offices, hospital wards and classrooms. In most of these general lighting applications it is recommended to limit PstLM values to ≤ 1.

Ingress protection

The control gear will have an ingress protection rating (IP rating). The IP rating for the control gear must be considered if mounted remote from the luminaire or in outdoor applications. This includes dust and moisture protection classifications. See Chapter 23 for information on IP ratings.

Inrush current

Inrush current caused by control gear during the first few milliseconds of initial lamp start up is also a consideration. Manufacturers of luminaires should publish inrush current tables so that the lighting designer is aware of the maximum quantity of luminaires to allow per circuit and, if needed, the correct circuit protective device required for the circuit. See also section 7.8 below.

Local control

Some control gear has provision for a momentary action switch (sometimes called a retractive switch) that allows the switch to turn the luminaire on and off via a single short press, but if the switch is held for a longer period of time, the luminaire will dim up or down.

Power factor correction

Nearly all control gear will also have a power factor correction, which is one means to fulfil the EMC requirements of the international standard IEC 61000-3-2 (IEC, 2018b). This harmonized standard defines the limits for harmonic line currents emitted by electric equipment and is listed under the EMC Directive (EU, 2014). In addition, there may be also other regional and/or national requirements for the power factor itself. Control gear with a low power factor may lead to increased power losses within the supply grid. It is therefore a recommendation that all control gear has a power factor correction rating (also referred to as λ) of at least 0.9.

Pulse width modulation (PWM)

Some dimmable LED drivers use this method to decrease the average driving current through the LEDs and thus dim their light output: The DC output of the PWM driver is pulsed or switched on/off at high frequency by the driver's internal circuit. The width of the 'on' and therefore the 'off' periods can be varied in time. If the 'off' time is increased the output of the driver is reduced and causes the LED light source to dim.

The PWM frequency under all lit conditions for a PWM driver should be greater than 100 Hz otherwise visible flicker may be apparent. Well-designed PWM drivers will provide accurate and repeatable dimming at PWM frequencies between 100 Hz and 200 Hz and can also accurately maintain the luminaire correlated colour temperature (CCT) as the luminaire is dimmed.

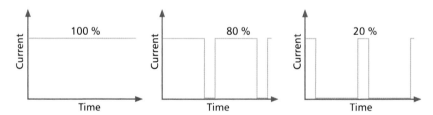

Figure 7.1 Pulse width modulation; the pulse width is measured in microseconds (μs)

Remote communication

Drivers will rely either on hard-wired control signals or wireless (e.g. radio frequency or infrared) based signals. These signals derive from a control system used to switch, adjust or communicate with the control gear/luminaire.

Consideration should be given to the communication type (i.e. hard-wired or wireless based) in respect of stability and technical maturity, but also regarding 'scalability' and long-term availability of support/maintenance. The appearance and cost of the infrastructure of a wired system needs to be considered. With wireless systems, potential problems with low signal strength, causing intermittent communication in some areas of a building or space, need to be considered.

7.2   Transformers for low voltage Incandescent lamps

Incandescent lamps that have a voltage rating compatible with the local mains electricity supply can be powered directly from the mains supply and no other form of control gear will be required.

Some incandescent lamps have a voltage rating lower than the local mains electricity supply and such lamps would usually be wired as a parallel circuit. This means that the control gear will be a transformer (magnetic or electronic) and will step down the mains supply voltage to a voltage compatible with the voltage rating of the low voltage incandescent lamp(s).

Consideration should also be given to the amount of low voltage lamps to be connected to the low voltage side of the control gear as the control gear will also need to be able supply ample current for the correct operation of the lamps.

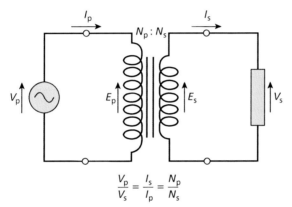

$$\frac{V_p}{V_s} = \frac{I_s}{I_p} = \frac{N_p}{N_s}$$

Figure 7.2 Magnetic step-down transformer used as control gear for low voltage incandescent lamps

Most modern transformers for halogen lamps use electronics. They usually contain high frequency oscillators to permit the use of smaller transformers that have smaller power losses. With the introduction of electronics, it is possible to introduce additional features such as constant voltage output and soft starting of the lamps.

7.3   Electronic control gear for high frequency fluorescent light sources

Operating fluorescent lamps at high frequency has a number of advantages and nearly all control gear is now of this type. Most electronic ballasts for fluorescent lamps are integrated into a single package that performs a number of functions. These functions are:

●   a low-pass filter, which limits the amount of radio frequency interference, protects the ballast against high voltage mains peaks and limits the inrush current

●   the rectifier, which converts the AC power from the mains supply into DC

●   a buffer capacitor, which stores the charge from each mains cycle thus providing a steady voltage to the circuits that provide the power to the lamps

- the HF power oscillator, which takes the steady DC voltage from the buffer capacitor and, using semiconductor switches controlled by the ballast controller, creates a high frequency square wave

- the output of the power oscillator is fed through a small HF coil that acts as a stabilisation coil to the lamp.

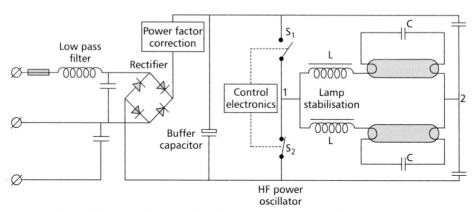

Figure 7.3 Circuit diagram of an electronic ballast for two fluorescent lamps

In some ballasts the electronics that control the power oscillator can vary the frequency at which the power oscillator runs, as the frequency increases the current passing through the coils decreases and thus it is possible to dim or regulate the lamps via an external signal. This is usually a digital signal such as DALI. Chapter 10, 'Controls' provides more detailed information on DALI and other protocols.

7.4 Control gear for discharge lamps

Most high-pressure sodium lamps and metal halide lamps require a high voltage pulse to start the arc in the lamp. This is usually provided by an electronic igniter. There are several types of igniter circuits, the two most common are the semi-parallel and the superimposed pulse types (Figure 7.4).

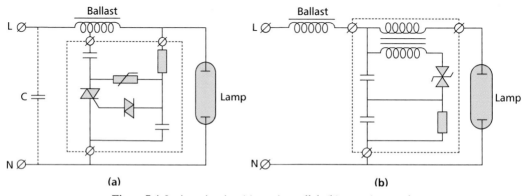

Figure 7.4 Igniter circuits; (a) semi-parallel, (b) superimposed

The semi-parallel igniter relies on the tapped ballast coil to generate the ignition pulse whereas the superimposed type igniter has its own coil to generate the pulse. The semi-parallel has many advantages in that it consumes no power when the lamp is running and is cheaper and lighter but, as it relies on the ballast, it may only be used with ballasts for which it has been specifically designed.

Igniters sometimes have other features built in such as self stopping igniters that will not continually try to re-strike a lamp that has come to the end of its life. There are also some that are designed to produce extra high voltages that can re-strike hot lamps.

7.5 Control gear for LED/OLED light sources

Many LED light sources will require some form of control gear and is most often referred to as a driver. Drivers have different characteristics, depending on the application and LED array they are controlling. Popular driver types are:

- constant current drivers and constant voltage drivers

- galvanic insulated 'SELV' drivers and non-insulated drivers

- indoor drivers and outdoor drivers

- dimmable and non-dimmable drivers

- dimmable drivers with DALI, and with 1–10 V (or other) control interfaces (e.g. DMX)

- drivers with amplitude and PWM dimming (type of dimming)

- DMX drivers (type of dimming command input method)

- single-channel and multi-channel drivers

- built-in and independent (remote) drivers

- standard and industrial grade drivers

- linear and compact shaped drivers.

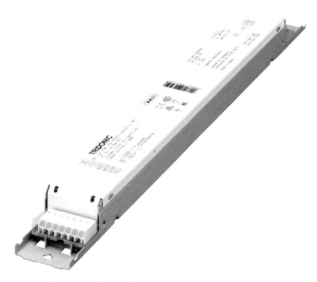

Figure 7.5 Typical linear driver for incorporating within LED luminaires (image © Tridonic.com)

7.5.1 Cable length from remote drivers

Care should be taken to ensure the correct cable is used between a remote driver and the luminaire(s) to ensure that excessive cable lengths do not cause a voltage drop outside of the LED array/luminaire specification and that the cross-sectional area of the cable conductors is adequate for the luminaire(s) load (amperes). The output of a driver can be extra low voltage DC and a higher current than expected.

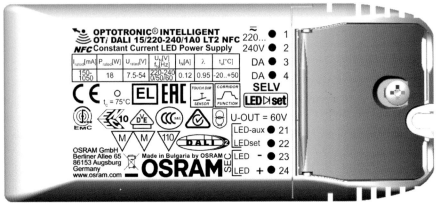

Figure 7.6 Typical compact driver for independent (remote) mounting (© OSRAM.com)

7.5.2 Amplitude modulation drivers

These can be used where the dimming curve needs to maintain as far as possible, the quality of delivered light, particularly in the 30% down to 1% dimmed range relative to full output. This is because some forms of dimming at low light levels can introduce acoustic noise, flicker, unacceptable electromagnetic emissions and general instability that may not be acceptable for the lighting application. However, with this method some colour temperature shift in the LEDs may be experienced at very low levels.

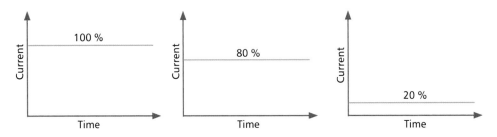

Figure 7.7 Amplitude modulation of LED

7.5.3 Constant current drivers

These control the output current of the driver and are used where high brightness LED arrays are used and highly efficient LED systems are targeted.

Due to the steep I/V characteristics of LEDs, a constant current supply is much better suited to obtain stable operating conditions for LEDs compared to a constant voltage supply.

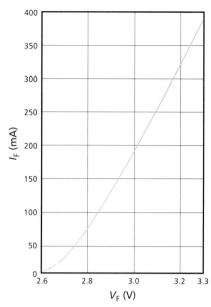

Figure 7.8 Typical I/V-characteristic of an OSRAM mid-power
DURIS S 5 LED (© OSRAM.com)

Constant current drivers adapt their output voltage automatically according to the specific characteristics of the connected LED module (within a defined range) so that the predefined output current level is achieved.

Constant current 'window' drivers allow flexible setting of the output current within a defined current window, either via software programming, connecting LED-set resistors or other means.

More than one LED module in series may be connected to a constant current driver as long as the total LED load voltage is still within the rated output voltage range of the driver. Parallel connection of identical LED modules may also be possible if they are specifically designed for such an operation.

7.5.4   Constant voltage drivers

Constant voltage drivers are used with LEDs/LED arrays that have an integrated current control circuit for that specific supply voltage. This kind of system architecture makes it easy to connect many LED arrays — each of them having their independent current control — in parallel, even when they are set to individually different current levels. The only limiting factor is that the total output power of the driver is not exceeded.

Constant voltage drivers are often used with luminaires designed for effect lighting, rather than general lighting. The overall efficacy of constant voltage systems is usually a bit lower compared to constant current systems.

Common luminaire applications would include LED light tape, light rope and rigid strips or bars of LED lights.

It is possible to use constant voltage drivers where dimming is required. Commonly DALI, 1–10 V and DMX types are available, as well as mains phase-cut controlled types, but this particular method can have some limitations in performance.

7.5.5   DMX drivers (digital multiplexing)

DMX drivers are often used to control stage and effect luminaires that require to change brightness and/or colour when prompted by a control signal. DMX multi-channel drivers mix the primary colours of individual red, green and blue LEDs to create the required colour in what is referred to as an RGB luminaire. If a good quality white light is also required, then an RGBW luminaire will be required. This fourth white LED in the luminaire will demand a '4-channel' DMX driver capable of controlling an RGBW luminaire.

The DMX signal is normally provided by an external DMX lighting controller and is programmed to send digital signals to the DMX control gear that determine the luminaire colours, light output, on/off state and when to change any of these combinations.

DMX drivers can be either constant voltage or constant current types, depending on the RGB/RGBW luminaire type and application.

Figure 7.9 RGBW driver

7.5.6   Phase-cut dimmers

Phase-cut dimmers are designed to reduce AC mains power and were initially developed to dim incandescent lamps and provide an acceptable performance.

They have had to evolve to operate with LED luminaires that are capable of being 'mains dimmed', but the dimming curve may no longer be as linear with LED arrays as it was with incandescent lighting. This means in practice, and subject to performance expectations, that phase-cut dimmers have limited applications.

Phase-cut dimmers use thyristors as the prime means of limiting or 'chopping' the output current from the dimmer and are defined as being either leading or trailing edge types, also called forward phase-cut or reverse phase-cut, respectively, depending on the section of the sine wave that is 'cut'. It is therefore important to ensure that the driver/luminaire can be controlled by a phase-cut dimmer of a leading edge (forward phase-cut) or trailing edge (reverse phase-cut) type.

They may reliably dim only down to 30% of luminaire output and can be erratic in operation at start-up and at lower dimming levels. The luminaire load also has to be of a minimum power (but not exceed the maximum safe working load of the phase-cut dimmer) otherwise the dimmer/driver/luminaire combination will not work to the product specification.

Figure 7.10 illustrates how the AC supply is 'cut' by the dimmer circuit to achieve a dimming effect.

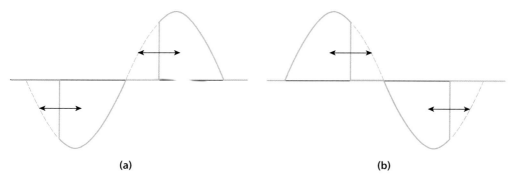

Figure 7.10 Phase-cut dimming; (a) leading edge phase dimming, (b) trailing edge phase dimming

7.5.7 Galvanic insulated 'SELV' drivers and non-insulated drivers

Galvanic insulation of the LED supply can have several advantages. In applications where the LED modules or the LED output circuits can be touched, a driver with SELV ('safety extra low voltage') and reinforced insulation to the mains is mandatory and protects from accidental electrical shock. Outdoor drivers mostly have insulated LED supply circuits, even when they are not touchable, because their capability to withstand high voltage surges is supported by that insulation. Compact shaped drivers for spot and downlight applications as well as constant voltage drivers are usually insulated. Galvanic insulation within LED drivers is accomplished by a special transformer with separated primary and secondary windings, operating at high frequency.

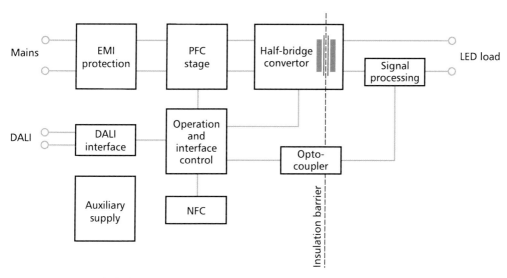

Figure 7.11 Block diagram of a galvanic insulated LED driver with DALI dimming interface and NFC configuration of operating parameters (© OSRAM.com)

Non-insulated drivers do not require expensive insulating transformers and are usually more efficient compared to insulated drivers. Luminaire manufacturers that manage to provide reliable protection from touching non-insulated LED supply circuits can benefit from these advantages. Especially for linear and area applications the relevance of non-insulated drivers is steadily increasing.

7.5.8   Outdoor drivers

Outdoor drivers have special requirements due to their application environment. They need to be reliable and 'ruggedized' for extreme operating temperatures, high humidity, mechanical vibrations, and also regarding high voltage surges on the mains supply.

Some outdoor drivers withstand voltage surges up to 6 kV or more. City municipalities often require street lights that can reduce their light levels and power consumption during dedicated night periods or can be adapted to specific use cases. Programmable drivers with autonomous night time dimming or with DALI and other control interfaces may be required.

7.6   Control gear for emergency lighting applications

Nearly all emergency lighting types have now adopted LED light sources and as a consequence, the control gear has to work with LEDs. Emergency lighting luminaires are either dedicated emergency luminaires or can be integrated into a general purpose luminaire, subject to space availability and ambient temperature considerations. Such integrations may use separate drivers for general and emergency lighting functions or a single driver that can control both the standard and emergency luminaire functions (Figure 7.12).

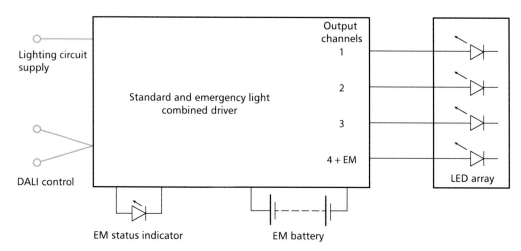

Figure 7.12 Single driver with automatic control and remote monitoring; only channel 4 remains in operation during emergency conditions

7.6.1   Emergency lighting: self-contained batteries

The control gear will consist of a driver for the LED array and additionally a charger for the batteries contained within or adjacent to the emergency luminaire.

The emergency lighting function will have some form of test method, usually by the following methods:

- *Manual testing*: disconnection by local normally closed key switch of the charger-maintained live supply to force the emergency luminaire to operate from the internal batteries for a set period in order to establish that the luminaire operates under power loss conditions and for the required duration.

- *Self testing*: an internal timer within the driver's charger module firmware will automatically make periodic disconnections of the maintained live and check the battery and driver performance as part of the self testing function. There are two types of self-test:

  — *Monthly self-test*: drivers that are currently in monthly self-test mode may cause the normally green (status healthy) indicator to rapidly flash on/off at four times per second on a weekly basis. *Note*: some manufacturers drivers carry out this test at weekly intervals and/or indicate in a different way.

  — *Annual self-test*: drivers that are currently in annual self-test mode may cause the green status indicator to slowly flash twice, over a test period of one hour or, more commonly, three hours.

- *Automatic testing and monitoring*: these drivers have a communications port (e.g. DALI) to enable all the emergency drivers to be connected to a network that allows a central controller and display to communicate with/monitor the driver/battery integrity and also carry out automated testing of the emergency luminaire and confirm the results of the tests or system faults at the central monitoring display.

The emergency luminaire status LED is connected to the driver and may also provide local information about the emergency system as follows:

- *battery and luminaire healthy*: steady green indication

- *battery low*: two slow red flashes

- *battery charger fault*: three rapid red flashes

- *lamp failure*: steady red indication.

7.6.2 Emergency lighting: central battery systems

There are various forms of central battery system. Systems that supply either AC or DC power to luminaires under emergency conditions are available. DC output systems require that luminaires connected to such systems use a driver that can be operated with both AC and DC input power.

Such drivers are fitted to luminaires that normally operate from 230 V AC mains supplies and ideally with digital control rather than conventional manual switches in order to maintain a permanent lighting circuit connection to all required luminaires. This means that the luminaire drivers are permanently powered-up as the driver also uses the supply to maintain its communications with the lighting control system. In the event of an AC supply failure to the driver, the incoming supply changes to a nominal 230 V AC or 213 V DC under emergency conditions via a battery/static inverter arrangement forming the central battery system.

A driver capable of also operating from a DC input may detect a DC supply voltage and then reduce its output to the LED array to typically 10–30% of nominal. This then allows the same luminaire to operate as an emergency luminaire until the AC mains supply is restored.

These driver types usually have a communications connection (e.g. DALI) to enable the driver to communicate its status to a host monitoring system and to switch the luminaire during normal operating conditions.

7.7 Control gear for circadian lighting luminaires

This control gear is required to shift the range of a 'tuneable white' LED light source in terms of correlated colour temperature (CCT) over a range of, typically, 2700–6500 K.

The LED driver will need an external control signal to shift the CCT as required. IEC 62386-209 (IEC, 2011) type 8 drivers are a popular choice for this application and will require a compatible DALI control device capable of controlling a type 8 (2-channel) driver.

Automatic brightness and colour temperature profiles can be processed during the course of the day via light controls with an integrated real-time clock.

In order to achieve a good match between the desired and actually achieved colour temperatures of a tuneable white system, LED modules and LED drivers must be matched to each other and ideally provide a calibration option.

7.8 Inrush current

Most electrical and electronic equipment has an inrush current whereby the initial switch-on current drawn by the equipment is many times higher than the operating current. The inrush current may only be apparent for a few milliseconds but needs to be taken into account when specifying control gear and specifically some types of LED drivers, even though the running current seems very low and efficient.

Most reputable manufacturers will supply details of the inrush current of their products and provide a table of the maximum number of a given product that can be connected to a given type and rating of circuit breaker.

Figure 7.13 below shows one manufacturer's product webpage, which includes a drop-down table against 'Miniature circuit breaker' that shows how many of those luminaires can be connected to a circuit breaker selected for a final lighting circuit. In this example it shows a maximum of 13 luminaires on a 10 A type-B MCB. The luminaire's load of 33.5 W would have allowed over 60 luminaires on the same circuit if it were not for the inrush current tripping this fast-acting type of circuit breaker. Even with a slower operating type C breaker, it would allow only 21 of these luminaires to be connected to it without a risk of tripping when switched on.

ZUMTOBEL

OVERVIEW

PRODUCT DATA

Description	LFE E LED4400-830 M600Q LDO KA SRE
Article no.	42 181 841
EAN number	9008709606302
Light Source	LED
Luminaire luminous flux*	4360 lm
Luminaire efficacy*	130 lm/W
Colour Rendering Index min.	80
Ballast	1 x 28000657 DRV TR LCA 75W 400mA 220V D #O4A lp PRE
Miniature circuit breaker	quantity with B10: 13 pcs.
Correlated colour temperature*	3000 Kelvin
Chromaticity tolerance (initial MacAdam)*	3
Rated median useful life*	50000h L80 at 25°C
Luminaire input power*	33.5 W Lambda = 0.9
Standby Power*	0.5 W
Dimming	LDO dimmable to 1% over DALI
Maintenance category	D - Enclosed IP2X

IP20   halogen   CE   650°C

Figure 7.13 Typical manufacturer's data relating to inrush current (courtesy of Zumtobel)

References

EU (2014) 'Directive 2014/30/EU of the European Parliament and of the Council of 26 February 2014 on the harmonisation of the laws of the Member States relating to electromagnetic compatibility (recast) Text with EEA relevance' *Official Journal of the European Union* **L96** (29.3.2014) 79–106 (available at https://eur-lex.europa.eu/legal-content/EN/TXT/?uri=CELEX%3A32014L0030) (accessed September 2018)

IEC (2011) IEC 62386-209: 2011: *Digital addressable lighting interface — Part 209: Particular requirements for control gear — Colour control (device type 8)* (Geneva: International Electrotechnical Commission)

IEC (2014) IEC 62386-101: 2014 : *Digital addressable lighting interface — Part 101: General requirements — System components* (Geneva: International Electrotechnical Commission)

IEC (2017) IEC TR 61547-1: 2017: *Equipment for general lighting purposes — EMC immunity requirements — Part 1: An objective light flickermeter and voltage fluctuation immunity test method* (Geneva: International Electrotechnical Commission)

IEC (2018a) IEC 34/508/CDV [draft] *IEC 63128: Lighting control interface for dimming — Analogue voltage dimming interface for electronic lamp controlgear* (Geneva: International Electrotechnical Commission) [IEC 63128 due for publication June 2019]

IEC (2018b) IEC 61000-3-2: 2018: *Electromagnetic compatibility (EMC) — Part 3-2: Limits — Limits for harmonic current emissions (equipment input current ≤16 A per phase)* (Geneva: International Electrotechnical Commission)

Chapter 8: Luminaires

The lighting industry produces many thousands of different luminaires. Given below are thumbnail sketches of the main types of luminaire used in interior and exterior lighting. Each main type has a predominant direction of the flow of light and will affect the distribution of light over the various parts of the lit scene. By choosing one type over another you are affecting the look and feel of an interior or space, as well as potentially the task-to-background lighting levels and the efficiency of the system. Details of any specific luminaire are best obtained from the manufacturer.

8.1 Interior luminaire types

8.1.1 Direct luminaires

Direct luminaires are luminaires in which the light distribution is predominantly downward. Such luminaires are typically recessed into or surface mounted on the ceiling. They are widely used in offices where the ceiling height is restricted. The usual light source is LED or a fluorescent lamp, either linear or compact. Many different forms of optical control are available, from diffusers through prismatic refractors to parabolic reflectors and louvres. Consequently, direct luminaires are available with a wide range of luminous intensity distributions. Direct luminaires are available for operation in dirty, corrosive or hazardous conditions. Direct luminaires are available with dimming or switching facilities linked to manual, occupancy sensor and photocell control. The most common problems with lighting installations using direct luminaires is the creation of a dark ceiling and poor illuminance uniformity in obstructed spaces. This problem can be overcome by choosing direct luminaires with a little upward light output or by having high reflection factors in the space. Figure 8.1 shows a selection of direct luminaires.

Figure 8.1 Examples of direct luminaires

8.1.2 Indirect luminaires

Indirect luminaires are luminaires in which the light distribution is predominantly upward. Such luminaires can be suspended below the ceiling, wall-mounted or free standing. They require a clean, white ceiling for efficient operation. They cannot be used where the ceiling height is less than about 2.6 m. The usual light source in suspended indirect luminaires is LED or a linear fluorescent lamp. Wall-mounted and free-standing indirect luminaires tend to use a high-output LED or discharge lamp. Optical control is confined to ensuring that the light output from the luminaire is widely spread across the ceiling so that no hot spots of high luminance are apparent. While indirect luminaires have a high light output ratio, lighting installations using indirect luminaires are usually less energy efficient than those using direct luminaires because of the losses caused by having to use the ceiling as a secondary reflector. This is compensated by the bright appearance of the space, the high level of illuminance uniformity and the absence of discomfort glare. Figure 8.2 shows examples of indirect luminaires.

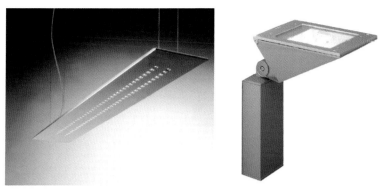

Figure 8.2 Examples of indirect luminaires

8.1.3 Direct/indirect luminaires

Direct/indirect luminaires are luminaires in which the light distribution is evenly divided between the upward and downward directions. In many ways, direct/indirect luminaires provide the best of both worlds. The energy efficiency of a lighting installation using direct/indirect luminaires will be higher than that of one using indirect luminaires, the problems of dark ceilings and poor illuminance uniformity are reduced by the indirect component and it reduces any discomfort glare from the direct component. Direct/indirect luminaires are suspended below the ceiling. They cannot be used where the ceiling height is less than about 2.7 m. The usual light source in direct/indirect luminaires is LED or a linear fluorescent lamp. Optical control is different for the two directions of light output, being much tighter for the downward component than for the upward. Direct/indirect luminaires are available with individual dimming of the direct component, allowing the indirect to provide a constant background illumination for the space. Figure 8.3 shows a selection of direct/indirect luminaires.

Figure 8.3 Examples of direct/indirect luminaires

8.1.4 Downlights

Downlight luminaires are usually recessed into the ceiling, so they direct all of their light output downward. Some downlights have optics or reflectors that can be tilted to wash walls or highlight objects in similar ways to spotlights. They are widely used in shops, hotels and other places where a lighting installation with a discreet appearance is desired. Many different light sources have been used in downlights, the most common now being LED with some compact fluorescent and metal halide still being made. Using reflectors, louvres, lenses and refractors many different beam spreads and beam sizes are possible (see section 8.3.2). Some downlights allow for adjustable aiming, which is useful when the intention is accent lighting. A number of downlights are fitted with decorative elements directly beneath the downlight aperture to give an impression of brightness to the luminaire. The most common problems with lighting installations using an array of downlights to create uniform illumination, are poor illuminance uniformity caused by over-spacing, potential harsh 'scalloping' on walls, and dark ceilings. Care is necessary to avoid a fire hazard when recessing downlights into an insulated ceiling. Figure 8.4 shows a selection of downlights.

Figure 8.4 Examples of downlights

8.1.5 Spotlights

Spotlights are luminaires with beam spreads in the range 10 to 60 degrees. They are usually mounted on either a base plate or lighting track. When track mounted, spotlights can be obtained for operation at mains voltage, low voltage or extra low voltage, the last of these requiring the installation of a step-down transformer. Spotlights are widely used in shops, hotels and museums for accent lighting. Spotlights are available that use LED, tungsten-halogen, metal halide and extra high-pressure sodium light sources of small physical size. Some of these sources come with integral reflectors and can be used as spotlights themselves. Other light sources come as a bare 'bulb' and have to use reflectors to attain optical control. Filters mounted in front of the spotlight can be used to change the light colour. Irises and baffles mounted in front of the spotlight can be used to modify the beam shape. Care is necessary when using spotlights to avoid glare to passers-by. Figure 8.5 shows a selection of spotlights.

Figure 8.5 Examples of spotlights

8.1.6 Wall washers

Wall washers are wide beam luminaires with optics or reflectors designed to give an even illumination level up a wall. They can be designed to be recessed into ceilings or attached to a lighting track. They can be long linear units using linear LED arrays or linear fluorescents, or spotlights with compact discharge or LED lamps/optics. Wall washers require careful positioning or aiming to achieve their best effect. Figure 8.6 shows examples of wall washers.

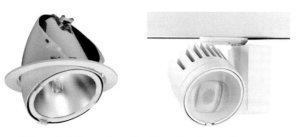

Figure 8.6 Examples of wall washer luminaires

8.1.7 Task lights

Task lights are a necessary part of a task/ambient lighting system, with a moderate level of even background illumination being provided across the space by indirect or direct systems. They provide local lighting of a specific area by bringing the light source closer to the task. The value of task lights is that they enable the user to have some control of the amount and distribution of light on the task by switching or dimming the light source and by changing the position of the luminaire relative to the task. Some LED types allow adjustment of the colour appearance of the light from warm to cool as preferred by the user. Typically, the light sources used in task lights are LED or compact fluorescent. The degree of adjustment available can vary widely as can the amount of desk space taken. When selecting task lights attention should be given to the coverage area for common positions and the likelihood of glare to the user. Figure 8.7 shows a selection of task lights.

Figure 8.7 Examples of task lights

8.1.8 Use for emergency lighting

Most systems discussed above can be used for emergency lighting with the exception of task lighting as this can be moved and is likely to provide poor uniformity across a space. See Chapter 3, 'Emergency lighting' for more details on requirements.

8.2 Exterior luminaire types

8.2.1 Road lighting luminaires

Where the road lighting is for traffic routes, the luminaires are designed to deliver light to a road so that the surface is seen to be of uniform luminance and objects on the road can be seen in silhouette. Generally, there should be no direct upward light from these luminaires. Roundabouts, pedestrian areas and residential roads are designed to more usual illuminance criteria. The light distribution is therefore dependent on the position of the luminaire relative to the road. Most road lighting luminaires are mounted on columns placed at regular intervals at the side of the road or between crash barriers in the median. At complex junctions and large roundabouts high mast luminaires may provide the best solution. A few installations use a catenary system in which the luminaires are suspended over the median in a continuous series. The light sources used in road lighting luminaires are typically LED, high pressure sodium or metal halide. Road lighting luminaires are often provided with adjustable LED optics, adjustable lamp holders and/or reflectors so as to allow the light distribution to be optimized for the light source and road layout. Two broad classes of road lighting luminaire are semi-cutoff and full cutoff (see section 8.3.2.3, Table 8.2) these classes reflecting a different balance between luminaire efficiency and the control of glare. Road lighting luminaires need protection against dust and moisture and so are classified according to the IP system (see Chapter 23, 'Extreme environments'). They are almost always fitted with a photoelectric control package. Figure 8.8 shows a selection of road lighting luminaires.

Figure 8.8 Examples of road lights

8.2.2 Post-tops

Post-top luminaires are a form of road lighting luminaire but unlike the road lighting luminaires described above, which are intended for the lighting of high speed traffic routes, post-top luminaires are intended for urban areas, where pedestrians are considered as important as drivers and the decorative aspect of the luminaire is as important as the functional. Generally, there should be no direct upward light from these luminaires. Post-top luminaires are available with either rotationally symmetric or road lighting light distributions, so that the same luminaire can be used to light both carriageways and open pedestrian areas in a city. Post-top lanterns take many different forms, some mimicking traditional styles for historic areas, while others represent the latest design trends. Because of their use in urban areas, the most common light sources being LED, high pressure sodium, metal halide. Post-top luminaires need protection against dust and moisture and so are classified according to the IP system (see Chapter 23, 'Extreme environments'). Because of their relatively low mounting heights, post-top lanterns are often constructed of materials that resist attacks by vandals. They are almost always fitted with a photoelectric control package. The most common problem with post-top lanterns is glare. This is to be balanced against achieving good vertical illuminance of people's faces. This problem can be avoided if there is no direct view of the light source. Figure 8.9 shows a selection of post-top luminaires.

Figure 8.9 Examples of post-top luminaires

8.2.3   Secondary reflectors

Secondary reflector luminaires are designed for use in pedestrianized places such as city squares and parks. In these luminaires, light is directed from the light source at the base of the mounting column, up the column, and then distributed by diffuse reflection from a large surface at the top of the column. Care must be taken to ensure there is no spill light past the reflector, which would give direct light up into the sky, both wasting energy and creating sky-glow. By changing the area and tilt of the reflecting surface, the light distribution can be altered. Secondary reflector luminaires are inevitably inefficient compared to post-top luminaires, but they do not cause glare, are not easily damaged by vandals and can provide a pleasing ambience. Figure 8.10 shows examples of secondary reflector luminaires.

Figure 8.10 Examples of secondary reflectors

8.2.4   Floodlights

Floodlights can be used to wash a large surface with light or to pick out a specific feature of a building. Floodlights vary enormously in their size, power and light distribution. The smallest floodlights consist of little more than a small LED pad with a spread reflector. Small floodlight types are generally used for small area lighting such as pub car parks, play areas, etc. The largest consist of a large array of LED optics or a high intensity discharge lamp with power in the kilowatt range and a carefully shaped reflector. These floodlights are mainly used for sports, industrial and entertainment area lighting. The light distribution of a floodlight can be rotationally symmetric, symmetrical about one axis or asymmetrical about one axis. This distribution is usually classified as narrow, medium or wide beam (see section 8.3.2.2, Table 8.1). Floodlights need protection against dust and moisture and so are classified according to the IP system (see Chapter 23, 'Extreme environments') and are often soundly constructed of materials that resist attacks by vandals. Filters mounted in front of the floodlight can be used to change the light colour. Barn door baffles mounted on the floodlight can be used to modify the beam shape. Care is necessary when using floodlights to avoid glare to passers-by. Figure 8.11 shows a selection of floodlights.

Figure 8.11 Examples of floodlights

Small floodlights are in general mounted from building structures or columns typically up to 6 m height. Large floodlights in general are mounted on the canopy of stadia or in frames mounted on towers, typically 25 m height. Local Authorities may require planning permission for columns/towers over, typically, 6 m.

8.2.5   Wallpacks

As their name suggests, wallpacks (also known as bulkheads) are designed to be mounted on walls so as to provide a low level of illumination in the nearby area. They are widely used for security and amenity lighting. The light distribution is usually wide and is achieved by a combination of reflecting and refracting elements that also restrict the upward emission of light. The light sources used in wallpacks are usually LED, high pressure sodium or metal halide. Wallpacks need protection against dust and moisture and so are classified according to the IP system (see Chapter 23, 'Extreme environments'). Because of their relatively low mounting heights, wallpacks should be solidly constructed of materials that resist attacks by vandals. The most common problem experienced with wallpacks is glare. This problem is much reduced if there is no direct view of the light source. Figure 8.12 shows a selection of wallpacks.

Figure 8.12 Examples of wallpacks

8.2.6 Bollards and ground recessed luminaires

Bollards are outdoor lighting luminaires mounted in the ground or on a surface plate having a height of typically 1.2 m. These are normally used for the illumination of pathways and gardens. They need to be constructed with a high level of robustness, protection, and securely fitted so unauthorised entry to the luminaire is restricted as far as possible. The light sources used are LED, CFL, and small HID lamps.

There are also ground recessed luminaires that are set flush with the ground surface and designed to emit upward light — often to light up walls or features. These luminaires use the same types of light source as bollards. These types of luminaire are used in amenity areas and the luminaires must be selected with care for the maximum mechanical loads for people or vehicles moving or standing on it and the maximum surface temperatures that would be acceptable for users of the installation area. Figure 8.13 shows examples of bollards and ground-recessed luminaires.

Figure 8.13 Examples of bollards and ground-recessed luminaires

8.3 Certification and classification

8.3.1 Certification

The principal EU Directives for electrical products are the Electromagnetic Compatibility (EMC) Directive (EU, 2014a) and the Low Voltage (LV) Directive (EU, 2014b). The LV Directive requires products put on the EU market to be safe and the EMC Directive requires products not to cause or be affected by electromagnetic phenomena (e.g. radio interference) Products complying with specified EuroNorm (EN) safety and EMC standards are presumed to comply. EN standards are based upon existing international standards, e.g. an IEC standard. In most instances, there is an equivalent British Standard (BS), known as a BS EN. (For established products a compatible BS may still be used, but preference should be given to the EN).

Electrical EN standards are issued by the EU-sponsored organization CENELEC. They are type tests, and manufacturers are required to associate them with controls for conformity of production.

Responsibility for compliance of a product with the Directives and with the specified EN standards rests on the person or organisation putting the product on the EU market, usually the manufacturer.

In Europe CE marking is a legal requirement (passport of the product for which a product must conform to specific applicable directives). For luminaires, this includes the EMC, LV and Energy-related Products (ErP) Directives (EU, 2014a/b, 2009) in conjunction with the CE Marking Directive (EU, 2008), requiring complying products to have a technical file that substantiates all conformity claims.

The CE mark must be on the product and preferably also on the packaging. Responsibility for marking rests on the person putting the product on the EU market.

It is important to note that CE marks on components in the luminaire does not imply that a luminaire complies. The luminaire as a whole must comply and carry the CE mark. Further, if a luminaire is modified for use in the EU (e.g. with emergency lighting) the modifier takes over responsibility and must make a new CE mark.

A lighting product outside the LV Directive (e.g. an ELV product) comes under the General Products Safety Directive (GPSD) (EC, 2001).

Luminaires incorporating a device using radio waves (transmitter or receiver) need to comply with the Radio Equipment Directive (RED) (EU, 2014c).

The ENEC mark indicates independent confirmation that the product complies with all relevant EN Safety standards and, where available, EN performance standards. The ENEC mark is not obligatory. Testing and approval are carried out by national Certification Bodies, e.g. in the UK by BSI. The XX in the example is replaced by a number from 01 to 25, e.g. 12 for BSI. The ENEC mark of each of the Certification Bodies is valid throughout the EU.

Again, it is important to note that ENEC marks on components do not imply that a luminaire has an ENEC mark. Further, if a luminaire is modified the modifier must remove the ENEC mark.

Recently an 'ENEC+' mark has been established to verify the performance claims for luminaires and LED modules. ENEC+ certified luminaires must also carry the ENEC mark (for safety) as a prerequisite.

8.3.2   Classification

8.3.2.1   Spotlights: luminous intensity distribution

Spotlights are characterized by their tight beam control. Most have a rotationally symmetric luminous intensity distribution. The most common way of classifying spotlights is by their beam spread. The beam spread of a spotlight is the angle over which the luminous intensity is 50% or more of the maximum luminous intensity in the beam.

It is important to note that beam spread, expressed in this way, is not a good indication of the appearance of the beam. A better classification of the appearance of the beam is the beam size often referred to as an 'illuminance cone'. The beam size is derived from the distribution of illuminance across a uniformly reflecting surface at a given distance from the spotlight. This distribution is differentiated to obtain the illuminance gradient. The locations of the peaks in the illuminance gradient distribution define the edges of the beam. The beam size is given as the angle subtended at the spotlight by distance between the two edges and is expressed in degrees. The magnitude of the peaks in the illuminance gradient profile indicate the sharpness of the edge of the beam; the higher the peaks, the sharper is the edge of the beam.

8.3.2.2   Floodlights: luminous intensity distribution

Floodlights are classified according to their beam spread. The beam spread is the angle over which the luminous intensity drops to a stated percentage of the maximum, usually 50% or 10%. For a floodlight having a rotationally symmetric luminous intensity distribution, only one figure is necessary to specify the beam spread. For a floodlight with an asymmetrical luminous intensity distribution, as is usual with rectangular floodlights, two beam spreads are needed, one for the vertical plane and one for the horizontal plane. If the luminous intensity distribution in either of these planes is itself asymmetrical relative to the beam axis, two angles are given for that plane and one for the other plane. A simple classification of beam spreads is sometimes used (Table 8.1).

Table 8.1 Floodlight beam spread classification

Luminaire classification	Beam spread at 50 percent of maximum luminous intensity
Narrow beam	< 20°
Medium beam	20° to 40°
Wide beam	> 40°

8.3.2.3   Road lighting luminaires: luminous intensity distribution for glare control

Road lighting luminaires have traditionally been classified as full cutoff or semi-cutoff, according to their luminous intensity distribution. BS EN 13201-2 (BSI, 2015) has introduced a finer classification designed to give better control of disability glare and obtrusive light. This classification uses the maximum luminous intensity per 1000 lamp lumens at different angles from the downward vertical in any direction as a criterion. Table 8.2 shows the limits for each of the six classes (G levels) and their relationship to the traditional semi-cutoff and full cutoff terms.

Table 8.2 BS EN 13201: Part 2: 2003 road lighting luminaire classification

Cutoff classification	G level	Maximum luminous intensity/1000 lamp lumens, at 70° from downward vertical	Maximum luminous intensity/1000 lamp lumens, at 80° from downward vertical	Maximum luminous intensity/1000 lamp lumens, at 90° from downward vertical	Other requirements
Semi-cutoff	G1	—	200	50	None
Semi-cutoff	G2	—	150	30	None
Semi-cutoff	G3	—	100	20	None
Full cutoff	G4	500	100	10	0 at greater than 95°
Full cutoff	G5	350	100	10	0 at greater than 95°
Full cutoff	G6	350	100	0	0 at greater than 95°

8.3.2.4 Operating conditions

The International Protection (IP) system classifies luminaires according to the degree of protection provided against the ingress of foreign bodies, dust and moisture and an IK rating for impact protection. See Chapter 23, 'Extreme environments' for details of the IP and IK rating systems.

8.3.2.5 Electrical protection

Luminaires are also classified according to the protection they provide against electric shock. Table 8.3 shows the luminaire classes in the IEC classification.

Table 8.3 The classification of luminaires according to the degree of electrical protection

Luminaire class	Degree of electrical protection
I	A luminaire having at least functional insulation throughout and provided with an earthing terminal or earthing contact that must be connected to a protective earth
II	A luminaire with double insulation and/or reinforced insulation throughout and without provision for earthing
III	A luminaire designed for connection to extra-low voltage circuits and which has no circuits, either internal or external which operate at a voltage greater than extra-low safety voltage

8.3.2.6 Flammability

The temperature of a luminaire may limit the surfaces on which it can be mounted. If the surface is non-combustible, then any luminaire may be mounted on it. But when the surface is either normally flammable or readily flammable, restrictions may apply. A normally flammable surface is one having an ignition temperature of at least 200 °C and that will not deform

or weaken at this temperature. A readily flammable surface is one that cannot be classified as normally flammable or non-combustible. Readily flammable materials are not suitable for direct mounting of luminaires. The IEC recommends a two-part classification system. For luminaires suitable for direct mounting only on non-combustible surfaces, a warning notice may be required.

For luminaires not suitable for mounting on a combustible surface must be marked with one of the following symbols (depending on suitability for surface or direct mounting).

Surface   Recessed

For recessed luminaires not suitable for covering with thermal insulation material the warning symbol shown must be marked on the luminaire.

References

BSI (2015) BS EN 13201-2: 2015: *Road lighting. Performance requirements* (London: British Standards Institution)

EC (2001) 'Directive 2001/95/EC of the European Parliament and of the Council of 3 December 2001 on general product safety (Text with EEA relevance)' ('The General Products Safety Directive') *Official Journal of the European Communities* **L11** (15.1.2002) 4–17 (available at https://eur-lex.europa.eu/legal-content/EN/ALL/?uri=CELEX:32001L0095) (accessed September 2018)

EU (2008) 'Regulation (EC) No 765/2008 of the European Parliament and of the Council of 9 July 2008 setting out the requirements for accreditation and market surveillance relating to the marketing of products and repealing Regulation (EEC) No 339/93 (Text with EEA relevance)' ('The CE-marking Directive') *Official Journal of the European Union* **L218** (13.8.2008) 30–47 (available at http://eur-lex.europa.eu/legal-content/EN/TXT/?uri=celex%3A32008R0765) (accessed September 2018)

EU (2009) Directive 2009/125/EC of the European Parliament and of the Council of 21 October 2009 establishing a framework for the setting of ecodesign requirements for energy-related products (Text with EEA relevance) ('The ErP Directive') *Official Journal of the European Union* **L285** (31.10.2009) 10–35 (available at http://eur-lex.europa.eu/legal-content/en/ALL/?uri=celex%3A32009L0125) (accessed September 2018)

EU (2014a) 'Directive 2014/30/EU of the European Parliament and of the Council of 26 February 2014 on the harmonisation of the laws of the Member States relating to electromagnetic compatibility (recast) Text with EEA relevance' ('The EMC Directive') *Official Journal of the European Union* **L96** (29.3.2014) 79–106 (available at http://eur-lex.europa.eu/legal-content/EN/TXT/?uri=CELEX:32014L0030) (accessed September 2018)

EU (2014b) 'Directive 2014/35/EU of the European Parliament and of the Council of 26 February 2014 on the harmonisation of the laws of the Member States relating to the making available on the market of electrical equipment designed for use within certain voltage limits Text with EEA relevance' ('The Low Voltage Directive') *Official Journal of the European Union* **L96** (29.3.2014) 357–374 (available at http://eur-lex.europa.eu/legal-content/EN/TXT/?uri=CELEX:32014L0035) (accessed September 2018)

EU (2014c) 'Directive 2014/53/EU of the European Parliament and of the Council of 16 April 2014 on the harmonisation of the laws of the Member States relating to the making available on the market of radio equipment and repealing Directive 1999/5/EC Text with EEA relevance' ('The Radio Equipment Directive') *Official Journal of the European Union* **L153** (22.5.2014) 62–106 (available at http://eur-lex.europa.eu/legal-content/EN/TXT/?uri=CELEX:32014L0053) (accessed September 2018)

Chapter 9: Power to lighting systems

9.1   Introduction

The provision of power to lighting installations is obviously a fundamental requirement and lighting designers and installers need to be aware of the methods by which this can be achieved. In the following, 'lighting designer' and 'electrical designer' are referred to separately in discussing the separate roles, but it is recognised that in many cases these can be the same person. This chapter looks only at the power distribution to the luminaires from local distribution boards; it does not concern itself with main power distribution through the building to those distribution boards. For a full coverage of this aspect see CIBSE Guide K: *Electricity in buildings* (CIBSE, 2004).

To carry out the electrical design the electrical designer will need to know the planned locations and loads of the luminaires. From this they can work out the optimum distribution of cabling and the sizes of those cables. From this a cable containment (conduit, tray, trunking) system can be designed to route the cables to the luminaires in an economic fashion. See Chapter 5, 'Coordination with other services', for more on the issues of allocating space within ceiling voids for cable distribution and coordination with other building services.

9.2   Design process

There are two basic requirements associated with the distribution and use of electricity and these are:

- make sure people are safe

- make sure that the risk of fire is not introduced.

No matter how complex an electrical installation becomes, it should not compromise these requirements.

Most countries around the world have a set of national standards that set a benchmark for electrical installation work and certain elements can be subject to regulation. In the United Kingdom, BS 7671: *Requirements for electrical installations* (BSI, 2018) sets the accepted minimum standard for general electrical installations within buildings.

In addition to BS 7671, in the UK certain electrical works are subject to regulations. An example would be certain domestic installation work, which falls under the building regulatory requirements for England, Wales, Scotland and Northern Ireland.

To meet the requirements of safe design, regulation or recommendations of guidance, electrical designers and installers will utilise the following approach if using conventional power distribution systems:

- Identify any hazards and consider how to address any risks they present.

- Determine the electrical load on each lighting circuit.

- Determine location of local distribution boards.

- Size cables from local distribution boards to luminaires.

- Determine how the cables will be installed to reach the points where power is needed.

- Chose a type of cable and containment appropriate to the installation.

- Chose a type and rating of over-current and short circuit protection for each circuit.

- Chose a method of switching and control.

Lighting designers and installers can help the electrical designer by considering the following specific items:

- Cables have to be able to reach the location of luminaires.

- Other than dwellings, emergency lighting may be required in most buildings and its installation should be considered alongside the general lighting designs to aid in wiring and coordination on the ceiling.

- Control of large groups of luminaires will add complexity to the electrical design.

- Certain light sources, such as some types of LED or metal halide, can have high inrush currents. High inrush currents will require suitable circuit protection and may limit the number of luminaires per circuit, see Chapter 7, section 7.8.

- Luminaires in certain locations, such as high up on buildings externally, may require specific surge protection to be included.

- Control gear and LED drivers are electronic components and can generate harmonic distortion through their power supplies back into the electrical system. Electrical engineers will need to account for any unusual situations.

- High pressure discharge lighting can place stresses on electrical systems and the electrical designer will need to limit the number of luminaires per circuit in order to avoid nuisance tripping of circuit protective devices.

9.3 Final circuit distribution

Electrical installations are made up of circuit protective devices (CPD) such as circuit breakers and fuses, along with various sections of cable which together create circuits.

Ideally those circuits should be as short as possible, which allows the CPDs to work more efficiently and reduces energy losses as well as maintaining the voltage level at the luminaires. Energy is lost due to the resistance of the copper or aluminium cables and the longer they are, the more energy is potentially lost. Voltage is 'dropped' as cables get longer and, in order for equipment to operate properly, the electrical designer will need to address this.

Cables within installations consist of mains cables, sub-mains cables and final circuit cables. The mains and sub-mains cables will carry the electrical load from a number of circuits and the final circuits will be dedicated to specific uses.

Final circuits to lighting are usually protected by either 6 amp (6 A) or 10 amp (10 A) circuit breakers or fuses. Occasionally 16 A devices will be used on high pressure discharge lamps due to the characteristics of the lamp and the current it draws until it warms up. An example would be the lighting to a sports pitch.

Conventional circuit protection works on the basis that in normal conditions, the load connected draws a current that is lower than the rating of the device. For example, a 6 A lighting circuit may draw 4 A under normal conditions. In the event of a fault developing, which creates a short circuit between the live and neutral conductors or an earth fault between the live conductor and any earthed metalwork, the impedance of the circuit falls. As the voltage is a fixed value of 230 V in the UK, the current rises due to the fall in impedance. Once the current rises to a value above the CPD rating, the circuit will be broken either by the fuse 'blowing' or the circuit breaker operating. The quicker this can happen the better as the exposure to any risk will be minimised.

The cables themselves will have an impedance and the longer they are, the higher the impedance will be. This needs to be accounted for in calculating how long a CPD would take to operate, so the aim of the electrical engineer is to keep circuits as short as possible. Lighting designers can help by considering, during the initial design phase, how luminaires are grouped for control and by discussing how cables will reach various parts of the building.

9.4 Conventional cabling systems

Conventional wiring to luminaires can be installed in a number of ways and use a number of cable types but all are similar in that the final connection to luminaires, switches etc., is made locally by an electrician and tested in situ. The way the cable is installed and the number of cables bunched together affect the current carrying capacity of the cables. For example, a given number of cables installed in a single layer clipped to an open tray can dissipate heat better than the same number of cables in closed trunking. The temperature of the space through which cables pass also affects their ability to dissipate heat and hence their maximum current carrying capacity. Cable manufacturers provide charts to adjust cable current carrying capacity based on installation method and ambient temperature. BS 7671 (BSI, 2018) in the UK, and similar standards/regulations elsewhere, cover this issue in detail to ensure that cables operate within their tolerances to ensure safety of the electrical system.

BS 7671 recommends that cables installed in or above escapes routes or passing through them should be non-flame propagating or be enclosed in non-flame propagating containment. As lighting is a key component of an escape route, this restriction will apply and may have an impact on where luminaires can be located.

9.5 Modular cabling systems

When electrical installations suffer failures, those failures tend to be where cables are terminated or joined. As each joint and termination in a conventional cabling system is created on site in conditions which are not always ideal, there is always the risk of a joint failure.

Modular wiring systems are factory built and tested in a controlled environment so benefit from a tested and repeatable assembly process. Cables have their connections made in the factory so they can simply be plugged together on site. Whilst this approach should improve the reliability of the finished installation and improve on installation time, it does rely on having a detailed design beforehand and, of course, is not capable of being changed easily once it has been manufactured. Late alterations to the layout of luminaires should therefore be avoided.

Care will also need to be taken in planning cable routes as the recommendation on BS7671 regarding non-flame propagating cables in escape routes will still apply. It may be prudent to have the whole system manufactured from the appropriate cable if escape routes are not fully identified or may be subject to change.

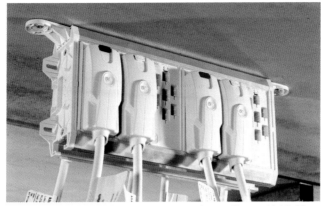

Figure 9.1 Modular cabling system in use in a ceiling void (© Hager)

9.6   Connection methods

There are a number of ways to connect luminaires, depending on their application, location and need for flexibility. Direct connection where final circuit cables enter and are terminated within the luminaire is the most common, particularly in domestic and low-cost installations. Where cables are terminated directly, care needs to be taken to ensure that they are suitable for any heat exposure within the luminaire and, if the luminaire has an IP rating, the connection does not reduce that rating. See Chapter 23 for details of IP ratings.

Plug and socket arrangements have been used for domestic lighting since the early days of the electric light. Five-amp plug tops and sockets have also been a popular choice for table and standard lamps over the years, especially in historic interiors. These separate lighting circuits can be switched from the doors, as with ceiling lighting circuits, or dimmed if all luminaires/lamps plugged into the 5 A lighting circuit are suitable for dimming.

9.6.1   Single point connectors

By using a plug-in connector between the fixed wiring system and the luminaire the electrical installation can be completed and tested without the luminaire itself being plugged in. The luminaires can be plugged in and tested later when site conditions are suitable for their installation and these potentially expensive and/or fragile items remain clean and are not exposed to risk of damage during the construction process.

Both 13 A and 5 A plug tops and sockets only offer a final power connection and the introduction of plug tops and sockets with four pins, dedicated to lighting were introduced in the 1980s (Figure 9.2). These allow control functions to be included as well and are now available with more pin connections and in a number of configurations, which can work with both conventional and modular cabling systems.

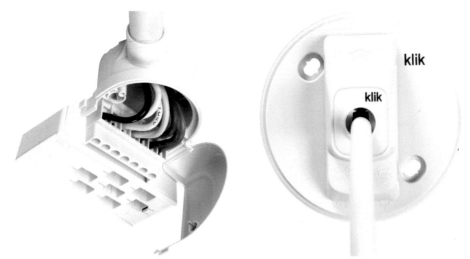

Figure 9.2 (*a*) Connector for single luminaire being installed in ceiling void; (*b*) the plug on a cable from a luminaire inserted into a ceiling rose version of a fixed base socket (© Hager)

9.6.2   Busbar systems

Busbar systems for lighting are available in 25 A, 40 A and 63 A ratings in different circuit arrangements to allow for separate control of different lighting circuits fed from the busbar. Each busbar is fed from one end and regular connection points along the length of the busbar allow luminaires to be connected where required via compatible tap-off connectors. If the rooms' spaces or task needs in the area being lit change, then it is fairly simple to move luminaires and reconnect them to a different tap-off position.

They come in a system that allows various lengths of busbar to be connected via corners, T- and X-joints to distribute connection points over an area. Some systems have simple clip-in tap-off connectors where they are under no strain, such as where used in office ceiling voids (Figure 9.3). Other systems have robust lock-on or screw-on tap-off connectors where the luminaires are suspended from the busbar, as in some industrial applications.

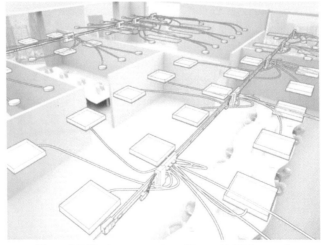

Figure 9.3 Busbar system in ceiling void (© Legrand)

9.6.3 Lighting track systems

Lighting track is a form of busbar that operates at a lower current that its counterpart. It is generally used for direct connection of luminaires where a flexible approach to lighting positions is required, such as in a retail space.

9.7 Distributed power and control systems

There are a number of systems that provide power and control functions to lighting systems through a primary and secondary distribution system. The primary section is usually the main power route either via cable or powered busbar trunking, and sometime a high-level control function (such as the ability to switch off all luminaires at once). At convenient places along the primary section, connection boxes, often referred to as 'nodes' or 'lighting control modules' (LCMs) are placed to allow secondary connection to luminaires, switches, presence detectors etc. Such systems are often factory built to a pre-determined design such as modular wiring systems and can use either mains or extra low voltage control functions.

Figure 9.4 shows how an LCM is connected to the mains power supply and BMS and provides output connections for a variety of equipment including manual switches, presence detectors and of course luminaires.

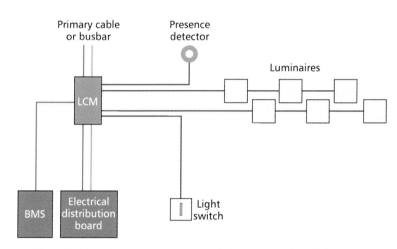

Figure 9.4 Luminaires connected to a lighting control module (LCM)

Sophisticated LCMs can operate as standalone controllers, receiving instructions from a primary controller such as a building management system (BMS), or through local connection to a computer accepting programming information directly. See also Chapter 10, 'Controls'.

9.8 Direct current power supplies

We have become accustomed to lighting in buildings being supplied at mains voltage from an alternating current (AC) supply. Incandescent lighting as well as low- and high-pressure sodium and mercury based lamps all require relatively high voltages generated by internal control gear either to strike or to directly produce any meaningful lighting output.

In addition, alternating current supplies have traditionally been easier to manage from a circuit protection point of view. However, they have a number of disadvantages, most notably the issue of flicker in fluorescent lighting and some LED products.

The introduction of LEDs and the use of microprocessor control of circuits has allowed the possibility of direct current (DC) supplies to be considered for a variety of applications, lighting being one of them. One driver for this is the possibility of reducing the number of individual drivers needed for LED lights and effectively consolidating these into one DC supply per lighting circuit.

Whilst a wide scale direct current alternative to 230 V AC within buildings is in its infancy and not expected to become mainstream for some time, a lower voltage system, which combines data and power over the same cables, has been available since the 1990s — Power over Ethernet (PoE).

9.9   Power over Ethernet (PoE)

Providing power supplies across Ethernet connections has been common practice for some time, most notably in telephony where voice over internet protocol (VoIP) has seen data cabling used to provide the power to the telephone handset as well as the voice signal. The ability to increase the working load of power supplies over Ethernet connections has improved considerably though and there is now the opportunity to consider such power supplies for DC LED luminaires.

PoE makes use of the same cabling as used in offices to provide a data connection between the main data switch equipment and each computer in the office. Additional cables of the same type can be installed at the same time as the data cabling with the advantage of reducing cost of installation. There would also be no need to install additional power cabling for the lighting installation if it was required in the same vicinity as the data cabling.

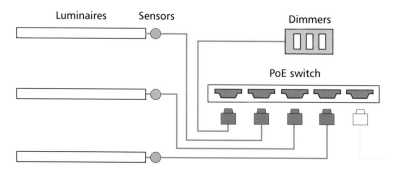

Figure 9.5 Example of Power over Ethernet lighting distribution circuit

For lighting designs utilising a localised approach to task lighting, PoE could easily be used to provide power at the data connection points for a DC powered LED desk light.

Traditionally, power supplies to lighting have been on the basis of power being available regardless of the need to use it. This has meant that a 'live' cable has been present, either within a luminaire or within a light switch. PoE is an active system that requires any connected luminaire to request power from the supplying power switch. Connected items are known as 'powered devices' (PDs) and each PD has an associated class it operates within. Table 9.1 below shows the relevant classes and their associated power limitations.

LED lighting supplied via PoE is most likely to use either Type 3 or 4. These systems are capable of supporting loads of up to 60 W and 100 W respectively at the power switch. It should be noted that these will be lower at the luminaire due to circuit losses, but should not be allowed to fall below the values shown in the Table 9.1.

Table 9.1 Categories of Power over Ethernet (PoE) as of 2017

Feature	Type (IEEE classification)			
	802.3at Type 1	802.3at Type 2	802.3bt Type 3	802.3bt Type 4
Common reference	PoE	PoE+	4-pair Power over Ethernet (4PPoE)	4-pair Power over Ethernet (4PPoE)
Maximum power per switch port	Up to 15.4 W	Up to 30 W	Up to 60 W	Up to 100 W
Maximum power to powered device	Up to 12.95 W	Up to 25.5 W	Up to 51 W	Up to 71 W
Cable type	Cat 5e, Cat 6 or Cat 6A	Cat 5e, Cat 6 or Cat 6A	Cat 5e, Cat 6 or Cat 6A	Cat 5e, Cat 6 or Cat 6A
Minimum number of pairs used	2	2	4	4

References

BSI (2018) BS 7671: 2018: *Requirements for Electrical Installations. IET Wiring* (London: British Standards Institution)

CIBSE (2004) *Electricity in buildings* CIBSE Guide K (London: Chartered Institution of Building Services Engineers)

Chapter 10: Controls

10.1 Introduction

Controls for electric light take many forms, starting with a manually operated one way switch through to an automated DMX control system capable of controlling a complex series of luminaires fitted to a building façade.

Lighting controls are specified for a number of reasons:

- conservation of energy

- automation of electric lighting for architectural enhancement

- providing lighting tailored to the needs of users of the space.

Lighting control technology is currently at a technological crossroads. Established protocols such as DALI® (digital automated lighting interface) and DMX (digital multiplexed) are well proven and in widespread use. New control technologies incorporated into emerging lighting technologies such as PoE (power over Ethernet), RF Bluetooth technologies, Li-Fi (data transmission via the emitted light of electric lighting) and IoT (the internet of things) are emerging, and will mature to a degree, in the next few years into established methods of lighting control.

The lighting designer should be aware of established lighting control technologies and how to apply lighting controls to a lighting design.

Further detailed information on lighting controls that expand on the information contained in this chapter, can be found in SLL Lighting Guide 14: *Control of electric lighting* (SLL, 2016).

10.2 Common terminology

10.2.1 Manual control

Manual switches are either the traditional 'hard wired' type or more recently of the wireless/battery-less type, where the physical switch operation momentarily generates an electrical pulse allowing the switch to act as a transmitter to an associated receiver containing the switching device usually located adjacent to or within the luminaire.

Figure 10.1 The simplest form of lighting control
(courtesy of MK by Honeywell)

At the opposite end of the spectrum to a hard-wired manual switch, control can be local and personalised via a hand-held device such as a smartphone or a tablet device communicating to the lighting installation via a wireless medium.

Manual scene setting switches are also common and usually allow the user to recall different lighting scenes and may also incorporate a manual dimming override and automated/manual operation of associated window blinds. The switch may also be an infrared remote-control device or a smartphone/tablet communicating with the lighting control device via Bluetooth or Wi-Fi.

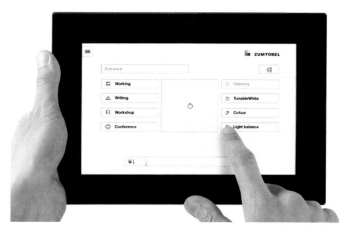

Figure 10.2 A Wi-Fi enabled scene select switch via a tablet application
(courtesy of Zumtobel Lighting)

10.2.2   Occupancy detection: presence detection

Presence detection automatically switches lighting on when presence is detected. If no presence is detected, the detector automatically switches the lighting off after a pre-set time. Presence detectors are typically based on passive infrared (PIR), microwave or ultrasonic/acoustic detector types.

PIR detectors operate when sensing two criteria: (1) infrared emissions at a wavelength emitted by humans and some animals, and (2) movement measured across more than one of the faceted lenses that make up the PIR lens array.

Some detectors also contain photo cells to measure light levels at the detector position and an infrared (IR) photo-sensor as a communications port to enable remote programming/adjustment.

Figure 10.3 PIR with adjustable lens
(courtesy of Ex-Or by Honeywell)

It should be noted that all types of lighting control occupancy detectors have manufacturers' application information that confirms the maximum fixing height and area of coverage.

In addition, line of sight from detector throughout the defined area of coverage will be required for reliable detector operation. Care should be taken when specifying microwave based detectors as the microwaves can pass though glazing and partition walls and therefore be triggered by the occupants of an adjacent space.

10.2.3 Occupancy detection: absence detection

Absence detection does not automatically switch lighting on when presence is detected. Absence detection relies on a local switch(s) that allow a user to turn on the lights — the detector will turn off the lights if no presence is detected for a pre-set time. The absence detector looks exactly like the presence detector shown in Figure 10.3, but will have additional connections for momentary push-to-make switches, often referred to as a retractive switches, or be capable of being programmed to receive switch commands where the detector is connected to a network or local controller. These switching commands may be received via an IR photo-sensor used as a communications port built into the absence detector.

The lighting is manually switched on, the detector monitors for presence and if no presence is detected, automatically switches the lighting off after a pre-set time. The switch may additionally allow manual switching off of lighting and, if the luminaires are capable of being dimmed (regulated), also allow manual dimming. Absence detectors are typically based on PIR and microwave detector types, but it is always wise to confirm with the supplier that the chosen detector can work as an absence detector.

Switch inputs may be either at the detector, or mapped to the detector(s) via an input module or lighting control module input.

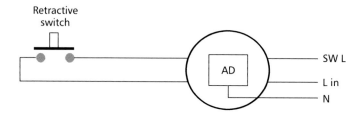

Figure 10.4 Basic absence detector operation

10.2.4 Photocells

Photocells are used to measure available light at a specific location in real time and can be used to automate a simple on/off lighting switch function or provide a digital signal to lighting control devices/systems that can either switch the lighting off if the received light reaches a pre-set level, or dim or regulate the lighting as daylight levels increase. More sophisticated photocells or photocell arrays can be used to measure real time available light levels (daylight and/or electric light) and use the information in real time to dim or regulate electric lighting and operate mechanised window shading. Such applications help to create a pleasant environment for people and also contribute to lighting energy efficiency. Photocells can either be separate items of lighting control equipment for either internal or external siting or can be incorporated into automatic detectors.

Thought should be given to the type of photocell (separate or incorporated) and the location to ensure the required level of performance is achieved by the lighting control design.

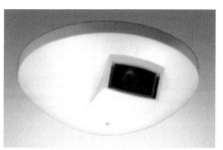

Figure 10.5 Photocell for internal use
(courtesy of Zumtobel Lighting)

10.3 Application examples

10.3.1 Daylight linking

Daylight linking uses a photocell or series of photocells to monitor available daylight and either switch off or regulate (dim) the associated lighting installation. Daylight linking works by 'blending' the available daylight and electric light to deliver the required lighting level on the working plane in real time.

It is important to ensure the photocells are correctly sited for effective daylight linking.

Further information on daylight linking can be found in section 3.5 of SLL Lighting Guide 10: *Daylighting — a guide for designers* (SLL, 2014).

Figure 10.6 Daylight linking of luminaires from left to right
(courtesy of Sophie Parry)

10.3.2 Constant illuminance adjustment

A maintenance factor (MF) is added during lighting design to allow for the lamp/LED's output to degrade to a lower lumen output over time due to the diffuser becoming dirty and the room's surfaces degrading or becoming dirty. This ensures that the required level of task lighting is still delivered at the lowest point in the installation's maintenance cycle. This means that the performance of the lighting installation still meets the design intent unless the assumed maintenance regime is not maintained by the owner/user of the installation.

However, applying a maintenance factor also means that, initially, excess energy is consumed and that the space may well be over-lit for some considerable time.

'Constant illuminance adjustment' addresses the excess energy consumed by a lighting installation by real time regulation of the light output of luminaires that are dimmable. The associated lighting is calibrated to a low set point equal to or just above the required lighting level. Over time, a feedback loop detects the lamp, luminaire and room surface degradation and alters the regulated level of the lighting to maintain the required lighting level.

Once the degradation over time reaches a low point and the lighting system is not able to deliver the required lighting level, it will become necessary to re-lamp, replace and/or clean the luminaire diffuser and room surfaces.

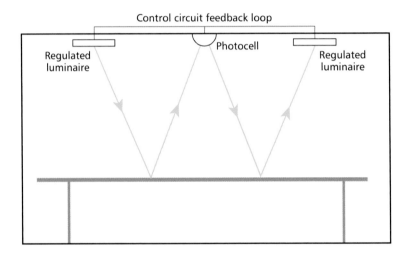

Figure 10.7 A photocell is used to measure the reflected light from the working plane to adjust the light from the luminaire to the required output

10.4   Dimming and regulation

10.4.1   Dimming

Dimming involves the reduction of the mains input power to luminaires in order to reduce the luminaire light output to the desired level.

Figure 10.8 230 volt trailing edge rotary dimmer (courtesy of MK by Honeywell)

10.4.2 Regulation

Regulation refers to the analogue or digital signal used to reduce the output of a compatible electronic ballast or driver. Typical regulation signals are a function of the 1–10 volt (analogue), DALI, DSI or DMX (digital) control protocols.

It is important to ensure the luminaire ballast or driver is matched to a compatible dimming or regulating lighting control device, see Chapter 7, 'Control gear'.

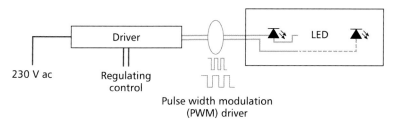

Figure 10.9 A DALI-regulated driver

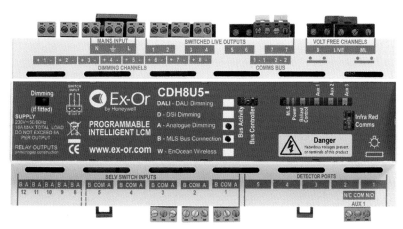

Figure 10.10 Multi-channel I/O module with analogue regulating outputs.
(courtesy of Ex-Or by Honeywell)

10.5 Basis of lighting control design

The lighting controls should be applied to a completed luminaire design by categorising the various spaces within the project and the specifying the required lighting control equipment to meet the performance objectives of the lighting controls specification, see Table 10.1 and Figure 10.11.

Table 10.1 Space classification

Classification	How used	Examples
Owned space	Small rooms, individual space	Cellular offices, consulting rooms
Managed space	Spaces where lighting scenes are predetermined by use	Retail spaces, hotel foyers, reception desks, sports halls, places of worship, front-of-house areas in entertainment venues
Shared space	Spaces of multiple occupation but would require some local or personal space control	Open plan offices, library study areas, hospital wards of multiple occupancy
Occasionally visited space	Periodic use for short periods	WCs, storerooms, warehouse aisles
Temporarily owned space		Classrooms, lecture theatres, meeting rooms, single patient hospital rooms
Unowned space	General open spaces, usually unsupervised	Circulation spaces, general open spaces

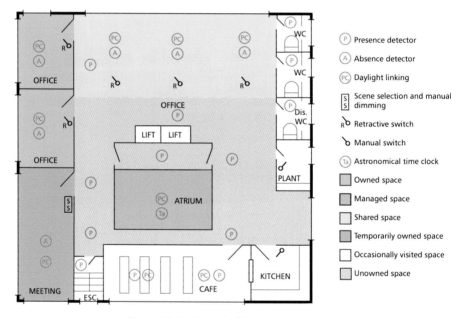

Figure 10.11 Typical office area arrangement

Notes:

- *Owned spaces*: the two offices have absence detection and daylight linking shown. Absence detection will always require a local switch(es), to manually switch the lighting on.

- *Managed space*: the atrium lighting could be regulated/switched off outside of business hours via an astronomical time clock arrangement. During business hours a welcoming environment would be required for visitors but also governed by daylight linking.

- *Shared space*: the open plan office uses daylight linking together with absence detection over defined work areas so that the lighting is only switched on based on office use by desk row.

- *Temporary owned space*: the meeting room has absence detection, a means of creating pre-set scenes and a manual dimming facility to ensure the correct lighting for most activities and/or AV presentations.

- *Occasionally visited space*: the WCs and canteen incorporate presence detection so that lighting is switched off when nobody is in the space. For the plant room and kitchen, a project risk assessment showed that lighting controls were not appropriate for these spaces, apart from a simple manual switch by the door.

- *Unowned spaces*: the circulation, and open office circulation route has presence detection and where appropriate, daylight linking is shown.

- *Plant room and kitchen*: a project risk assessment showed that lighting controls were not appropriate for these spaces, apart from a simple manual switch by the door.

Further guidance on space classification and choice of lighting controls is given in the BRE Digest 498: *Selecting lighting controls* (Littlefair, 2014).

10.6   Lighting control for visual effects

For many years, building features have been enhanced by the use of electric light. The lighting usually creates one fixed scene during the hours of darkness and is likely controlled by a time clock and photocell arrangement.

Technology such as LED light sources RGB/RGBW and DMX controls have enabled static and dynamic artistic lighting installations to be created that can often enhance the internal and external features of a building. The visual effects and luminaires required should be confirmed with the relevant project stakeholders. A compatible control system can then be specified.

Figure 10.12 DMX-controlled feature lighting
(courtesy of Kevin Stubbs)

10.7   Control of circadian lighting

The principle of circadian lighting is to enable the luminous intensity and correlated colour temperature (CCT) of the light source to be varied between a typical CCT range of 2500 K up to about 6000 K. This variable CCT lighting control can either be via manual control or can be automated to mimic the real time CCT of received daylight at a given time. See Appendix 2, 'Circadian lighting'.

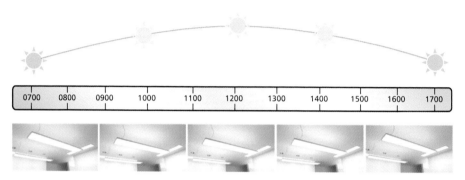

Figure 10.13 Circadian lighting tracking the CCT of received day light
during a typical day (courtesy of Zumtobel Lighting)

Circadian lighting may also be referred to as tuneable white or diurnal controlled lighting. Circadian lighting requires luminaires to have compatible ballasts/drivers fitted and a lighting control system that can tune or shift the luminous intensity and the CCT (light source correlated colour temperature expressed in kelvins) of the luminaires. A typical example would be where the luminaire driver meets the requirements of IEC 62386-201/207/209 (device type 6 or 8) (IEC, 2015/2009/2011) and the lighting control system also supports IEC 62386-207/209.

10.8   Lighting control for energy efficiency

The energy consumption of a lighting installation can be significantly reduced by the addition of automatic lighting controls, and the decision to incorporate controls has now moved from 'nice to have' to, in many instances, 'essential' for design compliance with current building regulations and/or energy performance requirements.

Care should be taken when incorporating lighting controls to ensure that the overall performance requirement of the lighting design is not compromised in the sole interests of energy conservation. The common method for calculating lighting installation energy over time is the Lighting Energy Numeric Indicator (LENI). LENI is an area-weighted annual lighting energy requirement measure, for use to indicate the energy performance of the lighting system, which also includes lighting controls. LENI is a reasonable starting point in lighting energy prediction over time, but the actual energy savings will be governed by the specific application and human factors.

To run a LENI calculation will require lighting load and hours of lighting operation information as well as information on standby energy (luminaire stand by and lighting control equipment) and the application of de-rating factors, subject to the type and configuration of lighting controls incorporated into the overall lighting design.

Throughout this chapter, reference is made to Building Regulations Approved Documents L2A and L2B (NBS, 2016a/b), which apply to England only. Separate documents apply in Northern

Ireland (DFPNI, 2012), Scotland (Scottish Government, 2017) and Wales (Welsh Government, 2017a/b). All references and examples in this chapter are based on the English versions and the designer should check on current local building regulations for all parts of the UK and other countries, where appropriate.

In order to comply with the recommendations in Approved Documents L2A, *Conservation of fuel and power in new buildings other than dwellings* (NBS, 2016a), and L2B, *Conservation of fuel and power in existing buildings other than dwellings* (NBS, 2016b), lighting loads should have dedicated energy metering. Existing installations can therefore be energy assessed over time to determine actual lighting energy consumption as opposed to predicted energy consumption at the design stage.

Guidance on compliance with L2A and L2B also recommends LENI ('lighting energy numeric indicator') calculations, see below. Information on de-rating factors can be found in the *Non-Domestic Building Services Compliance Guide* (NBS, 2013; Scottish Government, 2018). See also Appendix 3, 'Building Regulations and environmental labelling schemes'.

LENI calculations are also recommended in order to comply with BS EN 15193-1: 2017: *Energy performance of buildings. Energy requirements for lighting* (BSI, 2017a).

10.8.1   Predicting lighting energy where lighting controls are incorporated

It is important to be able to measure and benchmark the performance of a lighting installation as the lighting energy load is usually a significant consumer of energy in the majority of buildings. Benchmarks can be specified as a project performance criterion or from tables advising maximum lighting energy loads over time (typically expressed as kW·h per annum). An example of such tables can be found in section 12 of the *Non-Domestic Building Services Compliance Guide* (NBS, 2013; Scottish Government, 2018).

Section 12 of the *Compliance Guide* also states that lighting energy should also be separately metered. This is usually at the incoming supply for a dedicated lighting distribution board or alternatively as individual outgoing lighting circuits if the distribution board is not solely used for lighting. Some lighting control detectors and equipment can also monitor energy loads and make the data available as part of the lighting load measurement solution.

The use of automatic lighting controls, as opposed to manual switching or no switching, will usually reduce the overall lighting load and save energy. When calculating lighting loads de-rating factors can be applied for the use of automatic controls and may make the difference between compliance and non-compliance of a lighting design when the consumed energy is compared with the recommendations given in the *Compliance Guides* and/or the customer expectation.

From a lighting controls perspective, it will therefore be necessary to take into account the stand by and operating load of lighting control equipment and factor the standby/operating energy into any LENI calculations.

10.8.2   Lighting Energy Numeric Indicator (LENI)

LENI is the calculation of all aspects of energy consumption by a lighting installation over a stated period when the lighting installation is both in use (on) and not in use (apparent off).

The LENI output metric is expressed as kW·h/m² per annum and the result is compared against advised or recommended maximum permissible lighting power consumption for various applications.

LENI is area weighted and can be used for comparison of lighting system energy performance. LENI is usually used for the whole building but the same calculation procedure can be used for areas, zones or rooms when it is referred to LENISUB. BS EN 15193-1: 2017 (BSI, 2017a) now includes procedures to calculate and present the energy required for lighting at hourly, monthly and annual intervals as these are needed by the HVAC designers for their energy calculations.

There are three recognised ways of calculating the LENI for a defined area:

(1) The 'Quick Method', where the parameters other than the lighting loads are fixed and taken from tables detailed in the *Non-Domestic Building Services Compliance Guide* (NBS, 2013; Scottish Government, 2018).

(2) The 'Comprehensive Method', based on the formulae, values and tables found in BS EN 15193: 2017 (BSI, 2017a)

(3) Metered lighting load: this method is only applicable where LENI is benchmarked retrospectively for completed installations.

Further information on the application of LENI can be found in the following documents:

- BS EN 15193: 2017 (BSI, 2017a)

- CIBSE TM54: *Evaluating operational energy performance of buildings at the design stage* (CIBSE, 2013)

- *Non-Domestic Building Services Compliance Guide* (NBS, 2013; Scottish Government, 2018)

The lighting controls related information required to complete a LENI calculation:

- lighting load (daytime)

- lighting load (night time)

- hours of operation per annum (usually divided between day and night)

- proposed lighting controls configuration (for de-rating factors)

- luminaire (standby load) and lighting controls parasitic load (standby and operational parasitic load)

- the maximum permissible kW·h/m² acceptable lighting load.

This section will concentrate on the two items of information required to complete a LENI calculation and that are influenced by lighting controls. A typical LENI calculation using the quick method is then set out step by step at the end of this section.

10.8.2.1 Proposed lighting controls

The de-rating factors for lighting controls used in a LENI calculation are referred to as:

- F_c = constant illuminance

- F_d = daylight linking

- F_o = occupancy dependency

The de-rating factors vary for different modes and combinations of automatic lighting control operation and can be found in BS EN 15193: 2017 (BSI, 2017a), CIBSE TM54: *Evaluating operational energy performance of buildings at the design stage* (CIBSE, 2013) and the *Non-Domestic Building Services Compliance Guide* (NBS, 2013; Scottish Government, 2018). The values in the *Compliance Guide*, being targeted at regulatory compliance, are different from those in BS EN 15193.

For example, in the *Compliance Guide* de-rating does not apply to manual switches, whereas in BS EN 15193 the provision of manual switches can affect F_o. In principle, the method in BS EN 15193 gives a more realistic prediction of the actual energy performance of a lighting control system, but the method in the *Compliance Guide* should be used if it is required to demonstrate compliance with the requirements of Part L of the Building Regulations for England.

10.8.2.2 Standby energy within luminaires

Initially it is essential to ensure the luminaire data expresses the power of the proposed luminaire(s) as input power to the luminaire when lit to 100% illumination output.

Based on the above, the control gear standby energy is therefore accounted for in the day/night lighting load section of the LENI calculation.

The luminaire data should also include the standby power consumption of the luminaire when the lamp is not lit and the luminaire appears to be switched off. This load needs to be added to the lighting standby energy.

The reason for this 'apparent off' load is that many luminaires contain a ballast or driver which, for a variety of reasons, is fed with a permanent power supply.

Typical reasons for a permanent supply are where the ballast or driver constantly monitors the luminaire for data on performance and/or fault conditions or the ballast/driver is part of an emergency lighting system with an integral battery charger and/or automated test/feedback features.

If the luminaire data are not available expressed as input power and standby power consumption, then the standby energy will have to be determined by other methods. Assumed wattage per m² can be found in BS EN 15193-1: 2017 (BSI, 2017a), BS PD CEN/TR 15193-2: 2017 (BSI, 2017b) and the *Non-Domestic Building Services* England) (NBS, 2013; Scottish Government, 2015), for instance.

10.8.2.3 Standby energy within lighting control equipment

Note: some publications refer to standby energy as 'parasitic load'.

Lighting control devices such as detectors, photocells, hard-wired scene selection switches, lighting control modules, controllers and input/output (I/O) devices will almost certainly have a standby energy derived from the lighting circuit or a network driver associated with the lighting circuit, both in standby and operational mode.

The lighting control standby energy (standby and operating) should be calculated and applied to the LENI calculation.

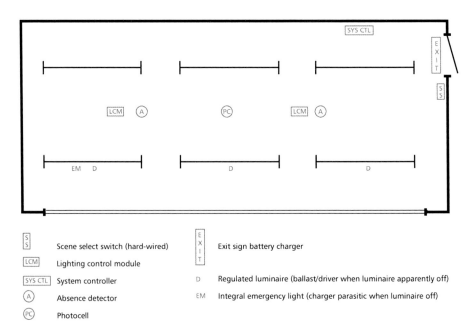

S
S — Scene select switch (hard-wired)

LCM — Lighting control module

SYS CTL — System controller

A — Absence detector

PC — Photocell

E
X
I
T — Exit sign battery charger

D — Regulated luminaire (ballast/driver when luminaire apparently off)

EM — Integral emergency light (charger parasitic when luminaire off)

Figure 10.14 Typical standby energy locations when lighting installation is switched on and apparently switched off to the observer

Note: D, EM and EXIT would normally be accounted for in LENI (E_d and E_n in equations 10.1 and 10.2 below) when the luminaires are switched on. At other times the standby load would be incorporated in the standby energy use E_p.

In summary and based on the above information, in order to accurately determine the overall standby energy, the following information will be required:

● luminaire standby load

● emergency lighting load whilst charging batteries/batteries charged, where the emergency lighting is based on local battery/charger type emergency luminaires

● lighting control equipment standby/operating load.

10.8.3   Typical step by step LENI calculation based on the Quick Method

The lighting design may have to be divided into sections for individual calculations if the typical hours of use and control type vary.

Step 1: Determine daytime energy use (E_d)

$$E_d = \frac{P_1 \times F_o \times F_d \times F_c \times T_d}{1000} \tag{10.1}$$

where P_1 is the total consumed by the luminaires (W), F_o is the occupancy de-rating factor ($F_o = 1$ if not incorporated), F_d is the daylight de-rating factor ($F_d = 1$ if not incorporated), F_c is the constant illuminance factor ($F_c = 1$ if not incorporated) and T_d is the daytime hours of lighting operation (h).

Step 2: Determine night time energy use (E_n)

$$E_n = \frac{P_1 \times F_o \times F_c \times T_n}{1000} \qquad (10.2)$$

where T_n is the night time hours of lighting operation (h), F_o is the occupancy de-rating factor ($F_o = 1$ if not incorporated) and F_c is the constant illuminance factor ($F_c = 1$ if not incorporated).

Step 3: Determine the standby energy associated with the lighting installation (E_p)

This calculation will need to be the sum of the standby energy associated with the E_d hours (step 1) and the E_n hours (step 2) as the load may vary between the two periods.

Note: some publications refer to standby energy as 'parasitic load'.

Step 4: Calculate the total lighting energy expressed as kW·h/m² per year (LENI)

$$\text{LENI} = \frac{E_d + E_n + E_p}{A} \qquad (10.3)$$

where A is the area of the lit space subjected to calculation (m²).

The calculated energy expressed as kW·h/m² per year should then be less than or equal to the lighting performance criteria specified for the project.

A typical example of acceptable performance criteria can be found in section 12, Table 44, of the *Non-Domestic Building Services Compliance Guide* (NBS, 2013; Scottish Government, 2018).

It should be noted that the calculated energy consumption may, over time, be compared with the actual energy consumption as recorded by any sub-metering devices that form part of the lighting installation. These comparative data may be used to verify the design intent against the actual performance over time of the lighting installation.

The performance modelling of lighting control systems is additionally covered in section 7.9.1 of CIBSE AM11: *Building performance modelling* (CIBSE, 2015).

10.9 Automatic testing and monitoring of emergency lighting

Emergency lighting luminaires can be monitored and tested via a separate, dedicated lighting control system, or as a function of a single multi-functional lighting control system. These forms of control are applicable to both stand alone and central battery emergency lighting installations.

It is important to ensure that any emergency lighting integration uses compatible components and that the performance criteria meet the requirements of the current editions of BS 5266-1: *Emergency lighting code of practice for the emergency escape lighting of premises* (BSI, 2016), BS EN 50171: *Central power supply systems* (BSI, 2001), IEC 62034: *Automatic test systems for battery powered emergency escape lighting* (IEC, 2012) and SLL LG12: *Emergency lighting design guide* (SLL, 2015).

Automated emergency lighting systems can be:

- separate dedicated control systems conforming to IEC 62034 (IEC, 2012)

- part of a lighting control system where the emergency lighting automated test function conforms to IEC 62034, with a data connection additionally integrated into a BMS/BEMS.

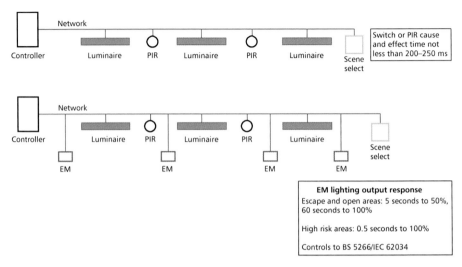

Figure 10.15 Network scenarios and configuration examples

10.10 Commissioning and handover

Lighting control systems will require set up and function testing, prior to full commissioning as part of the completed lighting installation and the hand over and demonstration to the facilities manager/end user.

Systems designed for effect and/or visual comfort will require setup and testing to provide the desired visual effect.

The equipment manufacturer or their agent should be employed as a minimum, to set up:

- agreed time delays

- detector coverage and sensitivity if applicable

- photocell calibration/set points

- scene select devices and scenes/animations required

- zoning

- user or graphical user interfaces to display graphics/information as required by the end user

- interface connections to other services/systems.

If seasonal re-commissioning is specified, some or all of the above functions may require periodic adjustment.

In order to verify design intent, historical sub-metering data for the lighting installation should be checked to ensure the delivered lighting/lighting control system is performing as intended. If not, adjustments to the installation/lighting control devices may be required.

Further information on commissioning/ post occupancy checks can be found in CIBSE Commissioning Code C: *Automatic controls* (CIBSE, 2001), CIBSE Commissioning Code L: *Lighting* (CIBSE, 2018) and section 8, 'Post occupancy evaluation' of CIBSE TM54: *Evaluating operational energy performance of buildings at the design stage* (CIBSE, 2013).

On completion and set-up/commissioning of the lighting controls as part of the lighting installation, the handover process should include the demonstration and, where specified, the training of the facilities manager and end user on the reason for and benefits of the lighting controls. This approach will enable both parties to understand the lighting controls system and its benefit.

References

BSI (2001) BS EN 50171: *Central power supply systems* (London: British Standards Institution)

BSI (2016) BS 5266-1: *Emergency lighting code of practice for the emergency escape lighting of premises* (London: British Standards Institution)

BSI (2017) BS EN 15193-1: 2017: *Energy performance of buildings. Energy requirements for lighting* (London: British Standards Institution)

BSI (2017b) CEN/TR 15193-2: 2017: *Energy performance of buildings. Energy requirements for lighting. Explanation and justification of EN 15193-1, Module M9 PD* (London: British Standards Institution)

CIBSE (2001) *Automatic controls* CIBSE Commissioning Code C (London: Chartered Institution of Building Services Engineers)

CIBSE (2018) *Lighting* CIBSE Commissioning Code L (London: Chartered Institution of Building Services Engineers)

CIBSE (2013) *Evaluating operational energy performance of buildings at the design stage* CIBSE TM54 (London: Chartered Institution of Building Services Engineers)

CIBSE (2015) *Building performance modelling* CIBSE AM11 (London: Chartered Institution of Building Services Engineers)

DFPNI (2012) *Technical Booklet F2: Conservation of fuel and power in buildings other than dwellings* (Belfast: Department of Finance and Personnel, Northern Ireland) (available at http://www.buildingcontrol-ni.com/assets/pdf/TechnicalBookletF22012.pdf) (accessed August 2017)

IEC (2009) IEC 62386-207: *Digital addressable lighting interface. Part 207: Particular requirements for control gear — LED modules (device type 6)* (Geneva, Switzerland: International Electrotechnical Commission) (published in the UK as BS EN 62386-207: 2009)

IEC (2011) IEC 62386-209: *Digital addressable lighting interface. Part 209: Particular requirements for control gear — Colour control (device type 8)* (Geneva, Switzerland: International Electrotechnical Commission) (published in the UK as BS EN 62386-209: 2011)

IEC (2012) IEC 62034: *Automatic test systems for battery powered emergency escape lighting* (Geneva, Switzerland: International Electrotechnical Commission) (published in the UK as BS EN 62034: 2012)

IEC (2015) IEC 62386-201: *Digital addressable lighting interface. Part 201: Particular requirements for control gear — Fluorescent lamps (device type 0)* (Geneva, Switzerland: International Electrotechnical Commission) (published in the UK as BS EN 62386-201: 2015)

Littlefair P (2014) *Selecting lighting controls* BRE Digest 498 (Garston: Building Research Establishment)

NBS (2013) *Non-domestic Building Services Compliance Guide* (2013 edition for use in England) (plus addendum) (Newcastle Upon Tyne: NBS) (available at https://www.gov.uk/government/publications/conservation-of-fuel-and-power-approved-document-l) (accessed September 2018)

NBS (2016a) *Conservation of fuel and power in new buildings other than dwellings* Approved Document L2A (2013 edition with 2016 amendments) (Newcastle upon Tyne: NBS/RIBA Enterprises) (available at https://www.gov.uk/government/publications/conservation-of-fuel-and-power-approved-document-l) (accessed September 2018)

NBS (2016b) *Conservation of fuel and power in existing buildings other than dwellings* Approved Document L2B (2010 edition incorporating 2010, 2011, 2013 and 2016 amendments) (Newcastle upon Tyne: NBS/RIBA Enterprises) (available at https://www.gov.uk/government/publications/conservation-of-fuel-and-power-approved-document-l) (accessed September 2018)

Scottish Government (2018) *Non-domestic Building Services Compliance Guide for Scotland* (Edinburgh: Scottish Government) (available at https://www.gov.scot/Topics/Built-Environment/Building/Building-standards/techbooks/techhandbooks/ndbscg) (accessed September 2018)

Scottish Government (2017) *Energy* ch. 6 in *Technical Handbook 2017: Non-domestic* (Edinburgh: Scottish Government) (available at http://www.gov.scot/Topics/Built-Environment/Building/Building-standards/techbooks/techhandbooks/th2017nondomenergy) (accessed September 2018)

SLL (2014) *Daylighting — a guide for designers* SLL Lighting Guide 10 (London: Society of Light and Lighting)

SLL (2015) *Emergency lighting design guide* SLL Lighting Guide 12 (London: Society of Light and Lighting)

SLL (2016) *Control of electric lighting* SLL Lighting Guide 14 (London: Society of Light and Lighting)

Welsh Government (2017a) *Conservation of fuel and power in new buildings other than dwellings* Approved Document L2A (2014 Edition with 2016 amendments) (Cardiff: Welsh Government) (available at http://gov.wales/topics/planning/buildingregs/approved-documents/part-l-energy/?lang=en) (accessed September 2018)

Welsh Government (2017b) *Conservation of fuel and power n existing buildings other than dwellings* Approved Document L2B: (2014 Edition with 2016 amendments) (Cardiff: Welsh Government) (available at http://gov.wales/topics/planning/buildingregs/approved-documents/part-l-energy/?lang=en) (accessed September 2018)

Part 3: Applications

Chapter 11: Common building areas

11.1   Introduction

Many building types have the same generic types of internal spaces. Most buildings have corridors, staircases and lobbies as part of the circulation routes used to move through buildings. These spaces generally need to be lit so that people can orientate themselves, view signage easily and recognise faces of people approaching them. Hospitals, factories and many offices will have staff changing rooms, cleaners' rooms and store rooms. For successful lighting it is important to consider the finishes and reflectances of all the bounding surfaces. Avoiding black or dark colour surfaces will enhance the feeling of welcome and brightness in these areas.

This chapter gives overall guidance on the lighting of such common building areas. There may be specific overriding requirements for some building types that will affect this guidance, but the recommendations presented in this chapter will provide a good starting point. All recommended illuminance values given below are maintained average values. The colour rendering index figure given is a recommended minimum and can be exceeded. Glare limits for most of these spaces are given in the schedule of recommendations in the *SLL Code for Lighting* (SLL, 2012a).

In many of these common building areas, the provision of good emergency lighting is essential and this should be considered and planned jointly with the normal lighting scheme. Guidance on emergency lighting is available in Chapter 3 and in more detail in SLL Lighting Guide 12: *Emergency lighting* (SLL, 2015a).

11.2   Entrance halls

- *Recommended lighting levels*: 100 lux at floor level, uniformity 0.4; 200 lux vertical on principal vertical surfaces; 200 lux over seating areas in waiting areas where casual reading may take place.

- *Colour rendering*: R_a80.

These spaces vary enormously in size and sophistication. Some are simple spaces for visitors to arrive, to be booked in and to sit and wait. Others are lavish or grand spaces designed to make an impression on the visitor of the size, wealth or sophistication of the building owner or its tenants.

A flow of light across the space is required both to make the entrance hall seem well lit and to aid in the visibility of visitors and staff to other people and to CCTV cameras. A flow of light across the space also provides lighting to walls where there may be company names, logos or artwork displayed.

Seating areas need to be lit in a relaxing way to allow for casual reading of magazines or documents and to allow visitors to relax before a meeting.

Some large pieces or art or trees may require special lighting. Some trees and large horticultural species require specific light levels to flourish and for the light to be on for periods beyond normal working hours — a horticultural specialist should be consulted if in doubt.

Most entrance halls will be provided with windows or full-height external glazing. This is mainly to provide views in and out, but also allows for the useful ingress of daylight and sunlight. This needs to be carefully considered and integrated with artificial lighting and lighting controls.

Emergency lighting will normally be needed to cover all of the open area of the entrance hall as anti-panic lighting at 0.5 lux. Clear exit signage will need to be positioned to clearly identify which doors to use for evacuation. The size of the signs needs to be appropriate for the maximum viewing distances across the entrance hall.

The entrance lobbies in many building operate late into the night or throughout the night. Many will have a security guard visibly located in the entrance area as a deterrent. Some entrance lobbies in prominent locations will be required to have some or all of the lighting on after hours to act as advertising of the location and, perhaps, prestige of the company. Other lighting in the lobby would normally be under management control so that some can be on for cleaning and the remainder on when the building is open to the public or during working hours.

11.3   Reception desk

- *Recommended lighting levels*: 200 lux at desk top; 300 lux on any lower working surface on receptionist's side of desk.

- *Colour rendering*: R_a80.

The reception desk needs to be lit so that the visitors and receptionists can each see each other's faces well to aid communication. The top surface of the desk should be uniformly lit where visitors may need to sign-in or fill out forms. The workspace on the receptionists' side of the desk needs to be well lit so that they can consult both screen-based and paper-based information. They may also be handing-out passes and/or logging people into the building.

The front of the desk may carry a company name or logo, which may need lighting in some way — either by back lighting or possibly downlighting from the overhanging top surface of the desk.

The wall behind the desk may also need to have lighting integrated into it or be lit if there are displays, company names or logos there. Note that there may be large screens mounted on or integrated into this wall or adjoining walls for the display of fixed or moving information or videos — avoid positioning lights that could be reflected in such screens towards the viewers. There may need to be dedicated emergency lighting at or over the receptions desk if it is used for security or emergency control, or as a location for fire and emergency crews to work from.

11.4   Atria

- *Recommended lighting levels*: 100 lux at floor level, uniformity 0.4; other lighting levels dependent on use of each part of the space.

- *Colour rendering*: R_a80.

Atria form large voids within the hearts of buildings. They can fulfil many functions — arrival points, meeting spaces, connecting spaces, workspaces, circulation, promenading, social and dining areas. They also provide a high-quality visual outlook to occupants of the spaces abutting the atrium and can contribute to the environmental conditions within these occupied or transitory spaces. By providing access to daylight for workers on the 'inside' of the building, atria buildings can offer greater efficiency in space planning, leading to increased user satisfaction.

Planting, artwork, water features, seating and reception areas are often provided within the atrium, enhancing its social function. Similarly, they are often central to the grand circulation statement, with escalators, feature observation lifts and staircases forming major elements. Dining facilities, retail and workspaces may also be incorporated into the atrium design.

The atrium is therefore an extremely important space within a building and will require lighting that is appropriate to these multi-functional provisions. It is essential that the designer is fully aware of all the functions that the atrium is to provide and their intended locations.

For a full coverage of the electric and daylight design, controls and for specialist lighting for planting, see SLL Lighting Guide 7: *Offices* (SLL, 2015b).

Figure 11.1 Different lighting being used in the different functional areas of this hotel atrium (courtesy of Paul Ruffles)

Figure 11.2 Variety of uses of the spaces require different lighting systems for this office atrium (courtesy of Iguzzini Ltd.)

11.5   Corridors

- *Recommended lighting levels*: 100 lux at floor level, uniformity 0.4.

- *Colour rendering*: $R_a 60$ in back-of-house and industrial spaces, $R_a 80$ in others.

Corridors vary considerably in size, use and sophistication. Some are simply routes for individual pedestrians through parts of buildings where they are unlikely to linger. Others are wide routes for trolleys in hospitals or goods in factories; each needs appropriate lighting for their functions.

The lighting on the floor of the corridor should be fairly uniform and avoid any shadows that may be misinterpreted as a step. The lighting on the walls can vary to provide some visual variety. Ensure that intended locations for signs, artwork and notice boards on walls are well lit.

For corridors with rows of numbered rooms, such as hotel bedroom corridors and office meeting room corridors, ensure that room numbers or names and the locks or key-card slots/panels are well lit.

Figure 11.3 Simply lit corridor with borrowed daylight through glass walls from adjacent meeting rooms (courtesy of Paul Ruffles)

Figure 11.4 The decorative ceiling lights leave the dark carpeted floor looking poorly lit; the exit sign points to an unlit doorway (courtesy of Paul Ruffles)

There are some environments, such as galleries, hospital wards at night, cinemas and theatres, where corridors lead up to or link spaces lit to low lighting levels. If these corridors were lit to standard levels, they may be distracting or cause an adaptation problem. In these cases, the lighting level in a linking corridor should respond to the lighting level in the spaces being connected. Where a corridor leads from a much brighter space to a dimly lit space then ideally the lighting level along the corridor should be at an intermediate level to aid adaptation of those approaching the dimly lit space.

Emergency lighting is normally needed along all corridors. Exit signs with an arrow pointing upwards should be located above smoke doors along the corridor to indicate the need to continue along this route to an exit. Where the exit door from the corridor is on one side of the corridor, an exit sign should be mounted centrally in the corridor with arrow pointing left or right, as appropriate to that door.

Figure 11.5 (*Left*) Exit signs visible along corridor until….
(*Right*) smoke doors close on fire alarm, obscuring exit signs

For frequently used corridors in some offices the lighting would be on during all times that staff are in the building. In other buildings, such as some hotel corridors that are infrequently used during parts of the day, presence detectors can be used. These need to be carefully sited so that they bring on the lights in the sections of corridor ahead of an approaching person and stay on whilst they are in that section. Detectors must also trigger when someone emerges from any room along a corridor. Normally some background lighting should be provided in all corridors so that when someone looks along a long corridor the sections far ahead are not in complete darkness.

11.6   Waiting areas

- *Recommended lighting levels*: 100 lux horizontal on floor generally; 200 lux over seating areas where casual reading may take place.

- *Colour rendering*: R_a80.

Whilst strictly not strictly part of a circulation route, these areas are often open to and an extension of a corridor, such as in many hospitals.

The lighting should provide direct illumination on wall mounted signs, information boards and art work. There should be a good flow of light across the space to light people's faces so that people can easily recognise the faces of others.

11.7   Ramps

- *Recommended lighting levels*: 100 lux at floor level as part of corridor; 150 lux at floor level as part of loading dock or similar; uniformity 0.4.

- *Colour rendering*: R_a60 in back-of-house and industrial spaces; R_a80 in others.

Ramps used in buildings are normally of limited incline so that they can be safely traversed by wheelchairs and push-chairs. For design purposes, they should be treated in the same way as corridors although, with an inclined floor and possibly flat areas to allow rest, they need more attention paid to lighting at the start and stop of each section of ramp, so that users can quickly and easily identify them.

Where ramps form part of an exit route, emergency lighting should be provided with additional emphasis on the start and stop of the incline.

11.8   Lift lobbies

- *Recommended lighting levels*: 100 lux horizontal on floor generally, but 200 lux in front of lift doors.

- *Colour rendering*: R_a60 in back-of-house and industrial spaces; R_a80 in others.

Whilst many lift lobbies are simply wider sections of a corridor, they should be lit in a way that emphasises any signs, artworks or furniture in the space, as well as the lift doors themselves. By lighting the lift doors, light is also provided on the threshold into the lift once the doors open.

These open spaces where people wait for lifts or emerge from lifts need to be lit so that people can easily orientate themselves and easily read signs and quickly recognise the faces of others in the space.

11.9   Staircases

- *Recommended lighting levels*: general buildings: 100 lux horizontal; schools: 150 lux; railway stations: 50 lux for small and medium stations, 100 lux for large stations.

- *Colour rendering*: R_a40 in escape stairs; R_a60 in back-of-house and industrial spaces; R_a80 in others.

In most buildings, there are two types of stair: those used constantly by the occupants to pass up and down the building, normally referred to as accommodation stairs, and the escape stairs that are rarely used except to evacuate the building. Escape stairs are considered in the next section.

The main or accommodation stair can vary from simply decorated and lit, as in a typical hospital or factory, to lavishly decorated and lit in some more up-market shops, offices and hotels. See SLL Lighting Guide 16: *Lighting for stairs* (SLL, 2017) for more details on this subject.

Lights are often positioned at each landing, as this ensures that the top and bottom of flights of steps are easily lit. The landing also provides a flat platform to erect step-ladders or other access equipment for safe access to the lights for cleaning and maintenance.

The average maintained lighting level on the main landings should be the same as the recommended lighting level for the stair and the normal criteria for uniformity apply. In general, the lighting should be as even as possible with no sudden changes of light level. No shadows should occur across the landings, as this may be misinterpreted as a step.

It is important to light small quarter landings where a stair turns, so that users can accurately judge the end of one flight and the start of the next. It is similarly important to light any 'rest' landings that are used to break up long continuous flights into shorter sections. This ensures that users can see that what might appear to be one very long flight suddenly has a much wider 'step' that is in fact a landing to allow users to pause safely if they cannot make the whole long flight in one go.

Luminaires must not be positioned such that they reduce the width of the stairs, as this might infringe local building regulations on minimum widths. They should also not be placed in locations where they could be hit by the body or head of those passing up or down the stair or crossing landings. They should not be positioned above the stair flights themselves, as access for maintenance is difficult and access equipment may compromise the use of the stair. Luminaires should not be positioned above doors that open onto a landing, as there is a risk of impact on any access equipment being used and again such equipment may impede escape.

Refuge areas for wheelchair users to wait for assistance in an emergency, are normally located to one side of the main landings. This area needs to be lit to aid transfer from the wheelchair to a stair lift. for transport down the stairs. If a stair-chair is permanently located in or adjacent to the refuge area, normally wall mounted, it will also need to be lit to aid location, removal and assembly.

Good vertical illumination will be needed on any information signs and any intercom system located in or adjacent to the refuge area.

Other than in a single dwelling, the occupants of a building are only occasional users of a communal staircase and do not feel responsible for the lighting. Placing switches in such a stair leads to the danger of the lights being turned off whilst people are using the stair or lights being left on permanently. If switches are ever used, they need to be at every door into the stair to avoid people entering a dark stair at levels where there is no switch. Because of these problems, it is normal for the lighting of staircases in most public, civic and commercial buildings are centrally switched under management control. This means that the staircase lighting is on whenever the building is occupied. In frequently used staircases this is sensible, assuming the staircase lighting uses the minimum energy necessary to provide the required level of lighting. Where staircases are only occasionally used then there are other control systems that can be considered as a way of saving energy. See SLL Lighting Guides 16: *Lighting for stairs* (SLL, 2017) and 14: *Control of electric lighting* (SLL, 2016) for more detail.

11.10   Emergency lighting of staircases

In the event of a failure of the normal power supply to the lighting, an emergency lighting system is normally required to provide lighting to the stairs and landings to allow safe evacuation of people from the building.

Even if a staircase has been designated by someone as 'just for emergency' or 'escape' use, this does not remove the need to light them adequately for normal use.

On loss of main power the emergency lighting must provide along the centre line of the stairs not less than 1 lux, with each step being lit and the ratio of maximum to minimum illumination being less than 40 to 1. See SLL Lighting Guide 12: *Emergency lighting* (SLL, 2015a) for full requirements and design options.

In practice this lighting level has been found to be adequate for controlled escape — once people are descending the stairs (if they are regularly spaced) they just follow the person in front. Where the stairs are not even, or turn in unusual ways, increased emergency lighting levels of 5 lux should be provided.

Emergency lighting must be located in disabled refuge areas to illuminate all key signs, intercoms and physical features; BS 5266-1 (BSI, 2016) recommends 5 lux horizontal on the floor and 5 lux vertical on signs and communications equipment.

Escape stairs that are not intended for normal use are often left undecorated and simply lit as they are not normally seen or accessed. The lighting is normally off unless access is needed. Particular consideration is needed to ensure that the lighting in the stair comes on wherever and whenever someone enters the stair and stays on whilst they are moving up or down the stair.

11.11 Escalators

- *Recommended lighting levels*: 100 lux horizontal on treads; uniformity 0.4.
- *Colour rendering*: R_a60 in back-of-house and industrial spaces; R_a80 in others.

Escalators can normally be specified with lighting integral to their structure. These lights are often under the moving handrail or in the side skirts of the lower step covers. Where integral lighting is not specified, lighting will need to be provided above the escalator to light down between the sides, which may be solid. It is especially important to light the threshold as a person enters the escalator, as someone approaching must judge the speed and pitch of the steps so that they can match their pace to the moving steps. It is similarly important to light the end of the escalator so that the person on the escalator can clearly judge the timing of their leaving step. Some manufacturers provide integral lights in the side truss at the entrance and exit threshold to alert users.

Emergency lighting should be provided with emphasis on the bottom and top of the escalator.

11.12 Toilets

- *Recommended lighting levels*: 100 lux on floor with uniformity 0.4; 200 lux on basins and surrounding surface; 100 lux horizontal at 0.6 m in toilet cubicles; 200 lux horizontal at 0.8 m in toilet cubicles for disabled people; 200 lux horizontal over baby changing tables.
- *Colour rendering*: R_a60 in back-of-house and industrial spaces; R_a80 in others.

The overall principles given below apply to most toilets but, for some, aesthetics and visual interest are likely to guide the selection of luminaires, but for others durability or even vandal resistance is likely to drive selection. Consider the range of people likely to use the toilet from those used exclusively by staff, to those in theatres, in schools and finally to those fully accessible to the general public.

Individual fully enclosed toilet cubicles require their own light, which needs to come on when the cubicle is entered and stay on whilst it is occupied.

For toilets that are used by disabled people the lighting needs to light the walls so that any assistance equipment, sinks and alarm cords/buttons can easily be seen.

Lighting over the wash hand basins should ideally come from above to left and right of someone standing in front of it, so that light is not obstructed if they lean forward. This also means their face appears well lit if they look into a mirror on the wall in front of them. This is especially important where the mirror may be used for shaving or applying make-up — 'light the person, not the mirror'.

Emergency lighting is required in toilets for people with disabilities and in other toilets over 8 m² in area.

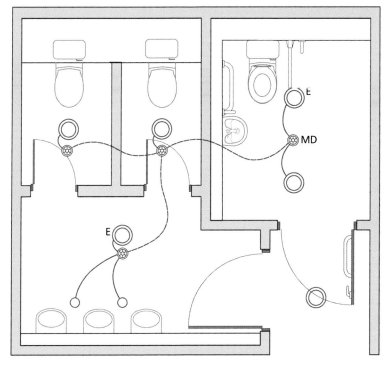

Figure 11.6 Typical locations for PIRs in toilets

Where toilets are likely to be left unoccupied for long periods the lighting should be controlled by presence detection so that the lights come on as someone enters and remain on whilst the space is occupied. Note that detectors need to be positioned such that they can detect movement of people in each cubicle and in the open area of the toilet, including urinals and washbasins. This is often achieved economically by positioning a detector over the partition between cubicles and the open space. Luminaires are available with presence detectors built-in.

11.13 Staff changing rooms

- *Recommended lighting levels*: 100 lux horizontal on floor; 100 lux vertically across face of lockers.

- *Colour rendering*: $R_a 60$ in industrial premises; $R_a 80$ in others.

These facilities vary in size and extent from a small room for one or two uniformed members of staff to change, to large-scale facilities for most of the workforce.

The lighting should directly illuminate the fronts of any lockers so that some light is likely to enter the locker when the door is open to light the content. Where there is a wall mirror for staff to stand and check their appearance before leaving, a luminaire should be positioned above the space between the mirror and where the staff member will stand so that their front is lit when looking into the mirror.

Emergency lighting will be required in most staff changing rooms.

Generally, presence detectors should be provided so that the lighting should come on when staff enter the room and turn off after a period of absence.

11.14 Staff showers

The IET Wiring Regulations, BS 7671 (BSI, 2018), govern the type of luminaires used in wet areas. At present this requires waterproof luminaires (IP44 or better, e.g. IP54, IP65) in Zone 2 near baths and showers, see Chapter 19, Figure 19.1. Any lighting directly above showers is in Zone 1 and is recommended to be IP65 waterproof. With substantial changes of temperature, condensation can still form inside a waterproof luminaire, hence it is better not to position luminaires directly over showers, especially if the ceiling is low.

Emergency lighting will be required in most staff shower areas.

11.15 Tea points and refreshment areas

- *Recommended lighting levels*: 200 lux horizontal on work surfaces; 200 lux vertical across fronts of cupboards.

- *Colour rendering*: to match that of adjacent areas.

The lighting should directly illuminate the fronts of any cupboards, so that some light is likely to enter them when the door is open to light the content.

If there are food preparation or cooking areas, then luminaires should be positioned to wash light over the preparation or cooking areas from one or both sides to avoid anyone having to work in their own shadow.

Emergency lighting will be required, with emphasis on any preparation areas and on cooking/ heating equipment.

If the space is a separate enclosed kitchen, presence detectors should be provided so that the lighting comes on when staff enter the room and turn off after a period of absence.

11.16 Sick bay/first aid room

- *Recommended lighting levels*: 200 lux horizontal on floor; 500 lux on examination beds/ chairs.

- *Colour rendering*: $R_a 80$; examination light $R_a 90$.

The lighting should be restful with minimum glare to resting patients and provide good levels of illumination on walls where there may be restful art work, posters outlining emergency procedures and/or cabinets of equipment.

Where there is a bed or patient chair, an adjustable wall-mounted, or ceiling suspended, inspection light should be provided to assist in examination and diagnoses. This needs to have a colour rendering of $R_a 90$ or above to aid diagnosis.

Emergency lighting should be provided, with emphasis on medical cupboards and any treatment chairs/beds.

For large facilities see SLL Lighting Guide 2: *Hospitals and healthcare buildings* (2008).

11.17 Cleaners' rooms

- *Recommended lighting levels*: 100 lux horizontal on sinks; 150 lux vertical across face of shelving.

- *Colour rendering*: R_a60.

These rooms normally contain a sink for filling and emptying a floor wash-trolley, space for vacuum cleaners and brushes, and storage shelves for cleaning materials and chemicals. The lighting needs to provide light on the sink, even when someone is leaning over it, and vertical illumination on any shelving.

Generally, presence detectors should be provided so that the lighting should come on when staff enter the room and turn off after a period of absence.

Emergency lighting will not normally be needed in the typical 'one person' cleaners' room.

11.18 Store rooms

- *Recommended lighting levels*: 100 lux horizontal on open floor areas; 200 lux vertically across shelving and filing systems; 300 lux where small components are selected or sorted.

- *Colour rendering*: R_a60.

These facilities vary in size and extent from a small room for stationary on an office floor, up to central stores of equipment, goods or merchandise. The lighting needs to directly illuminate the items stored so that they can be quickly surveyed and picked as needed.

The lighting should directly illuminate the fronts of any racks or storage lockers so that some light is likely to enter the locker when the door is open to light the contents.

Generally, presence detectors should be provided so that the lighting should come on when staff enter the room, or part of a larger store, and turn off after a period of absence. In large store rooms, detectors will be needed between any racks or high storage units to ensure all occupants are 'seen'. See also Chapter 13, section 13.3.2, 'Storage'.

Whilst emergency lighting will not be needed in small office floor store cupboards, they will be needed in larger storage rooms, especially where there are high storage racks or items stored on the floor.

11.19 Loading bays

- *Recommended lighting levels*: 150 lux horizontal on floor and any ramps; uniformity 0.4.

- *Colour rendering*: R_a60.

Loading docks can be simple semi-store spaces where vehicles park outside for deliveries to be brought in through standard double doors. They can also, however, be large spaces where lorries or vans back in to unload either down to ground level or onto a higher-level loading dock. The lighting in such areas needs to light the edge of any loading docks so that they can be seen by the driver of a reversing lorry and to aid unloading from the lorry onto the dock platform. Placing

border on providing a domestic type environment, further demonstrating how office life is changing. The lighting of such areas should be designed accordingly.

12.2.2   Screen type

An important consideration for office lighting is the optical and geometric properties of the computer screens in the office. The relevant optical properties are diffuse reflectance, specular reflectance, display polarity and display background luminance. The relevant geometric properties are screen tilt, curvature and orientation.

The optical properties of the screen matter because they determine the visibility of reflections from the screen relative to the visibility of the display itself. The higher the diffuse reflectance, the greater the reduction in contrast of the display. The higher the specular reflectance, the sharper the reflected image in the screen and the greater the probability that it will be distracting. The increasing use of tablets as replacements for traditional computers and laptops means that the orientation of screen surfaces relative to potential glare sources is unpredictable and users may have to move position to avoid such sources.

There are two main ways to present data on a screen: light characters or lines on a dark screen, which is described by the computer industry as negative contrast or polarity, and the presentation of dark characters and lines on an overall light screen, described as positive contrast or polarity.

Whilst some in the mathematical community might argue that the definition of 'positive' and 'negative' contrast should be the other way around, this *Handbook* keeps to the computer industry definition as that is the most commonly used and understood.

A negative polarity screen (bright characters on a dark background) will make reflected images more visible than a positive polarity (dark characters on a bright background) screen. The higher the background luminance of the display, the less visible will be the reflected image in the screen. What all this means is that a computer screen with anti-reflection treatment and a positive contrast display with a high background luminance, has a low probability of disturbing screen reflections. Conversely, a screen without anti-reflection treatment, using a negative contrast display with a low background luminance, will be very sensitive to the lighting conditions (Figure 12.1).

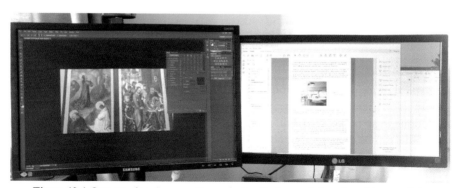

Figure 12.1 Screens showing negative polarity display on left and positive on right
(courtesy of Paul Ruffles)

Given that the optical properties of the screen are such that reflections are likely to be seen, then the geometry of the screen becomes important because it determines the probability that high luminances, such as those produced by luminaires, will be in a position to cause disturbing reflections on the screen. Office lighting installations are almost always installed in or on the ceiling, so the further the screen is tilted from the vertical the more likely it is that disturbing reflections will occur.

Wherever possible, it is desirable to know the optical and geometric properties of the screens that will be used in the office because different properties place different constraints on the design of the office lighting (see Chapter 8,'Luminaires').

12.2.3   Daylight availability

Most offices have access to daylight through windows. Depending on the time of day and season of the year, the weather conditions, the size and shape of the windows, the orientation of the windows and the presence of external obstructions, the amount of daylight available in the office can vary over a wide range. It will always be necessary to install electric lighting for use after dark but whether or not to invest in a control system that automatically adjusts the electric lighting to supplement the available daylight will depend on the amount of daylight available. As a rough guide, in offices where the minimum daylight factor is less than 2%, there is little to be gained from modifying the electric lighting. Where the minimum daylight factor is more than 5%, controlling the electric lighting to blend with daylight should always be considered. See chapter 2, 'Daylighting', for more guidance on this issue.

Of course, daylight will only be available if the window is unobstructed and a short walk around any business district will show how frequently windows are obstructed. Windows may be obstructed for a number of reasons. Among them are visual discomfort caused by a direct view of the sun or bright sky; visual discomfort caused by the presence of high luminance patches of sunlight on the workstation; visual discomfort caused by reflected images of the windows in computer screens; and thermal discomfort caused by excessive radiant heating or cooling. Visual discomfort can be minimized by careful attention to external shading of the windows or the use of different types of glazing or internal screening (see SLL Lighting Guide 7: *Offices* (SLL, 2015)). The problem of reflections from computer screens can be solved by orienting the screens so that they are perpendicular to the plane of the windows.

12.2.4   Ceiling height

Ceiling height is important for office lighting design because it determines whether indirect lighting is an option. Floor-, furniture- and wall-mounted indirect lighting luminaires rely on height to shield the occupants of the office from a direct view of the lamp. This is the reason why the vast majority of floor-mounted luminaires are at least 1.8 m high and why wall and furniture mounted indirect luminaires should have their top surface at least 1.8 m above the floor.

This minimum height above the floor for luminaires sets a minimum ceiling height that can be used for indirect lighting. As a rule of thumb, floor furniture and wall mounted indirect lighting luminaires are best used with ceiling heights in the range 2.5 m to 3.5 m. Below 2.5 m there is a risk of high luminance 'hot spots' being produced on the ceiling. Above 3.5 m the additional energy consumption required for floor mounted indirect lighting becomes difficult to justify, however a mix of wall-mounted background indirect and desk-mounted direct lighting can work well.

Where indirect luminaires are suspended from the ceiling, the luminaires need to be well above normal head height. A minimum height of 2.3 m to the underside of the luminaire is recommended. As for the separation from the ceiling, this is a matter of luminaire design. Manufacturers usually specify a minimum separation from the ceiling. This minimum should not be ignored.

12.2.5   Obstruction

Obstructions in offices are created by the use of partitions between individual workstations and/or the use of full-height partitions to subdivide the office.

The degree of obstruction created by the use of partitions between individual workstations will depend on the height of the partitions — the higher the partition, the greater the obstruction. Partitions 1.2 m high provide visual privacy for anyone sitting at the workstation but not when standing. Partitions 2 m high provide visual privacy for both sitting and standing occupants. An office equipped with 2 m high partitions is effectively a collection of very small offices. This has both advantages and disadvantages for lighting. The advantage is that luminaires and windows are very unlikely to be seen reflected in the computer screen. The disadvantage is that the amount of light on the workstation will be reduced unless allowance is made for the additional light absorption in the design of the electric lighting. As for daylight, the presence of partitions between workstations limits the role of windows to providing a view out, the amount of daylight reaching the workstation being negligible.

Most office buildings constructed for lease show the office floor as one large open space but require the lighting to be designed so as to allow full height partitions to be installed to subdivide the space into offices of different sizes. The effect of these partitions will depend on the size of the offices created and the reflectance of the partitions. The smaller the office and the lower the reflectance of the partitions, the greater the reduction in illuminance. Ideally the designer needs to know the size of the smallest office in order to determine the most suitable type and layout of lighting.

Lighting designs that work for an open plan, may not work if partitions are added.

Thought will also have to be given to the control system for the lighting.

12.2.6   Surface finishes

The colour and reflectance of all the surfaces in an office influence the distribution of light. Table 12.1 gives recommended ranges of average cavity reflectances for floor and ceiling and the average wall reflectance. This is illustrated in use in Figure 12.2. (See also Appendix 1, 'Reflectance and colour'.

Table 12.1 Recommended reflectance ranges for common office surfaces

Surface	Reflectance
Ceiling	0.7–0.9
Walls	0.5–0.8
Partitions	0.5–0.8
Floor	0.2–0.4
Furniture	0.2–0.5
Window blinds	0.4–0.6

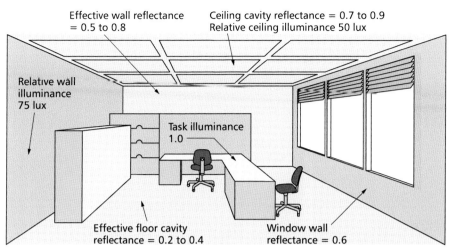

Figure 12.2 Illumination on walls and ceiling

When estimating the average reflectance of a cavity it is necessary to take into account the reflectances of each surface that forms the cavity. For example, if a painted wall is lined with filing cabinets, the average wall reflectance is made up of the reflectance of the painted wall and the filing cabinets weighted by the area of each. Appendix 1 gives the reflectance of some common materials found in buildings and some paint colours. Details of the reflectance of other materials can often be obtained from the manufacturers or by the methods described in SLL Lighting Guide 11: *Surface reflectance and colour* (SLL, 2001).

For direct lighting, where the luminaires are recessed into the ceiling, light reaching the ceiling and upper part of the walls is first reflected from the floor and workstations. To avoid a gloomy appearance caused by dark walls and ceiling it is necessary to have a floor cavity reflectance towards the top end of the range given in Table 12.1. Unfortunately, it is difficult to achieve this without using a light floor finish, something that is not practical in heavily occupied offices. The solution is a supplementary lighting installation designed to light the ceiling directly. Also, as the ceiling is illuminated primarily by light reflected from the floor, a strongly coloured floor will result in a strongly coloured ceiling.

There is much to be said for the use of high reflectance surface finishes of neutral or low chroma colour, particularly in small offices. Surface finishes of this type increase the inter-reflected component of the illumination, thereby diminishing shadows and reducing the probability that the occupants will experience discomfort glare or be annoyed by veiling reflections.

For indirect lighting (see section 12.4.2), it is important to provide a high ceiling cavity reflectance free from colour. Failure to do this will result in an inefficient installation producing coloured light. It is also desirable to use large areas of high reflectance on the walls to enhance the inter-reflected component of the illumination, with small areas of colour to offset the blandness of indirect lighting.

For direct/indirect lighting (see section 12.4.3), a high ceiling cavity reflectance free from colour is again desirable to ensure the efficiency of the indirect lighting. However, there is no need to have a high floor cavity reflectance as the ceiling is illuminated by the indirect lighting.

12.3 Lighting recommendations

12.3.1 Illuminances

Offices contain rooms with different functions. Tables 12.2 and 12.3 give the recommended maintained illuminances for the most common spaces in an office building. The recommended maintained illuminance is the minimum average illuminance that should be provided in the given space throughout the life of the installation. Unless specified otherwise, the recommended maintained illuminance is measured on a horizontal working plane at desk height. Table 12.2 gives the recommended maintained illuminances for the primary office spaces. A primary office space is a space where most of the work is done and where most of the staff spend most of their time.

Table 12.2 Recommended maintained illuminances on a horizontal working plane in primary office spaces

Space	Recommended maintained illuminance (lux)
Open plan office: mainly screen based work	300
Open plan office: mainly paper based work	500
Deep plan core area (more than 6 m from window)	500 or 750*
Cellular office: purely screen based work	300
Cellular office: mainly paper based work	500
Graphics workstations	300
Dealing rooms	300–500
Executive offices	300–500

* The maintained illuminance in the deep plan core area should be related to the illuminance of the area near the windows. For an illuminance of 300 lx near the windows, the deep plan core area should be lit to 500 lx; where 500 lx is used for the area near the windows, a maintained illuminance of 750 lx should be used in the deep plan core area.

Offices frequently contain a number of secondary spaces that are used intermittently for a wide variety of purposes. Table 12.3 gives the recommended maintained illuminances for these secondary spaces. These spaces can contain specialized equipment or furnishings that require lighting to different illuminances than the general lighting (see SLL Lighting Guide 7: *Offices* (SLL, 2015) for advice).

Table 12.3 Recommended maintained illuminances for secondary office spaces

Space	Recommended maintained illuminance	Recommended maintained illuminance for special situations (lux)
Meeting rooms	300 lx (for normal meetings)	500 (if more intense reading and writing is done)
Training rooms	300 lx (for normal meetings)	500 (if more intense reading and writing is done)
Conference rooms	300 lx (for normal meetings)	500 (if more intense reading and writing is done)
Board rooms	300 lx (for normal meetings)	500 (if more intense reading and writing is done)
Reprographics rooms	300 lx (vertical on reprographic equipment)	300 (on collating, binding and dispatch tables)
Libraries/information centres	300 lx (general)	200 (vertically on bookcases); 500 (on reading desks and counters)
Archives/document stores	300 lx (general)	200 (vertically on fronts of shelving)
Break rooms	200 lx (general)	300 (on serving and preparation areas)
Medical rooms	300 lx (general)	500 (on medical examination area)
Canteens/restaurants	200 lx (general)	300 (serveries); 500 (kitchens)

In addition to these secondary spaces, all offices have circulation areas, staff facilities and service areas. Chapter 11, 'Common building areas', gives full details of the lighting levels, controls and emergency lighting requirements of these areas.

12.3.2   Light distribution

The illuminances given above are averages. To avoid complaints about non-uniform lighting, it is necessary to have limits on how much the illuminance on any single work surface is allowed to drop below the average. For any individual work surface, e.g. a desk, the illuminance uniformity (the ratio of the minimum illuminance/average illuminance) should not be less than 0.6.

Most offices are furnished with many desks or workstations. To ensure different desks or workstations are perceived to be treated equally, the illuminance uniformity (minimum average illuminance on the desks/overall average illuminance) should not be less than 0.6. This illuminance uniformity criterion applies to electric lighting designed to produce a uniform illuminance across the whole working plane. Where there is daylighting from side windows, or where individual control of the light output from luminaires is used, this illuminance uniformity criterion can be ignored.

The appearance of the office will also be affected by the illuminance of the walls and ceiling as well as the working plane. Figure 12.2 above shows the recommended minimum illuminance level on the walls and ceiling. The illuminances achieved on the walls and ceilings will depend on the type of office lighting used. For a purely direct lighting design, the ceiling illuminance will be harder to achieve than for a design that includes some diffuse elements. If it cannot be achieved, some form of supplementary lighting to brighten up the ceiling is required. For indirect lighting, there may be a need to add some supplementary task lighting or risk illuminating the ceiling to a much higher level than is necessary. For direct/indirect lighting it should always be possible to achieve the minimum wall and ceiling illuminance.

12.3.3   Maximum luminance

One of the concerns of people working in offices is the reflection of high luminance objects in computer screens. Such reflections can be disturbing because they mask the display or distract attention from it. This used to be a major problem when screens used bright characters on a dark background and were highly reflective as well as convex, but the development of better quality, higher luminance flat screens that allow dark characters on a bright background, and the wider use of screen treatments to reduce both diffuse and specular reflections, made it less of a problem. The increase in tablets and touchscreens has introduced the need for resistance to finger marks and this has resulted in the use of glossy screens, which is bringing back the risk of specular reflections.

The obvious solution to reflections from screens used to be the purchase of a better-quality screen. However, screen quality has improved to the point where low-cost equipment is usually of a reasonable quality. Tablets are a bigger issue in that they can be used in any orientation and it may be that the user has to move in some situations to avoid reflections. If it is necessary to solve a screen reflection problem by doing something about the lighting, then the answer is not to exceed the maximum luminance limits set for luminaires. Table 12.4 gives the maximum luminance of any part of a luminaire that can be seen in a screen, for different screen types. The luminance limit is normally applied at and above a 65° angle of elevation where the screens are not tilted back more than 15°. Where screens are unusually sensitive to reflections, it may be necessary to use a 55° luminaire luminance limit angle.

Table 12.4 Average luminaire luminance limit for different types of computer screen

Screen type	High luminance screen $(L > 200 \text{ cd/m}^2)$	Medium luminance screen $(L < 200 \text{ cd/m}^2)$
Case A (positive polarity and normal requirements concerning colour and detail of the displayed information as used in offices, education, etc.)	≤ 3000	≤ 1500
Case B (negative polarity and/or higher requirements concerning colour and detail of the displayed information as used in CAD, colour inspection, etc.)	≤ 1500	≤ 1000

Limiting luminaire luminance is important to solving a problem of screen reflections because luminaires are often the highest luminance object in the office — but not always. Sometimes, the view out of the window will have a higher luminance and, with indirect, and direct/indirect lighting, the ceiling may have the highest luminance. For indirect lighting, it is recommended that the average luminance of the major surface reflecting light, which is usually the ceiling, should be less than 500 cd/m² and the maximum luminance at any point should be less than 1500 cd/m². Further, the luminance variation across the surface should change gradually and not suddenly. The same criteria can be applied to windows, which will usually mean fitting some form of blind.

12.3.4   Discomfort glare control

Discomfort glare is controlled by ensuring that the unified glare rating (UGR) of the lighting installation does not exceed the maximum recommended value.

Discomfort can also be caused by a view of the sun or bright sky through a window. This source of discomfort can be limited either by the use of light shelves and similar elements of the building structure or by blinds. The best blinds are those that shield the occupants from the excessive brightness while preserving some of the view out (see SLL Lighting Guide 7: *Offices* (SLL, 2015) for advice).

12.3.5   Light source colour properties

Light sources with a CIE general colour rendering index (CRI) of at least $R_a 80$ should be used in all parts of the office, except clearly separate service areas. For service areas, light sources with a CRI of at least $R_a 60$ are acceptable.

As for colour appearance, the correlated colour temperatures (CCT) of light sources commonly used in offices varies from 3000 K to 5000 K and sometimes as high as 6500 K. The choice between these different CCTs is a matter of individual preference. CCTs at the lower end of this range will give a warm appearance to the interior but do not blend well with daylight. Higher CCTs will blend better with daylight but give a cool colour appearance to the space. Very high CCTs will also produce a perception of greater brightness for the same luminance and enhance visual acuity. Whatever light source CCT is chosen, it should be used throughout the office.

12.3.6   Wellness

There is a growing interest in how the work environment affects the 'wellness' of its occupants and, in particular, how lighting can have an influence on that. The introduction of LED lighting has brought with it enormous opportunities to provide lighting in a way to suits individual spaces, people and their behaviours. It is unlikely that the properties of daylight will be able to be fully replicated through electric means, but research continues into the subject and developments over the coming years are expected. Refer to Appendix 2, 'Circadian lighting', for more information on the effects of colour, and to Appendix 3, 'Building Regulations and environmental labelling schemes', for information on some of the building certification schemes that take this into account.

12.4   Approaches to office lighting

12.4.1   Direct lighting

Direct lighting uses luminaires that are designed to emit the vast majority of their light output directly down onto the nominal horizontal working plane. Any upward light emitted plays an insignificant part in lighting the task. Direct lighting luminaires can be surface mounted, recessed into the ceiling or suspended (Figure 12.3).

Figure 12.3 Direct lighting in an office (courtesy of Acoulite)

The main potential problem with direct lighting is the fact that the ceiling and the upper parts of the walls tend to be under-lit resulting in a gloomy, cave-like appearance. This problem can be alleviated in a number of ways. One is by using high reflectance finishes to the floor, furnishing, walls and ceilings (see section 12.2.6). If this is not practicable, then supplementary wall mounted uplighting can be used or a direct lighting luminaire can be chosen that diverts a small amount of light onto the ceiling (Figure 12.4). This will have the effect of making the office appear brighter and more interesting although care has to be taken to avoid high luminance patches appearing on the walls or ceiling as these may be seen as high luminance reflections in computer screens.

Figure 12.4 Direct lighting luminaire with 30% upward component with a clear prismatic diffuser underneath (courtesy of RIDI Lighting Ltd.)

Undesirable high luminance reflections of the luminaires can be eliminated by choosing luminaires within the luminance limits specified in Table 12.4. The same luminance limits will minimize discomfort glare to occupants looking across the office. To eliminate overhead glare, it is necessary to shield any direct view of high luminance light sources such as point source LEDs. In addition, it is better not to use highly specular reflectors with such high luminance light sources as these reflectors can provide an image of the light source with almost the same luminance as the light source itself.

For comparable illuminance distributions on a horizontal working plane, direct lighting will almost always be more energy efficient than either indirect or direct/indirect lighting. However, the effectiveness of direct lighting may be compromised where there is a lot of obstruction from partitions in the space. It is also important to appreciate that surface mounted or suspended luminaires may interfere with air distribution in the office, thereby causing thermal discomfort. Coordination of luminaire layout and air distribution pattern is very desirable. See also Chapter 5, 'Coordination with other services'.

12.4.2 Indirect lighting

Indirect lighting uses luminaires where all, or almost all, of the light produced by the luminaire is reflected off some surface, usually the ceiling, before reaching the working plane. In the interests of energy efficiency, it is important to ensure that the surface from which the light is reflected has a high diffuse reflectance — at least 0.7 and preferably 0.8 or higher. In the interests of colour rendering, it is important that the reflecting surface is spectrally neutral in colour. The lighting effect produced by indirect lighting is typically diffuse, without strong modelling or shadows. Therefore, it is important to use the office décor to provide some visual interest and variety. This can take the form of small areas of strong colour associated with architectural features or gentle spotlighting of interesting features such as artwork or notice boards (Figure 12.5).

Figure 12.5 Indirect lighting of an office space (courtesy of Zumtobel)

Indirect lighting can be highly effective in a heavily obstructed office. Further, provided the maximum surface luminances given in Table 12.4 are not exceeded, there should be no problem with either discomfort glare to the occupants or high luminance reflection from screens.

Indirect lighting is most suitable for ceiling heights within the range 2.5 to 3.5 m. Indirect luminaires can only be used at ceiling heights in the range 2.3 to 2.5 m if careful attention is paid to light distribution to avoid high luminance spots occurring immediately above the luminaire. Ceiling heights greater than 3.5 m can be used but at extra cost in terms of installed power. Indirect lighting luminaires will usually be seen against the ceiling. To avoid excessive contrast, the outer surfaces of indirect luminaires should be light in colour.

Occasionally, ceiling recessed luminaires in which the vast majority of the light from the light source is reflected from the interior of the luminaire before exiting the luminaire, are described as indirect luminaires. This is misleading. Such luminaires should be treated as direct lighting luminaires.

12.4.3   Direct/indirect lighting

Direct/indirect lighting uses a luminaire or a combination of luminaires that provide some lighting on the working plane directly and some after reflection from a surface, usually the ceiling. Direct/indirect lighting can be very effective because the two components are complementary. By using direct/indirect lighting the office will have not only well-lit walls and ceiling but also some modelling (Figure 12.6).

Figure 12.6 Direct/indirect lighting in an office (courtesy of RIDI Lighting Ltd.)

The exact proportion of direct and indirect lighting is not critical in most circumstances although the appearance of the office will change with a change in proportions. As a rule of thumb, if the lighting is to be considered direct/indirect lighting, the minimum percentage for either component is 20%. The recommendations and limitations given above for direct lighting and indirect lighting should be applied to each component separately.

Direct/indirect lighting luminaires come in several different forms. One form uses the same light source or sources to provide the two components. Another uses different light sources for the two components. In the latter case, an option is often available to switch or dim the two components independently. This option may be used to allow occupants to adjust the direct lighting in their local area to match their own preferences but the extent of interaction between adjacent areas needs to be considered. Some direct/indirect lighting luminaires come with a canopy attached to provide a close-up reflector for the indirect component. This is useful in spaces with very high ceilings. Yet another form of direct/indirect lighting uses two entirely different luminaires for the two components, usually direct lighting luminaires and free standing or wall mounted uplighters.

12.4.4 Localized lighting

Unlike direct lighting, indirect lighting and direct/indirect lighting, which are most frequently used to provide a uniform illuminance across the whole working plane, localized lighting deliberately sets out to provide non-uniform lighting, with a higher illuminance around the workstations and a lower illuminance elsewhere. Workstations typically occupy about 25 to 30 percent of office floor area so this approach offers the potential for energy savings but with reduced flexibility unless care is taken to ensure easy movement and reconnection when workstations are relocated.

Localized lighting can take various forms such as luminaires in, or suspended from, the ceiling above each workstation, or free standing direct/indirect lighting adjacent to a workstation (Figure 12.7), or indirect lighting located in the centre of a cluster of workstations.

Figure 12.7 Localized lighting

Luminaires recessed into or surface mounted on the ceiling are usually part of a re-locatable ceiling tile system. Suspended luminaires can be connected to a ceiling mounted track system. The direct component of free-standing direct/indirect lighting adjacent to the workstation should ideally be positioned to throw light from either left or right side of the work surface and should cover the task area with a uniformity ratio of 0.6 or better. Lighting placed in front of the task area is likely to produce veiling reflections.

12.4.5   Supplementary task lighting

Supplementary task lighting consists of a task light attached to each desk or workstation.

Supplementary task lighting luminaires should allow the occupant some degree of control, both of light output and position. Control of light output can be provided either by switching or dimming. Position should be limited so as to ensure that the luminaire cannot become a source of discomfort to others. To avoid discomfort to those sitting at the desk, the supplementary task lighting should not be above sitting eye height. Further, the luminaire should not be positioned so low that deep shadows are cast across the work area. As a rule of thumb, the minimum height for the luminaire above the task area should not be less than 0.5 of the width of the task area. Task lighting luminaires need to be mechanically and electrically safe and not too hot to touch or work close to.

12.4.6   Cove lighting

Cove lighting aims to produce indirect lighting by throwing light across the ceiling from a ledge or recess high up on a wall. This approach has three limitations. First, great care has to be taken to avoid the wall immediately above the cove and the adjacent ceiling having a luminance higher than the maximum luminance limits given in Table 12.4. Second, depending on the cove's distance below the ceiling, it may be difficult to light the ceiling more than 2 to 3 m from the wall. Third, the energy efficiency is low. Apart from in corridors, this method is rarely used in offices today.

12.4.7   Luminous ceilings

Luminous ceilings usually consist of an array of light sources contained above a translucent diffusing ceiling. The surfaces of the cavity above the ceiling are finished in a high diffuse reflectance. The cavity itself has to be high enough for the individual light sources not to be detectable through the diffusing material. Although luminous ceilings are not a form of indirect lighting, they produce a very similar light distribution. Luminous ceilings vary widely in energy efficiency depending on the transmittance of the diffusing material and the light source used. However, they almost always pose problems for access and maintenance so are rarely used in offices today.

12.4.8   Daylight

Regulation 8(2) of the The Workplace (Health, Safety and Welfare) Regulations 1992 (HMSO, 1992) states that 'The lighting in [every workplace] shall, as far as is reasonable practicable, be by natural light'. This means that the provision and control of daylight should be considered for every office. Of course, most building footprints, and the fact that daylight predictably fails every night, means that reliance can rarely be placed on daylight alone. What is required is a useful combination of daylight and electric light. For guidance on some of the factors to consider about daylighting, see Chapter 2 of this *Handbook*. For a comprehensive guide to window and daylight design see SLL Lighting Guide 10: *Daylighting — a guide for designers* (SLL, 2014). For details of various approaches to combining electric lighting and daylighting in offices see SLL Lighting Guide 7: *Offices* (SLL, 2015)

References

HMSO (1992) The Workplace (Health, Safety and Welfare) Regulations 1992 Statutory Instrument 1992 No. 3004 (London: HMSO) (available at http://www.legislation.gov.uk/uksi/1992/3004) (accessed September 2018)

SLL (2001) *Surface reflectance and colour* SLL Lighting Guide 11 (London: Society of Light and Lighting)

SLL (2014) *Daylighting — a guide for designers* SLL Lighting Guide 10 (London: Society of Light and Lighting)

SLL (2015) *Offices* SLL Lighting Guide 7 (London: Society of Light and Lighting)

Chapter 13: Industrial premises

13.1 Functions of lighting in industrial premises

The basic problem of lighting for industry is the wide variability in the amount and nature of visual information required to undertake work in different industries. Some industrial work requires the extraction of a lot of visual information, typically the detection and identification of detail, shape and surface finish. Other types of industrial work require accurate eye–hand coordination and the judgment of colour. Yet other types of industrial work can be done with very little visual information at all. The materials from which visual information has to be extracted can be matte or specular in reflection or some combination of the two, and the information can occur on many different planes, implying many different directions of view. Further, the material from which the information has to be extracted can be stationery or moving. This variability means that the design of industrial lighting is inevitably a matter of tailoring the lighting to the situation. There is no 'one size fits all' solution to industrial lighting.

However, there is a limit to how closely the lighting can be tailored. This limit is set by the fact that many different tasks are likely to occur on the same industrial site, within the same building, on the same production line and, certainly, within the area lit by one general lighting installation. The usual solution to this problem is to provide general lighting of the whole area appropriate for the average level of task difficulty; localized lighting where work is concentrated (e.g. on an assembly line) and local lighting where fine detail needs to be seen (e.g. on a lathe in a machine shop), or where obstruction reduces the visibility of the task (e.g. on the work piece of a hydraulic press), or where there is an obvious hazard (e.g. on the feed to a circular saw). The only place where this general/localized/local lighting approach is impossible is where the scale of the equipment is so large that both the people and the lighting work within the equipment, e.g. a chemical plant. For such applications, lighting equipment is integrated into the plant.

13.2 Factors to be considered

Despite the variability faced by the designer of industrial lighting, the objectives are the same everywhere. They are:

- to facilitate quick and accurate work

- to contribute to the safety of those doing the work

- to create a comfortable visual environment.

To meet these objectives, it is necessary to consider many aspects of the situation.

13.2.1 Legislation and guidance

There are several different pieces of legislation relevant to industrial lighting, ranging from statements of general principle to specific requirements.

Under the Health and Safety at Work Act 1974 the employer must, as far as reasonably practicable, provide and maintain a safe working environment with adequate lighting.

Under Regulation 8 of the Workplace (Health, Safety and Welfare) Regulations 1992 (HMSO, 1992a) every workplace shall have suitable and sufficient lighting.

Most associated standards, Regulations and Acts call for adequate lighting and installation maintenance, some of which are:

- Directive 92/58/EEC: Safety and/or health signs ('the Signs Directive') (EU, 1992)

- Health and Safety (Safety Signs and Signals) Regulations 1996 (TSO, 1996)

- BS 5266-1: *Emergency lighting. Code of practice for the emergency lighting of premises* (BSI, 2016)

- BS EN 1838: 2013: *Lighting applications. Emergency lighting* (BSI, 2013)

- Building Regulations, as applicable in the country in which the building is located

- Fire Precautions (Workplace) Regulations 1997 (TSO, 1997)

- Health and Safety (Display Screen Equipment) Regulations 1992 (TSO, 1992b)

- Electricity at Work Regulations 1989 (TSO, 1989)

Guidance on lighting for specific industries is given in SLL Lighting Guide 1: *The industrial environment* (SLL, 2012).

13.2.2 The environment

Industrial lighting may be required to operate in extremes of temperature and humidity; may be exposed to atmospheres that are corrosive, explosive or dirty; and may need to be capable of withstanding water jets and vibration.

Some light sources are temperature sensitive. For example, fluorescent lamps only produce their full light output at a specific ambient temperature, higher or lower temperatures causing a significant reduction in light output. LEDs produce less light output and have shorter lives as the ambient temperature increases. Where ambient temperatures are low, for example in a cold store, care is necessary to avoid starting problems with discharge lamps.

Control gear has a maximum operating temperature above which its life will be reduced. Electronic control gear is more sensitive than electromagnetic control gear in this respect. Therefore, care should be taken in selecting and locating control gear when lighting industrial locations where the ambient temperature near the luminaires is high, such as in a foundry.

Luminaires designed to cope with damp, corrosive, explosive, flammable or dirty atmospheres are available, at a price. Luminaires capable of operating in damp and dirty conditions are classified using the ingress protection (IP) system (see Chapter 23, 'Extreme environments').

Some industrial activities produce considerable vibration, e.g. movement of an overhead crane. Light sources where a hot filament is used are sensitive to vibration.

13.2.3 Daylight availability

Many industrial premises have the potential to use daylight. For new buildings, this can be done through a special roof construction, such as a northlight (Figure 13.1). For existing roofs, it is sometimes possible to replace existing roof panels with simple translucent panels. The lighting objective for any daylighting system should be to provide diffuse daylight without direct sunlight. Direct sunlight can cause glare and strong shadows on the workplace and should be avoided.

Figure 13.1 Daylight provided by a sawtooth northlight roof

13.2.4   Need for good colour vision

Where colour is used to convey information, lighting with good colour rendering properties is required. Examples of applications where colour is used in this way are electrical assembly, where components are colour coded; food processing, where colour is used to judge freshness and suitability for consumption; and printing and painting, where consistency of colour is important. For such applications, a light source with a colour rendering index of at least R_a80 is recommended. For some tasks where very fine colour discrimination is required, e.g., grading diamonds, special lighting that enhances the relevant colour differences is used.

Where colours are used to identify the contents of pipes and conduits, it is essential that the lighting should make it easy to identify these colours correctly.

13.2.5   Obstruction

Many industrial premises contain obstructions. Obstructions tend to produce shadows. Shadows are cast when light coming from a particular direction is intercepted by an opaque object. Shadows can be minimized by:

- using a larger number of smaller wattage light sources rather than a smaller number of larger wattage light sources so that light is incident from many directions

- using luminaires with a widespread light distribution

- having high-reflectance surfaces in the space

- providing local lighting of the shadowed area.

Figure 13.2 shows a small workshop where shadows have been minimized by using a large number of fixtures and high reflectance surfaces.

Figure 13.2 A small workshop with high reflectance walls and lit by a regular array of luminaires with wide luminous intensity distribution; the result is a shadow-free environment

At the very least, a proportion of the light emitted by luminaires should be emitted upwards, to be reflected from a high-reflectance ceiling or roof.

Although shadows can be a problem, it should be noted that they are also an essential element in revealing the form of three-dimensional objects.

13.2.6   Directions of view

Directions of view in industry can vary widely, from vertically downward into a case where components are being assembled, through horizontal for work on a press, to upward for a forklift truck driver picking a pallet off the top of a rack (Figure 13.3). This wide variety of directions of view mean that care has to be taken to avoid both disability and discomfort glare.

This can be done by:

- using smaller wattage light sources so that the source luminance is lower

- using luminaires which do not allow a direct view of the light source

- using large area luminaires with an upward light component

- having high-reflectance surfaces in the space.

Figure 13.3 Directions of view for a fork lift operator
(courtesy of the Lighting Research Center,
Rensselaer Polytechnic Institute)

13.2.7 Access

All lighting installations require maintenance. For this to occur, access is necessary. When designing an industrial lighting installation, it is essential to consider how access is to be achieved without disrupting operations.

13.2.8 Rotating or reciprocating machinery

Where rotating or reciprocating machinery is present a stroboscopic effect is possible. A stroboscopic effect is evident when oscillations in the illumination of a moving object cause that object to appear to move at a different speed from the speed at which it is actually moving, or even to appear to be stationary. All light sources operating from an alternating current electrical supply produce oscillations in light output. Whether these oscillations are enough to produce a stroboscopic effect will depend on the frequency and amplitude of the oscillation. The closer the fundamental frequency of light oscillation is to the frequency of rotation and the larger the amplitude of light oscillation, the more likely a stroboscopic effect is to occur. The probability of a stroboscopic effect occurring can be reduced by:

- using high-frequency electronic control gear for discharge lamps

- mixing light from light sources operating from different phases of the electricity supply before it reaches the relevant machinery

- supplementing the general lighting of machinery with task lighting using a light source with inherently small oscillation in light output, such as an LED luminaire with a high-frequency driver with low ripple.

It should be noted that LEDs are not flicker free and so need to be treated as if they could cause a stroboscopic effect at some rotating machine frequencies.

13.2.9 Safety and emergency egress

Some consideration of the impact of lighting on safety is appropriate in all lighting applications but it is particularly important in industrial situations. This is because of the complex layout of many plants, the hazards associated with some manufacturing processes and the dangers from moving equipment. Minimum illuminances are recommended for safety whenever the space is occupied, ranging from 10 lx where there is little hazard and a low level of activity to 50 lx where there are definite hazards and a high level of activity. But illuminance alone is not enough. Hazardous situations can arise whenever seeing is made difficult by disability glare, strong shadows and sudden changes in illuminance.

Emergency lighting is required in all industrial premises (see Chapter 3, 'Emergency lighting'). When designing emergency lighting, it is essential to understand the hazards associated with different operations so that the appropriate form of emergency lighting can be determined, i.e. which areas can be evacuated immediately, which areas contain operations that need to be shut down before leaving, and which areas contain operations that need to be maintained.

13.3 Lighting recommendations

There are many different industrial operations but there are also some areas common to many industrial premises. These will be discussed here. Details on lighting for a range of specific industries are given in SLL Lighting Guide 1: *The industrial environment* (SLL, 2012).

13.3.1 Control rooms

Control rooms are often crucial for the production and safe operation of a wide range of processes. Staff monitor and act upon incoming status information (e.g. plant, fuel, product etc.), which is normally displayed on visual display terminals or mimic diagrams (Figure 13.4). The work is often multi-functional and the lighting scheme must enable a wide range of visual tasks to be performed whilst revealing incoming status information with absolute clarity. The lighting should be as flexible as possible to meet the different visual tasks with general dimming or alternative switching arrangements and/or local lighting. The luminaires should blend with the room as far as practicable to avoid being sources of distraction. Low glare or shielded, flicker-free high frequency lighting is preferred where possible.

The lighting designer will need to establish precisely how and where the information will be displayed such that the layout geometry and light distribution of the luminaires can be co-ordinated.

Often incoming information will be displayed in a vertical or near vertical plane and the display screen(s) or dial(s) will often be fronted by glass or clear plastic. It is essential to avoid veiling reflections in these displays. There are three ways to do this:

- position downlighter luminaires to avoid the critical luminaire/screen/eye geometry

- select downlighter luminaires with low luminance at the critical luminaire/screen/eye geometry (see Table 13.1)

- treat the ceiling/upper walls as a low luminance source by uniform uplighting with uplighter luminaires.

For uplighting, the maximum average ceiling luminance is 500 cd/m^2 and the maximum point luminance is 1500 cd/m^2.

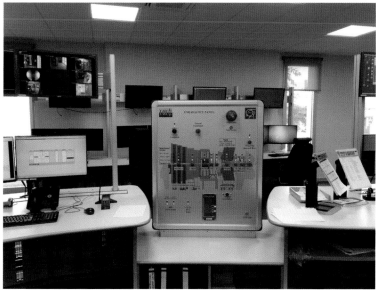

Figure 13.4 Control room showing display screens on desks and walls, paper information and mimic panels of plant; lit by low-luminance lights and with bright sky through windows screened by blinds (courtesy of CCD Design & Ergonomics Ltd.)

Table 13.1 Average luminaire luminance at elevation angles of 65° and above from the downward vertical, radially around the luminaires, for workstations where display screens which are vertical or inclined up to 15° tilt angle are used

Screen high-state luminance	High luminance screen ($L > 200$ cd/m^2)	Medium luminance screen ($L < 200$ cd/m^2)
Case A (positive polarity and normal requirements concerning colour and detail of the displayed information as used in offices, education, etc.)	< 3000 cd/m^2	< 1500 cd/m^2
Case B (negative polarity and/or higher requirements concerning colour and detail of the displayed information as used for CAD, colour inspection, etc.)	< 1500 cd/m^2	< 1000 cd/m^2

Note: screen high-state luminance (see BS EN ISO 9241-302: 2008 (BSI, 2008)) describes the maximum luminance of the white part of the display screen; this value is available from the manufacturer of the display screen.

13.3.1.1 Horizontal display screens

These will reflect large areas of ceiling and it will often be extremely difficult to plan a satisfactory downlighter scheme that avoids veiling reflections, leaving uniform low luminance uplighting or local lighting as the only viable solutions.

When uplighting, it is important that the ceiling and upper walls have matt finishes to provide a diffuse reflection. High reflection factors are essential for high efficiency lighting. Uniform ceiling luminance is the key objective and it is preferable to use more low output uplighters than fewer with a high output. Ceiling ventilation grills or other obstructions should be painted a matching finish to the ceiling to avoid luminance imbalances reflected in screens.

13.3.1.2 Mimic diagrams

These need to be evenly illuminated and the level of illuminance will depend on the detail, the viewing distance, and if the display is self-luminous (where over-lighting will wash out the luminous detail). Dimming is advisable and asymmetric 'wall washer' luminaires are available, which can be surface or recessed mounted.

13.3.1.3 Room surface luminances

Surface luminances need to be controlled to ensure no excessive contrasts between the screen and other objects within the same field of view, or other items, that are regularly looked at. In general, light coloured matt finishes are preferable for all room surfaces and furnishings.

13.3.1.4 Windowed control rooms

These often provide operatives with an essential view of the processes under control. As with display screen lighting it will be necessary to avoid veiling luminaire reflections in the glass and the same principles will apply. Reflections of room surfaces must also be controlled, especially if the average luminance outside the control room is significantly lower than within. Dimming controls will often be necessary to provide the requisite balances.

13.3.1.5 Emergency lighting

This deserves careful consideration in control rooms, since high-risk processes may need to be continued or shut down in the event of an emergency. This may require lighting levels in excess of the normal escape route levels, even up to 100% of the normal lighting levels. In these circumstances it is often necessary to consider uninterruptable power supplies to the lighting rather than self-contained battery operated luminaires, which deliver only a relatively low light output.

Table 13.2 Lighting recommendations for direct lighting in control rooms

Activity	Average illuminance (lx)	Minimum colour rendering index	Maximum unified glare rating
Display screen tasks, self-luminous mimic diagrams	300	80	19
Paperwork tasks, general display boards	500	80	19
Low contrast mimic diagrams	1000	80	19

13.3.2 Storage

Many industrial premises contain areas where raw materials or finished product are stored. In such areas, many visual tasks are performed on vertical surfaces at different heights (Figure 13.5). The lighting designer will require a lot of information regarding the movement of goods and proposed stocking arrangements if all the lighting needs are to be met. In particular, the location of fixed items such as racking is critical, as luminaire layouts must be planned according to the layout of the aisles.

Luminaires are available with optics tailored to the requirements of high rack lighting (> 5 m). These luminaires have a high downward luminous intensity to maximise penetration into the aisles. A sharp cut-off in transverse plane ensures minimal light waste on the tops of racks and a broad axial light distribution maximises luminaire spacing along the aisles.

Figure 13.5 Lighting of a storage area

In 'concertina' storage mechanisms (bins or racks that push together to reveal access aisles) continuous fluorescent trough reflectors are mounted above the bins and at 90° to the aisle openings. Consideration should be given to localising the lighting according to occupation of the access aisles, e.g. pull cord switching or presence detection controls. This will avoid wasted energy due to all the luminaires being needlessly switched on.

With random bulk storage it is best to use wide distribution luminaires in a closely spaced array. This will help to minimise the effects of shadows due to stacking and maximize vertical illuminance.

Cold stores should be illuminated with luminaires that are reliable and efficient at the temperatures concerned. Advice from manufacturers should be sought before luminaires are specified. See Chapter 23, 'Extreme environments'.

Automated picking warehouses need only sufficient lighting for safe access. However, any maintenance work will need additional portable lighting.

Direct glare from luminaires can be particularly problematic, especially for forklift truck drivers. The selection of a greater quantity of low luminance luminaires is preferable to fewer quantity high luminance luminaires. Fitting louvres or diffusers can help but may compromise the light distribution. Uplighting onto a reflective ceiling background will reduce the brightness contrast between the source and background to lessen direct glare. This may be achieved by selecting downlighter luminaires with an upward light component, or by secondary uplighting. Reflected glare from floors etc can also be problematic and matt should always be used in preference to glossy finishes.

Table 13.3 Lighting recommendations for storage areas

Activity	Minimum maintained illuminance (lx)	Minimum colour rendering index	Maximum unified glare rating
Automated aisles	20	40	—
Manned aisles	150	60	25
Continuously occupied areas with little perception of detail required	200	60	25
Continuously occupied areas with perception of detail required	300	80	22

13.3.3 Ancillary areas

13.3.3.1 Circulation areas

When lighting circulation areas such as corridors or stairs, visual guidance is as important as illuminance. Care should be taken to ensure sufficient light is directed onto the walls thereby preventing the corridor appearing oppressive. Luminaires should be positioned in stairways so as to provide sufficient contrast between the treads and the risers. Provision should be made for emergency lighting in all areas particularly those defined as escape routes. The reader should consult SLL Lighting Guide 12: *Emergency lighting* (SLL, 2015).

13.3.3.2 Canteens and mess rooms

Many ancillary areas can be illuminated with a regular array of luminaires. However, some areas such a receptions, canteens and rest rooms benefit from a more imaginative approach, thereby creating a better visual impression. In these situations the recommended illuminances should only be treated as a guide — the 'feel' of the lighting is far more important than the illumination level achieved.

Table 13.4 Lighting recommendations for ancillary areas

Area	Minimum maintained illuminance (lx)	Minimum colour rendering index	Maximum unified glare rating
Lifts, corridors and stairs	100	80	22
Mess rooms	100 to 300	80	22
Canteens	200	80	22
Toilets	200	80	25
Store rooms	100	60	25
Plant rooms	200	60	25

13.3.4 Speculative factory units

Speculative factory units are typically simple shed-type buildings. Often these are built before a tenant is found and therefore there is no knowledge of what the building will be used for.

Typically the lighting is provided by a combination of daylight and electric light. Roof lights usually provide the daylight, supplemented by general lighting from a regular array of luminaires. The purpose of the electric lighting is to illuminate the space uniformly, using conventional equipment. No extreme conditions such as high temperature, high dust levels etc are catered for.

Table 13.5 Lighting recommendations for speculative factory units

Activity	Minimum maintained illuminance (lx)	Minimum colour rendering index	Maximum unified glare rating
Workshop units	300	80	22

13.4   Approaches to industrial lighting

Industrial lighting usually consists of some combination of general lighting, localized lighting and local lighting. For some visual inspection tasks, special lighting arrangements are needed to reveal any defects.

13.4.1   General lighting

General lighting is designed to produce a uniform illuminance on the working plane throughout the area involved. A minimum illuminance uniformity of 0.80 is recommended. General lighting is usually provided by a regular array of luminaires. This approach offers considerable freedom in the location of workbenches and machinery. The choice of light source to be used for general lighting is influenced by the level of colour rendering required and the mounting height. Some examples of the level of colour rendering required are given in section 13.3. The influence of available mounting heights is shown in the Table 13.6. The lower the mounting height, the greater the care that needs to be taken to control glare. Where common viewing directions are upward towards the lighting installation, large area, low luminance luminaires should be used. Where linear fluorescent luminaires or LEDs are used, orienting the luminaires to run parallel to the direction of view and at right angles to rows of workbenches or machines is usually the best layout.

Table 13.6 The usual light sources used for general lighting at different mounting heights

Mounting height (m)	Usual light source
2.5 to 3.0	LED or fluorescent
3.0 to 6.0	LED, fluorescent or low wattage, high pressure discharge
Above 6.0	LED, fluorescent or high wattage, high pressure discharge

13.4.2   Localized lighting

Localized lighting is characterized by higher illuminances in one part of a workshop and lower illuminances in another. Localized lighting is appropriate where the arrangement of work positions is permanent and the visual demands of the work are different in different areas where there is large scale obstruction to general lighting, or where the visual demands of the work call for additional illumination or a different light distribution.

13.4.3   Local lighting

Local lighting is designed to illuminate the task and its immediate surround. Local lighting should be regarded as a supplement to general lighting or localized lighting, not a substitute. Local lighting can be fixed or adjustable by the worker.

13.4.4 Visual inspection

Rapid visual inspection calls for off-axis detection of defects. How well this can be done will depend on the visibility of the defect and, if there are other objects in the area to be searched, the conspicuity of the defect. There are many different methods of lighting for visual inspection. All depend on the use of lighting to make the defect more visible and more conspicuous. Figure 13.6 shows raking light across fabric, revealing a defect.

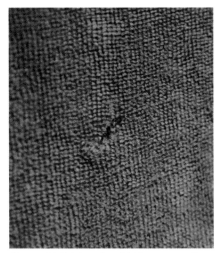

Figure 13.6 Directional lighting revealing damage in cloth

13.4.5 Visual aids

There are some features of products that can be much more easily seen with the use of visual aids. Such aids include magnifiers, stroboscopes and ultraviolet lamps.

Magnifiers can be head mounted or hand-held. Magnifiers are useful for inspecting very fine detail but there is a trade-off to be made against field size. The greater is the magnification, the smaller is the field size. The lowest magnification necessary to see the required detail should be used.

It is sometimes necessary to examine machined parts while they are in motion. A stroboscope will help with this by apparently stopping the motion. To do this it is necessary for the frequency of the stroboscope to be adjustable so that it can be matched to the frequency of motion.

Seals can be tested by placing a fluorescing dye in the sealed container and searching for leaks using an ultraviolet lamp.

References

BSI (2013) BS EN 1838: 2013: *Lighting applications. Emergency lighting* (London: British Standards Institution)

BSI (2016) BS 5266-1: *Emergency lighting. Code of practice for the emergency lighting of premises* (London: British Standards Institution)

EU (1992) 'Directive 92/58/EEC on the minimum requirements for the provision of safety and/or health signs at work (ninth individual Directive)' *Official Journal of the European Communities* **L245** (26.8.1992) 23–42 (available at http://eur-lex.europa.eu/legal-content/EN/TXT/?uri=celex:31992L0058) (accessed September 2018)

SLL (2012) *The industrial environment* SLL Lighting Guide 1 (London: Society of Light and Lighting)

SLL (2015) *Emergency lighting* SLL Lighting Guide 12 (London: Society of Light and Lighting)
TSO (1989) Electricity at Work Regulations 1989 Statutory Instrument 1989 No. 635 (London: TSO) (available at http://www.legislation.gov.uk/uksi/1989/635) (accessed September 2018)

TSO (1992a) Workplace (Health, Safety and Welfare) Regulations 1992 Statutory Instrument 1992 No. 3004 (London: TSO) (available at http://www.legislation.gov.uk/uksi/1992/3004) (accessed September 2018)

TSO (1992b) Health and Safety (Display Screen Equipment) Regulations 1992 Statutory Instrument 1992 No. 2792 (London: TSO) (available at http://www.legislation.gov.uk/uksi/1992/2792) (accessed September 2018)

TSO (1996) Health and Safety (Safety Signs and Signals) Regulations 1996 Statutory Instrument 1996 No. 341 (London: TSO) (available at http://www.legislation.gov.uk/uksi/1996/341) (accessed September 2018)

TSO (1997) Fire Precautions (Workplace) Regulations 1997 Statutory Instrument 1997 No. 1840 (London: TSO) (available at http://www.legislation.gov.uk/uksi/1997/1840) (accessed September 2018)

Chapter 14: Educational premises

14.1 Functions of lighting for educational premises

Learning, whether by discussion, interaction, practical application or formal lecture, requires sufficient light to enable the learner to see the visible information presented around them. Whether in a primary school classroom or a professional lecture theatre, for the young or old, the quality of light provided will directly affect the learning experience and indeed the motivation to learn. If students cannot see clearly what is written on the board or within printed materials, identify true colours, or read the facial expression and body language of teachers, lecturers or compatriots, then their learning and experience will fail to meet their needs. Along with temperature and noise, light impacts greatly upon the ability to learn.

Guidance on the lighting of some parts of educational premises is given elsewhere in this *Handbook*, e.g. see Chapter 28 for the lighting of sports halls and swimming pools and Chapter 3 for emergency lighting. Bear in mind that emergency lighting should be based on a risk assessment, including the planned and actual use of spaces by the community outside of daylight hours.

Further guidance on the lighting of educational premises is published by the Department for Education in the form of Building Bulletins, some of which are now quite old, and documents by the Education Funding Agency. Detailed guidance is also given in SLL Lighting Guide 5: *Lighting for education* (SLL, 2011). The lighting that will be considered here is that of the functional parts of educational premises, such as classrooms and other learning spaces.

14.2 Factors to be considered

14.2.1 Students' capabilities

A classroom may contain students with seeing and hearing difficulties, or who are autistic and therefore sensitive to sudden changes in the environment. For students who have difficulty hearing, it is important that the movements of the teacher's lips are clearly visible. For students who are partially sighted, it is important to control glare from luminaires and windows, to minimize veiling reflections and to use the décor to give high contrast to salient details of the environment, such as the position of the door (Figure 14.1).

Figure 14.1 The lighting in this classroom provides good horizontal light on the desks but, once daylight fades, may only be lighting the lower part of the walls (courtesy of Cundall)

For autistic children, it is necessary to avoid sudden and dramatic changes in the environment. This implies that slow dimming control is better than simple switching and that control of any changes should reside in the classroom so students can be warned about any changes. More advice is given in Building Bulletins 77: *Designing for Pupils with Special Educational Needs and Disabilities in Schools* (DfES, 2005) and 102: *Designing for disabled children and children with SEN* (EFA, 2014).

14.2.2 Daylight or electric light

Most school premises in the UK are now required to make extensive use of daylight but electric lighting is always installed for use after dark and to supplement daylight in some parts of the space. Daylight should be used as the primary light source whenever it is available and should be made available without causing visual or thermal discomfort. This means that care has to be taken to control the admission of daylight (see Chapter 2, 'Daylighting').

Minimum daylighting qualities are specified using either daylight autonomy (DA) or usable daylight index (UDI). For DA, 50% of the working plane should achieve 300 lux for at least 50% of the core hours. Alternatively, daylighting should achieve a UDI (i.e. in the range 100 lux to 3000 lux) for 80% of the core hours.

The range of 100–3000 lux is to allow the sunlight to have a controlled impact and bring some natural animation to the space. The minimum required illuminance on the task is 300 lux and thus a level of 100 lux from natural and electric light in combination would not be acceptable. Where electric lighting is used during daytime, it should be fitted with a control system that will minimize its use of energy, such as occupancy sensors to switch off the lighting in unoccupied class rooms. See section 14.3.6 and Chapter 10, 'Controls'.

14.2.3 Lines of sight

Formal teaching spaces such as lecture theatres will have common lines of sight. For example, the lines of sight in a lecture hall are commonly from the seating towards the lecturer's podium, demonstration bench and projection screen, and from the lecturer towards the seating area. These common lines of sight allow the lighting designer to pick the location and shielding of luminaires and windows so as to eliminate glare (Figure 14.2).

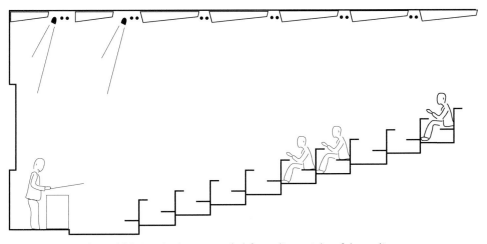

Figure 14.2 Luminaires concealed from direct sight of the audience

Commonly a classroom will be a multifunctional learning space and may have to accommodate a range of ages, learning styles and furniture layouts through a typical day. Here there may be no common line of sight, although the board position will be well defined. Care should be taken to account for a more personal level of interaction where face-to-face communication may take place anywhere around the space, combined with reading and creative learning styles. Lighting should be from more than one direction and glare should be carefully considered.

14.2.4   Flat or raked floor

Small rooms in educational premises almost invariably have a flat floor, but large lecture halls often have a raked floor. The problem these pose is that the effective height of the room decreases from the front to back of the lecture hall and this will influence the spacing of the luminaires if a constant illuminance is to be provided. The alternative is to keep even spacing of luminaires, but to programme in progressive dimming of the rows as the ceiling height reduces.

14.2.5   Suspended or open ceiling

The style of ceiling may be dictated by the thermal or daylight strategy. This can have an impact on the positioning and type of luminaires, the location of other building services, the provision of accoustic absorption materials and the reflective properties of the major surfaces. It will also alter the possible position of luminaires relative to the task — lower in height near corridor/service bulkheads, higher nearer to windows. Obviously, these elements should be considered and may require the services of a professional lighting designer to assess the full impact on both daylight and electric lighting. Care must be taken to ensure any luminaire that relies on uplight is not positioned below open acoustic ceiling panels or structure.

14.2.6   Presence of visual aids

Group learning using notes on a whiteboard is often supplemented by visual aids such as TVs, computer screens or projected images. Uncontrolled lighting, both daylight and electric light, can make it difficult to see these aids, though this is becoming less problematic. However, the presence of such aids makes it necessary to be able to dim the lighting of the classroom and to control the admission of daylight. With the growing use of gloss screens, care should be taken to control veiling luminance, particularly where daylight falls directly onto whiteboards or other screens (see section 14.3.3).

14.2.7   Surface finishes

While strongly coloured surfaces can be stimulating, their use in classrooms should be limited to small areas (LRC, 1998). The majority of classroom surfaces should be finished in low chroma, high reflectance materials. This will increase the amount of inter-reflected light which, in turn, will distribute daylight more evenly across the room and reduce the strength of any shadows and veiling reflections. It should be remembered that many classrooms tend to contain a significant amount of wall displays and/or storage, which will have a direct impact on the amount of reflected light. A realistic average wall reflectance figure must be used in lighting calculations.

14.3   Lighting recommendations

14.3.1   Illuminance

Table 14.1 summarises the minimum maintained illuminances recommended for the more common functional areas of educational premises. These illuminances should be provided on the relevant plane. For classrooms, this may be on the plane of the desks and may also extend to the walls if there are benches or worksurfaces at the perimeter of the room; for art rooms it may be the vertical plane of a canvas.

In all teaching spaces, it is important to obtain a good balance of directional illumination to the face of the teacher and the students. In addition to Table 14.1 all teaching spaces should provide a cylindrical illuminance of 150 lux between 1.2 m and 1.6 m above floor level and a modelling index of 0.3 to 0.5.

Table 14.1 Lighting recommendations for functional areas

Room	Minimum maintained illuminance (lx)	Minimum illuminance uniformity	Maximum unified glare rating (UGR)	Minimum CIE general colour rendering index
Classrooms, IT, seminar and tutorial rooms	300	0.6	19	80
Classrooms used for adult education, lecture theatres and auditoriums	500	0.6	19	80
Arts room	500	0.6	19	90
Science laboratory	500	0.6	19	80
Library	200 vertical (shelves) 500 horizontal (reading areas)	—	19	80
Assembly hall	200	0.4	22	80
Music room	300	0.6	19	80
Drama studio	300	—	19	80

14.3.2   Illuminance uniformity

Illuminance uniformity is important where the lighting needs to be perceived as uniform or where activities may take place anywhere within the lit area. So, for classrooms, lecture halls, IT rooms, art rooms, science laboratories and assembly halls a minimum illuminance uniformity of 0.6 is recommended.

Where the space is likely to be obstructed, e.g. a library, or where light should be centred on a performer, e.g. a music room, the illuminance uniformity requirement is limited to the task area. Even where illuminance uniformity over the whole working plane is important, it may be necessary to provide additional lighting in a specific area to give emphasis, e.g. on the whiteboard in a classroom or theatrical lighting in a drama space.

14.3.3   Glare control

Glare control should be applied to both luminaires and windows. For luminaires, this is a matter of limiting the light distribution so that the unified glare rating (UGR) is 19 or less. One point that calls for care is the lighting of the main board or projection screen in a classroom, where reflected light (veiling reflections) can impair students' ability to read the board or screen. Figure 14.3 shows a space with low-glare luminaires, daylight coming from high clerestory windows, and light décor, which all help in reducing direct glare to users and reflected glare from screens.

For windows, the glare should be controlled to shut out a direct view of the sun and sky, restricting the brightness to acceptable levels on bright days, preferably while leaving some view out. See Chapter 2, 'Daylighting' for more details on blind types and uses.

Figure 14.3 PC-based activity (courtesy of Kirsten McCluskie/Cundall)

14.3.4 Light source colour properties

Light sources with a CIE general colour rendering index (CRI) of at least R_a80 should be used in all functional parts of a school, remembering that even circulation spaces may be used as social or teaching break-out zones. Care should be taken to look at rendering across all 15 possible reference colours to ensure the light source used is not deficient in any part of the visible spectrum. For instance, in LED often the R9 value underperforms leaving reds poorly rendered.

As for colour appearance, the correlated colour temperatures (CCT) of light sources commonly used in schools varies from 3000 K to 5000 K and sometimes as high as 6500 K. CCTs at the lower end of this range will give a warm appearance to the interior but do not blend well with daylight. Higher CCTs will blend better with daylight but give a cool colour appearance to the space. Whatever light source CCT is chosen, it should be consistent throughout the school. If rooms are to be used in the evening then warmer lighting should normally be provided. Some LED luminaires have tuneable white control allowing the colour of the light to be changed dynamically by local user or by central control.

Great care should be taken where high CCT is being proposed as a way of boosting performance or on energy efficiency grounds as research in these areas is still not clear.

14.3.5 Flicker

To avoid perception of flicker the control gear of any fluorescent lighting should be of 'high frequency' type.

Where LED lighting is used the drivers and luminaires should, as a minimum, comply with the flicker limits in IEEE Standard 1789-2015 (IEEE, 2015), namely no less than 162 Hz with a flicker factor < 3%.

14.3.6 Control systems

Lighting controls should be installed in educational premises for three purposes:

- to minimise the use of electricity when there is sufficient daylight available
- to avoid the waste of energy by turning off the lighting when the space is empty
- to provide some flexibility in the use of the space.

To minimise the use of electricity when there is sufficient daylight available, it is necessary to connect the installation so that luminaires at the same distance from the windows can be switched or dimmed together (Figure 14.4). Ideally, a dimming system should be used with a photosensor to detect the amount of daylight available.

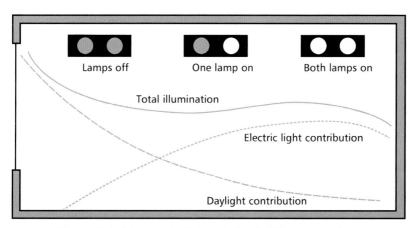

Figure 14.4 Balancing daylight and electric light across a classroom

When a space is unoccupied the lighting should be turned off to avoid the waste of energy. This can be achieved automatically using motion sensors with an automatic switch-off and a manual switch-on. See Chapter 10, 'Controls', for further guidance.

To provide some flexibility in the space, a switching or dimming system should be provided under the control of the teacher or instructor.

14.4 Approaches to lighting educational premises

14.4.1 Classrooms and lecture halls

Classrooms can be used for formal or informal teaching. Lecture halls are solely for formal teaching. During formal teaching, the students are all looking towards the teacher and the whiteboard or screen and reading/writing notes on their desks. During informal teaching, the students may be working in groups with the teacher circulating amongst them or the whole class may be arranged around the teacher.

For classrooms used for formal teaching, a regular array of direct or direct/indirect luminaires can be used, the long axis of the luminaires being arranged parallel to the windows (Figure

14.3). The use of direct/indirect luminaires is specifically recommended to ensure good communication and room surface brightness. The whiteboard should be provided with its own lighting system, designed to eliminate glare and veiling reflections. This can be done by mounting luminaires on the ceiling or wall, shielded from the students and located so that the light reaches all parts of the board at an angle of less than 30 degrees from the plane of the board. Whilst it is tempting to use a few high output luminaires to minimise installation cost, it is normally better to use a larger number of lower output luminaires to reduce shadowing across the space and reduce possible glare from the luminaires. The teacher needs to be able to control the lighting. The windows should be fitted with blinds to facilitate the use of visual aids.

Lecture halls often have raked seating and very little daylight. Appropriate lighting would be a regular array of dimmable luminaires shielded from students and arranged parallel to the seating (Figure 14.2). The lighting of the instructor, any demonstration bench and the whiteboard should be provided by a separate installation. Both installations should be dimmable and under the control of the instructor. More adaptable spaces can have lighting that is more suitable for the range of uses of the space, see Figure 14.5, where retractable seating can leave the whole floor area free for activities.

Figure 14.5 Direct/indirect lighting provides low-glare lighting of the space for a range of activities and lights the ceiling and walls well (Harris Boys' Academy) (© Howarth Litchfield Partnership)

For classrooms dedicated to informal teaching, flexible lighting is desirable. This can take the form of a low level of ambient lighting from a regular array of luminaires supplemented by dimmable spotlights mounted on track if needed for highlighting areas, benches or displays. It should be assumed that some form of connected tablet or screen based learning will take place in most classrooms and thus all should comply with the lighting requirements for use with display screens. Further advice can be sought in SLL Lighting Guide 7: *Offices* (SLL, 2015).

14.4.2   IT room

The IT room is characterised by the installation of many computer screens for use by students. The lighting of this room faces the same problems as those in a modern office and therefore should be lit in the same way, particularly as regards the methods used to minimize high luminance reflections from computer screens. The only difference is the need for the students to see a projected image of the instructor's screen. This need implies that the lighting should be dimmable by the instructor.

14.4.3 Arts studio

Arts studios have three special lighting requirements; good colour rendering, an emphasis on lighting vertical as well as horizontal planes to ensure good modelling and some flexibility in control. Ideally, the windows in an arts room should deliver large amounts of north sky daylight. The electric lighting should blend with north sky daylight and should have a CIE general colour rendering index greater than 90. Both good modelling and flexibility can be delivered by an installation consisting of a low level of ambient lighting from a regular array of luminaires supplemented by aimable and dimmable spotlights mounted on track.

14.4.4 Science laboratories

Science laboratories require special lighting in that the atmosphere may be humid and corrosive. Luminaires should be sealed against ingress of dirt and damp to IP44, see Figure 14.6 (see also Chapter 23, 'Extreme environments'). The electric lighting in a science laboratory should provide the required illuminance uniformly over the horizontal working plane. Supplementary task lighting may be needed.

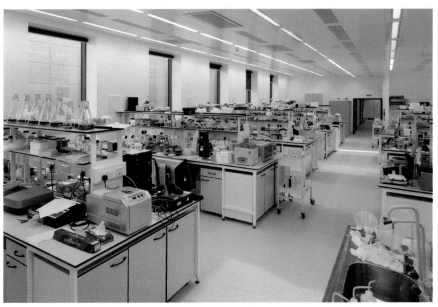

Figure 14.6 Sealed luminaires in a chemistry laboratory (Newcastle University) (courtesy of Martine Hamilton Knight)

14.4.5 School street or atrium

These central connecting spaces vary hugely and the lighting of each will need to provide lighting for the various activities that take place in them. See the first few sections of Chapter 11, 'Common building areas', for guidance on entrance halls, atria and corridors. Figure 14.7 shows one such street with a variety of feature lighting as well as stair and corridor lighting, in addition to plenty of daylight from rooflights.

Figure 14.7 Variety of lighting systems used to light different parts of this space (Harris Boys' Academy) (courtesy of © Howarth Litchfield Partnership)

14.4.6　Seminar room

The seminar room is rather like a small classroom used for informal teaching. The key word as far as the lighting is concerned is flexibility. This can take the form of a low level of ambient lighting from a regular array of luminaires supplemented by downlights, wall washers or dimmable spotlights mounted on track. At least one line of luminaires on a separate control circuit should run parallel with the front of the room so that a more formal presentation can be made when desired. The wall spaces should be well illuminated but kept free for display boards and working space during workshops.

14.4.7　Library

The lighting of library spaces must be coordinated but appropriate to a number of different functions. In addition to general lighting, lighting for vertical book stacks, lighting for study, lighting for using computers and accent lighting for display purposes may be required. It is important that the lighting arrangements are designed so that there is no conflict between the appearance of the different parts of the installation or with the light distribution throughout the space.

14.4.8　Assembly hall

The assembly hall is a place where all or most of the school meets. As such it has an important multifunctional and social space. It may also be used for school ceremonies, concerts, theatrical performances and community events. The general lighting should be designed to provide uniform illumination over the main seating area, using dimmable luminaires that blend with the architecture. Luminaires with louvres or containing relatively loose optics/components should not be used as they may vibrate during musical events. The stage should be able to be lit using theatrical lighting techniques. Daylight should be available during the day, but blackout blinds will be needed to exclude daylight during performances.

14.4.9   Music room

Music rooms require illumination on many different planes, depending on the instrument(s) being played, the position of the music and the location of the instructor. Daylight is desirable provided it does not cause glare and is evenly distributed around the room. Suspended direct/ indirect lighting in a room with high surface reflectances is a good approach. Luminaires with louvres should not be used as they may vibrate during performances.

14.4.10 Drama studio

The drama studio is essentially an open space in which different types of activity occur. The principle requirement for the lighting is variation in position, distribution and amount of light. A series of mounting bars and a stock of theatrical lights combined with a control desk will provide the necessary flexibility. Ambient lighting using surface mounted luminaires is also required for setting up and cleaning up.

References

DfES (2005) *Designing for Pupils with Special Educational Needs and Disabilities in Schools* Building Bulletin 77 (London: Department for Education and Skills)

EFA (2014) *Designing for disabled children and children with SEN* Building Bulletin 102 (London: Education Funding Agency) (available at https://www.gov.uk/government/publications/building-bulletin-102-disabled-children-and-children-with-sen) (accessed October 2017)

LRC (1998) *Delta Portfolio: Mary McLeod Bethune Elementary School* (Troy, NY: Lighting Research Centre) (available at http://www.lrc.rpi.edu/publicationDetails.asp?id=172) (accessed October 2017)

SLL, 2011) *Lighting for education* SLL Lighting Guide 5 (Society of Light and Lighting)

SLL (2015) *Offices* SLL Lighting Guide 7 (Society of Light and Lighting)

IEEE (2015) IEEE 1789-2015: *IEEE Recommended Practices for Modulating Current in High-Brightness LEDs for Mitigating Health Risks to Viewers* (IEEE Standards Association)

Chapter 15: Retail premises

15.1   Functions of lighting in retail premises

For the retailer, lighting is an essential part of 'setting out the stall'. Lighting has four major roles in retail premises. They are:

- to attract attention

- to send a message to would-be shoppers about the nature of the shop

- to guide shoppers around the shop and make sure they are safe

- to display the merchandise to advantage.

Subsidiary lighting systems may be needed to provide facilities for cleaning and maintenance as well as security after closing. Emergency lighting is normally needed to allow evacuation if power to the main lighting fails.

Data from web-connected devices is a powerful source of information and is set to make the retail experience much more specific to individuals. Lighting is well positioned in such future development as it can, through technologies such as Li-Fi (using modulated light to carry information) or 'visible light communications' (VLC) systems, convey information to shoppers' mobile devices. LED lighting is ideal for the dual function of providing this service along with the obvious visible light aspect.

For a full guide to lighting retail premises of all types, refer to SLL Lighting Guide LG17: *Lighting for retail premises* (SLL, 2018).

15.2   Factors to be considered

15.2.1   Shop profile

Retail premises differ in the type of customer they want to attract. Essentially, the profiles can range from high turnover, low profit to low turnover, high profit and anywhere between. It is important to determine with the store owner the type of business they want to attract and how they see the interior design, including the lighting, contributing to attracting their chosen customer base. Many retail outlets, which could be categorised as essential everyday retail premises, such as grocers, newsagents, general clothing, pharmacies etc. may not be too concerned with the lighting design. If the customer finds the store an attractive place to visit and can easily see the merchandise on offer, the lighting will be doing its job. Figure15.1 shows a general high street store with well-lit uniform distribution, typical of the kind of stores customers use regularly.

In stores such as high-end jewellers or clothing boutiques, the experience of shopping is often as important as the purchase itself and customers will expect to be treated to some luxury. This can extend to the quality of their surroundings and ambience, which the lighting can influence significantly.

High-end stores may have a low level of general lighting with significantly more accent lighting to produce a dramatic effect in highlighting merchandise displays. Figure 15.2 shows the dramatic effect often used in high-end stores to complement the interior design and draw the eye to displays.

Figure 15.1 Soft general lighting with additional spotlighting on wall displays
(courtesy of Iguzzini)

Figure 15.2 Spotlighting of central displays as well as wall displays
(courtesy of Lamp Lighting)

15.2.2 Daylight or electric light?

Many retail premises do not allow much daylight penetration into the shop, so this question is moot. However, in many large, out-of-town stores, daylight may be admitted through roof lights or even fully glazed facades, as is often the case with stores selling large items such as bathrooms or cars. The use of daylight adds an attractive dynamic element to the store and can be used as part of an energy saving strategy. Care needs to be taken though if direct sunlight is permitted to enter the sales area, as it could cause glare to shoppers and staff and some merchandise may fade due to its brightness and ultraviolet content. In some retail environments, such as car showrooms, the merchandise on display is quite large and needs space around it in order to stand out. The prospective purchaser needs to be able to take in the whole scene and this requires a lot of light. The stock is regularly moved around and so the issue of potential damage due to ultraviolet light may not be significant. Discomfort glare to customers, and particularly staff who work in one position for long periods, may be an issue requiring careful consideration of the interior layout. Providing accent lighting where such large quantities of daylight are present will prove challenging and require significant amounts of energy to achieve.

Electric lighting can be provided from ceiling-mounted luminaires to try and replicate as much as possible the bright, uniform effect of daylight.

Figure 15.3 General lighting in a car showroom (courtesy of Paul Ruffles)

15.2.3   Nature of merchandise

The type of lighting and the colour properties of the light sources used depend on the nature of the merchandise. Merchandise such as bedding may need to be displayed in a warm, cosy atmosphere, which calls for low light levels and light with a warm colour appearance. Conversely, free standing white goods are best shown at high light levels with light of a cool colour appearance, although when incorporated into displays simulating a home setting, lighting that looks like attractive home lighting is desirable. Merchandise such as meat, fish, fruit and vegetables needs lighting that emphasizes whatever characteristic indicates freshness, e.g. redness for meat, coolness for fish. Therefore, understanding the nature of the merchandise is essential when designing retail lighting.

15.2.4   Obstructions

Some stores, such as DIY stores, have more in common with warehouses than shops. The store is divided into many aisles and the merchandise is displayed in racks extending to head height and above. Where such obstruction occurs, it is essential that the layout of the lighting and any aisles with high racking is coordinated. See section 13.3.2 for more guidance.

15.2.5   Integration with the interior design

Integrating lighting with the interior design of a retail space has been a key part of high-end installations, which in the past have suffered from the difficultly of incorporating physically large fittings and the heat produced. LED technology has allowed the use of miniature luminaires with lower temperatures, opening up many possibilities for closer integration of lighting and interior designs.

15.2.6   Self-pay terminals

Increasingly, stores are introducing self-pay terminals where customers can purchase goods without having to engage sales staff. By doing the exercise normally associated with the sales assistant, the customer must carry out unfamiliar and sometimes detailed tasks. Self-pay terminals should therefore be provided with a level of illumination in line with screen-based office work. Some units include adequate lighting as part of their design. However, where this is not the case additional lighting may need to be added.

15.2.7   Energy

Retail lighting can be a large user of energy, particularly where a lighting design uses narrow beam display or accent lighting rather than a general lighting approach. As the colours and textures of the reflecting surfaces are as important as the light source themselves in delivering the appropriate lighting effect, using paler colours for internal finishes can help to reduce energy use.

The most common way of highlighting merchandise is to provide a higher level of illumination onto the subject than its background. This can be as high as 30 times the level of background lighting although at these levels there is a risk of the general shop areas appearing gloomy and there may be a higher risk of glare. As it is the relationship between background and foreground illumination levels that is important, rather than the actual level of illumination, consideration could be given to reducing the background level. That would allow a proportionally lower level of display lighting to achieve the same effect.

15.3   Lighting recommendations

15.3.1   Illuminances

Retail lighting is essentially a balance between general lighting, accent lighting and display lighting. This balance itself depends on the shop profile. Therefore, the illuminances to be used depend on the shop profile. For low budget shops, where there is no accent or display lighting, the average illuminance should be in the range 500 to 1000 lx. This illuminance should be provided on the merchandise. For a supermarket, this means on the vertical face of the shelves.

For a shop with an exclusive profile, which means the widespread use of accent and display lighting, the general background lighting illuminance should be in the range 50 to 200 lx. This lower background illuminance is necessary for the accent lighting to be effective and should be provided on a horizontal plane at counter level.

For shops with value for money and quality profiles, where some accent lighting is used, the general background lighting illuminance should be in the range 250 to 500 lx, and should be provided on the merchandise.

15.3.2   Illuminance uniformity

Regardless of the shop profile, general lighting on the floor for safe movement around the shop should be uniform. An illuminance uniformity (minimum/average) of at least 0.7 should be achieved by the general lighting alone. Where accent and display lighting is used, the overall illuminance uniformity is low, by design.

15.3.3   Luminance

For accent lighting to be effective, the luminance of the merchandise lit has to be higher than the luminance of its immediate background. Different luminance ratios will give different strengths of highlights and shadows. Table 15.1 indicates the luminance ratio for different strengths of accents.

Table 15.1 Luminance ratios for different strengths of accent lighting

Luminance ratio (accent/background)	Strength of accenting
1	None
3	Noticeable
5	Low theatrical
15	Theatrical
30	Dramatic
>50	Very dramatic

15.3.4   Light source colour properties

The colour appearance of the light used in a shop will contribute to the message the lighting sends to would-be shoppers. A cool light appearance tends to convey a business-like atmosphere while a warm colour appearance indicates a homely feel. As a rule, the colour appearance of the light sources used changes from cool to warm as the shop profile moves from low budget to exclusive. However, the use of LEDs has led to a move in some large stores to use a cooler colour for general merchandise. This approach should improve colour perception but can result in a dull and under-lit appearance if not done well. Where daylight is used in the shop, it is necessary to choose a light source having a colour appearance that blends well with the daylight. For some merchandise, the colour appearance of the light used is important. Chiller cabinets look fresher and white goods look crisper and cleaner under a cool light source. Conversely, gold looks more attractive when illuminated by a warm light source.

The other aspect of light source colour properties that needs attention is colour rendering. In general, light sources with a CIE general colour rendering index greater than $Ra80$ should be used in all retail premises. This will normally be satisfactory, but where the merchandise is most likely to be seen under different lighting, e.g. a coat is most likely to be seen under daylight, it is wise to use lighting that does not distort the colour of the merchandise relative to how the merchandise will be seen in use. This is why in some shops customers will ask to take clothes to the window to see how they will look in daylight. In other shops, it will be important to choose a light source with colour rendering properties that give an appealing appearance to human skin, particularly in areas where an individual's appearance may be closely examined, e.g. fitting rooms. While the CIE general colour rendering index is a useful guide, the final choice of light source is best made by viewing the lit objects of interest.

15.4   Approaches to retail lighting

15.4.1   General lighting

General lighting in shops selling low value items such as fresh food is usually provided from a regular array of luminaires (Figure 15.4). These luminaires range from bare fluorescent and LED battens through recessed fluorescent louvres to pendant metal halide globes. The purpose of such general lighting is to produce a uniform illuminance over the relevant plane without causing glare. Whilst LED is the dominant source of light for new projects, the nature of budget shops is likely to drive any refurbishment or maintenance work to the lowest cost option, which will be T8 or T5 fluorescent for some time to come.

Figure 15.4 Suspended linear lights over the whole display area (courtesy of Lamp Lighting)

Exchanging existing fluorescent tubes for LED equivalents is a popular choice as it removes the need to replace luminaires. However, not all ballasts in luminaires allow this to be undertaken safely and the original luminaire supplier should be consulted. Care should be taken as LED tubes may not have the same uniform distribution as fluorescent tubes and this may affect the light distribution from the luminaire. This, and a tendency for LED tubes to have a lower lumen output can, if not properly considered, result in a lighting scheme that looks dull with poor uniformity.

In shops with quality or exclusive profiles, the architecture is more likely to be a feature of the store and the general lighting will need to be integrated with it. This may involve the use of recessed downlights, cove lighting or suspended uplights rather than a regular array. Regardless of the lighting approach used, the appearance of the luminaires needs to be consistent with the style of the shop.

15.4.2   Store entrances, shop fronts and displays

A major part of attracting customers to a store is the entrance, its shop window and any media, particular video, that can catch the eye of potential shoppers. Designers will need to consider how these elements are intended to work with the architect or interior designer as there may be criteria that require a specific approach. For example, a south facing shop can be subject to strong sunlight during the day and any lighting used to enhance an entrance or shop window will struggle to make any impact. Taking the entrance inside as shown in Figure 15.5 can help avoid such a situation. Providing dramatic lighting for a shop that opens only at night will be much easier than for one that is open during the day as well. Where day and night have to be considered, two separate schemes may be required and this should be discussed with the shop owner or interior designer during the early development of the design.

Figure 15.5 Shop entrance with illuminated media displays
(courtesy of Paul Ruffles)

15.4.3 Accent lighting

Accent lighting in shop windows has to compete during the day with the image of the street outside reflected in the outside face of the window. In malls the lighting has to compete with the images of shops opposite reflected in the windows. Done well, accent lighting can guide shoppers through the shop and draw their attention to merchandise. The best form of accent lighting depends on the area to be accented. For large area wall displays, wall-washing luminaires fitted with LED arrays are used. For gondola displays, the lighting can be built into the gondolas (Figure 15.6 below). For small area accent lighting, 'aimable' spotlights attached to power track can be used. Whatever the form of accent lighting, some flexibility is required. This is because the nature and aiming of accent lighting will depend on the merchandise to be accented. As the nature and layout of the merchandise changes, the accent lighting will need to change.

It is popular for some clothes retailers to use only accent lighting to illuminate their stores. This approach can produce some dramatic and appealing effects, particularly if the clothing on sale is a mix of vibrant colours. Care should be taken though as customers still need to move around safely and sales staff have to be provided with adequate lighting at till positions.

Where wall-washing luminaires are used, one important characteristic of the luminaires is the light distribution, the ideal being a uniform illuminance from the top to the bottom of the wall. A similar consideration applies to accent lighting built-in to gondolas. The illuminance distribution from the top to the bottom of the gondola should be as even as possible. Where spotlights are used, the luminous intensity at the centre of the beam, the shape and dimensions of the resulting light spot with respect to the size and shape of the area to be lit are important.

Figure 15.6 Non-uniform lighting of wall and central displays
from spotlights (courtesy of Lamp Lighting)

15.4.4 Display lighting

The function of display lighting in shop windows is to gain the attention of passers-by and to make the merchandise look attractive. Inside the shop, the main purpose of display lighting is to emphasize the desirable features of specific merchandise. Inside the store, display lighting can be applied to merchandise open to examination (Figure 15.7) or to merchandise in showcases (Figure 15.8).

Figure 15.7 Dark interior with dramatic lighting of individual items
from adjustable track spots (courtesy of Lamp Lighting)

Figure 15.8 Light interior with soft spotlighting of merchandise (image courtesy of Lamp Lighting)

Display lighting is designed to gain attention by using an appropriate combination of brightness, colour and modelling. Relative brightness can be expressed in terms of the luminance ratios given in Table 15.1. The higher is the luminance ratio, the more likely the display is to gain attention. As for colour, strongly coloured light on an object of the same colour will deepen the colour whilst strongly coloured light on the background and surroundings will change the atmosphere. The modelling achieved depends on the relative strength of light delivered from different directions. Modelling is usually achieved by some combination of key light, fill light, back light and up light. Table 15.2 describes these types of light. Depending on the balance between the different components, the modelling can be changed from bland to dramatic. Figure 16.3 in the following chapter shows the same object modelled in different ways.

Table 15.2 Descriptions of the components of display lighting

Light	Description	Function
Key light	The principle source of directional illumination	To create sparkle and reveal texture
Fill light	Supplementary illumination from a different direction	To soften shadows so as to get the contrasts in the display at the desired level
Back light	Illumination from behind and usually above	To separate the object from its background, to reveal transparent elements
Up light	Light accentuating parts of the display close to the floor	To soften shadows, can be used for dramatic effects

Different materials require different display lighting techniques. Table 15.3 below lists some of the more common techniques for specific materials.

Table 15.3 Common display lighting techniques for particular materials

Material	Display lighting technique
Uniformly transparent materials	Transmitted light from a lit background; up-lighting possibly in colour
Glass and crystal	Highlighting; up-lighting, possibly in combination with translucent background lighting; coloured light
Transparent fibrous objects, e.g. fine textiles	Contour lighting from behind
Precious stones and jewellery	Small spotlights, black velvet background
Opaque, shiny objects, e.g. silver	Spotlights, black velvet background, highlighting
Opaque, textured objects	Light predominantly glancing across the surface

Reference

SLL (2018) *Lighting for retail premises* SLL Lighting Guide LG17 (London: Society of Light and Lighting)

Chapter 16: Museums and art galleries

16.1 Functions of lighting in museums and art galleries

Museums and art galleries come in many different forms, ranging from historic buildings to purpose-built facilities. Likewise, the objects they contain come in many different forms. Some are free standing, some are wall mounted, some are contained in showcases and some are there to be experienced. Despite this diversity, the lighting of all types of museums and art galleries has three main functions:

- to display the objects to advantage

- to minimize the damage done to the objects by exposure to light

- to show off the architecture of the building.

In addition, lighting is normally needed:

- to help maintain the security of the facility

- to illuminate signage and aid wayfinding through the building

- to provide emergency lighting if power to the main lighting fails.

Detailed guidance on all these topics is given in SLL Lighting Guide 8: *Lighting for museums and art galleries* (SLL, 2015).

16.2 Factors to be considered

One of the lighting designer's first considerations in many spaces with daylight, is the balance between daylight and electric light. For some exhibits, such as light art and digital projection, daylight has to be excluded. For others, such as sculpture, daylight is preferred, but the uncontrolled use of daylight can conflict with conservation if the exhibits are sensitive to light. With most exhibits the selection of the lighting level and control of the duration of illumination of the objects is important to control fading and degradation of the objects on display. Luminaires need to be selected to give the correct light quality and positioned to give the best lighting of the exhibits whilst avoiding direct or reflected glare.

16.2.1 Daylight and windows

If daylight is to be used as the primary light source, it is important that the designer should preserve the most attractive features of daylight, namely its changes in amount and colour. There is little point in controlling daylight so closely that it cannot be distinguished from electric lighting. Electric lighting will always be required for use after dark, but can be adjusted during daytime when sufficient daylight is available (see Chapter 2, 'Daylighting', and Chapter 10, 'Controls').

If a view out of the building is desired, then it is usually better to provide this from a window in a space off the main display areas. If a side window is provided in a gallery, then it needs to have neutral density glass and/or translucent blinds to reduce possible reflection of the window in the glass front of a showcase or glass covering a picture and to avoid a possibly bright window view next to relatively dark objects being displayed nearby.

16.2.2 Conservation of exhibits

Exposure to light can cause damage to objects by radiant heating and by photochemical action. Radiant heating causes surface layers to expand and moisture in the object to be driven out. For a painting, this can result in cracking and lifting together with a loss of colour. Photochemical action is a chemical change produced by the absorption of photons. Symptoms of photochemical damage are pigment colour changes and loss of mechanical strength.

The obvious first step to minimize such damage to exhibits is to shield them from both ultraviolet (UV) and infrared (IR) radiation. Such radiation does not contribute to vision but does cause damage. The strongest source of ultraviolet radiation per lumen of light is daylight, even after passage through glass. The strongest sources of infrared radiation per lumen of light are the incandescent light sources. Both these sources of light should be filtered to minimize ultraviolet and infrared radiation unless required for display purposes. One advantage of LED light sources is that there is little or no UV or IR radiation in the beam of light from them.

Radiation in the visible range can also cause damage, particularly the short wavelengths, i.e. the blue end of the visible spectrum. To minimize damage from light, it is necessary to limit the overall light exposure. Table 16.1 shows the limiting illuminances and limiting annual light exposures recommended for objects with different levels of responsivity to light. Determining the responsivity of an object to light is the responsibility of the conservator.

An illuminance of 50 lx is considered to be a minimum for displaying objects that require the perception of detail and colour. For high responsivity objects, using an illuminance of 50 lx implies restricting the annual hours of display to less than 300 hours. This means that such objects cannot be on continuous display and must either be rotated out of display into dark storage for most of the time and/or light exposure reduced when no one is looking at the object via presence detection and dimming.

Table 16.1 Limiting illuminance and limiting exposure recommendations for objects with different levels of responsivity to light

Responsivity to light	Limiting illuminance (lux)	Limiting annual light exposure (lux × hours on, per year)
High responsivity objects, e.g. silk, newspapers, some colorants	50	15 000
Moderate responsivity objects, e.g. textiles, furs, lace, fugitive dyes, prints, watercolours, some minerals, feathers	50	150 000
Low responsivity sensitive objects, e.g. oil paintings, wood finishes, leather, some plastics	200	600 000
Non-responsive objects, e.g. metal, stone, glass, ceramic, most minerals	Unrestricted (but must not be too bright if objects in the above categories are displayed alongside, as they may appear poorly lit by comparison.)	Unrestricted

16.2.3 Light source colour rendering properties

Electric light sources vary in their ability to render colours accurately. Light sources with a general colour rendering index (R_a) greater than 80 should be used in all museums and art galleries. However, the general colour rendering index is a single number describing a complex perception. Therefore, it is always advisable to view the objects to be displayed under the proposed light source before choosing the light source.

16.2.4 Adaptation

The low light levels in the exhibit rooms of many museums and art galleries mean that visitors need time for their vision to adapt from the higher light levels usually present in entrances, cafes etc. To achieve this there should be a transition zone of slowly decreasing illuminance between the brighter lit areas and the exhibition areas, especially if lit to 50 lux.

16.2.5 Balance

The balance between the lighting of the exhibits and the general lighting of the space can vary widely. At one extreme, the lighting on the exhibits is the only lighting in the space, with general lighting being achieved using spill light from the exhibits (Figure 16.1). Such lighting can be very dramatic but may pose problems for circulation. At the other extreme is a high level of diffuse ambient lighting without emphasis on the exhibits (Figure 16.2). This approach can be perceived as bland. A reasonable compromise is to aim for an illuminance ratio between exhibit lighting and ambient lighting of 3:1. If a strong emphasis on the exhibits is required an illuminance ratio of at least 10:1 is suggested.

Figure 16.1 Object directly lit with only reflected light from them lighting space around them (courtesy of Dr. Kit Cuttle)

Figure 16.2 Soft general lighting of the space with no emphasis lighting of exhibits themselves (courtesy of Dr. Kit Cuttle)

16.2.6   Shadows and modelling

The distribution of light around a three-dimensional exhibit determines the strength and form of the shadow pattern created and hence the strength of modelling (Figure 16.3). A large area luminaire and a high surface reflectance background will, together, minimize shadows and modelling. A narrow beam spotlight and a low reflectance background will, together, maximize shadows and modelling. What strengths of shadows and modelling are desired is a matter of judgment but exhibits with some modelling are considered more interesting and more attractive than those with none.

Figure 16.3 Soft diffuse lighting gives little modelling of features (left); just spotlighting loses detail in the dark shadow areas (right); spotlighting and diffuse gives modelling without losing detail in shadow areas (centre) (courtesy of Paul Ruffles)

16.2.7   Glare

The widespread use of spotlights in museums and art galleries makes glare a distinct possibility. Glare from spotlights can usually be avoided if spotlights are not aimed more than 35° above the downward vertical. In large spaces putting in extra rows of track, or individual spots, gives more chance to better light objects in the central part of the space without causing glare to viewers (see Figure 16.4).

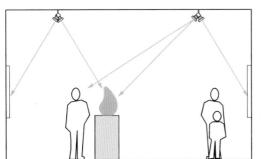 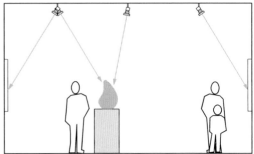

Figure 16.4 Trying to light across a large space can cause glare to viewers (left); adding extra tracks or spots adds cost, but allows better lighting angles and less glare to viewers (right)

16.2.8   Veiling reflections and highlights

Objects on display can vary dramatically in their reflection properties. Some have matt surfaces giving diffuse reflections of light falling on them, whilst others have shiny or specular surfaces that give a clear reflection of high luminance objects. The most usual sources of high luminance in a museum or art gallery will be windows and luminaires. Whether such high luminance reflections are desirable will depend on the object. For paintings and information presented on computer display screens, high luminance reflections can cause veiling reflections and will reduce visibility. For silver and glass objects, high luminance reflections provide highlights and are essential for revealing the nature of the material.

The likelihood of high luminance reflections will depend on the geometry between the luminaire, the object and the observer. The careful selection of and positioning of the luminaire relative to the object and control of its light distribution will allow high luminance reflections to be minimized or maximized, as desired.

16.2.9   Out of hours activities

Prior to opening and after closing, there are numerous cleaning and curatorial activities that need to be undertaken. During this time, the display lighting should be extinguished and the museum and gallery lit by energy efficient ambient lighting mainly lighting the floor. This is recommended by the *Non-domestic Building Services Compliance Guides* (NBS, 2013; Scottish Government, 2018) in support of the energy conservation requirements of Building Regulations (see Appendix 3). Further, extinguishing the display lighting will help to conserve those objects responsive to light exposure.

16.2.10   Security and emergency

The objects contained in museums and art galleries are often valuable so the security of the building is important. Different security systems require different lighting. Where patrolling after closing is in use, lighting systems that enable the guard to move safely and effectively through the spaces is necessary. A minimum illuminance at floor level of 20 lx should be provided for safe movement.

Museums and art galleries are open to the public, many of whom may be unfamiliar with the layout. Emergency lighting to help with egress in the event of a power failure is normally required (see Chapter 3, 'Emergency lighting').

16.2.11 Maintenance

For any lighting system to be effective it has to be maintained. Access for maintenance needs to be considered when designing the lighting of museums and art galleries, as it may not be safe or convenient to move exhibits.

16.2.12 Flexibility

Many museums and art galleries change their displays regularly or house temporary exhibitions. Different displays or exhibitions can require different positions for the lights and different light distributions from them, so it is essential to have flexibility. Flexibility of positioning can be provided by using a track system to power spotlights (see Figure 16.4). Flexibility in light distribution can be achieved by using spotlights with different beam widths — ideally with interchangeable lenses or reflectors. Flexibility in the amount of light can be provided by having different elements of the lighting on different dimming circuits or using individual spotlight control via DALI or similar control protocols, see Chapter 10, 'Controls'.

16.3   Lighting approaches for museums and art galleries

16.3.1   Wall mounted displays

Lighting paintings hung on a wall requires care if veiling reflections and shadows are to be avoided. Uniform lighting over the whole wall can be achieved using wall-washing luminaires. Uniform lighting over individual pictures can be achieved using spotlights. In this case, some spill light around each picture will soften the effect and illuminate any label. Where a painting is hung so that it can be viewed by a standing observer looking straight ahead, spotlights aimed so that the centre of the beam is on the centre of the painting and 30° from the downward vertical usually produce satisfactory conditions (see Figure 16.5). Where paintings are double hung, i.e. one above the other, the upper painting should be tilted down to minimize veiling reflections.

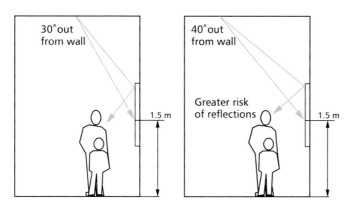

Figure 16.5 Spots or tracks located so that the light comes from about 30° from vertical gives a good compromise between avoiding reflections on object and shadowing from viewers

16.3.2   Three-dimensional displays

Most three-dimensional objects need to be lit from several different directions to reveal their form and texture. The usual approach is to provide a dominant flow of light across the object (key light) with a softer flow in opposing directions (fill light), and sometimes from below, to soften the shadows from the key light. The background lighting level determines the context in which the object will appear and sets the levels that will be required for key and fill light to be noticeable. Key lighting consists of a beam aimed to bring out the most important features of the object. This will create shadows and highlights on the object revealing the shape of the object and texture of its surfaces. However, key lighting on its own creates strong shadows which can hide detail. This needs to be offset by fill light from the opposite direction and perhaps up light to soften the shadows and diminishes contrast. By balancing key, fill and up light in direction and amount, relative to the background, a wide range of appearances can be created (Figure 16.6).

 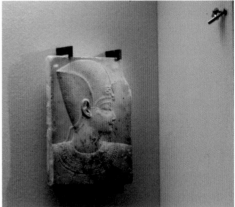

Figure 16.6 Glancing light across an object reveals surface texture (courtesy of Paul Ruffles)

A particular challenge in lighting three-dimensional displays is avoiding glare to the viewer, not from the object but direct from the luminaires. When the object is at eye level or lower and is lit from all sides with the beam angles less than 30 degrees from the downward vertical glare should not occur. Where the object is large and requires the viewer to look upwards, glare is a definite possibility. This can be dealt with by restricting the directions from which the object is viewed using narrower beams for the key light so that all the light is within the display, or lighting from below as long as appearance is not distorted.

16.3.3   Showcase lighting

Glazed showcases are used for displaying rare, valuable and delicate objects while protecting them from environmental changes, damage and theft. Showcases can be small or large; can be viewed from all sides or from a limited number of sides; and can be lit from outside or inside the case. The problems of showcase lighting are reflections from the glazing, shadows produced by viewers, and heat build-up in the case.

Reflections from the glazing will be worse when the interior of the case and the objects are dark compared to the brightness of surfaces and objects reflected in the glass of the case. Reducing the ambient lighting around the case and the luminance of surfaces near the case will reduce the impact of the reflections.

Shadows can be caused when viewers come between the external lighting and the objects being viewed. The impact of the shadows can be reduced by using multiple light sources from different directions and ensuring lights are not behind viewers when they stand in the principal viewing positions.

Using carefully aimed interior lighting for the showcase will eliminate problems with reflections from the glazing. However, shadows can still occur around and on the objects in the showcase depending on how the objects are positioned relative to each other and the lights and the reflectance of the surfaces in the case. The more directional the lighting and the lower the reflectance of the interior, the more likely it is that shadows will occur around the objects. One form of interior lighting is the light box on top of the showcase. This can provide soft diffuse light and/or directional lighting using adjustable spotlights. Light boxes need to be ventilated to prevent heat build-up and have easy access to the lamps and projectors for maintenance. There should be a glass or plastic barrier between any non-LED lamps in the light box and the case interior to filter out ultraviolet and infrared radiation. For most tall or narrow showcases, the top lighting will need to be supplemented by lighting from the sides, back or bottom to provide good modelling of objects on the lower shelves and to alleviate shadows from objects on higher shelves.

Another form of interior lighting is small spotlights mounted in the corners or down the edges of the showcase. These can be small LEDs, but note that whilst the beam of light from an LED is cool, the LED itself produces heat; if one puts 30 watts of LEDs in a case, that is 30 watts of heat generated in the case. Fibre-optic lighting has distinct advantages for internal lighting (Figure 16.7). The light source can be mounted outside the showcase thereby avoiding heat build-up. Further, the fibres can be fitted with different light distribution devices and can be individually aimed and even moved around the showcase as required. The case shown in Figure 16.7 has interchangeable lenses giving wide, medium and narrow spread — this allows the emphasis and/or light levels on individual exhibits to vary. In this case the sensitive objects are lit to about 50 lx, whilst others nearby are lit at 100 to 150 lx.

Figure 16.7 Using optics with interchangeable lenses enables different spreads of light over different objects giving appropriate lighting levels (courtesy of Paul Ruffles)

References

NBS (2013) *Non-domestic Building Services Compliance Guide* (2013 edition for use in England) (plus addendum) (Newcastle Upon Tyne: NBS) (available at https://www.gov.uk/government/publications/conservation-of-fuel-and-power-approved-document-l) (accessed September 2018)

Scottish Government (2018) *Non-domestic Building Services Compliance Guide for Scotland 2018* (Edinburgh: Scottish Government) (available at http://www.gov.scot/Topics/Built-Environment/Building/Building-standards/techbooks/techhandbooks/ndbscg) (accessed September 2018)

SLL (2015) *Lighting for museums and art galleries* SLL Lighting Guide 8 (London: Society of Light and Lighting)

Chapter 17: Hospitals and healthcare buildings

17.1 Functions of lighting in hospitals and healthcare facilities

The lighting of hospitals and healthcare facilities has two main functions. The obvious and most important function is to meet the task requirements in each area of the building. Some of the tasks to be carried out will require exacting levels of visual performance. Indeed, the safety of the patients may depend on the level of visual performance achieved. The second and equally important function is to create an environment that is visually satisfying, wholly appropriate and 'emotionally compatible'. Lighting can influence human emotions and feelings of wellbeing. Good lighting will also help promote an air of quality and competence within the hospital.

Extensive guidance on the lighting of hospitals is given in SLL Lighting Guide 2: *Hospitals and health care facilities* (SLL, 2008).

17.2 Factors to be considered

17.2.1 Daylight

The provision of some daylight and a view outside is much appreciated by patients, so daylighting and access to windows should always be considered when designing the lighting of hospitals. However, care is necessary to limit sun penetration so that thermal and visual discomfort does not occur. Further, the amount of light coming through the windows at night needs to be restricted if sleep is not to be disturbed. This means that windows should be fitted with adjustable blinds. Where daylight makes a major contribution to the lighting of the space, the electric lighting should be fitted with an automatic switching or dimming system so that energy waste is avoided.

17.2.2 Lines of sight

Hospitals differ from many places in that some common lines of sight are unusual. For patients in hospitals, common lines of sight are towards the ceiling and the upper parts of the opposite walls. Such common lines of sight mean that special care is necessary to avoid glare to patients while still providing good visibility to doctors and nurses.

17.2.3 Colour rendering requirements

Skin colour, eye colour and the colour of tissue and fluids can be important guides to diagnosis and treatment. Therefore, there are strict colour rendering requirements placed on the light sources used in the clinical areas of hospitals. Clinical areas include ward units, consulting rooms and operating departments. Ward units include bedded areas, ward corridors, nurses' stations and treatment rooms. All lamps within these areas should have a CIE general colour rendering index of at least *Ra*80.

In specialist areas such as those used for examination or treatment, a minimum CIE general colour rendering index of *Ra*90 is recommended. However, these areas generally do not require the general illumination to be provided by such lamps, only the immediate task area. This task area lighting will usually be provided by dedicated fixed or mobile examination lamps. It is essential that light sources with different colour rendering or colour temperature characteristics are not used in the same area. If the bed-head reading lights are intended to supplement the general illumination for the purposes of patient treatment, then the light sources used in the reading lights should have a CIE general colour rendering index of at least *Ra*90.

17.2.4   Observation without disturbance to sleep

Lighting in hospital wards suffers from a conflict of interest at night. The patients are trying to sleep, while the staff need to be able to see the patients, move around safely and do detailed work at the nurses' station. The differences between the visual requirements of these activities means that ward lighting needs to be flexible. Crude flexibility can be achieved using switching. Fine flexibility can be achieved using dimming.

17.2.5   Emergency lighting

Emergency lighting is required for the movement of patients, staff and visitors to a safe location in the event of the main lighting failing. Some of the people in a hospital will almost certainly be physically incapacitated and/or could be mentally impaired. Because of the likely condition of patients, hospitals do not normally fully evacuate in an emergency. Patients are generally moved by a process called progressive horizontal evacuation from high risk areas to low risk areas while the emergency is brought under control. The emergency lighting should be sufficient to allow easy progressive horizontal evacuation, particularly in those areas where elderly patients may be present. Emergency lighting should be designed to meet the requirements of BS 5266 (BSI, 1998–2016). Design guidance can also be obtained from SLL Lighting Guide 12: *Emergency lighting* (SLL, 2015) and from Chapter 3 of this *Handbook*.

For hospitals, the minimum illuminance on the centre line of a two-metre wide escape route should be 1 lx. A minimum illuminance of 0.5 lx should be provided over all open areas where people will need to move through to reach an escape. Fire muster points and dedicated refuge areas must be given special consideration to ensure they are illuminated to a minimum of 5 lx and are visible or stand out from the general surrounding area. Illuminated signs on the movement and escape routes should comply fully with BS ISO 3864-1 (BSI, 2011) and BS EN 50172 (BSI, 2004).

Standby lighting will be required in certain parts of the hospital to enable essential activities to be carried out in the event of a supply interruption. Hospitals normally work to two standards of illuminance for standby lighting. In critical areas, such as operating theatres, delivery rooms and high dependency units, the illuminance provided by the standby lighting should equal, or nearly equal 90 percent of the normal mains illuminance. Other non-critical but important areas will require standby lighting to a reduced illuminance, generally to 50 percent of the normal mains level.

Where standby lighting is provided by a generator, there will always be a break in the continuity of supply as the engine runs-up, so a battery back-up with a minimum of three hours capacity to power the lamp(s) or a light source should be provided to cover the start-up period and to cater for the possibility that the generator fails to start.

17.2.6   Luminaire safety

All luminaires used should comply with BS EN 60598-2-25 (BSI, 1995). They should all carry a CE mark with the manufacturer's declaration of conformity to all directives designated under the harmonized European Standards and certified to be in full compliance with the EMC Directive. In addition, all luminaires intended for use within clinical areas of healthcare buildings should specifically comply with the requirements of BS EN 60598-2-25.

Electrical safety should be considered a top priority for all electrical apparatus used within hospitals, especially in bed-head luminaires that are accessible to patients. Such luminaires should be either be of Class II construction or supplied from a safe extra-low voltage supply (SELV), as defined in BS EN 60598-1, section 1.2 (BSI, 2015). The construction should be robust and the luminaires should be capable of being securely mounted. Provision should be made for easy cleaning of the interior of enclosed luminaires without the risk of electrical shock.

Hand-held switches at mains voltage can be dangerous to patients so an extra-low voltage relay-actuated switch, at a maximum of 24 volts, should be incorporated into any nurse-call apparatus. Electrical connections should be accessible only with the use of tools.

It is also worth noting that any recessed emergency luminaires used on an escape route will have to retain the fire integrity and the rate of fire spread of the surrounding ceiling system. In practice this means that any attachment used will have to withstand the 850 °C glow wire test and be manufactured from a self-extinguishing material such as polycarbonate or a TP(a) based polymer.

17.2.7   Cleanliness

It is possible for airborne dust particles as small as 0.5 μm to transport harmful bacteria. Luminaires in common with other items of equipment can cause the transfer of infection by contact with the dust particles they may harbour. Therefore, luminaires for use in hospitals should have the minimum area of horizontal or near horizontal surfaces on which dust may settle and such dust should be easily removable by simple cleaning methods. In high risk areas it is advisable to use luminaires with no horizontal faces, only sloping and vertical faces. It is also advisable to use theatre luminaires that have glass diffusers since glass cannot be penetrated by bacteria and is unaffected by sterilizing materials and UV. A further measure in preventing the transmission of infections is to ensure that any space requiring ingress protection between the void and room (especially theatre luminaires), uses a luminaire that has integral mechanical measures to ensure the seal between the ceiling and the luminaire frame and does not rely on the luminaire being manually held while it is fixed into place.

17.2.8   Electromagnetic compatibility (EMC)

Many items of electrical equipment installed in hospitals can cause interference, either by radiation or by transients through the mains voltage supply. The prime nuisance factor from control gear within luminaires is the creation of radio interference.

The use of high frequency electronic control gear within the patient environment requires careful consideration with regard to EMC emissions and immunity. The testing and certification of a ballast or driver by a manufacturer as an independent component is not sufficient to ensure that its use within another housing or product will meet the overall technical requirements. Tests need to be performed by manufacturers on the complete assembly, as it would be installed. BS EN 60601-1-2 (BSI, 2015) defines the EMC test requirements for electrical medical equipment within the patient environment. The EMC elements of BS ISO 11197 (BSI, 2016) should be observed for bed-head service trunking systems that include lighting components.

All products in Europe have to be CE marked, which means that they have to be EMC certified and this means that they should not interfere with 'anything else'.

17.3 Approaches for the lighting of different areas in hospitals

The areas considered here are those most likely to be experienced by those visiting a hospital as patients. Hospitals contain many other areas. Details of the lighting required for all areas of hospitals are given in SLL Lighting Guide 2: *Hospital and health care buildings* (SLL, 2008).

17.3.1 Entrance halls, waiting areas and lift halls

In the main entrance of a hospital visitors will look for signage to direct them towards their destination. The lighting should be designed in conjunction with interior materials and finishes to clarify transit routes and points of arrival. A change of type, height or orientation of the luminaires can highlight the focal point of activity such as reception, waiting areas and lifts (Figure 17.1). This approach to design will also provide brightness variations that contribute to the pleasantness of the interior. A maintained illuminance of 200 lx on the floor is recommended.

Figure 17.1 A hospital entrance area
(courtesy of Charlotte Wood Photography)

17.3.2 Reception and enquiry desks

Maintained illuminances of 300 lx on the floor of the reception area and 500 lx on the task areas are recommended. The overall impression should be a welcoming one that avoids harsh contrasts (Figure 17.2). It is important to consider the vertical as well as the horizontal illumination, so that people's faces within the reception areas are properly lit as this will provide good facial modelling and help with the process of lip reading.

Figure 17.2 A hospital reception area (courtesy of Nicholas Bukorović)

17.3.3 Hospital streets and general corridors

Hospital streets form the major links between clinical departments and may include public waiting areas. They have a relatively high traffic density and can be in excess of 6 m wide (Figure 17.3). General corridors can vary from the minor, linking one or two offices, to the major, linking different departments. For both areas, a maintained illuminance of 200 lx on the floor is recommended. A lower maintained illuminance of 50 lx is recommended for use at night, the lower illuminance being achieved by either selective switching or, preferably, by dimming. If selective switching is used then care should be taken to maintain an illuminance uniformity (minimum/average) of at least 0.2. This will provide the staff with a more comfortable illuminance when moving to and from dark wards and will also avoid the patients being disturbed by the glow of bright lights from the corridor. Low glare luminaires should be used, positioned to avoid alternating brightness patterns being viewed by trolley-borne patients.

Figure 17.3 A hospital corridor (courtesy
of Charlotte Wood Photography)

17.3.4   Changing rooms, cubicles, toilets, bath, wash and shower rooms

A maintained illuminance in the range of 100 to 150 lx on the floor is recommended. The lower illuminance is considered adequate for small, enclosed cubicles. In the interest of cleanliness, these areas should be lit to minimize shadows and no areas should have to rely solely on reflected light. Bathrooms and shower rooms are humid; therefore, special attention is required in the selection and the location of the luminaires. In changing areas, the luminaires should be sited between clothes racks or lockers to provide adequate light into the lockers. The positions of wall-mounted mirrors and of the general lighting should be chosen to avoid troublesome reflections.

17.3.5   Wards

The lighting of wards must satisfy the requirements of both the patients and the nursing staff during the day, evening and night. In bed spaces, it is now common practice for the light levels required to administer medical or general patient care to be provided without the use of a separate portable luminaire. Lighting of bed spaces should be individually switched to encourage energy saving when the bed space is unoccupied. Lighting of the central ward area should be provided so as to enable safe circulation and general cleaning procedures to be carried out. Most importantly the lighting of the whole ward should aid in the provision of a general pleasant and amenable ambience.

For nursing care to be performed efficiently the maintained illuminance over the general area of the bed should be at least 300 lx with a uniformity (minimum/average) of 0.5 or better. The illuminance at the foot of the bed should be at least 200 lx. A combination of general and task lighting may be used. The maintained illuminance in the central space between the beds should be not less than an average of 100 lx at floor level. This level will be sufficient for the general activities of ambulant and recumbent patients without causing disturbance to other patients in the room who may want to rest.

It is common practice that when patients are being attended to by nursing or medical staff, their bed curtains will be pulled around to provide an element of privacy. When the bed curtains are pulled around, the average illuminance within the curtain area for both the general level and the nursing care level must not be reduced by more than 25 percent when compared to the unscreened bedded area. A minimum acceptable mean illuminance of 75 lx for the general ward lighting should be maintained outside the bedded area when all the bed curtains within the ward are drawn around simultaneously.

The lighting of wards can be done in several different ways. Ceiling-mounted ward luminaires are usually required but these can be supplemented with bed lighting consisting of ceiling-recessed luminaires positioned centrally over the bed area. Linear luminaires can be mounted on top of a strengthened curtain rail between beds to provide uplighting, although this approach will not be appropriate where the distance between the curtain rail and the ceiling is less than 1 m and/or where the ceiling height is more than 3 m (Figure 17.4).

Another possibility is to use luminaires that are integral within a wall-mounted bed-head services trunking system that also provides piped medical gas and cabled services, or are mounted on the wall above the bed-head (Figure 17.5). The optimum mounting height for such integrated luminaires is 1.8 m. Any luminaire mounted below 1.8 m will need careful light control if glare to standing patients and staff is to be avoided.

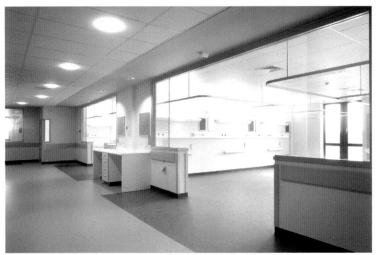

Figure 17.4 Ward and bed-head lighting (courtesy of Nicholas Bukorović)

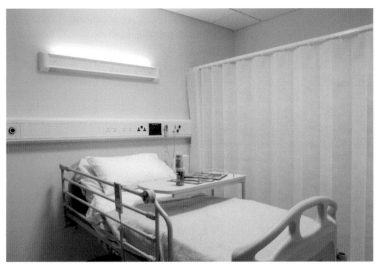

Figure 17.5 Bed-head lighting providing upward light for the ward and patient switchable downward lighting (courtesy of Thorlux Lighting)

Ceiling-mounted ward luminaires can be suspended, surface-mounted or recessed. The minimum ceiling height required for suspended luminaires to be considered is 3.5 m. This will ensure that adequate clearance is still possible for the use of mobile apparatus at the bedside. The mounting height above the floor should not be less than 2.7 m nor greater than 3.5 m. If the luminaire has an upward light component the suspension length should be between 700 mm and 1000 mm to achieve a satisfactory spread of light across the ceiling for surface-mounted luminaires, the ceiling height may be 2.7 m or less. It is usually convenient to mount luminaires to coincide with the bed spaces. Where luminaire spacing does not match bed spacing the illuminance in the circulation space could be less uniform and somewhat higher than the recommended value. In areas with ceiling heights between 2.4 m and 2.7 m, it is possible to provide the recommended illuminance at the bed-head by using surface-mounted luminaires alone.

Recessed and semi-recessed luminaires may be used in ceilings between 2.4 m and 3 m high. Luminaire spacing should generally be as described for surface-mounted luminaires.

It is also possible to illuminate wards using wall-mounted luminaires that combine an upward and a downward component. This method has numerous advantages. The downward component from luminaires by beds and seating areas allows patients to do visually demanding tasks such as reading or puzzles. The upward component provides non-glaring, soft illumination to the room, allowing the patients to relax. When combined, the upward and downward components can provide the higher level of illumination required for examination or nursing care.

Ward lighting should not cause glare to recumbent and ambulatory patients. Ceiling- or wall-mounted luminaires should be assessed for their average luminance value at elevation angles between and including angles a and b in Figures 17.6, 17.7. and 17.8. Surface-mounted luminaires should not exceed 1500 cd/m² for all angles of azimuth. For all ceiling recessed or semi-recessed luminaires the value should be reduced to 1000 cd/m². Wall-mounted luminaires should be assessed for their average luminance value, which should not exceed 700 cd/m² for all angles of azimuth, between and including angles a and b, as defined in Figure 17.8 where:

- h_1 is the minimum height of the mattress surface plus 200 mm

- h_2 is the maximum height of the mattress surface plus 600 mm

- h_3 is the height above floor level to the centre of the luminaire

- d_1 is the distance from the wall to the front edge of the pillow

- d_2 is the distance from the wall to front face of bed-head

- d_3 is the distance from the wall side to the luminaire centre

The average luminance value of 1500 cd/m² (1000 cd/m² for recessed or semi-recessed luminaires) is defined as the luminous intensity measured at each 5° angle between and including angles a and b, divided by the sum of all the orthogonally projected luminous areas at each of the elevation angles. This average applies at all angles of azimuth. The average value of 700 cd/m² for wall luminaires should not be exceeded anywhere between and including angles a and b for all angles of azimuth. The designer should use the measurement values relating to the actual or specific areas in question. However, in the absence of specific dimensional data for h_1, h_2, h_3, d_1, d_2 and d_3 the following values should apply:

- $h_1 = 850$ mm

- $h_2 = 1450$ mm

- $h_3 = 2.7$ m (ceiling mounted), 2.0 m (rail mounted), 1.8 m (wall mounted)

- $d_1 = 900$ mm

- $d_2 = 450$ mm

- $d_3 = 4.0$ m (ceiling mounted), 5.0 m (rail mounted), 8.0 m (wall mounted)

For wall-mounted luminaires fixed at ≥ 2.0 m, angle b is the actual measured value. At mounting heights of ≥ 1.8 m but < 2.0 m from finished floor level, angle b must always be 90°. For mounting heights below 1.8 m, angle b must always be 120°. The maximum luminance must not exceed 700 cd/m² at any angle of azimuth between and including the angles of assessment detailed in Figure 17.8.

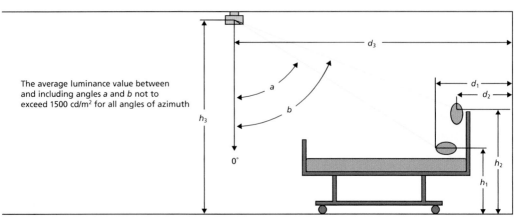

Figure 17.6 Elevation angles for ceiling-mounted luminaires

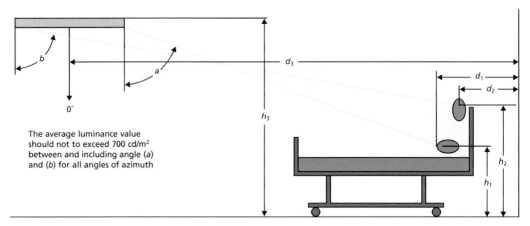

Figure 17.7 Elevation angles for bed-head rail-mounted luminaires

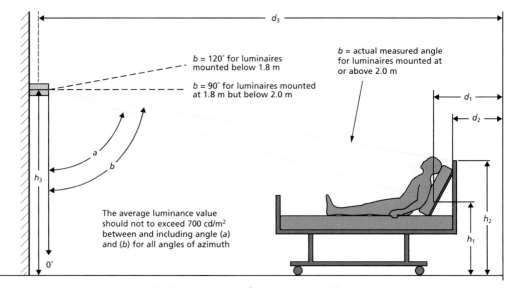

Figure 17.8 Elevation angles for wall-mounted luminaires

Luminaires must not cause excessive luminance spots (bright patches) on the room surfaces when viewed by the patients. The average luminance of all the major reflecting surfaces should not exceed 600 cd/m^2 and the maximum measured spot level should not exceed 1500 cd/m^2. In addition there should be no sudden change in the values of luminance on any of the major reflecting surfaces, i.e. they should change gradually.

17.3.6 Reading lighting

When reading, most people will rest with their head or back against the pillows. A reading light should provide an average illuminance of 300 lx over a horizontal area of 1 m × 1 m, centred at the bed-head and directed towards the bottom of the bed at 1.0 m above floor level, after taking into account the shielding effect produced by the patient's head and shoulders. The reading light switch should be conveniently positioned within reach of the patient, remembering that some will have difficulty in turning or stretching. Suitable reading lights, especially if they are articulated, may also be used for general nursing activities at the beds. All reading lights should be cool to the touch and easy to clean. Ideally, wall-mounted fixed bed-head type reading lights should be installed at a mounting height of 1.8 m but can be mounted below 1.8 m provided care is taken to control glare and shadows. Articulated wall-mounted reading lights and ceiling-mounted reading lights can also be used.

17.3.7 Night lighting

Night lighting needs to fulfil three functions: to provide enough light for the safe movement around the ward, to allow the nursing staff to see facial features and a patient's general condition, and to allow patients to sleep. The average maintained illuminance for the central ward circulation space should be 5 lx on a horizontal working plane 0.85 m above floor level, with a maximum illuminance measured on the pillow of 0.5 lx. To avoid disturbing glare the luminance of any luminaire left on during the night within the ward should not exceed 30 cd/m^2 at an angle of 35° or more from the downward vertical at all angles of azimuth.

In addition, any luminaire positioned at the bed-head or within the bedded area defined by the screening curtains should not exceed 30 cd/m^2 at an angle of 20° and more from the downward vertical at all angles of azimuth.

Moving shadows cast by car headlamps, trees or from nearby road lighting can be particularly disturbing to patients, it is recommended therefore that blinds or curtains be drawn over the windows at night where external sources are considered to be a likely issue.

17.3.8 Night observation lighting (watch lighting)

Watch lighting may be required for the observation of a particular patient after the general lighting has been switched off. It should avoid any visual disturbance to other patients so it is unlikely that the general use of a patient's reading light, which has not been designed for this purpose, will be successful. An illuminance of 15–20 lx at the bed-head is considered adequate for this task, provided the night lighting is of the recommended level.

17.3.9 Clinical areas and operating departments

Clinical areas and operating department are locations where surgical, clinical or medical procedures are carried out. The main function of lighting in such areas is to provide sufficient light for the critical examination of patients, for carrying out operating procedures and for the use of life support apparatus. It is essential that the general lighting should have a CIE general colour rendering index of *Ra*90 or more and should provide an even distribution of illuminance throughout the department.

Ceilings and walls should have a semi-gloss or eggshell finish. The walls should not produce reflected images of the luminaires, especially where they might occur at the eye-height of operating theatre staff. The ceiling reflectance should be 0.7 to 0.9, which can be achieved by the use of off-white or a pale shade, other than blue or green. This will assist in controlling the luminance contrast between the ceiling and the general lighting luminaires. The walls should have a tinted finish, rather than white, with a reflectance of 0.5 to 0.8. The floor should have a light-tone finish with a reflectance of at least 0.3 to maintain an adequate inter-reflected light component, especially within the actual operating theatre.

All luminaires used within a theatre complex should have ingress protection of at least IP54. In addition, all luminaires must be constructed to allow for easy cleaning.

17.3.10   Operating theatres

European Standard BS EN 60601-2-41: 2009 + A1: 2015 (BSI, 2009/2015) provides detailed information on the requirements of 'luminaires for diagnosis', 'minor (treatment) surgical luminaires' and 'major and system surgical luminaires'.

The illuminance in the surgical field will be determined by the type of surgical procedure, the depth of the body cavity to be illuminated, and the angle of illumination. Consequently, different surgical procedures will require operating luminaires of varying luminous intensities and illuminated field sizes. In a large operating theatre suite each theatre may be equipped with an operating luminaire specifically suited to the type of surgery to be undertaken in each theatre. In smaller suites where various types of surgical procedures will be undertaken in the same theatre, it will be necessary to select an operating luminaire that will provide the best all-round solution (Figure 17.9).

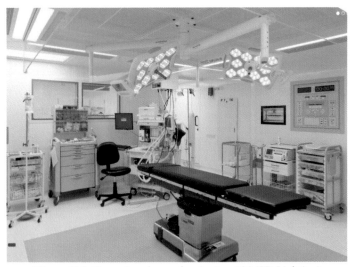

Figure 17.9 Operating theatre luminaires (©MID Lighting)

The maintained illuminance for general lighting of operating theatres is 1000 lx. This is usually adequate for performance of ancillary tasks by theatre staff. To minimize the possibility of bacterial transmission the general theatre luminaires should have ingress protection that is

≥ IP65 void to room with the front frame fixed on, and ≥ IP54 when the frame is off for lamp replacement.

The general lighting is required to provide both horizontal and vertical components of illuminance, vertical being required for good visibility of swab count racks, wall mounted equipment, life support equipment etc., the surfaces of which should not be glossy.

For ophthalmic, ear, nose and throat (ENT), and micro-surgery, much lower levels of general illuminance will be required. A value of between 10 to 50 lx is recommended. Dimming will provide the flexibility that is often required in theatres to permit multi-functional use.

Surface-mounted or, in some instances, wall-mounted luminaires may be required where theatre ceilings are not suitable for recessed luminaires. If wall-mounted luminaires are used care should be taken to ensure that the minimum horizontal light requirement is achieved without glare to theatre staff.

Practice has shown that glare should not be a problem in the comparatively small areas of modern operating theatres, provided that the recommended illuminances, colours and reflectances are used and linear recessed or surface luminaires having a downward light output ratio of approximately 0.6 are specified.

Failure of the lighting during an operation may have serious consequences and it is essential to provide sufficient and reliable standby lighting. Instantaneous change-over to the standby supply is required for the 'major surgical luminaire' or 'surgical luminaire' system.

References

BSI (1995) BS EN 60598-2-25: 1995/IEC 60598-2-25: 1994: *Luminaires. Particular requirements. Luminaires for use in clinical areas of hospitals and health care buildings* (London: British Standards Institution)

BSI (1998–2016) *BS 5266 Emergency lighting. Code of practice for the emergency lighting of premises* (various Parts) (London: British Standards Institution)

BSI (2004) BS EN 50172: 2004/BS 5266-8: 2004: *Emergency escape lighting systems* (London: British Standards Institution)

BSI (2009/2015) BS EN 60601-2-41: 2009 + A1: 2015: *Medical electrical equipment. Particular requirements for basic safety and essential performance of surgical luminaires and luminaires for diagnosis* (London: British Standards Institution)

BSI (2011) BS ISO 3864-1: 2011: *Graphical symbols. Safety colours and safety signs. Design principles for safety signs and safety markings* (London: British Standards Institution)

BSI (2015) BS EN 60598-1: 2015: *Luminaires. General requirements and tests* (London: British Standards Institution)

BSI (2015) BS EN 60601-1-2: 2015: *Medical electrical equipment. General requirements for basic safety and essential performance. Collateral Standard. Electromagnetic disturbances. Requirements and tests* (London: British Standards Institution)

BSI (2016) BS ISO 11197: 2016: *Medical supply units* (London: British Standards Institution)

SLL (2008) *Hospitals and health care facilities* SLL Lighting Guide 2 (London: Society of Light and Lighting)

SLL (2015) *Emergency lighting* SLL Lighting Guide 12 (London: Society of Light and Lighting)

Chapter 18: Places of worship

18.1   Functions of lighting in places of worship

Religion and worship have been part of world culture for several thousand years. From the roots of paganism and sun worship many different religions and churches have developed over the centuries. The list is extensive and therefore reference should be made, in many cases, to the types of building and fabric rather than the religion itself. A place of worship is taken to be a building, or a particular room within a building, where people congregate to carry out prayer and activities relevant to their faith. Associated areas such as offices, vestries, boiler rooms and bell towers should also be considered to assist the designer in carrying out the design for the building in its entirety.

It must be stressed that it is as important to apply the correct source of lighting as it is to accurately achieve a particular illuminance. The success of an installation should not be judged by light meters but through the eyes of those who have to perform the ceremonies as well as those who watch them. Similarly, efficiency should not be rated simply by the effectiveness of gathering all the lamp lumens and exclusively directing them onto the task plane, but rather by the ease with which the task can be seen and by the contribution of the lighting installation to making the environment more agreeable. It is important to analyse the visual task and the lighting problem. If members of the congregation or assembly tend to sit in one particular area this should be focal to the design brief. If certain parts of the service or ceremony appear better with the aid of daylight try to understand why.

For detailed guidance on the issues outlined below see SLL Lighting Guide 13: *Lighting for places of worship* (SLL, 2013).

18.2   Factors to be considered

Lighting, as used in places of worship, has four main objectives:

- to enable participants in the religious activity or ceremony to see what they are doing
- to enable the congregation or assembly to see what is happening around them
- to contribute to the safety of everyone within the room or building
- to create a good visual environment.

To enable these objectives to be met it is necessary to consider all the aspects of the activities taking place, which will differ from religion to religion, and indeed from building to building. However, there are certain points which require a deeper understanding.

18.2.1   The illuminance of the task

Most places where both natural and artificial lighting are put to use contain at least one task area. Places of worship are no exception as tasks are part of a particular ritual or ceremony. The illuminance in the task area is the main quantitative criterion used for all forms of functional lighting. It is the illuminance on the task which, in combination with the reflectiveness of the materials from which the task is constructed and the immediate surroundings to the task, determines the sensitivity of the visual system. The illuminances recommended in this *Handbook* are given in the form of maintained illuminances, that is, the illuminances on the task averaged over the relevant area and over one complete maintenance cycle of the installation. The relevant area can be the immediate task, or a part of a room, or the complete building. The illuminances recommended in this section are consistent with those recommended in SLL Lighting Guide 13: *Lighting for places of worship* (SLL, 2013) and BS EN 12464-1 (BSI, 2011). As such, they represent good lighting practice. However, they are based on additional considerations, such as theatrical performance and the appearance of the room or building. As an example, it is recommended that uniformity within a prayer or worship area can be lowered if a particular lighting effect is justified. Such an example could be a narrow beam spotlight over the font in a Christian church. Likewise, a similar spotlight could be used to light the Koran in a mosque or the Scriptures in a synagogue.

18.2.2   Modelling

In addition to lighting the task, the volume of space occupied by any people should be lit. This particular light is required to illuminate objects, reveal texture and improve the appearance of people within the space. The terms 'mean cylindrical illuminance', 'modelling' and 'directional lighting' describe the lighting conditions. See *SLL Code for Lighting* (SLL, 2012) for definitions and descriptions of calculation methods for these parameters.

Good visual communication and recognition of objects within a space are essential within any religious building. This is achieved by providing adequate mean cylindrical illuminance (E_z) in the space. The maintained mean cylindrical illuminance (average vertical plane illuminance) in all public areas should be at least 50 lx, with uniformity $U_o \geq 0.1$ on a horizontal plane at a specified height. This height would normally be 1.2 m for seated or kneeling persons and 1.6 m for people standing.

It should also be noted that in those areas where good visual communication is important, such as altars, lecterns and circulation areas, E_z should be at least 150 lx with $U_o \geq 0.1$.

18.2.3   Daylight availability

Daylight is always a useful instrument for the lighting designer. The use of daylight as a primary source of lighting is strongly recommended in any building and places of worship are no exception. The amount of control which the designer has over daylighting in most religious buildings is of course very limited. Existing churches that have stood for centuries can hardly be changed to suit a designer's whim, no matter how good the reason may be. Sometimes existing obstructions such as adjacent trees or buildings will limit the effect of daylight entering a building, but nevertheless some daylight can help to save energy.

The daylight factor is an expression of how much outside light on an overcast day arrives at a particular place in a room or area. The defined luminance distribution of a CIE (Commission Internationale de l'Eclairage) overcast sky is used in the calculation. In designing a space with appropriate daylight, we are providing a space that allows the reduction in use of electric lighting for general areas during daylight hours. The savings from automatic dimming controls are directly related to daylight factor. The daylight factor is affected by the building form, materials, glazing, façade etc. See Chapter 2, 'Daylighting', for more guidance.

In large buildings such as Christian churches, some mosques and certain synagogues, whilst the window design is out of the lighting designer's control, use can be made of the available daylight. Windows can be very high and wide giving excellent daylight penetration. In such buildings consideration should be given to an electronic daylight dimming system on the general lighting layout, whereby luminaires can be dimmed according to the amount of daylight available. One must remember that this type of system will work very well to ensure energy saving, but is not available for all light sources. Another factor is that due to the possible low hourly usage in some of these buildings, the payback time can be very high and not justifiable. This type of control should be limited to the general lighting scheme and not to those luminaires which are used to spotlight people and objects.

The ideal daylit environment is one where the fixed architectural form provides both good daylighting and effective solar protection. This will not always be the case in certain buildings. Solar protection where stained glass windows are present would be difficult to instigate. There have been attempts to control solar heat gain through these windows by covering them with plastic panels on the outside. This has been done mainly to limit vandalism, but the results can be unsightly and have limited effect on solar heat gain. The potential for the building fabric to control the daylighting of the space depends on the building type, specifically on the richness and variety of the fixed architectural form. For places of worship consisting of a single rectangular room, the scope to control the daylit environment is limited to a few basic building parameters such as glazing ratio and window transmissivity.

Optimisation of these will have some beneficial effect, but the occupants will still have to resort to frequent use of blinds or shades to prevent undue ingress of daylight and to prevent glare. The greater the richness and variety in the architectural form the greater the opportunity for controlling the daylit environment through an integrated design approach that combines effective solar control with good daylight practice. Often the more successful daylighting designs are those that offer a combination of daylighting strategies.

Low-rise buildings offer the greatest opportunity to realise a controlled daylit environment because the designs can, in principle, accommodate various daylighting features and devices. In addition, low-rise building designs can also feature skylights, clerestory windows, lightwells, overhangs, deep self-shading reveals etc. Window areas and ceiling heights can be chosen by the architect to achieve high daylight factors because the benefit of carbon savings, especially when the rooms are subjected to frequent use, is so significant that the extra cost of larger windows and high ceilings may be effective in terms of the cost of carbon reduction. They will also aid natural ventilation. For further information on daylight, reference should be made to SLL Lighting Guide 10: *Daylighting — a guide for designers* (SLL, 2014).

Figure 18.1 Good daylight penetration enables the use of lighting controls

18.2.4 Lighting for people with disabilities

Society in general must recognise that all people should have access to places of worship. The issue of accessibility and the partaking in religious ceremonies has become more critical with the increasing percentage of older persons in the world's population. Whilst not all elderly persons have disabilities, the majority of those who have disabilities is highest amongst this group.

In the UK, for example, the Equalities Act 2014 (TSO, 2014) requires that, as far as is reasonably practical, disabled people are able to use the building and have access to the services that it provides. Making 'reasonable adjustments' will assist in complying with the legislation. However, what is 'reasonable' depends on a number of factors, in particular the size and resources of the place of worship.

The needs and abilities of people change as they get older and the abilities of individuals in any particular age group vary considerably. It is important to recognize that physical as well as mental limitations vary from relatively low effect, such as temporary hearing difficulties or the use of glasses for reading, to being totally blind, completely deaf or need to use a wheelchair or walking aids. It should be noted also that whilst some limitations may be minor in nature, in combination these can be severely limiting. Apart from the obvious necessity for making places of worship more accessible by older persons and persons with disabilities, there are a number of economic benefits. The most obvious is the increase in possible worshippers. This can help the church or movement grow and in turn attract more to the congregation.

It is therefore important that the requirements of all disabled worshippers are taken into consideration at the beginning of the design stage rather than later, as this enables architects and building services engineers to design and produce religious buildings and environments that more people can use. A well thought-out building can be much more economical to the client than having to adapt premises at a later date. The following points should be borne in mind:

- Lamp flicker, flashing or blinking text, or objects or video screens should avoid frequencies that are most likely to trigger visually induced seizures. This is common with people who suffer from certain forms of epilepsy. The use of high frequency electronic control gear will generally limit the effect of lamp flicker in most cases and should be encouraged. It would also be wise to avoid any form of stroboscopic lighting unless absolutely necessary for a particular performance, and even then must be used with caution. Warnings should be given to every attendee and/or their carer in these circumstances.

- Suitable and adequate lighting will ensure that those with a visual impairment are better able to see instructions and controls. This can often be resolved by increasing the vertical illuminance on these items. It is also true for those with a hearing problem. Lighting that has a good vertical component will assist with lip reading or sign language communication.

- The lighting levels suitable for a particular room or area should be considered. Adjustability of lighting levels may be desirable to suit different needs, but sudden changes in lighting levels should be avoided. Therefore, consideration should be given to the use of dimming circuits.

- The recommended illuminance levels given in this *Handbook* are minimum maintained values. On the other hand, if the illuminance levels are very high, or if the light is concentrated in a particular direction, this can result in deep shadows or glare.

High reflectance surfaces on signage and information panels should be avoided to reduce the possibility of glare.

- Colour contrast is important for the ease of recognition and ease of seeing. Certain colour combinations are also more effective than others. For example, some colours, such as red and green, are not distinguishable by a significant minority of the population, in particular those with colour blindness. The best colour combinations depend on the purpose of information, whether it is for guidance or a hazard warning, and the lighting conditions under which it is most likely to be viewed. For example, black on yellow or light grey are general purpose combinations that provide strong definition without too much glare. Pastel shades on pastel backgrounds or red lettering or symbols on light grey are difficult to see and should normally be avoided. All information conveyed with colour should also be available without the perception of colour. Colour coding should not be used as the only means for conveying information, indicating a response or distinguishing a visual element.

- Similar thought must be given to the exterior environment, including car park access and signage, external entrances and pathways. Such consideration is particularly valuable for those with impairments in seeing, balance, dexterity, manipulation, movement, strength and cognition.

- Surfaces that may be touched inadvertently during normal operation should not get excessively hot. The choice of lamps to be used, for example in ground mounted floodlights, should be made to avoid burns being received by people accidentally falling against them. It is possible for appropriate outer housings to be constructed with protective wire mesh guards in these circumstances. Internally, care should also be taken with the siting and construction of wall mounted luminaires. Warnings of where temperatures may be excessively high for functional reasons are of particular benefit to those with limited sensitivity in their touch receptors. The format of the warnings should be accessible to people with visual or cognitive impairment.

- It is essential that emergency escape routes are obvious, intuitive and accessible to wheelchair users and others with a movement or visual impairment. In particular, emergency lighting should be adjacent to or above ramps that allow a change in level, or indeed thresholds at entrances over which wheelchairs travel.

- The use of automatic lighting controls must be seriously considered at the design stage of a project. A choice that may be suitable for an able-bodied person may not be suitable for those with a disability. If absence or presence detection is to be used in public areas such as toilets, they will need to be set correctly. Whilst a five minute hold-off delay may be a normal setting in a WC or washroom, this value may need to be increased to 20 or 30 minutes in a disabled toilet. Whilst at first view this may appear overly cautious there is still plenty of opportunity for energy saving in reality.

18.2.5   Listed buildings

A listed building is a building that has been placed on the 'Statutory List of Buildings of Special Architectural or Historic Interest'. This status has been applied to around half a million buildings in the UK, and is controlled by Historic England, Historic Environment Scotland, CADW (Wales) and the Northern Ireland Environment Agency (NIEA). Similar bodies serve the same function in other countries. These bodies have a broad remit of managing the historic built environment in their country and advising the relevant Secretary of State on policy and in individual cases such as registering listed buildings and scheduled ancient monuments.

A listed building may not be demolished, extended or altered without special permission from the local planning authority. Consultation then takes place with the relevant central government agency, particularly for significant alterations to the more notable listed buildings. Exemption from secular listed building control is provided for some buildings in current use for worship, but only in cases where the relevant religious organisation operates its own equivalent permissions procedure. Owners of listed buildings are, in some circumstances, compelled to repair and maintain them and can face criminal prosecution if they fail to do so or if they perform unauthorised alterations.

It is important, therefore, before commencement of any repair or maintenance work, that advice be sought primarily from the local authority under whose jurisdiction the religious building is located. National heritage bodies can be sympathetic to renovation projects on listed buildings where project managers work with them, rather than against them. New luminaires designed to blend in with the surrounding architecture, albeit with modern high efficiency lamps, are often acceptable if designed well. See Appendix 4, 'Heritage buildings and spaces'.

18.3   Lighting recommendations

18.3.1   Areas for prayer and service

Generally speaking, the areas within a place of worship can be split between those where a service, ritual or prayer is performed, and those which are of an ancillary nature. In an Anglican or Catholic church the former area would be the nave. Alternatively, in a mosque or synagogue this area would be the prayer hall or main sanctuary.

The main tasks within this type of area are being able to read hymn books or prayer books as well as seeing the person or persons leading the service. The lighting should be practical in nature but also attractive in appearance and able to create an interesting environment. There may be other issues peculiar to a particular building which will be important to consider, such as height, temperature and ease of maintenance. In addition, if the hours of usage permit, or there is sufficient daylight during the services, controls may be considered as part of the lighting design.

In general terms consideration should also be given to the mean cylindrical illuminance within any areas where congregations meet. It is important that people can be seen easily and identified accurately, and that extreme vertical shadowing is avoided. Therefore, a minimum mean cylindrical illuminance of 100 lux would be considered acceptable in most circumstances.

Table 18.1 below shows suggested general minimum illuminance levels to be considered for prayer and congregation areas, although care must be taken when using these values as there are many factors which may influence the designer for a specific project.

Table 18.1 Suggested general minimum illuminance levels for prayer and congregation areas

Activity	Minimum maintained illuminance (lx)	Minimum colour rendering index	Maximum unified glare rating	Minimum uniformity
Nave or prayer hall where public congregate	150	60	25	0.4
Choir stalls	300	80	22	0.6
Altar area or main focal point	500	90	19	0.6
Organ or piano keyboard/music stand	500	80	19	0.6
Lectern/pulpit	300	80	19	0.6

18.3.2   Ancillary areas

In practical terms, all other rooms within a place of worship are considered ancillary areas. As such it is worthwhile considering what the activity is for a particular room or area and relating the requirements to areas mentioned in Chapter 11, 'Common building areas'. Table 18.2 below shows suggested general minimum illuminance levels to be considered for ancillary areas.

Ancillary areas need to accommodate various activities and tasks, and range from Sunday schools and community halls to vestries, storerooms, libraries, offices and toilets. Consideration should be given to energy conservation in all these areas and controls should be used where the designer feels they are appropriate and can be used effectively. In areas such as libraries and offices advice given in other chapters of this *Handbook* should be followed, even though the areas may be quite small in comparison to larger commercial types of room.

Table 18.2 Suggested general minimum illuminance levels for ancillary areas

Activity	Minimum maintained illuminance (lx)	Minimum colour rendering index	Maximum unified glare rating	Minimum uniformity
Entrance vestibule	200	80	22	0.4
Multi-purpose/communal room	300	80	22	0.6
Bell tower/minaret	200	40	28	0.4
Stairs	100	40	25	0.4
Kitchen (cooking of meals)	500	80	22	0.6
Tea/coffee counter	300	80	22	0.4
Dining room	200	80	22	0.6
Vestry/robing	200	80	25	0.4
Toilets	200	80	25	0.4
Boiler room	200	60	25	0.4
Storerooms	100	60	25	0.4
Office	500	80	19	0.6
Library bookshelves	200	80	19	0.4
Reading areas	500	80	19	0.6

18.3.3   Multi-purpose rooms

It is possible that a Sunday school building or community centre annex may be separate to the main church and connected by cloisters or pathway. In this case, the lighting should be considered separately to the church itself. The cloisters would need access lighting with suitable weatherproof luminaires.

Inside the annex building there may be a general hall together with a theatrical stage. This area would normally be multi-purpose in nature, ranging from badminton matches and youth group assemblies to audience seating when the stage is used for a theatrical production. 'Gang Shows' by the Scout and Guide movements used to be frequent events in this type of building. Members of the community, as well as youth groups associated with the community, may put on shows or performances of various types in these spaces. Larger buildings have separate classrooms for religious education and should be treated exactly the same as if in a school itself. Other rooms could include changing rooms, toilets, kitchen facilities and storerooms. Emergency lighting will be required and advice is given in Chapter 3, 'Emergency lighting', SLL Lighting Guide 12: *Emergency lighting* (SLL, 2015) and BS EN 5226-1 (BSI, 2016).

It is possible that a community room may be part of the main building. In this case, the lighting should be considered as part of the overall scheme with lighting to match the general theme. Sometimes, lectures and drama presentations take place with additional facilities such as video screens and overhead projectors. Again, the lighting should be designed accordingly and scene setting equipment may be required, together with spotlights to enhance the speaker or reader. In multi-purpose rooms it must be obvious that different levels of illuminance will be required, depending on the use. In addition, emphasis of certain objects or tasks may also be required.

Figure 18.2 A typical multi-purpose room

18.4 Approaches to lighting for places of worship

18.4.1 General lighting

In most cases the basic approach to lighting churches will follow the objective of drawing the viewer's attention towards the altar in the east. Therefore, the method of having three steps of illuminance (and also luminance) from the nave to the chancel and to the altar will suffice. The designer will need to consider the fabric of the church and use luminaires that are visibly suitable as well as efficient. Uniformity can be achieved over each of the separate areas and mean cylindrical illuminance checked. For other religions there are similar areas of focus that need special treatment.

Any points or areas where illuminance needs to be increased can then be looked at, such as pulpits, lecterns, organ or piano areas and fonts. How far one can go with the lighting design may be limited by restrictions beyond the designer's control. This could be in the form of mounting positions, lack of power supply, obstructions or the building being a listed property. It is suggested that for a more detailed look at the approach to lighting solutions the reader is directed to SLL Lighting Guide 13: *Lighting for places of worship* (SLL, 2014).

18.4.2   Lighting of the general surround

Except in those areas where it is detrimental, illuminance of the walls and overhead surfaces will improve the appearance of the room or building. Luminaires having a sharp cut-off, i.e. with no upward light component, when used in areas with low reflectance create a tunnel-like appearance which can be depressing. In high buildings where the ceiling consists of dark oak panelling or similar low reflectance material, it would be appropriate to use some upward light so that the ceiling form can be seen. It is not necessary in this case to use large amounts of light but rather ambient levels to reduce the tunnel effect.

There are of course certain times when rituals or ceremonies are performed by candlelight. In these circumstances the artificial lighting generally is not used. However, consideration should be given to the use of uplighting, with light sources of a warm colour, to illuminate the ceiling and upper walls and blend in with the candlelight at the lower levels.

The reflectances of the surfaces in an individual interior can make an important contribution to the quality of the lighting. By making use of high reflectances for the surfaces in the interior, the installation will be made more efficient, the shadowing effect of any obstructions will be reduced and the magnitude of discomfort glare will be reduced. Ideally, the reflectance of the floor should be at least 0.2 and the walls at least 0.5. If light is being deliberately reflected off a ceiling as part of an indirect lighting scheme, then this surface should have a reflectance of at least 0.7. There will be occasions when these values cannot be met due to the building or room construction. In these circumstances it is the responsibility of the lighting engineer or designer to ensure that these factors are taken into consideration during the design process.

18.4.3   Task lighting

Most places where both natural and artificial lighting are put to use contain at least one task area. Places of worship are no exception as tasks are part of a particular ritual or ceremony. The illuminance in the task area is the main quantitative criterion used for all forms of functional lighting. It is the illuminance on the task which, in combination with the reflectiveness of the materials from which the task is constructed and the immediate surroundings to the task, determines the sensitivity of the visual system.

The illuminances recommended in this *Handbook* are given in the form of maintained illuminances, that is, the illuminances on the task averaged over the relevant area and over one complete maintenance cycle of the installation. The relevant area can be the immediate task or a part of a room or the complete building. The illuminances recommended in this section are consistent with those recommended in the *SLL Code for Lighting* (SLL, 2012) and BS EN 12464-1 (BSI, 2011). As such, they represent good lighting practice. The illuminances recommended here are generally similar to those for equivalent tasks or actions within other guides. They are, however, based on additional considerations, such as theatrical performance and the appearance of the room or building. As an example, it is recommended that uniformity within a prayer or worship area can be lowered if a particular lighting effect is justified. Such an example could be a narrow beam spotlight over a font in a Christian church. Likewise, a similar spotlight could be used to light the Koran in a mosque or the Scriptures in a synagogue.

It is common in places of worship for tasks to occur on different planes, horizontal, vertical and anywhere in between. The illuminance recommendations given in this *Handbook* are to be produced on the plane in which the task lies.

A common failing of lighting in Christian churches is the provision of low illuminances on the vertical plane. The usual causes are the use of narrow distribution luminaires, choice of luminaire by lay people, and/or the over-spacing of luminaires. Illuminance on the vertical plane in buildings with high ceilings is much more sensitive to changes in spacing between luminaires than is illuminance on the horizontal plane. Therefore it is possible to have conditions in which the illuminance on the horizontal plane meets the illuminance recommendations but the illuminance on the vertical plane is much reduced and markedly non-uniform. Typically, the best approach to avoiding this problem is to use luminaires with a wide distribution, at a reduced spacing. Higher room surface reflectances can also be beneficial, although it is appreciated that this particular aspect cannot always be controlled by the lighting designer.

18.4.4 Architectural considerations

It is a common feature of many religious buildings that there is extensive obstruction to the distribution of light from the lighting installation. Large vertical stone pillars, wooden cross beams, heaters and banners can all cause such obstruction. If obstruction and the consequent possibility of shadowing are thought likely to be a problem then special care is required in the design of the installation.

There are a number of approaches that can be used to reduce the problems caused by obstructions. First, if the obstruction is by overhead cross beams etc., the possibility of positioning the lighting below the obstruction should be considered. Second, if there are a few large obstructions in the space such as stone pillars, a suitable approach is to check that all parts of the space are lit by at least two luminaires. These luminaires can be roof mounted or can be floodlights mounted on the walls or pillars themselves. This approach, together with high surface reflectances in the interior, should eliminate any patches of low illuminance. Third, and most generally, the spacing between luminaires can be reduced, the amount of reduction being greater the larger the size and number of obstructions and the lower the reflectances of the obstructions. Typically a one-third reduction in the maximum spacing/mounting height ratio may be required.

In places of worship it is not usually necessary to make accurate colour judgements. Where this is the case light sources with a CIE General Colour Rendering Index (CRI) of greater than $R_a 90$ are recommended. These light sources would not generally be used for the complete installation but, if the colour judgements are to be done in a specified location, localised lighting using a high CRI could be used. It should be noted that with modern light sources it is possible to have a high CIE General Colour Rendering Index as well as a high luminous efficacy (amount of light per watt). However, in many types of religious buildings lamp colour is used for overall effect rather than critical reasons. Most churches, and many synagogues and mosques, are large areas that are difficult to heat in cold weather and benefit greatly by being illuminated with a 'warm' light source having a colour temperature of 2700 K or 3000 K. In addition, when the designer wants to highlight a particular area or action, the use of light sources with different colour temperatures for the task area and surrounding areas can be very beneficial and economical.

Most places of worship are heated in some way nowadays. However, as some churches may be used for only a few hours each week it would be uneconomical for heating to be turned on whilst the building is unoccupied. This will result in some cases during the winter months where the light fixtures are in a frozen state when being switched on. Apart from the possible presence of moisture this is where incandescent lamps had the advantage over other light sources, being able to be turned on at very low temperatures. With modern light sources such as compact and linear fluorescent lamps they will usually be operated on electronic control gear which is susceptible to low temperatures, to the point of refusing to start. Where such conditions occur the lighting equipment has to be selected with care.

References

BSI (2011) BS EN 12464-1: *Light and lighting. Lighting of work places. Indoor work places* (London: British Standards Institution)

BSI (2016) BS EN 5226-1: 2016: *Emergency lighting. Code of practice for the emergency lighting of premises* (London: British Standards Institution)

TSO (2014) Equality Act 2014 (London: The Stationery Office) (available at http://www.legislation.gov.uk/ukpga/2010/15) (accessed August 2017)

SLL (2012) *SLL Code for Lighting* (London: Society of Light and Lighting)

SLL (2013) *Lighting for places of worship* SLL Lighting Guide 13 (London: Society of Light and Lighting)

SLL (2014) *Daylighting — a guide for designers* SLL Lighting Guide 10 (London: Society of Light and Lighting)

SLL (2015) *Emergency lighting* SLL Lighting Guide 12 (London: Society of Light and Lighting)

Chapter 19: Communal residential buildings

19.1 Introduction

Communal residential buildings generally use domestic-style lighting although they are usually managed as a commercial operation. Examples of such buildings are student residences, hostels, NHS staff accommodation, school boarding houses, hospices and residential homes for the elderly. The lighting in such locations has two main functions. The first is to enable residents to see what they want to see effectively without discomfort. The second is to create a visual environment that is at best attractive and interesting and at least one that avoids looking institutional. The balance between these two functions varies within and between each application.

Good practice in this context means utilising efficient light sources with effective controls to provide a suitable standard of illumination and a pleasant ambience for residents. Communal residential buildings need not look institutional: well-planned lighting and décor can produce a welcoming atmosphere.

For detailed coverage of lighting these types of building, see SLL Lighting Guide 9: *Lighting for communal residential buildings* (SLL, 2013).

19.2 Factors to be considered

There are many factors to be considered when planning the lighting for communal residential buildings and these vary in importance depending on the exact type of home and the types of residents. The function of a particular room type may be the same in a care home and a student flat, but the abilities of the users of that room differ and this needs to be taken into account.

19.2.1 Occupants' capabilities

Different communal dwellings may house people with very different visual capabilities. The occupants of student residences are likely to be young with good visual acuity. Conversely, the occupants of homes for the elderly are likely to have some form of visual impairment. Guidance on lighting for people with low vision is given in SLL Factfile 10: *Providing visibility for an ageing workforce* (SLL, 2006) and in *Housing for People with Sight Loss* (Goodman, 2008).

A realistic assessment of the visual capabilities of the occupants and what visual tasks they need to perform is necessary before starting to design the lighting.

19.2.2 Daylight

Most people strongly desire access to daylight and a view out. The more daylight is available, the less the need for electric lighting. For a bed-sitting room or study bedroom the recommended daylight factor of 2.0% would be considered good practice. See Chapter 2, 'Daylighting', for further guidance.

Ideally all rooms would get direct sunlight at some time during the day. Buildings consisting almost entirely of bed-sitting rooms or study bedrooms would ideally be constructed on a north–south axis, so the rooms face east or west and thus all receive some sunlight. For new buildings with significant communal and/or service areas, a good orientation is on an east–west axis with bathrooms, toilets, storerooms, kitchens and corridors on the north side, with bedrooms and lounges on the south side. Suitable curtains and/or blinds are needed for both privacy and control of solar glare.

19.2.3 Colour rendering and colour temperature of light sources

The appearance of bedrooms, lounges and bathrooms is important: they constitute a resident's living space. Consequently, it is important to use light sources with good colour rendering, CRI ≥ 80, and a warm colour temperature of 2700–3000 K. This facilitates a domestic atmosphere and provides accurate rendering of fabric colours and skin tones. In communal areas (other than lounges) the CRI should be similar; however, a warm colour temperature is less critical and so 3000–4000 K can be used.

19.2.4 Energy efficiency

Part L of the Building Regulations (TSO, 2010/2015a/2017) applies to communal residential buildings in England and Wales. Similar legislation applies in Scotland and Northern Ireland (TSO, 2004/2015b/2016a, 2012/2016b). Communal residential buildings are normally classified as non-domestic, hence in England and Wales Building Regulations Approved Documents L2A (new buildings) (NBS, 2016a) or L2B (existing buildings) (NBS, 2016b) will apply. The equivalent documents for Scotland and Northern Ireland are, respectively, *Technical Handbook 2017 Non Domestic — Energy* (Scottish Government, 2017) and Technical Booklet F2: *Conservation of fuel and power in buildings other than dwellings* (DFPNI, 2012).

In the context of Building Regulations, energy efficiency covers many aspects of the building fabric and services, of which lighting is only one. Nevertheless, lighting should be planned to meet the basic efficiency target, which, in 2018, is an average for the building of at least 60 lamp lumens per circuit watt.

That precludes the use of halogen lamps over most areas but they could be used in small numbers, provided that the average figure is met for the whole building. However, the latest ranges of high colour-quality LED spotlights should be used where halogen lamps were used previously. See Appendix 3, 'Building regulations and environmental labelling schemes' for further guidance.

A simple checklist for energy efficiency is:

- use efficient light sources, such as fluorescent or LED
- select well-designed luminaires with a high light output ratio (LOR)
- use high-frequency electronic control gear with fluorescents
- include appropriate controls, e.g. daylight-linking, presence/absence detection for interiors; solar time-clock or presence detection for exteriors.

19.2.5 Safety

There are two aspects of safety to be considered: luminaire safety and lighting for residents' safety.

Luminaires must be safe from the risk of electric shock: in the case of portable luminaires such as table lights or desk lights a suitable portable appliance test (PAT) regime must be set up. Appliances must be safe from heat build-up that might cause a fire and, in bathrooms and showers, they must be safe from water ingress.

Some luminaires reach a high surface temperature when in use; in this case they should be positioned out of reach of vulnerable residents and away from curtains or other soft furnishings. Recessed luminaires should be installed with sufficient air space to avoid excess heat build-up in the ceiling void. LED luminaires are very sensitive to heat build-up, which has a detrimental effect on both light output and the life of the LED. The luminaire should have a heat sink adequate to ensure good thermal management and, if recessed, it must be installed with the recommended air space above it.

Waterproof luminaires will be needed for shower rooms, some bathrooms and any exterior lighting. They are classified by reference to the ingress protection (IP) system, see Figure 19.1 and Chapter 23, Tables 23.3 and 23.4, for details of the system.

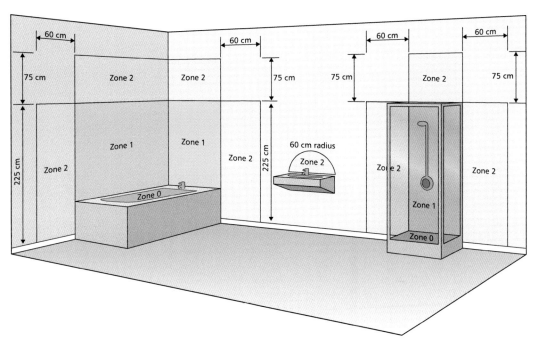

Figure 19.1 Electrical zones

A luminaire classified as IP44 is generally suitable for bathrooms and exterior use, though if it is in zone 1 or is installed in a very exposed external position IP65 classification will be required. See Chapter 9, 'Power to lighting systems' for more details of zone requirements.

Lighting for residents' safety is important on stairs and at building entrances. An emergency lighting system will be required for the safe exit of residents in the event of an emergency involving failure of the main power supply (see Chapter 3, 'Emergency lighting'). This must take into account the mobility of the residents; in some care homes there will be occupants who are physically or mentally incapacitated and so good lighting of refuge areas for those awaiting evacuation will be important.

19.2.6   Security

One feature that distinguishes communal residential buildings from private dwellings is that not all residents necessarily recognise each other, and strangers may be encountered inside the building. This part private, part public nature of the building means that security is a specific concern. Lighting around the entrance, both external and internal, is important especially if CCTV security cameras are in use. Facial recognition is essential in halls, stairways and corridors, hence lighting needs to be designed to provide good vertical illumination.

19.3   Lighting recommendations

The lighting recommendations for communal residential buildings are relatively straightforward. Most of the bedrooms, bed-sitting rooms and study bedrooms are small spaces. There is less concern for illuminance uniformity and more with ambience. Glare should be avoided, so light sources should be specified with diffusers or lampshades. The recommendations in Table 19.1 are based on adults with normal vision. When designing lighting for homes for the elderly, higher lux levels are likely to be needed (see SLL Factfile 10: *Providing visibility for an ageing workforce* (SLL, 2006) and *Housing for People with Sight Loss* (Goodman, 2008)).

Table 19.1 Recommended illumination levels

Location	Recommended illuminance (lux)	Notes
Entrance	200	
Reception desk	300	
Corridor	100	
Stairs	100	
Study bedroom	100	150–200 on desk
Bed-sitting room	100	100 at bedhead
School dormitory	100	
Small kitchen	200	
Dining area	150	
Utility room	200	
Toilets	100	
Bathroom	150	
Lounge	100	Plus local reading lights
TV lounge	50	
Games room	300	500 over a billiard/pool table
Children's play area	200	
Exterior: paths, car parks	10	
Exterior: care homes	20–30	50 around entrances and steps

19.4   General aspects of lighting in communal residential buildings

Whilst the size, type and form of communal residential buildings differ greatly, there are some areas that are common to them all. The general guidelines for lighting these areas need to be read with an understanding of the competence and fitness of the actual residents of the building being designed for. A bathroom for an elderly person is likely to be laid out slightly differently and need lighting in a different way from a similar bathroom for an able-bodied student.

See also general guidance in Chapter 11: 'Common building areas'.

19.4.1   Entrances

The entrance gives visitors and residents their first impression of a building; lighting is one of the most important constituents of this impression. It is essential to light entrances adequately: a dingy vestibule is not only unattractive and unwelcoming but also creates a feeling of insecurity, especially for people returning alone late at night. Lighting should be designed to provide good vertical illuminance to aid facial recognition. Direct or indirect lighting can be used depending on the size and shape of the space. Some entrance spaces have pigeon holes for post or notice boards, which should be well lit. In some larger blocks there may be waiting areas or vending machines that may need specific lighting.

19.4.2   Corridors

Many corridors in larger residential blocks have little or no natural light, so lighting is likely to be in constant use. The recommended illuminance for a corridor is 100 lux.

Ceiling height and corridor width are important determinants of the lighting method. The aim is to light the walls as well as the floor so that signs and door numbers can be seen easily and the space appears well lit.

In a narrow corridor cove lighting can be installed along one side. Where there is a high ceiling, uplights are recommended. If linear light sources are used, they should run parallel to the corridor. Spacing of luminaires needs to ensure adequate light outside each door off the corridor, to allow for residents locking and unlocking doors and to identify a person who calls at their door.

Automatic lighting controls are recommended: when nobody is present lighting can be dimmed as low as 20% of its specified level, with either manual or automatic switching to return to 100%. If the latter option is chosen, a sufficient number of sensors must be installed to ensure this happens when any resident's door is opened.

19.4.3   Stairs

Lighting on stairs is important for safety reasons, given the possibility of serious injury if someone falls. A low level of lighting should be provided whenever daylight is insufficient, with manual or automatic control for full illumination (100 lux) when required.

Stairs should be lit so that there is a flow of light from top to bottom, thus ensuring that all treads are illuminated. The top step and bottom step of each section must be clearly lit to indicate where stairs begin and end.

It is important to avoid glare — uniform diffuse lighting is recommended. A larger number of lower output luminaires is generally preferable to fewer, more powerful ones. Narrow stairs are best lit from the ceiling, for example using circular flush ceiling luminaires with opal, rather than prismatic, diffusers. Wide stairs give greater scope for variety of lighting methods: wall lights, ceiling lights, or a combination of both can be used. (See SLL Lighting Guide 16: *Lighting for stairs* (SLL, 2017)).

Figure 19.2 Light on landing is central to and almost above bottom steps, giving good shadow-free lighting of them as someone approaches (© Craig Auckland/Fotohaus)

19.4.4 Study bedrooms and bed-sitting rooms

Study bedrooms and bed-sitting rooms require lighting that is flexible to enable the resident to adapt lighting to a wide range of visual tasks, such as reading, writing, working at a computer, watching TV, dressing, cleaning, bed-making. A study bedroom in a student residence, a bed-sit in a hostel and a bedroom in a care home all constitute a resident's only private space. Many hours may be spent here, so light fittings need to be decorative rather than utilitarian.

The room should be provided with one (or more) main lights — either ceiling luminaire or pendant — to provide general light throughout the room. The main room light should provide diffuse light of 100 lux at floor level. This will be easier to achieve if the room surfaces have good reflectance values. For the main lighting a combination of a direct and an indirect luminaire, separately switched, is good practice as this allows the resident to vary the ambience easily. In addition, one (or two) task light(s) will be needed for each separate task area in the room, such as on a desk, by a reading chair and at the bed head. These should have individual, local controls.

Room lights and cupboards should be sited such that their interiors are not in deep shadow, especially where residents are elderly. For larger or walk-in cupboards, interior lights could be provided that come on automatically when the door is opened.

Figure 19.3 Study bedroom in a student residence with a variety of lighting positions (courtesy of Unilife Ltd.)

19.4.5   Kitchens

Communal kitchens have many formats, depending on the number of residents expected to use them and whether they are designed for the preparation of main meals or just hot drinks and snacks. Kitchen/utility/dining (KUD) rooms are typically found in student residences, usually purpose-built, incorporating a kitchen area and a dining area for up to 12 people. Where there is no lounge this becomes the residents' social centre.

The kitchen section requires low-glare uniform illuminance, for which ceiling luminaires are recommended; they should be enclosed with glass or polycarbonate covers designed to be easily removed for cleaning. A practical way of providing shade-free task lighting on a worktop is to fit linear LED lights under the base of wall-mounted cupboards over work-tops.

The dining area is distinct from the kitchen and it is recommended that the lighting should reflect this. Decorative wall or ceiling lighting, such as wall brackets or pendants, creates a pleasant atmosphere. These should be on a separate control to those in the kitchen area. Automatic lighting control through absence detection is recommended (see below).

Figure 19.4 Kitchen/utility/dining area in a student residence (© Craig Auckland/Fotohaus)

19.4.6   Lounges

Lounges are social areas where people gather to read, converse or watch television. Lighting has more effect on the atmosphere of a large communal lounge than any other aspect of its design. Such areas benefit greatly from the interest and flexibility provided by a combination of different types of lighting that are separately switched. The lighting should contribute to a relaxing atmosphere. This can be achieved by avoiding uniform illuminance, lighting both walls and ceilings, avoiding reflections of light sources in TV screens, and by emphasising features of the space such as pictures or alcoves. It is recommended that lights be provided near chairs and tables, which may be used for reading, craft work or card games. Where appropriate, socket outlets should be provided for additional table or floor lamps.

19.4.7   Recreation areas

Recreation spaces encompass a wide range of room sizes and configurations matching the range of activities. A hospice or children's home will have play areas suitable for different age groups — a student residence or hostel is likely to have a games room, an old people's home will include a room with tables for card and board games. The required illuminance depends on the anticipated activities. Generally, 300 lux is recommended, with minimal shadowing or glare, and good uniformity across the room to avoid too great a contrast between the task area and its surroundings. Additional task lighting may be required, e.g. for a dart board or above a billiard table. Automatic lighting control is recommended (see 19.4.10 below).

19.4.8   Bathrooms

Bathrooms should have at least two luminaires: a main light on the ceiling or wall and a separately switched light over the mirror, which together provide at least 150 lux. Where elderly residents are likely to need to use the lavatory during the night, it is recommended to provide an additional LED night light, left on continuously, providing illuminance of 20–30 lux for reassurance and guidance. The principles for lighting bathrooms are the same whether they are individual or communal.

19.4.9   Exterior lighting

This is required to mark the access route to the entrance and to provide basic safety and security for residents, staff and visitors during the hours of darkness.

Where there are steps on the approach to the building, these should be lit using integrated step lights, column-mounted luminaires or bollards. Floodlights mounted low on the building are not recommended because they tend to produce glare for those approaching the building. Lighting should be provided at the entrance so that keypads, bells, lists of residents, card readers or keyholes are visible. A good method is to use low luminance diffuse lighting on either side of the door.

19.4.10   Lighting controls

Areas occupied sporadically, such as lounges, games rooms and kitchens, are recommended to be fitted with absence detection. Residents switch lights on manually, but if the room is unoccupied for a pre-determined length of time, the absence detector switches the lights off automatically. In homes for the elderly, no automatic controls should turn all the lighting off in a room, as residents are far more likely to have fallen asleep in a chair and therefore not be triggering movement detectors. On waking up they need light to enable them to orientate themselves without panic and get up from their chair safely.

Main circulation areas, such as entrance halls, stairs and corridors, should not be left in darkness; in these cases it is good practice to switch or dim lighting to approximately 50% via an absence detector. See chapter 10, 'Controls'.

For more detailed information see SLL Lighting Guide 14: *Control of electric lighting* (SLL, 2016).

19.5   Nursing and care homes

Most of the general principles outlined above apply here. However, many residents will have poor eyesight and their adaptation to changes in levels of illuminance is relatively slow.

It is important to minimise glare; hence indirect lighting is useful and spotlights should only be used with care. Sudden changes in illuminance between adjacent areas are not recommended. Lighting should be designed to produce a generally domestic atmosphere. In lounges, dining rooms and bedrooms an average illuminance of about 200 lux is recommended, using decorative luminaire types. Selective switching or dimming should be available to allow for different activities, e.g. the dining room may also be used to watch TV. The use of automatic lighting controls will be restricted by safety considerations; for example, corridor lighting will normally not be automatically dimmed but manually set once all residents are in bed for the night.

See also SLL Lighting Guide 2: *Hospitals and health care buildings* (SLL, 2008), for detailed information for clinical areas of nursing homes.

Circadian lighting

Human circadian rhythms are affected by light, both its intensity and its colour temperature. The generally accepted principle is that bright cool morning light broadly resets the body's natural wake/sleep cycle. It is recognised that where people are living in an environment of constant illuminance, with only limited exposure to daylight, they may not receive sufficient stimulus to reset their wake/sleep cycle, which may lead to erratic sleeping and waking patterns.

From lighting a building purely to meet target illuminances, it is a logical step to design lighting to contribute to the wellbeing of residents, hence the term human-centric lighting. However, many factors contribute to wellbeing; lighting is only one of them and it alone should not be seen as a simple solution.

New LED luminaire designs incorporate tuneable white, allowing a variation of colour temperature. This, combined with dimming, makes it possible to design a control system to provide a high level of light at a cooler colour temperature (say 4000 K or even 6000 K) in the morning, and a dimmer, warmer setting (say 2700 K) in the late afternoon and evening, thereby to some extent mimicking natural changes in daylight. Such controlled settings can be beneficial in lounges and communal rooms where residents spend much of the day. It could also be provided in bedrooms with little access to natural morning light to stimulate the residents to wake and thereby help to establish the natural wake/sleep cycle.

See Appendix 2, 'Circadian lighting' for more detailed information.

References

DFPNI (2012) *Conservation of fuel and power in buildings other than dwellings* Technical Booklet F2 (Belfast: Department of Finance and Personnel) (available at http://www.buildingcontrol-ni.com/regulations/technical-booklets) (accessed September 2018)

Goodman C (2008) *Housing for People with Sight Loss: A Thomas Pocklington Trust Design Guide* (EP 84) (Garston: BRE Press)

NBS (2016a) *Conservation of fuel and power in new buildings other than dwellings* Approved Document L2A (2013 edition with 2016 amendments) (Newcastle upon Tyne: NBS) (available at https://www.gov.uk/government/publications/conservation-of-fuel-and-power-approved-document-l) (accessed September 2018)

NBS (2016a) *Conservation of fuel and power in existing buildings other than dwellings* Approved Document L2B (2010 edition incorporating 2010, 2011, 2013 and 2016 amendments) (Newcastle upon Tyne: NBS) (available at https://www.gov.uk/government/publications/conservation-of-fuel-and-power-approved-document-l) (accessed September 2018)

Scottish Government (2017) *Technical Handbook 2017 Non Domestic — Energy* (Edinburgh: Scottish Government) (available at http://www.gov.scot/Topics/Built-Environment/Building/Building-standards/techbooks/techhandbooks/th2017nondomenergy) (accessed September 2018)

SLL (2006) *Providing visibility for an ageing workforce* SLL Factfile 10 (London: Society of Light and Lighting) (available at http://www.cibse.org/Knowledge/knowledge-items/detail?id=a0q20000008I732AAC) (accessed September 2018)

SLL (2008) *Hospitals and health care buildings* SLL Lighting Guide 2 (London: Society of Light and Lighting)

SLL (2013) *Lighting for communal residential buildings* SLL Lighting Guide 9 (London: Society of Light and Lighting)

SLL (2016b) *Control of electric lighting* SLL Lighting Guide 14 (London: Society of Light and Lighting)

SLL (2017) *Lighting for stairs* SLL Lighting Guide 16 (London: Society of Light and Lighting)

TSO (2004) The Building (Scotland) Regulations 2004 Scottish Statutory Instruments 2004 No. 406 (as amended) (London: The Stationery Office) (available at http://www.legislation.gov.uk/ssi/2004/406) (accessed September 2018)

TSO (2010) The Building Regulations 2010 Statutory Instrument 2010 No. 2214 (as amended) (London: The Stationery Office) (available at http://www.legislation.gov.uk/uksi/2010/2214) (accessed September 2018)

TSO (2012) The Building Regulations (Northern Ireland) 2012 Statutory Rules of Northern Ireland 2012 No. 192 (as amended) (available at http://www.legislation.gov.uk/nisr/2012/192) (accessed September 2018)

TSO (2015a) The Building Regulations &c. (Amendment) Regulations 2015 Statutory Instrument 2015 No. 767 (London: The Stationery Office) (available at http://www.legislation.gov.uk/uksi/2015/767) (accessed September 2018)

TSO (2015b) The Building (Scotland) Amendment Regulations 2015 Scottish Statutory Instruments 2015 No. 218 (London: The Stationery Office) (available at http://www.legislation.gov.uk/ssi/2015/218) (accessed September 2018)

TSO (2016a) The Building (Scotland) Amendment Regulations 2016 Scottish Statutory Instruments 2016 No. 70 (London: The Stationery Office) (available at http://www.legislation.gov.uk/ssi/2016/70) (accessed September 2018)

TSO (2016b) The Building (Amendment) Regulations (Northern Ireland) 2016 Statutory Rules of Northern Ireland 2016 No. 412 (available at http://www.legislation.gov.uk/nisr/2016/412/contents/made) (accessed September 2018)

TSO (2017) The Building (Amendment) Regulations 2017 Statutory Instrument 2017 No. 856 (London: The Stationery Office) (available at http://www.legislation.gov.uk/uksi/2017/856) (accessed September 2018)

Chapter 20: Places of entertainment

20.1   Introduction

Places of entertainment vary widely in size and use, but have some common factors: they have many visitors who may be unfamiliar with the premises; they may have lighting that needs to create a certain atmosphere that may change during the day; and often have special lighting effects and dimming requirements. In addition, many spaces are licensed premises, which means in the building or parts of the building alcoholic beverages are sold for consumption on the premises. They include:

- public houses

- restaurants

- 'gastropubs'

- nightclubs

- sports and social clubs

- health clubs and sports halls

- theatres and cinemas

- areas within airports and railway stations

- universities and colleges

- hotels and guest houses

- licensed tea rooms

- conference halls and function rooms.

Lighting must meet two distinct objectives: (1) to be appropriate for the style/feel/mood/ brand of the premises and (2) to meet legislative requirements for safety and escape. Even in the most moody or 'edgy' of premises, stairs and escape routes must be lit with safety in mind. Exit signage must be present, even if reduced to the minimum permitted size for the viewing distance for each sign, and emergency lighting is usually required. Likewise, legal requirements for places of work and building regulations must be complied with.

More details can be found in the SLL Lighting Guide 18: *Lighting for licensed premises* (SLL, 2018).

20.2   Principles of lighting

20.2.1   Character and atmosphere

Many factors contribute to the character and atmosphere of places of entertainment, but decoration and lighting are the most important. Different atmospheres suit different kinds of premises. A small pub in the country may call for a very relaxed and welcoming atmosphere, whilst a town centre bar aimed at a younger clientele aims for a more stimulating, vibrant one, potentially themed. In some cases, the atmosphere will need to alter at different times of day. For example, a theatre bar may need a brisk and bright atmosphere when drinks have to be served rapidly during intervals, but a more relaxed one if it is open for pre- and after-show drinks.

The style of the luminaires also contributes to the atmosphere. Even when switched off they are part of the décor and should be chosen accordingly. Domestic style luminaires may be suited to a small village pub, whereas industrial types suit the warehouse style of some restaurant chains. It is advisable that all the luminaires in any one space should complement one another.

20.2.2 Lighting and decoration

Lighting and decoration complement one another to a marked degree. At any point in a room, much of the light comes not directly from the luminaires, but will have been reflected off the floor, ceiling or walls. A warm atmosphere is generally expected. In general, the darker the décor, the greater the lighting input required to achieve a given level of illumination in the room or area.

Figure 20.1 The colour of the decor can have a profound effect on the atmosphere within a room (courtesy of Chelsom Ltd.)

The height of the ceiling is an important determinant of lighting design. Low ceilings should preferably be white or an off-white colour, otherwise the room risks appearing gloomy and oppressive. Higher ceilings allow a much wider range of lighting methods to be used and the choice of colour is wide; for example, a room could have the ceiling painted a deep colour for effect. Very high ceilings pose a different challenge: whether to light right up to the top; to leave the ceiling dark; or to set a lower height with a translucent stretch fabric false ceiling (Figure 20.2), which then allows lighting either above or below the ceiling material.

Figure 20.2 Lighting made into a feature in the bright and lively Joker Café in Ankara (courtesy of Barrisol®)

Light coloured walls help to create a bright environment, especially in an old country pub or retail-style café-bar with little daylight. On the other hand, a warehouse-style bar or restaurant will use exposed brick, concrete and ironwork as a feature, with a variety of spotlights creating pools of light in sharp contrast to the dark materials on walls, ceiling and probably floor as well.

20.2.3 Daylight

Many licensed premises such as bars and sports clubs operate during daylight hours. As a light source, natural daylight is excellent and has good colour rendering. However, daylight should not be considered as 'free'. Large window spaces providing excellent daylighting of an area have implications on heating and ventilation. They often result in large heat losses in cold weather, with consequent additional heating costs, whereas in summer considerable heat gains and solar glare require investment in blinds and, possibly, air conditioning.

Problems can also arise in the transition between areas lit by daylight to areas that are much darker. Examples include (*i*) entrances where patrons walk from a bright street into a dark bar, (*ii*) where a conservatory has been added to an old building with few windows, (*iii*) where the staff serving meals to patrons outdoors pass frequently between sunlight and darker kitchens. These problems are more acute for older people, whose vision adapts slowly to large changes in light level.

Electric lighting should be designed to complement daylight in all premises, particularly those with large window areas. In large spaces, the switching should be arranged in rows parallel to the windows so that lights may be brought on in groups as daylight fades. See Chapter 2, 'Daylighting', for more information on all aspects of daylighting and integration with electric lighting.

20.2.4 Colour rendering and colour temperature

Good colour rendering is important in all areas of licensed premises used by patrons; the faces of both staff and patrons should be well lit; food and drink should look appetizing; and cards and banknotes need to be easily distinguishable. The minimum colour rendering index (CRI) should be 80 in all areas; ideally lighting in front of house areas and the kitchen should have a CRI of 90.

To create a warm and welcoming atmosphere, lamps with colour temperature in the range 2700–3500 K are recommended. Cool white light sources are not generally suitable unless aiming for a specific feel, such as an 'ice-bar' or similar. It is important to avoid cold lighting in service areas that are visible in the bar or restaurant when a connecting door is opened, hence passages leading to front of house areas need to be considered with the front of house lighting. See Appendix 1, 'Reflectance and colour', for a more in-depth consideration of this topic.

20.2.5 Modelling, glare and sparkle

The appearance of people is critical. If light is provided by a few small bright light sources, strong shadows will be produced that lead to an unflattering appearance. Equally if the light is made very diffuse in character, it may make things look flat and uninteresting. One solution to this problem is to provide one style of lighting to provide general lighting with supplementary spotlights to provide highlights.

The positioning of luminaires is important; luminaires that are close to the usual sight lines, such as those mounted on a low ceiling, may produce objectionable glare. Wall-mounted luminaires may do likewise, hence ones with a suitable shade for the light source are recommended.

Spotlights can be used to emphasise key areas or displays and to add visual interest to a bar or restaurant area. Lighting to produce highlights can be achieved with carefully positioned spotlights.

20.2.6 Energy-efficient lamps

Energy-efficient lamps are required throughout: a wide choice of LED lamps is available. Their use results in a considerable reduction in running costs without sacrificing interest or sparkle, see Figure 20.3.

Figure 20.3 LED 'filament' lamps used in a bar to introduce points of visual interest without undue radiant heat onto customers or staff (courtesy of Bright Goods®/LED Eco Lights)

20.2.7 Lighting controls

It is well worth investing in suitable controls for any lighting installation. This makes the lighting scheme more flexible and enables it to be used more economically in terms of energy use. Building Regulations (**NBS, 2013; Scottish Government, 2018**) recommend that display lighting controls should be separate from those for the general lighting.

20.2.7.1 Switches

Where straightforward switches are used, it is advisable for them all to be on a single panel at a central point not accessible to the public. It is recommended that the switch panel be engraved so that the function of each switch is clear: staff turnover in places of entertainment is notoriously rapid. Additional light switches should be provided at each entrance door to the building for basic access lights.

20.2.7.2 Dimming controls

Care is required with LED lamps. Some operate with a standard (leading edge) rotary dimmer switch, but others require the less common trailing edge version. Dimmers need a minimum load, usually 25 W, which may not be reached if only a small number of LED bulbs is in use on a circuit. A number of manufacturers now offer 'intelligent' dimmer switches, which detect the circuitry of the lamps and provide the most suitable dimming method. For this reason, it is sensible to avoid mixing brands and/or types of LED on the same circuit and to select a compatible dimmer switch. Check with the dimmer switch manufacturer that the product is compatible with the proposed lamp type(s).

- *1–10 V dimmers*: LED and fluorescent lamps can use this type of dimming equipment, which requires additional 1–10 V control wiring. The dimmer switch operates via the low-voltage control circuit on the driver or ballast of the luminaire to adjust the light output.

- *DALI dimming*: for larger premises and spaces, DALI dimming control could be considered. Here all the luminaires or drivers are individually addressed via a data cable looping to each. This allows each to be set to a specific lighting output and assigned to scenes. Limitations on numbers of devices per cable and distance limits means that careful design is required.

20.2.7.3 Control systems

There is a wide variety of control systems available with various degrees of complexity, and corresponding cost:

- *Electronic single room systems and electronic multi-room systems*: these can be hard-wired to a switch plate or keypad, or operated wirelessly. Wireless control is a convenient way of retro-fitting a control system without the need for new cabling. A wireless receiver is installed in the circuit of every light fitting to be controlled; the transmitter in the controller sends instructions to switch on/off or dim. This can be operated from a fixed control panel or from a smartphone or tablet computer. The only limitation is the Wi-Fi coverage in the building. An override switch is required within easy reach of bar staff in case of emergency.

- *Daylight control*: a light sensor monitors the level of daylight, switching 'on' when it fades below a trigger point. This type of control is used to maintain a specified level of light in a room, which can ensure that lights are dimmed or switched off in a room when there is plenty of daylight available, leading to significant energy savings. For exterior use a dusk-to-dawn sensor operates to switch security lights on at dusk and off again with the morning light.

- *Presence or absence detection*: a passive infrared (PIR) or microwave detector senses whether there is anyone present in a room. This can be used either to switch lights on when someone enters a space, or to switch off lights when rooms are left empty, or both. This is useful for meeting rooms, toilets, cellars and store rooms. See Chapter 10, 'Controls', for a full discussion of options and limitations.

20.3   Lighting design: interior

20.3.1   General design considerations

Patrons enjoy a relaxed atmosphere and the lighting should be designed accordingly. The best results will be achieved by using a variety of light sources to achieve good vertical and horizontal illuminance, and contrasting some areas against others. Having arrived at a target level of overall ambient illumination, smaller and more directional light sources may be added to highlight specific areas. Spotlights should be sited with care and used advisedly.

Luminaires need to be robust, and readily replaceable. Luminaires within reach of patrons must not be hot to the touch, and should be secured to walls, tables or floors to comply with health and safety requirements and to prevent theft. Luminaires should be carefully positioned so as to avoid glare, which is often a problem in premises with low ceilings — luminaires will be viewed from both sitting and standing positions. It is advisable to select luminaires where the light source is not directly visible from a normal viewing angle.

Each area within the building will have a different function and the visual tasks involved for each of these will vary. The tasks will also vary for the staff and the patrons. It is important to consider all the tasks that may need to be carried out at different times of the day and by different people.

The fundamental considerations in planning the lighting layout are:

- Who is going to use the area?

- What will they be doing?

- For how long will they be doing it?

It is also important to assess the degree of difficulty of the task: reading a menu may appear to be a simple task, but small or intricate print is difficult for people with lower visual acuity.

20.3.2   Bars and pubs

Table 20.1 Recommended illuminances for bars and pubs

Area	Recommended illuminance (lux)	Notes
Bar counter	100	Vertical illuminance important
Till and display area	200	
Games area	200 – 300	
TV viewing	50	
Steps and stairs	100	See 20.3.2.10 below
Toilets and urinals	100	
Washbasins and mirrors	200	Good colour rendering essential
Cellar, storeroom, passage	100	
Staff room	200	
Kitchen	500	
Office	300	

20.3.2.1 Entrances and exits

The lighting should ensure that the door and approach(es) to the door(s) stand out from the surrounding area(s). This applies both to people leaving and to those arriving from outside, particularly in strong sunlight. Additional illumination will be needed at such points.

Suggestions include:

- providing extra ambient light (i.e. additional luminaires)

- skirting level lighting in passageways

- providing extra luminaires for use only during daylight hours to help people adjust when entering from sunlight outside.

20.3.2.2 The bar walk

This is the area adjacent to the bar counter where patrons stand to be served. The aim is to achieve contrast with the surrounding area, so that the eye of a new patron is drawn to the bar. Suggested approaches include:

- using downlights to mark out the floor passage

- ensuring that adjacent lighting is less bright to enhance the effect of the pathway to the bar

- using a lighter coloured (i.e. more reflecting) floor covering than that in the surrounding drinking areas.

20.3.2.3 Bar counters

Good vertical illuminance is important, without glare, so that bar staff can discern the features of patrons and vice versa; patrons and staff need to see the colour of drinks and money.

20.3.2.4 Bar backs

The choice of lighting will depend on the type of display (bottles, optics, etc.) envisaged. Possible approaches are: wall-washing, illuminated panels in the bar back, edge lighting of shelves, illuminated shelving.

20.3.2.5 Display areas and tills

It is vital that staff can see money clearly. In dim environments such as night clubs 200 lux is not practical; rather, till lighting should be one 'level' above that of the surroundings. Excessively bright till lighting may impede the ability of the staff to see what is going on in drinking areas. Downlights or spotlights can be used over displays and tills but care must be taken with the positioning of such luminaires to prevent glare or unwanted reflections from till touch screens.

20.3.2.6 Staff areas

Task rather than decorative illumination is required in cellars, storerooms, changing rooms, passages and offices, ensuring that there is sufficient light to enable the various tasks to be carried out safely. Kitchens require fully enclosed and moisture-proof luminaires (IP65) with easily cleanable surfaces.

20.3.2.7 Drinking areas

The lighting system needs to be flexible to respond to differing needs at different times of day, i.e. brighter lighting at lunchtime, early evening and for morning cleaning, with softer lighting for the later evening.

Where there is fixed seating in the form of banquettes, the lighting can be designed accordingly using wall lights, ceiling lights, recessed lighting or wall washers from above or below. More often there is an area with movable tables and chairs.

Some options are:

- provide lighting all round on the walls, e.g. wall lights, uplighters, picture lights or a combination

- ceiling lights: if these are recessed good diffusers are recommended; recessed downlights alone make the ceiling appear dark, whereas the use of surface-mounted luminaires has the benefit of lighting the ceiling itself

- pendants or chandeliers where the ceiling height is adequate.

Many bars have a television for watching sport. Spotlights or other bright sources are not recommended near a screen, nor should direct light fall on it since this greatly reduces the contrast of the picture. It is advisable to have two set lighting levels, one subdued for TV viewing and a brighter one for when the TV is not in use.

20.3.2.8 Restaurants and eating areas

Lighting needs to be flexible to respond to differing requirements, e.g. Sunday lunchtime or Friday evening. It needs to reach each table so that patrons can see to read the menu, but without making them feel exposed. In most pubs it is better to illuminate the whole space than to provide individual table lighting; one can choose a direct or indirect lighting scheme, or a mixture of the two. The more diffuse the light, the softer the ambience.

- *Direct lighting options*: wall lights, pendants, chandeliers.

- *Indirect lighting methods*: wall uplighters, concealed lighting in coving on ceilings, along beams or in window embrasures; wall washers set behind fixed seating or recessed in the ceiling.

20.3.2.9 Games areas

These areas generally need higher overall illumination than drinking areas.

- Separate games rooms: high levels of ambient lighting without shadowing:

  — *Indirect*: wall uplights or lighting in ceiling coving.

  — *Direct*: ceiling lights, wall lights, pendants.

- If games are within the bar area, specific items such as a pool table or dartboard need to be highlighted by direct lighting such as pendants or spotlights over tables or downward wall washers for dartboards.

20.3.2.10 Steps and stairways

In many older premises there are small changes in level between various parts of the same room. These represent a hazard to users, so good lighting and marking are essential. Similar hazards exist on staircases. Various measures are recommended:

- Edging of a contrasting colour to the floor surface on stair treads, across their whole width.

- Increased ambient lighting on steps and stairways, i.e. one 'level' brighter than surrounding areas.

- Low-level lighting at the side of stair treads to target the light where it is needed.

- Edge-strip lighting along stair treads; LED strips are very effective.

The advantage of the last two methods is that they have little impact on the ambient lighting in the area.

More detailed advice on lighting stairs is given in SLL Lighting Guide 16: *Lighting for stairs* (SLL, 2017).

20.3.2.11 Toilets

The style of luminaire chosen will depend on the establishment and its clientele. Fully enclosed decorative or bulkhead luminaires are recommended, ceiling or wall mounted, easy to clean, moisture-resistant and appropriate to the interior design. In some places vandal-proof luminaires are advisable.

Lighting for mirror and baby changing areas is important. Spotlights and downlights immediately above mirrors cause harsh shadows and are therefore not recommended; it is more effective to install lights on the wall or ceiling, to either side of the mirrors.

20.3.2.12 Lighting for cleaning

In larger premises it may be worthwhile installing a secondary lighting system to boost the lighting levels for cleaning and restocking outside opening hours.

20.4 Lighting design: exterior

20.4.1 General considerations

Exterior lighting enables patrons to locate the premises; makes gardens and external smoking areas available after dark; covers safety needs; and provides security.

The first consideration is whether external lighting is necessary at all. Premises in a brightly lit city centre may not need any if well designed signage is used. If external lighting is needed, start by lighting those parts of immediate interest to patrons, such as the façade, entrances, access ways, car parks and gardens, and leave the rest. Light should not trespass into adjacent properties where it is not wanted, nor should it be allowed to spill into the night sky.

20.4.2 Location of luminaires

When planning exterior lighting it is sensible to consider the security of the lighting equipment. Cabling, connection boxes and light fittings are all vulnerable to damage, theft or vandalism, so it is recommended that cabling is, as far as possible, positioned out of reach of customers or passers-by, and suitably robust luminaires chosen. Lighting needs to be waterproof, generally IP44, but IP65 in exposed areas subject to pressure washing, sea spray or regular water coverage from fountains etc. See Chapter 23 'Extreme environments' for full requirements of IP designations.

Luminaires should be located where they produce minimum glare for residents of the premises, neighbours or passers-by. They should be visually unobtrusive but accessible for maintenance. Luminaires placed high up can be seen from a great distance, especially in rural areas.

20.4.3   Control

In general, the external lighting, including advertising signage, should only be on during those trading hours which are in darkness. Solar-time controls to switch lights off when they are not needed should always be included. Security lighting can be controlled by passive infrared movement detectors (PIR). However, some security lighting may need to be on all night in which case dusk-dawn photocell control is recommended.

Figure 20.4 External lighting not only provides light for the users but can act as an advertisement of the premises location and use (© Ieva Saudargaite/iGuzzini)

20.4.4   Gardens and terraces

It is important to decide on the colour temperature — warm white or cool white — and to have consistency across the various different types of luminaire used.

Paths and especially steps need to be lit, ensuring the treads are lit across their full width. Low-level luminaires, which can be recessed into an adjacent wall, are a good way of doing this. If there is a flight of more than four steps, it is essential to light the top and bottom step effectively.

Low-level lighting is recommended to reduce the possibility of glare at the tables and as people go in and out of the building. This could be achieved with low bollards, low light fittings which light downwards, or lights on walls or fences with a hood or eyelid to avoid upward light. Where decking is installed small recessed indicator lights on either side are a good method of marking paths and steps.

Up+down lights or wall lights with effective diffusers are recommended for general illumination. It is usually better to install a larger number of lower output luminaires than two or three high-output ones. Accent lighting can be provided by carefully placed spotlights, either fixed to structures or at ground level. Festoon lighting can be placed in trees, shrubs or along the top of fences for a decorative effect.

20.4.5   External smoking areas

A smoking area is generally sited either on the pavement in front or in the garden/yard behind the building. This may be a shelter or simply tables protected by large parasols.

Where large parasols are used, suitable options are:

- a small pendant lantern under each parasol

- small bulkhead lights on the wall of the building just below the height of the parasol.

In a shelter it is practical to install a ceiling luminaire or wall-mounted lights. It is advisable to use waterproof luminaires given the risk of condensation forming in cold weather after lights are turned off at night.

20.4.6   Façades

There are numerous options, depending on available space and location of power supplies:

- ground level floodlights positioned away from the building

- uplights on the wall, or in the ground at the base of the wall

- festoons of mini LED lights above the windows and/or along the eaves of the roof

- neon tubes forming the name of the establishment or delineating the façade

- small spotlights on the wall picking out architectural features.

Table 20.2 Recommended levels of lighting for outdoor areas and car parks

Area		Average illuminance (lux)
Rural	Environmental Zones E1 and E2	15
Urban	Environmental Zones E3 and E4	30
Car parks	Light traffic	5
	Medium traffic	10
	Heavy traffic	20

In zones E1 and E2, there should be no sky glare; elsewhere it should be kept to a minimum. Care should be taken that light does not shine directly into windows of neighbouring properties.

20.4.7   Car parks

Car parks used during the hours of darkness must always be lit, both for security of patrons and for safe movement of cars and people. It is particularly important to avoid glare to drivers.

Unless it is a very small car park (less than 10 spaces) it is recommended that luminaires be mounted on poles or outbuildings and have flat glass diffusers and suitable cowling to ensure that light is effectively directed downwards and not spilled sideways or up into the sky.

If closed circuit television (CCTV) is in use, lighting needs to be compatible. See Chapter 27, 'Security lighting', for more comprehensive information.

20.5 Emergency lighting

Emergency lighting is a vital part of any lighting system. It is required to enable people to leave a building safely in the event of mains power failure; it also has to allow for specific tasks, such as cooking, to be stopped safely. Emergency lighting is closely involved with safe evacuation: safety signs and escape routes have to be considered together. There are three categories of emergency lighting, known as escape, safety and standby lighting. In smaller premises, it is usual only to provide escape lighting.

In some premises safety lighting may be specified to enable occupants to stay in an area of the building during a power failure but is not enough for business to continue.

Standby lighting can be provided to enable normal activities to continue within the building during a mains failure using a generator or UPS system. Standby lighting can also be used as escape lighting provided it meets all the specific requirements for escape lighting: this is common in larger buildings such as airports.

See Chapter 3, 'Emergency lighting', for the full descriptions of these and detailed requirements.

20.6 Specific types of premises

20.6.1 Restaurants

Style and atmosphere constitute an important part of a restaurant's image: lighting plays a major role in this. Those offering fine dining will probably look for soft, shadow-free background lighting with a candle(s) on each table; by contrast a warehouse-style bistro typically highlights each table with a bright spotlight and this effect is enhanced by leaving the ceiling and background in shadow.

20.6.1.1 Fine dining restaurants

The atmosphere is generally opulent and relaxed to enable customers to savour gourmet food and fine wine. Many such restaurants make a significant investment in internal decoration and furniture.

Principles for lighting design: indirect background lighting; direct main lighting; some accent lighting to add variety and interest; flexibility of switching to allow a brighter setting for lunch (approx. 100 lux on the tables) and a softer evening one for dinner (50–75 lux).

20.6.1.2 Bistros

A town centre or city bistro has a lively atmosphere, frequently with music, which presents a modern and fashionable image. Emphasis is on high seat occupancy, rapid service and social 'buzz'.

Options for lighting design:

- track system with spotlights
- large pendants with metal or brightly coloured shades
- pencil pendants over tables

- up+down wall lights

- cove lighting with colour-settable LED strips or tape

- distinctive surface-mounted spotlights

- several switched settings to cover various scenes, or a lighting control system with pre-sets

- daylight control for lighting circuits near windows.

20.6.1.3 Small, informal restaurants

Many restaurants in towns and villages are sited in typical retail premises with a capacity of no more than 40 covers. There will be an entrance and large windows at one end, but otherwise no daylight; ceiling heights can vary considerably; there may or may not be a bar for coffee and drinks.

Both the size of the space and budget considerations favour a simple general lighting scheme with all-purpose luminaires. Automatic daylight control for lights at the front of the premises is recommended. The ceiling height is a major consideration:

- *Low ceiling*: flush or recessed ceiling lights; wall lights.

- *High ceiling*: uplights; pendants; chandeliers; cove lighting using flexible LED tape; some accent lighting.

20.6.1.4 Hotel restaurants

These are often multi-purpose spaces serving three meals a day, each of which has different requirements. Breakfast is likely to be self-service with emphasis on lighting the buffet tables and coffee machines; lunch may be informal with fairly quick service of a limited menu, while dinner is a big meal served in a formal manner. Above all the lighting needs to be versatile. This can be achieved by a single lighting scheme with overall dimming to suit the ambience for different meals, or it can be designed with several distinct but complementary types of lighting from which a combination is chosen to create the desired atmosphere. In the latter case a lighting control system with pre-sets would be advantageous.

Options for lighting design: indirect background lighting; direct main lighting; some accent lighting; picture lights contributing to indirect lighting; automatic daylight control recommended for lights near windows.

20.6.1.5 Function rooms

Hotels, clubs and some pubs have function rooms of varying sizes, many without daylight. They may be used for meetings, conferences, coffee breaks, buffets, dances and formal meals. Here the lighting needs to be multi-purpose to cope with different room layouts and different levels of illuminance.

Options for lighting design: indirect lighting; direct lighting; recessed ceiling lights if the ceiling is low; some accent lighting; a lighting control system with pre-sets is advantageous; automatic control of main lights, or all lights, via an absence detector is recommended.

Figure 20.5 Function room with wall, picture and downlights to allow the lighting of the room to vary with use (image © Benedict Cadbury)

20.6.2   Clubs

Style and atmosphere are very important for a club: lighting plays a major role in this, to an even greater extent than décor. Unlike almost all other licensed premises, where generally the entire area is lit, clubs choose to leave areas dark, hence the perception of lighting is as much about what is not lit as what is. Nevertheless, safety considerations require access routes and particularly steps to be adequately illuminated; lighting in the bar area has to be sufficient for the tasks staff undertake.

Lighting requirements are likely to include:

- indication of access routes to the bar, exit and toilets

- subdued ambient lighting in seating areas

- accent lighting for the stage, performance area and bar(s)

- colour-settable lighting

- dimming control for all lighting

- additional luminaires to boost light levels during cleaning and maintenance.

Considerations for lighting design:

- Ambient lighting can be provided by deeply recessed directional ceiling lights, wall lights with no direct forward light (such as LED cubes or pucks, which light up, down or sideways), uplights recessed behind fixed banquette seating.

- General lighting may need to link to any show or performance lighting system.

- Cove lighting is an effective form of background lighting: recessed LED strips or tape can be used; this provides great opportunities for scene-setting if it is dimmable and colour settable.

- Access routes must be clearly identifiable by customers and staff. A good option is to install low-level recessed lighting with no upward light spill either side of the route. The recommended average illuminance is 20 lux.

- Steps are a particular hazard. The principle is to ensure that unexpected isolated steps and the top and bottom step of any flight of stairs are lit more brightly than their immediate surroundings and have a suitable contrasting nosing on each step. The first step should be lit to a lighting level one standard lighting interval (see Appendix 5, 'Glossary') above ambient, e.g. for an average floor lighting level of 20 lux, the step should be lit to 30 lux.

- Exit signs must be of the prescribed size and be lit whenever the premises are in use. They should be sufficiently bright that they can be clearly seen by patrons on the dance floor or in seating areas. Emergency lighting must be installed in accordance with the regulations, which means that the escape route must be lit all the way to a place of safety outside the building. See Chapter 3, 'Emergency lighting', for a full coverage of the requirements.

Figure 20.6 Various lighting techniques are used here to put light where needed for functional use whilst keeping the general atmosphere relaxed (courtesy of Bignell Shacklady Ewing)

20.6.3   Theatres and concert halls

Throughout these generally large, busy buildings general lighting requirements are likely to include:

- interface with the performance lighting control system

- lighting for CCTV monitoring

- safe access to luminaires in high spaces must be planned and discussed with the lead designer and the venue operating team

- emergency lighting to all stairs and exit routes, and anti-panic levels over all open spaces

- exit signs, which must be of the correct size for the various viewing distances across any large open spaces and be lit whenever the premises are in use.

Discuss with Building Control the use of the alternative 'green on black' exit signs adjacent to any performance areas, to avoid distraction during performances.

20.6.3.1 Entrance and exterior

Entrances act as a gateway into the building but also an opportunity to display the activity within the building to be seen from outside, particularly at night.

Lighting requirements are likely to include:

- the creation of a sense of welcome and anticipation of the performance to come

- a well-lit entrance guides patrons to the public entrance; it should be arranged to give a significantly enhanced light level to the pavement or forecourt area

- accent lighting to display boards along the façade and beneath the entrance canopy is of equal importance to emphasise the advertising of current and future productions

- automated lighting control to articulate façade features and advertising boards out of hours during night time

- steps or ramps to be clearly illuminated

- safe access to luminaires, both inside and externally

- emergency lighting externally, to allow crowds to disperse safely in the event of a local area power cut.

20.6.3.2 Foyer

Foyers constitute an important transition space and often account for around a quarter of the built area of a project and can be larger than the auditorium in area. Foyers provide an opportunity to showcase the building but also highlight its presence at street level. Foyers act as the showcase for the venue operator — a place to see and be seen.

Foyer lighting can aid navigation, helping to draw audience members to the box office, bars and the auditorium entrance doors. Lighting can be coordinated with way-finding to highlight the position of key signs.

It is important that some means of adjusting the light levels and general mood of the front-of-house (FoH) lighting is incorporated. This could take the form of a programmable scene-setting control system that can dim or switch individual circuits and store pre-programmed lighting scenes. Centralised control systems of this type are also important in the reduction of energy usage.

Lighting considerations are likely to include the following:

- Colour temperature selection should consider the material used in the space. Natural wood finish would require a warmer colour such as 2700 K, for example.

- Facility for colour accent lighting to create bespoke atmospheres. Colour-settable lighting to adapt to the event content or theme.

- Indication of access routes to all areas of the venue.

- Localised lighting for display cases or boards.

- Good vertical illumination is essential to illuminate faces as well as the boundaries of the space.

- Required lighting levels that can be varied up to 200 lx depending on the activities. Some events will require reduced illumination level to suit the desired atmosphere.

20.6.3.3 Retail

Show merchandising offers opportunities for theatre and performance venue operators to generate additional income. Venues with resident companies may operate their own shop while touring companies may operate a temporary merchandising service themselves — this may be in dedicated areas or in 'pop-up' stands or tables in corners of the foyer. The lighting of any dedicated retail space should therefore be flexible to cater for all operational modes. See also Chapter 15, 'Retail lighting'.

Lighting requirements are likely to include the following:

- Track and spot arrangements: it is recommended to use spot luminaires with on-board dimming. This option will enable the operator to customise the desired lighting effect for the merchandise on display.

- Include local scene setting controller if required.

- Use high-CRI light sources.

- Good vertical illumination.

- Discuss electronic point of sale (EPoS) location and CCTV monitoring lighting requirements. This specific location may require an enhanced lighting level.

- Retail facilities are also workplaces. These should be designed so that staff can see to serve and take money and process credit cards.

20.6.3.4 Circulation areas

The circulation area links all spaces and aids the safe and efficient flow of large numbers of people between these spaces. The types of spaces off the circulation area or combined within it vary depending on the size and type of venue but can include ticket office, cloakrooms, sales points (confectionery and programmes), stairs and lift lobbies, toilets, bars, cafés, restaurants and shops.

Lighting requirements are likely to include:

- Extend the dramatic atmosphere of the entrance and foyer, directing users to their destination. Any architectural features or finish textures could provide visual interest using a combination of indirect and direct lighting.

- A separate layer of lighting may be needed to illuminate any display boards/materials provided along corridors leading to the auditorium.

20.6.3.5 Bars

Theatre and concert goers expect all facilities to be efficient and of a high standard. The bar is the focal point during the interval when most of the audience gathers there to drink and socialise, and to a lesser extent before and after the performance. Bars in such locations are increasingly utilised during the day when rooms are hired out commercially for conferences and events. It is important that the lighting is separately controlled from the main foyer and/or landing lighting, thereby enabling the bar to operate independently.

References

NBS (2013) *Non-Domestic Building Services Compliance Guide* (plus addendum) (Newcastle Upon Tyne: NBS) (available at (available at https://www.gov.uk/government/publications/conservation-of-fuel-and-power-approved-document-l) (accessed September 2018)

Scottish Government (2018) *Non-Domestic Building Services Compliance Guide for Scotland* (Edinburgh: Scottish Government Building Standards Division) (available at http://www.gov.scot/Topics/Built-Environment/Building/Building-standards/techbooks/techhandbooks/ndbscg) (accessed September 2018)

SLL (2017) *Lighting for stairs* SLL Lighting Guide 16 (London: Society of Light and Lighting)

SLL (2018) *Lighting for licensed premises* SLL Lighting Guide 18 (London: Society of Light and Lighting)

Chapter 21: Courts and custodial buildings

21.1   Courts

The lighting of courtrooms and their associated areas needs to be carefully considered. The wide range of users, their differing tasks, timescales and the emotional engagement with the various spaces require differing lighting approaches.

During the past five years, the importance of cylindrical illuminance in working environments has come to the fore. In courtrooms this metric is paramount as facial and emotional recognition are vital tasks in such spaces. However, this metric must be balanced against the relatively stringent unified glare rating (UGR) for courtrooms themselves which, in the past, has led to many modern courtrooms and associated spaces being lit with direct/indirect systems.

Judges, court officials, lawyers, witnesses and jurors may require different lit conditions, while the gravitas of such spaces should always be at the forefront of the designer's mind.

21.1.1   Courtrooms (Crown, Magistrates' and County)

Courtrooms are complex spaces with a visual hierarchy that needs to be considered. As well as horizontal illuminance, cylindrical illuminance is now a key factor encompassing, as it does, facial modelling, which is a requirement for the business of a court.

The need for controlled glare rating is paramount as eye strain, a function not only of the eye but also of brain fatigue, is a common complaint, reflected in the requirement for a maximum UGR of 16. Combined with the need for a range of illuminance levels, from 500 lux for the reading of critical evidence documents by court officials through to witness recognition, both in the box and behind screens, and adequate lighting for councils and jurors, many factors, products and variable positions must be considered. Clearly a 'one size fits all' approach is not appropriate.

Careful attention should be paid to ensure that screens used for video conferencing with witnesses are free from veiled reflectance. A common approach to the lighting of courts is the use of direct/indirect luminaires hanging from cables or rods, and such fittings could cause problems if the screens are not resistant to glare. Therefore, this approach must be combined with an understanding of the location of video conferencing monitors. This is especially important when a screen is viewed collectively by a jury as, unlike court officials who may have access to individual monitors, a juror may not be able to change position to avoid veiled reflections on the screen.

The need for hierarchy is best observed and executed at the bench, where the judge or judges preside over the court proceedings. In modern court rooms this area is frequently delineated by light; for example, by a specific row of downlights. The wall behind the bench is also important as it is the usual position for the Royal Coat of Arms. The Royal Arms appears in every courtroom in England and Wales (with the exception of the magistrates' court in the City of London), demonstrating that justice comes from the monarch and a law court is part of the Royal Court (hence its name) (HMTCS, 2016). Its lit appearance, therefore, needs careful consideration. See Figure 21.1 below.

Figure 21.1 Modern court environment (courtesy of
Hoare Lea/Hurd Rolland Partnership)

Finally, all electric light generated will fall short of the quality and feel of daylight — the light
that the eye and brain have evolved to respond to. Admitting daylight into courtrooms should
therefore be a priority. The full spectrum of natural light and the connection it brings to the
external environment will benefit those occupying a space, in which the nature of the work
undertaken inevitably means it is likely that occupants will experience high levels of anxiety
and stress. Due to the need for privacy many courts have clerestory windows. However,
when this is not possible, full windows can be used if the glass is opaque. Flat roof lights
are not recommended due to solar glare, although north lights can be considered in certain
circumstances if high levels of natural light can be limited to avoid high contrast ratios in the
courtroom.

21.1.2   Defendant and witness areas

Lighting in defendants' areas should have a calming effect and be free from high contrast ratios
and glare. High lighting levels may be required to facilitate the reading of legal documents of
variable text size. Access to natural light is a benefit, assisting in creating a more comfortable
environment.

21.1.3   Child witness waiting suite

Lighting in witness suite areas should have a calming effect and be free from high contrast
ratios and glare. High lighting levels are required to facilitate the closed loop video conferencing
facilities for remote witness evidence to ensure cameras can adequately convey body language
and facial expressions. Cameras must be free of lens flare and careful consideration must
therefore be given to luminaire positions. Unlike other areas, daylight is not recommended due
to the possibility of high contrast ratios that natural light, on a bright sunny day, might create.

Light fittings should be positioned to the left and right of the seated subject, so that light is cast
from both sides onto the face. Light fittings directly in front of the subject should be avoided
as these can cause glare or veiled reflections (lens flare) on poorer quality cameras. Careful
attention should be paid to balancing contrast ratio.

21.1.4 Jurors' areas

Lighting in jurors' areas should have a calming effect and be free from high contrast ratios and glare. High lighting levels may be required to facilitate the reading of legal documents of variable text size. Access to natural light is a benefit. Lighting in such environments should help to enhance the impression and therefore the look and feel of luminaires could be more akin to a domestic environment rather than a commercial one.

21.1.5 Judges' accommodation

The judges' accommodation can vary in design from modern, private business accommodation to rooms in listed buildings. In all cases illumination levels should be adequate for the reviewing of legal documentation; it is also likely that task lighting will be required on desks and close to lounge furniture. Finally, special attention should be paid to the uniform lighting of legal textbook shelving and libraries. Such shelving can house a variety of text books with different sized text and with different contrast ratios, therefore visual acuity is a key factor.

21.1.6 Associated circulation areas

Circulation areas need to be well lit to create a calming effect; they should be free from high contrast ratios and have reasonable glare control. Circulation spaces are critical to the judicial process as they are where defendants, witnesses, court officials and the public gather before, during and after court proceedings. These spaces can be simple corridors, but may also comprise break-out space, defendant's waiting areas and impromptu consultation areas. See Figure 21.2.

Figure 21.2 Waiting and circulation area with plenty of daylight and views out (courtesy of Hoare Lea/Hurd Rolland Partnership)

21.1.7   Lighting recommendations

The figures given in Table 21.1 below are based on the now withdrawn *Court Standards and Design Guide* (HMCTS, 2010). Some of the Home Office figures appeared unusually precise and the rationale of why a judge needs 25 lux more in a toilet than a child witness is not explained. However, the figures are a guide that should be discussed with any potential court client during design.

Table 21.1 Lighting recommendations for courts (source: HMCTS, 2010)

Location	Maintained illuminance (lx)	UGR	Notes
Magistrates' court suite	500	16	Lighting level in areas of high activity to be as shown, reducing to a lower general level in the public area (not less than 350 lux). Artificial lighting design should be directed towards enhancing the working environment.
Crown court suite	500	16	Lighting level in areas of high activity to be as shown, reducing to a lower general level in the public area (not less than 350 lux). Artificial lighting design should be directed towards enhancing the working environment.
County court suite	500	16	Lighting level in areas of high activity to be as shown, reducing to a lower general level in the public area (not less than 350 lux). Artificial lighting design should be directed towards enhancing the working environment.
Courtroom entrance	300		
Defendants' secure waiting	200	19	
Defendants' toilet	125		Emergency lighting required
Jury waiting room	300	19	
Jury toilet	125		Emergency lighting required
Child witness waiting suite	300	16	
Child witness toilet	150		Emergency lighting required
Judge's (all court types) retiring suite	175		
Judge's (all court types) toilet	175		
Judges' library/lounge	350	16	
Judges'/justices' lounge	350	16	
Judges'/magistrates' restricted circulation	175	19	

21.1.8   Lighting control and energy efficiency

As the use of LEDs is now commonplace, with the energy efficiency that they offer, it is through lighting control, both automatic and manually operated, that energy efficiency can be optimised. Reducing energy use in any artificially lit environment is always preferable, but unlike other working environments, when courtrooms are in session, it is essential that recommended illuminances are maintained.

As such, although dimmable ballasts and drivers can be utilised throughout a court building, it is recommended that PIRs and other presence detection controls be kept to areas other than the courtroom itself, where manual and astronomical clock lighting controls systems can be installed. Where PIRs are used, it is recommended that lighting is reduced only to a minimum of 10–15% of the areas recommended maximum illuminance level to ensure that completely dark rooms are avoided.

21.1.9   Emergency lighting

Self-contained emergency luminaires with localised batteries can be used throughout a court building, although self-testing and reporting systems are strongly recommended to ensure a functioning system at all times. For larger premises, a central battery system may be more economic. See Chapter 3, 'Emergency lighting', for more details.

Due to the high volume of people unfamiliar with these buildings, it may be prudent to consider higher emergency lighting levels in some key areas. In particular, BS EN 1838 (BSI, 2013) states:

> 'The objective of high risk task area lighting is to contribute to the safety of people involved in a potentially dangerous process or situation and to assist proper shut down procedures to be carried out for the safety of other occupants of the location.'

As such, courtrooms should be considered high-risk task areas and should be lit in accordance with the BS recommendations, which state 'shall be not less than 10% of the required maintained illuminance for that task'.

All other rooms in court building can follow standard emergency lighting recommendations for their room use.

21.2   Custodial lighting

Lighting of custodial applications requires careful consideration. Safety is paramount, particularly in accommodation areas, and the technical requirements of the luminaire can be stringent. Impact resistance and anti-ligature design are highly important features, as are aesthetics and energy efficiency. However, a luminaire succeeding in all of these areas can often be a challenge. Typical custodial lighting applications would be prisons, police custody suites, custom and immigration centres, court premises and secure units.

Currently there are two governing bodies, these being the Home Office and the Ministry of Justice Estates Department. Although the Home Office comes under the Ministry of Justice Estates Department it is still currently operating independently. However, this may change at some point in the future. The Home Office is responsible for police custody, border force, immigration centres and any establishment where a person might be detained (e.g. airport, football ground etc.). The Ministry of Justice Estates Department, previously known as the National Offender Management Service (NOMS), is responsible for prisons, courts and high secure units.

21.2.1   Prison standard cell and 'safer cell' lighting requirements

Prison custodial accommodation lighting is broken down into two types: standard cell and 'safer cell'. First and foremost, where individuals may be unsupervised or be under limited supervision, in order to limit the likelihood of suicide, luminaires must protect against electrocution and must not provide any positions for the attachment of a ligature. (Prisoners have used belts, shoe laces and various cords to commit suicide by hanging themselves.) The lighting must be sufficient to allow inmates to carry out tasks such as reading and writing, and also allow supervision, either from the viewing window in the door or via CCTV.

Typical standard cell applications would apply to prison accommodation, accommodation within immigration centres, courts, and secure units such as violent offender institutions as typical examples. Here the lighting must be tested and certified by the Ministry of Justice Estates Department, which regulates the procurement and supply to prisons of all manner of products including lighting. It sets strict safety and quality standards where a rigorous programme of testing is undertaken before a luminaire is approved. Testing is considerable and includes impact testing for robustness, which simulates repeated and sustained physical attack using a variety of different implements that might be obtainable, and a naked flame test to ensure that no part of the luminaire is damaged if subjected to flame. The design must also be 'anti-ligature' to prevent self-harm, even after physical attack. Typically, the luminaire is part of a system that incorporates other services such as CCTV and speakers, etc. These systems are often bespoke, therefore careful co-ordination is required between the design/construction teams and the luminaire manufacturer, see Figure 21.3.

Figure 21.3 A typical standard cell solution with bespoke cornice lighting (courtesy of Thorlux]

'Safer cells' are specifically designed to house individuals who are assessed to be at risk of self harm or suicide. 'Safer cells' therefore have similar requirements to those outlined in standard cells above; however, the luminaire requirements and testing is more onerous. A very high level of robustness is required where the luminaire must withstand a severe physical attack from a metal bedhead frame. In this situation, it is often expected that the luminaire will not remain functional and deformation may occur. However, any damage to the luminaire must not allow the opportunity to attach a ligature. It is assumed that such an attack will generate noise alerting the prison staff, so the robustness of the luminaire then affords them time to locate the cell and deal with the situation.

21.2.2   Police cell lighting requirements

The Home Office sets out the guideline requirements for a police custody suite. Where the detainee is left unsupervised, the requirements of a 'safer cell' standard of luminaire apply. All other areas including corridors, interview rooms etc. require a luminaire that is fit for purpose. This means that it needs to be impact resistant and secure with no sharp edges and does not require the application of anti-pick mastic.

21.2.3   Security and inspection areas in prisons

Positioning of luminaires within inspection areas is important to ensure good uniformity of light over the inspection area where searches are carried out. The space should be lit from multiple luminaires to avoid shadowing providing staff with the visual conditions needed to carry out the task. A level of 500 lx at 750 mm from the floor should be achieved. Although these spaces will be supervised, luminaires will still need to be robust, anti-ligature and contain tamper-proof fixings.

Lighting within the visitor room needs to be sufficient with good uniformity. Tables tend to be quite low, typically just 500 mm high, therefore 300 lx at 500 mm is required. Good uniformity over the whole space is needed, $U_0 > 0.6$, to allow staff to monitor interactions and help identify any passing of contraband. Luminaires should be suitable for the space with robustness, and tamper resistance still being important.

Thought is needed at security gates and windows to ensure that there is enough light provided to clearly see the person on the other side. Often this requires good vertical light levels as well as horizontal. Luminaire distribution and positioning are therefore important. An example of a well-placed luminaire at a security window can be seen in Figure 21.4.

Figure 21.4 Light above prisoner side of window so that staff can clearly see the face and activity of those at the window (image courtesy of Thorlux)

21.2.4 Circulation and association areas in prisons

These spaces will usually be supervised, therefore Ministry of Justice Estates Department approval for the luminaire is not required although many of the same principles used in accommodation areas still apply. Anti-ligature design, robustness to IK10 (see Chapter 23, Table 23.5) and tamper proof fixings are still highly important specifications. This level of specification will also be required in non-prisoner areas but where visitors may be unsupervised (toilets, baby change facilities etc). The lighting design should be such that good lighting levels are achieved, typically 300 lx at floor level, and special attention should be given to uniformity and avoidance of shadowing. Good vertical illumination should also be considered to aid face-to-face recognition and communication. This is particularly important for the feeling of safety by the staff.

The same is also true of activity/dining rooms. Often these spaces are multi-purpose and will have a servery hatch for meal times. A light level of 300 lx at floor level is required and again attention will need to be paid to good uniformity. The choice of luminaire in this application tends to be very industrial, therefore glare should be considered and managed so as to not cause discomfort to prisoners and staff. Ideally, UGR should be less than 22.

Other activities will include TV rooms, craft rooms and gyms. Here too robustness and anti-ligature design are just as important. Good light levels, typically 300 lx at floor level are required. In craft rooms, workshops, classrooms and study areas 500 lx at 750 mm above the floor is more appropriate. Again, glare should be kept to a minimum whilst maintaining a robust and impact-resistant solution.

21.2.5 Daylight

For obvious reasons, the provision of daylight is often not practical, particularly in accommodation areas. However, it can be advantageous for the wellbeing of the person(s) within the cell. A connection to the outside world, even if just to establish weather conditions, can be beneficial. The provision of daylight is strongly recommended within non-critical areas such as offices, staff rest areas, general circulation and activity spaces. As well as the safety aspect, solar gains will also need to be considered so any direct sunlight does not overheat the space or cause discomfort glare. The Home Office guidance also recommends that all police cells have natural light where possible.

21.2.6 Lighting recommendations

Safe and functional lighting are the main requirements for custodial areas. Sufficient and good quality lighting is important for both staff and inmates, but it will also increase the feeling of safety for the custodial staff. Good quality lighting is also important for the effective use of CCTV equipment. In areas where face to face communication is important, vertical light levels and cylindrical illuminance levels should be considered. See SLL Lighting Guide 7: *Offices* (SLL, 2015) for further guidance on appropriate levels of cylindrical illuminance.

For cell and accommodation lighting, the luminaire system is often required to provide a variety of different light outputs, which can be achieved through lamp switching or more commonly nowadays with LED technology; e.g. pre-configured dim levels using digital control gear such as DALI. As a general rule there are two lighting modes required: a maintained level of 300 lx for general use and 15 lx for night/safety lighting. A 500 lx level should also be considered for occupants who may have a visual impairment, or for times where inspection and/or deep cleaning is carried out.

Due to the size of the cell accommodation rooms, the uniformity of light is not normally an issue. However, consideration of the light fitting location is important, particularly with respect to any desk/activity area in the room. If the luminaire is behind a person sitting at a desk, then strong shadowing will prevail producing an unsatisfactory result. It is therefore appropriate to mount the luminaires above the desk. This is particularly relevant for cornice style systems.

Table 21.2 Lighting recommendations for custodial buildings

Location	Maintained illuminance (lx)	Plane of measurement
Cells (day)	300/500	750 mm above floor
Cells (night)	15	Floor level
Corridors	300	Floor level
Holding room	500	750 mm above floor
Charge room	300/500	Charge desk level
Custody officer's room	500	750mm above floor
Interview room	500	750mm above floor
Stores	300	Floor level
Medical room	750	750 mm above floor
Toilets	100	Floor level
Plant room	300	Floor level

21.2.7   Lighting control and energy efficiency

Due to the nature of the application there is very little opportunity to use automatic controls, particularly within the custody envelope. However, within staff and public areas there is greater scope for the use of automatic dimming systems where daylight is present and automatic switching through presence detection. Within the custody envelope all lighting should be controlled by the custody staff, particularly cell lighting. All cell lighting should be controlled from the outside of the room or from remote locations such as the custody officers' office.

Energy efficiency is a key consideration, as is maintenance and reliability. As a result, luminaires with LED light sources are now the preferred option to take advantage of better energy efficiency and reduced maintenance. The lower power of LED luminaires is also beneficial for managing the loads connected to the UPS or central battery system.

21.2.8   Light source colour properties

Given all of the luminaire technical requirements, the quality of the light source is often an over looked factor. Cell accommodation areas can be occupied for many hours a day, the wellbeing of the inmate therefore needs to be considered. There may also be situations where the health of the individual needs to be established. Poor quality light or inappropriate correlated colour temperatures may hinder this process and/or provide and uncomfortable environment. To avoid any issues and ensure good quality lighting, it is recommended that a light source with a CIE general colour rendering index (CRI) of at least 80 should be used with a correlated colour temperature (CCT) of between 3000 K and 4000 K. High-CCT light sources are not advisable as, while these may be appropriate during the day, they are not advisable in the evening or at night when a calming ambiance is required in preparation for sleep.

21.2.9   Emergency lighting

Emergency lighting is required to allow the safe evacuation should the need arise under an emergency situation. The Home Office generally advises that emergency lighting should maintain the current working lighting conditions, whether this is in day or night mode. This requirement is significantly higher than normal emergency lighting provision.

To deal with the enhanced levels, either a UPS or central battery should provide the emergency lighting provision. This provision is needed for two hours. Self-contained emergency luminaires with localised batteries are not advised due to the risk of local failure and issues with access for maintenance.

Self-testing and reporting systems are also strongly recommended, again, to avoid disruption and/or access issues when carrying out periodic testing. See Chapter 3, 'Emergency lighting', for more guidance.

References

BSI (2013) BS EN 1838: 2013: *Lighting applications. Emergency lighting* (London: British Standards Institution)

HMCTS (2010) *Court Standards and Design Guide* (London: HM Courts and Tribunals Service) (withdrawn)

HMCTS (2016) *Traditions of the courts* [online] (London: HM Courts and Tribunals Service) (https://www.judiciary.gov.uk/about-the-judiciary/the-justice-system/court-traditions) (accessed September 2018)

SLL (2015) *Offices* SLL Lighting Guide 7 (London: Society of Light and Lighting)

Chapter 22: Transport buildings

22.1 Introduction

Transport buildings are about people in transition: moving through spaces, navigating decision points, and locating exits and entrances. All types of transport buildings should ensure the safe and effortless movement of those passing through the facility, boarding and alighting from vehicles and transferring between different transport modes. Good lighting design significantly enhances the legibility of potentially visually incoherent spaces and encourages intuitive wayfinding for passengers who will often be unfamiliar with their surroundings. Detailed lighting design principles should be determined at the outset of each project, by considering the guidelines contained in this chapter.

For a comprehensive guide to all aspects of lighting a wide variety of transportation buildings, both inside and out, refer to the SLL Lighting Guide 15: *Transport buildings* (SLL, 2017).

22.2 Identification of tasks

When considering how a space should be lit, it is important to first define the visual tasks and how the lighting should address them. Lighting should be layered and task-specific rather than generic and undifferentiated, as it is widely accepted that human visual perception and the processing of visual information is based on phototropic behaviour using a brightness and contrast hierarchy within the visual field. Horizontal illuminance and lighting uniformity should never be the sole consideration because the way in which the eye responds to light does not correspond with linear illuminance scales only, where a range of visual step changes should be applied.

The levels of illuminance applied should correspond to the complexity of each identified visual task. To give a perceptual difference with ambient illuminance levels recommended step changes in illuminance are illustrated in Figure 22.1.

Figure 22.1 Visible variations in illuminance (lux)
(source: BS EN 12464-1: 2011: section 4.3.2 (BSI, 2011))

In both interior and exterior environments, consideration should also be given to levels of illuminance of the immediate area surrounding the task area, together with the background ambient illuminance (Figure 22.2, below). This is to avoid extreme variations in illuminance that may cause visual discomfort and possible fatigue.

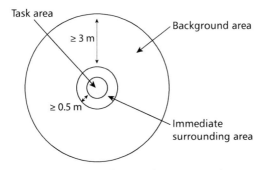

Figure 22.2 Relationship between task, immediate surrounding area and background

When standing or walking, the visual field typically includes more vertical surfaces than horizontal ones. In transport environments passengers are naturally drawn to brighter vertical backdrops rather than brighter floors, whilst either moving or standing. Indirect lighting and wall washing will therefore place greater emphasis on the ceiling and vertical surfaces rather than the floor surface.

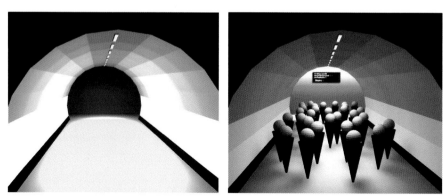

Figure 22.3 The lighting design strategy should consider that spaces are usually occupied
(courtesy of Zhang Qiting; © GIA Equation)

22.3 Design priorities and strategies

22.3.1 Orientation and safe movement

Passengers are often unfamiliar with the environment and wayfinding decisions will need to be made quickly to avoid congestion, particularly at transition points, thresholds and changes in direction.

22.3.2 Hazard identification

Obvious hazards include changes in level, junctions, changes in direction, platform edges and areas where there are moving vehicles or equipment. Local accent lighting should be used where necessary.

22.3.3 Wayfinding

This can be considered in four distinct stages: orientation, route decision, route monitoring and destination recognition. Signs, directory panels and maps should be adequately illuminated. It is important to ensure that ambient illumination does not create veiling reflections on self-illuminated signs and screens. Enhanced levels of illuminance provided in decision-making areas and at destination points will assist the passenger decision making process.

22.3.4 Safety and security

Appropriate illuminance levels with good levels of uniformity should be provided both internally and externally in transport environments. It is important that good facial recognition is achieved, particularly in the external environment (Figure 22.4).

Sufficient lighting also needs to be provided for CCTV cameras, so that staff can effectively monitor activity taking place after dark. It is important that lighting designers ensure that an adequate illuminance is provided in the field of view of CCTV cameras. Modern cameras can cope will low levels of illuminance but not extreme variations in luminance.

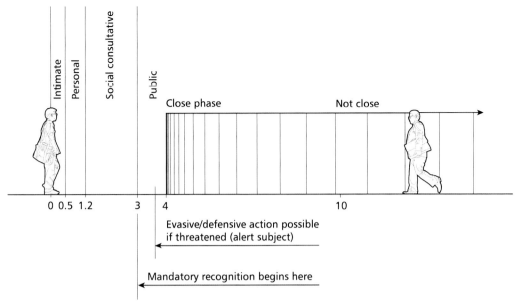

Figure 22.4 Good facial recognition (courtesy Zhang Qiting; © GIA Equation)

22.3.5   Visual adaptation

Light adaptation enables the human visual system to operate throughout the enormous range of luminances that occur in nature. There are many fast-moving transition spaces for both passengers and vehicles in transportation buildings where visual acuity and hazard recognition are important. Both light and dark adaptation need to be considered by the lighting designer. Once safe levels of task lighting have been provided, the lighting design should aim to create adaptation paths for the users. Lighting must be set at appropriate levels to allow the visual system to make a progressive transition from high to low luminance situations, and vice versa.

22.4   Accessible design considerations

The UK Equality Act 2010 (TSO, 2010) places a duty on transport service providers to make reasonable adjustments to remove potential barriers that passengers with disabilities may face when accessing both buildings and transportation services.

There are many degrees of disability experienced by a large percentage of transport users. In terms of visual impairment, this will vary between simple spectacle-corrected impairments to total loss of vision. Mobility impairments to be considered by designers will range from minor limb disability to those who use wheelchairs to access the facility. Good lighting at points of hazards, e.g. roadway edges and railway platform edges, will make the environment safer, easier and accessible for all passengers.

Spectacle wearers will experience veiling reflections if excessively bright light sources are positioned in the field of view, even at longer viewing distances. Glare should always be strictly controlled, whatever the type of visual impairment. Light sources, particularly high brightness LEDs should always be shielded from view.

People with visual impairment find it difficult to see effectively where there are high rates of change of luminance in the field of view. This can result in confused visual cues and loss of detail perception. Therefore, it is vital that luminance changes should be gradual. It is equally important that there is a difference in the luminance of adjacent horizontal and vertical areas at low level, e.g. step treads and risers, as the visually impaired often rely on shadow cues to determine the position of boundaries and obstacles.

Because all people with visual impairment suffer from a loss of contrast sensitivity, important signage and wayfinding information should be back-lit, so that a constant luminance across the surface of the sign is achieved together with optimal contrast ratios.

The lighting designer should also ensure that all visual information in the lit scene, both wayfinding and signage and environmental cues, can be easily interpreted from lower viewing positions for those who might be navigating a space in a wheelchair, rather than walking or standing.

22.5   Access, installation and maintenance

Due to the scale and complexity of most transportation projects, access and maintenance strategies become crucial for describing how each component can be constructed, accessed and maintained during both the design and operational stages of the project.

Access and maintenance become even more challenging in underground station environments and all other sub-surface spaces. Each component of the lighting installation will require a carefully considered construction method, plus an access and maintenance strategy. A typical access and maintenance analysis will cover the following:

- component overview with a summary of specific components regarding type, location and design life

- construction details that identify how each component can be installed on site and replaced (if required)

- access, cleaning and maintenance procedures throughout each component's life expectancy.

It is good practice to design lighting installations that use modular elements for simple removal and replacement, and use long-life luminaires to minimise maintenance. Ease of access to the light source and other separate lighting equipment parts that require replacement should be provided and the necessity for overhead work minimised in high-risk areas.

Equipment should be selected so that it is cost-effective to install and operate, as maintenance access periods in all transportation buildings are restricted. Where mounting heights are over four metres, careful consideration should be given to how easily the lighting equipment can be maintained.

Cleaning is also a key part of the life cycle of the lighting installation and should be planned carefully to provide sufficient cleaning to each luminaire type whilst avoiding any damage due to inappropriate luminaire handling. The ingress protection (IP) rating of the luminaire should be considered if strong, intrusive maintenance regimes including water splashing and/or water jets are anticipated.

All fixtures and fittings should be designed to be durable and easy to clean and maintain over their service life, allowing for easy installation and replacement (if required) and simple access to relevant switches, control gear and electrical connections. Key considerations during the luminaire specification process should be durability, robustness and sleek design that minimises the risk of dirt and dust build-up or damage. The luminaire manufacturer should provide simple and environmentally resilient fixing systems, with an adequate IP rating, to meet the design requirements.

In addition, the cable management system (CMS) strategy for the lighting installation should be designed to:

- provide continuous access to primary CMS

- allow regular access panels for cables that require pull-through installation

- minimise the necessity for overhead work

- allow for the use of mobile-elevating work platforms or scaffold towers for safe access when working at height

- maximise low level work

- allow for future modifications to the installation.

22.6 Risk assessment and emergency lighting

Transportation systems by their very nature accommodate large numbers of people who are mostly unfamiliar with the surroundings and therefore high integrity emergency lighting systems will be required. Higher minimum levels of illuminance than those set out in BS 5266-1 (BSI, 2016a) are likely to be needed in many areas. Local fire authority requirements should also be ascertained before commencing the emergency lighting design.

In all instances, transport buildings will require a Fire Risk Assessment to be carried out. This assessment should be reviewed and updated on a regular basis. Detailed advice for the preparation of Fire Risk Assessments for transport buildings in England, Wales and Northern Ireland is available in the Department for Communities and Local Government publication: *Fire Safety — Risk Assessment: Transport premises and facilities* (DCLG, 2007).

A transport building or facility may also be or become subject to other relevant legislation, such as European Directives covering fire safety in transport premises, be it an air, land (road or rail) or sea facility. Where this is the case, additional advice should be sought from the relevant enforcing authority.

Lighting designers should carry out a thorough evaluation of the emergency lighting requirements in terms of illuminance, uniformity, number and positions of luminaires and required duration of the emergency lighting, as this will influence equipment specification.

Because of the large number of people using transport systems, it will frequently be necessary to provide emergency lighting in open and outdoor areas. However, smaller structures such as bus stops will rarely require emergency lighting. See Chapter 3, 'Emergency lighting'.

Central power supplies with slave luminaires may be more economic in larger installations but these will offer a lower degree of integrity than self-contained battery emergency lighting. There are specific requirements for emergency lighting in sub-surface railways, as defined by the Fire Precautions (Sub-surface Railway Stations) (England) Regulations 2009 (TSO, 2009). If centralised emergency systems are installed, the use of enhanced fire survival cables will be required.

One aspect to be considered separately is that of standby lighting that enables the building to continue to function during a power failure. In most transport situations, there are processes that must continue during any evacuation and staff will need a working level of illuminance in public areas whilst safety procedures are carried out. This will require greater illuminance levels than for emergency escape lighting, and for a longer duration. If a building is going to be evacuated in the event of a power failure (e.g. a typical local bus station), then escape lighting should be provided. Some transport buildings may require escape lighting for the public areas, with standby lighting provided in a limited number of staff/operational areas. Refer to Chapter 3, 'Emergency lighting' for more information.

22.7 Typical transport building areas

22.7.1 Concourses

The use of natural light should be maximised and electric light integrated with the architectural design. Care should be taken to avoid glare and intense reflections from interior surfaces.

Levels of illuminance should be consistent in all areas occupied by passengers, both by day and night. There should be no extreme variations in illuminance level, and no areas should be excessively bright or dark. There should also be no areas of strong shadow.

Entrances, exits and ticket gates should be highlighted to facilitate the safe movement of passengers. Departure and arrival boards should be clear and legible and care should be taken to avoid veiling reflections on information displays and signage. Important elements such as ticket machines, ticket offices, information desks and changes in level should be emphasised. In large interior volumes, exaggerated devices such as large-scale signage elements will help passengers to navigate easily their way through the space.

Figure 22.5 Concourse daylighting design example
(© Felix Lipov/Shutterstock)

22.7.2 Check-Ins/counters/information desks

These may broadly be divided into two categories:

- *open*: where there is a counter top but no dividing screen between the customer and staff sides
- *protected*: where a clear screen, often ballistic glass, divides staff and public.

The task lighting considerations for the two typologies vary although the requirements are essentially the same. Good vertical illuminance is required each side of the counter to enable people to see each other's faces. A horizontal illuminance of 400–500 lux on each side of the counter top is a good target and the lighting should be glare-free. Lamps should be shielded and the luminaires should also have good optical shielding. For open counters, it may be possible to use a single lighting system to light both sides of the counter.

For protected counters, separate lighting elements will be needed to ensure that the staff and customers both have clear views of each other without the creation of veiling luminance on the glass partition. Because of the aural distortion created by these screens, and the audio systems associated with them, good visual cues are essential for successful communication and the creation of an appropriate lighting solution is paramount.

Display screen use on the staff side of protected counters should be considered. This will almost certainly require the provision of local lighting controls.

In all cases, task lighting that enables clear and rapid identification of coin, bank notes, credit cards and printed material should be provided. In most cases there will need to be a direct lighting component, and light source colour rendering should be $R_a 80$ or greater.

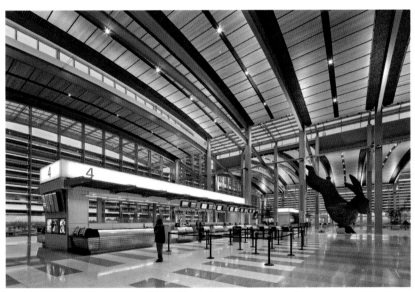

Figure 22.6 Check-in counter example
(courtesy of John Swain; © John Swain/ARUP)

22.7.3 Escalators and moving walkways

The most critical points are the landings and stepping on/off positions at the comb plate. The provision of higher values of illuminance in the area immediately around the landings should highlight this potential hazard and enhance passenger safety. Integral balustrade or skirting lighting is a good way of delivering the light to the task plane, but it must be designed such that the lighting does not create excessively high luminance contrasts in the step cavity. It is worth noting that although escalators are designed for standing, people may also be walking up or down.

Figure 22.7 Escalator lighting example
(courtesy of Carolina Florian; © GIA Equation)

22.7.4 Boarding and alighting points

These are encountered at quaysides, railway platform edges, bus stations and airports. The task plane is the threshold between the vehicle and the transport building or structure, which must be clearly defined. A maintained average horizontal illuminance of 100 lux is suggested at these transition points, although a lower value may be appropriate where there is a clear luminance contrast such as a white painted platform edge. At quaysides used after dark 200 lux minimum is advisable for safety reasons.

The contrast between lighting within the vehicle and its immediate surroundings should be addressed in the lighting design to avoid problems of visual adaptation for boarding or alighting passengers.

Figure 22.8 Boarding and alighting point example
(courtesy of Zhang Qiting; © GIA Equation)

22.8 Specific lighting requirements by transport mode

22.8.1 Railways

A fundamental consideration when designing for railway installations is the passenger/train interface (PTI), since moving trains present the greatest risk to passengers and staff in a station environment. The PTI at an open platform edge is a location where there is a significant risk of passengers falling onto the track and into the path of an oncoming train. In stations where the platform edge is enclosed by a screen this risk is eliminated, but appropriate lighting at the transition point between the train carriage and the platform will need to be provided.

Platform layouts vary considerably depending on the station environment but can be considered as two principal typologies; 'open' (uncovered) platforms with some free standing structures and enclosures or 'enclosed' where most of the platform space is covered by a canopy.

It is essential to provide good levels of illuminance and uniformity across the entire platform area, particularly the platform edge. For this reason, the task area of an open platform should be considered to extend up to 0.5 m trackside. This is to ensure that adequate levels of illuminance are achieved for passengers boarding and alighting from trains.

The platform lighting should not cause glare within the field of view of approaching train drivers. The avoidance of glare and stroboscopic lighting effects is essential. Ideally, light sources should not be visible, and luminaires with a controlled downward light distribution should be specified.

Figure 22.9 Platform lighting example (courtesy Bartenbach GmbH)

22.8.2 Airports

This guidance relates to landside facilities in passenger terminal buildings and associated areas such as circulation and concourses, customs and security, passenger amenity areas, staff accommodation, car parks, approach roads among others. Airside exterior areas such as aircraft aprons, stands, adjacent roads and taxiways should be illuminated in accordance with CAA document CAP168: *Licensing of Aerodromes* (CAA, 2014).

The activities and tasks undertaken in airports are more varied than in any other transport environment, and for this reason it is important that all visual tasks are considered and incorporated into the lighting design. Risk assessments should be carried out in instances where the significance of errors is serious, or where the design team wishes to depart from the airport operator's own standards and design criteria.

Most passenger tasks involve movement along a defined route, reading signs and display screens, and interaction with staff. Horizontal floor illuminance values are important for safe movement, but good vertical illuminance throughout the space is needed to enable signs to be seen clearly and good facial recognition to be achieved. Supplementary lighting should be provided where detailed tasks take place, for example at check-in desks, baggage reclaim conveyors and in customs halls.

There is frequently a visual conflict between the ambient lighting in terminals and the lighting of individual retail units. Lighting designers for both applications should consider the impact of their lighting proposals on adjacent areas, and integrate the schemes wherever possible.

For security reasons, passenger flows are usually separated (arrivals and departures) for the entry and exit parts of the terminal buildings, but there are also common areas, for example aircraft piers, where flow is bi-directional. For passengers entering a departure terminal from the street, orientation is the most important consideration as the environment will usually be unfamiliar and complex.

Good daylighting will aid adaptation and artificial lighting should ideally be daylight linked to achieve adequate illuminance values throughout the day as most airport buildings operate for 24 hours/7 days a week. It is important to provide sufficient daylight in waiting areas and departure lounges. Ensuring that adequate fenestration is provided to allow passengers and staff views out of the building is beneficial. Potential glare from direct sunlight should also be avoided.

Figure 22.10 Airport lighting example (courtesy Speirs and Major)

Consideration of the impact of artificial lighting at night on the aircraft aprons is a key factor, as it must not be distracting or interfere with aircraft movements. In addition, light pollution and glare should be limited to the minimum as airports are in the outskirts of cities and, therefore, belong to environmental zones with low artificial lighting values allowed at night.

22.8.3 Ports and harbours

The UK Dock Regulations 1988 (TSO, 1988) states that 'Each part of dock premises ... used for dock operations ... shall be suitably and adequately lighted'. The Dock Regulations also demand that hazards and obstacles should be made conspicuous, e.g. by lighting.

The design and provision of lighting for ports and harbours should consider site specific design factors, such as:

- the type of lighting used and the colour rendering of that lighting, which can significantly affect the visibility of people and objects regardless of the level of illuminance provided

- illuminance levels, which should be reasonably constant and uniform, minimising sharp contrasts and deep shadows

- avoidance of excessively high illuminance levels on the navigation of vessels in port areas, given the need for ships' pilots and masters to maintain 'night vision' adaptation of the eye

- minimising glare

- minimising environmental impacts and light pollution

- night-shift requirements for lower illuminance levels in the cabs of cranes, watercraft, vehicles, control rooms and security offices

- hazards/activities identified following a risk assessment may require increased levels of illuminance

- sufficient lighting to enable obvious damage to or leakage from packages, intermediate bulk containers (IBCs) and cargo transport units to be seen and to make warning signs clearly visible

- the protection of cargo from contamination by damaged lamps and lighting equipment

- collision protection of lighting towers and installations from vehicle impact, including heavy plant that might be operating nearby

- resilience to the environmental conditions and any other substances on site (adequate IP rating for the entire lighting installation and circuiting)

- redundancy built into any existing or planned lighting.

- safe access for maintenance of equipment, and reducing risks of working at height.

Figure 22.11 Quayside lighting example
(courtesy Zhang Qiting; © GIA Equation)

22.8.4   Trams and street running systems

Trams and street running light rail systems will generally run adjacent to highways that are illuminated to the requirements of BS 5489-2 (BSI, 2016b). Intermediate stops should be treated as bus stops. Principal stops and interchanges will require additional lighting for safety and to aid passenger orientation. A horizontal illuminance of 50 lux at boarding/alighting points is desirable, with a minimum average maintained illuminance of 30 lux on platforms. The lighting should not create disability glare for the tram drivers nor create adaptation difficulties for boarding and alighting passengers. The stops themselves should be lit in way that creates a feeling of security for passengers by promoting good facial recognition. Good colour rendering light sources of (at least R_a60) should be specified. The use of white light sources is preferred, and the lighting should be integrated into the architectural design of canopies, shelters and other structures. The integration of lighting columns and overhead line masts should be considered to minimise visual clutter.

Figure 22.12 Tram stop lighting example (© Schreder UK)

22.8.5　Bus and coach stations

Bus stops, which are generally on-highway, will mostly be illuminated by the ambient lighting on the street. Where bus shelter manufacturers provide integral lighting within the shelter itself, this should be glare-free and not exceed 50 lux at floor level.

In comparison with other transport buildings, bus station users are present for shorter lengths of time, so the most important issue after providing adequate task illuminance is to create an environment in which people feel secure. Most installations will have CCTV equipment, and the lighting should take account of this in terms of illuminance, glare, contrast and colour rendering. Vertical illuminance should be good so that people's faces can be seen clearly.

Where the bus station is situated at street level, a high degree of daylighting should be sought to avoid problems of adaptation. The electric lighting installation should be daylight linked, and care taken to avoid light pollution or light trespass after dark. Some exterior lighting to draw attention to the presence of the bus station is useful, but this should not generate unwanted light spill or light pollution. Covered bus stations may require a different approach as they will often have no access to daylight, except at the entrances. In these instances, enhanced levels of illuminance at the transition points between interior and exterior may be required. Generally, UK bus stations will share their lighting with the adjacent road network. Coordination with the local authority will therefore be required at the design stage, particularly if the lighting is to be adopted in future. Major coach stations may require an alternative design approach, where passengers may spend longer periods of time waiting. The provision of passenger lounges, catering facilities and other amenities will require the lighting designer to integrate the lighting of these with the main operational areas of the bus station.

Where the vehicle bays are open, care should be taken that vehicles do not block out the lighting or create strong shadows that can create a gloomy appearance to the space. As with all transport environments, the lighting should utilise good colour rendering light sources (R_a80 or better), with a colour temperature appropriate to the architecture and surface finishes.

To ensure pedestrian safety at crossing points or where there is a potential conflict between the movement of people and vehicles, additional glare-free lighting should be applied to enable vehicle drivers to clearly see pedestrians.

Figure 22.13 Bus station lighting example (©Belzer Holmes)

22.8.6   Routes and structures for bicycles

When considering lighting for cycle routes that are independent of main traffic routes, principle considerations should be highlighting the direction that the route takes enabling cyclists and pedestrians to detect potential hazards and orientate themselves correctly. Providing lighting which discourages crime against people and property should also be a key consideration when developing appropriate lighting solutions. The lighting designer should select an appropriate lighting class from BS EN 13201-2: Road lighting. Performance requirements (BSI, 2015).

Ensuring that good facial recognition is achieved is an important part of promoting a feeling of personal wellbeing after dark. This means providing good levels of vertical illuminance in addition to the required levels of horizontal illuminance and lighting uniformity.

The provision of local accent lighting can assist the easy identification of cycle racks and shelters in a visually competitive urban environment. Higher levels of local illuminance than the ambient street lighting in the immediate vicinity should be provided to enhance perceived personal safety and security. The relative scale of illuminances published in BS EN 12464-1: *Light and lighting. Lighting of work places. Indoor work places* (BSI, 2011) section 4.3.2 can be used as a reference when determining appropriate levels of local task lighting (see Figure 22.1).

Figure 22.14 Bermondsey cycle store
(© Mark Haddon Photography/Sarah Wigglesworth Architects)

References

BSI (2011) BS EN 12464-1: 2011: *Light and lighting. Lighting of work places. Indoor work places* (London: British Standards Institution)

BSI (2015) BS EN 13201-2: 2015: *Road lighting. Performance requirements* (London: British Standards Institution)

BSI (2016a) BS 5266-1: 2016: *Emergency lighting. Code of practice for the emergency lighting of premises* (London: British Standards Institution)

BSI (2016b) BS 5489-2: 2016: *Code of practice for the design of road lighting. Lighting of tunnels* (London: British Standards Institution)

CAA (2014) *Licensing of Aerodromes* CAP168 (Gatwick: Civil Aviation Authority Safety Regulation Group) (available at https://publicapps.caa.co.uk/docs/33/CAP%20168%20Licensing%20of%20Aerodromes.pdf) (accessed September 2018)

DCLG (2007) *Fire Safety — Risk Assessment: Transport premises and facilities* (London: Department for Communities and Local Government) (available at https://www.gov.uk/government/publications/fire-safety-risk-assessment-transport-premises-and-facilities) (accessed September 2018)

SLL (2016) *Transport buildings* SLL Lighting Guide 15 (London: Society of Light and Lighting)

TSO (1988) The Docks Regulations 1988 Statutory Instruments 1988 No. 1655 (London: The Stationery Office) (available at https://www.legislation.gov.uk/uksi/1988/1655) (accessed September 2018)

TSO (2009) Fire Precautions (Sub-surface Railway Stations) (England) Regulations 2009 Statutory Instruments 2009 No. 782 (London: The Stationery Office) (available at http://www.legislation.gov.uk/uksi/2009/782) (accessed September 2018)

TSO (2010) Equality Act 2010 Ch. 15 (London: The Stationery Office) (available at https://www.legislation.gov.uk/ukpga/2010/15) (accessed September 2018)

Chapter 23: Extreme environments

23.1 Introduction

Most of the lighting situations for which we design lighting are safe, stable and within normal bounds of temperature and humidity. However, there are many environments where the luminaires are subject to one or more extremes, be these high or low temperatures, impacts, corrosive or very dirty environments, or water. This chapter aims to assist designers and specifiers in choosing and applying the correct lighting systems for use in unusual situations where the environment will adversely affect the operation or performance of the system or pose a risk of fire or explosion.

The supplier or specifier needs to understand the impacts or restrictions each environment will impose on the luminaires and any supporting supplies and controls so that they can mitigate these effects and provide a robust, safe, maintainable and long-lasting solution. It must be borne in mind also that the lowest-cost luminaire may not be the cheapest solution over a long period of time. Making a higher initial outlay on luminaires that are designed to operate in a particular environment, using the best materials, will usually be the cheaper option over a ten-year period, during which cheaper and less robust products may have had to be replaced several times.

The sections below consider each form of extreme environment in turn, describe the problems likely to be encountered and suggest possible ways to compensate or protect against these problems. Following this there are sections on emergency lighting and remote lighting techniques, where standard lighting can be provided outside of the extreme environment.

Technical information is then provided on lamp performance outside standard temperatures and conditions in the form of a chart showing relative luminous flux due to starting conditions in various ambient temperatures.

23.2 Environments

23.2.1 Cold and freezing environments

There are many environments that can be described as being 'cold'. Theoretically, as luminaires for internal use are tested at an ambient temperature of 25 °C, then any constant level below this would be regarded as cold. However, for the purposes of this subject temperatures below 5 °C are more of concern. Internal areas of this nature would include cold storage rooms/warehouses, cold storage cabinets, freezer rooms and cabinets and retail premises selling frozen goods in open display cabinets. Also, certain farm and other buildings that are not heated could come under this category. Exterior environments would include cold countries and indeed the UK during the winter season when temperatures can fall to below zero.

The first consideration must be the choice of luminaire. At first view this would seem straightforward. However, it is important that internal parts are protected for safety reasons. Whilst choosing a luminaire with an ingress protection rating of IP65 (see section 23.2.5) may seem logical, this can prove problematic. The problem occurs when a luminaire has been switched on for a reasonable time and has become warm inside. When it is switched off the air inside begins to cool and the reduction in pressure starts to suck the external cold air into the body of the luminaire around or through gasket material, or through IP65 cable glands. The colder air entering the luminaire then forms condensation, which can be a safety concern for electrical parts and the operation of the luminaires. This is known as a capillary effect. To help prevent this it is recommended that quality luminaires with a rating of IP68 are considered. In addition, the materials that make up the exterior components of the luminaire need to be robust and strong such that cold temperatures have little or no effect. Type 306 stainless steel bodies with matching clips generally work very well. Glass diffusers in areas where food is not present are also acceptable. Where food is present then an alternative diffuser such as polycarbonate sandwiched with acrylic does the job well. Components such as lampholders and terminal blocks can become brittle when cold and care should be taken to ensure that live parts do not become exposed.

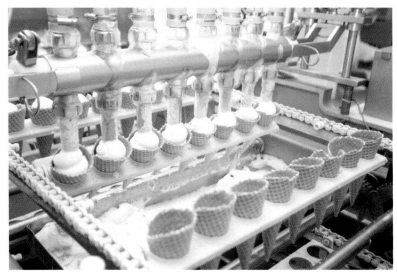

Figure 23.1 An ice cream factory (courtesy of ATM Lighting, Poland)

Electronic circuits within drivers and control gear do not like temperatures below –15 °C generally, but improvements in some LED driver designs do allow start-up operation in lower ambient temperatures than this, and special fluorescent circuits are available. One method of solving this problem is to have skylights in the ceiling of the room or area being illuminated and have standard luminaires outside the cold area shining through each opening. Again, the material of the skylight would need to be polycarbonate if the area is a food store or manufacturing base; see section 23.4, 'Remote lighting techniques'.

Light output on start-up in cold temperatures with fluorescent and discharge circuits can be very low. However, as the lamps warm up they give off heat, which increases the ambient temperature within a sealed enclosure. The length of time involved will depend on many different factors but generally speaking the luminaires will reach 90% of designed light output within a short period of time. The colour appearance of light sources can also vary with ambient temperature, but again this will usually rectify itself quickly.

Emergency lighting needs special consideration in cold environments. Self-contained luminaires with integral batteries are susceptible to premature failure as the batteries eventually refuse to hold their charge. Methods used to resolve this problem include the use of a central battery system in the building, with slave emergency units in the cold environments. Another solution is to mount the luminaires external to the room, as previously mentioned, and allow the light to enter the room via a skylight or other opening in the room fabric; see section 23.4, 'Remote lighting techniques'.

Finally, in any cold or freezing environment it is necessary to ensure that all products used in the lighting installation are suitable for the task in hand. Cabling and electrical connection boxes, including switches, glands and seals, should be chosen for suitability. If a control system, such as presence detection or timers are used they must be suitable for the intended use. A detector that fails to switch off unnecessary luminaires is neither use nor ornament in these situations.

23.2.2   Hot and humid environments

In the same manner as cold environments, theoretically any temperature above 25 °C can be described as being 'hot'. However, in most instances the hot or humid situation will be out of the control of individuals. Such internal areas will include production areas in factories where machinery generates heat as part of the process. Heat rises and when added to the heat from the sun on the building roof temperatures in excess of 40 °C may be experienced. Steam laundries and sauna rooms are also areas where high temperatures are expected, plus high levels of humidity in these cases. Boiler rooms in older buildings are also areas of concern. Externally, high ambient temperatures are rare in the UK, but on a hot day in summer an air temperature of 30 °C may cause the level in an enclosed luminaire to reach more than 50 °C when the heat from lamps and control gear is being generated. As most external luminaires are operated at night when the ambient temperatures have lowered, problems in the UK are thankfully few and far between. The same cannot be said for hotter countries in Europe and elsewhere, where high temperatures can be a big problem. Humidity is also of major concern in areas such as swimming baths, showers and industrial environments using water or steam as part of their processes.

Figure 23.2 Shopping centre kitchen, Ultra Lade, Trondheim, Norway
(courtesy of Sammode Lighting)

Again, the choice of luminaire is the first consideration. As previously discussed the cheapest option may not be the most economical in the long term. Good quality usually comes at a price, but it makes sense that an installation costing say, £50 000, and lasting 20 years, is more economically sound than one costing £10 000 and having to be replaced every two years, or indeed repaired every six months. Once the maximum ambient temperature has been established, there are several manufacturers who can provide luminaires that will operate efficiently at high temperatures. It is important that the materials used in such luminaires will withstand the particular environment and that a warranty exists to back-up any claims made by the manufacturer. In some process enclosures temperatures may soar to very high levels where the only option is a tungsten lamp, a metal enclosure and a thick glass cover. As a general guide acrylic material can withstand up to about 80 °C, and polycarbonate up to about 120 °C. High temperature glass can withstand temperatures up to around 300 °C or higher. This is a very specialised area but such luminaires are available. For areas with high humidity it will be necessary for ingress protection to be at least IP65. In practice, a rating of IP68 will ensure best protection and limit the possibility of capillary reaction when luminaires are switched off and cooling down. In humid environments it may be necessary to wash down the luminaires on a regular basis to avoid losing light output due to surface contamination.

The components of the luminaire must be able to withstand the high temperature concerned and need to be chosen carefully. Standard internal cables are usually rated at 105 °C and these may need to be upgraded. High temperature control gear and drivers can be obtained to withstand higher case temperatures than normal, but these will need to undergo full thermal testing in a luminaire body in the laboratory to ensure that they will not fail during operation. These tests must be carried out in accordance with BS EN 60598-1 (BSI, 2015a).

Emergency lighting can be used in hot and humid environments, but care must be taken in the methods employed. Integral batteries do not operate well in high temperatures and advice should be sought from the luminaire manufacturer as to their suitability for different temperatures. In extreme cases, it may be necessary to use only tungsten lamps with high-temperature rated cable and lampholder, in a basic metal and glass luminaire. In this case, any controlling electronics and relays would be mounted in normal conditions outside the high temperature area.

Finally, in any hot or humid environment it is necessary to ensure that all products used in the lighting installation are suitable for the task in hand. Cabling and electrical connection boxes, including switches, glands and seals should be chosen for suitability.

23.2.3 Dusty environments

As dust is present in all but specialist clean areas it is difficult to define what comprises a dusty environment. Under normal conditions, where small amounts of non-combustible dust are expected, a choice of an enclosed luminaire with an ingress protection rating of IP5X may be all that is needed. However, there are some environments that are normally very dusty and which, if dust is allowed to enter the luminaire, could be extremely dangerous. An obvious example would be working with explosive materials, such as in a fireworks or munitions factory. Less obvious situations are flour mills, woodworking areas and grain stores. It is a fact that flour and grain can ignite when they come in contact with electrical sparks. Therefore, it is most likely that a fire officer will have designated the area concerned as being 'ATEX Zone 22' rated and requiring luminaires to be of a suitable type; see section 23.2.9, 'Explosive environments', for more details on the ATEX zone system. If the area concerned is a new building or structure, or there is a change of use, then the building operator should have sought advice from the local fire service before any electrical or lighting design is carried out. It is not the opinion of the user or the electrical contractor that matters here, but it is the outcome of a risk assessment carried out by the designated competent person. The lighting designer has a responsibility to establish that the brief given to them is the result of such a risk assessment and to design in accordance. The areas that are merely dusty but have no explosion risk, and those that are dusty and are an explosion risk, must be clearly defined by the client.

Figure 23.3 Tunnel boring machine, CSM Bessac (courtesy of Sammode Lighting)

Once the room or area has been designated as a particular zone type, then and only then can a suitable luminaire be considered. It is possible, if the structure contains rooflights or large window areas, to use an external method of illumination, so that the luminaires are outside the zonal area and therefore do not need to be of a zone protection type; see section 23.4, 'Remote lighting techniques'. Floodlights can be successfully employed in this manner also, if they are above the height of the zone, and can provide the necessary light levels together with an acceptable level of uniformity. However, if this method cannot be employed it will be necessary to look at suitable zonal rated luminaires, if the area is classed as an explosive environment. It is important to select a fitting that not only has the correct zone rating, but also to ensure that the maximum surface temperature does not reach a level which can ignite the dust. This is given by a 'T-rating' for the particular luminaire. The design of the luminaire should also be considered such as to try to avoid a build-up of dust on the external surfaces. There are types available of tubular shape, which reduces the possibility of dust build-up and therefore reduces the chances of ignition. In all cases it will be necessary to clean the luminaires on a regular basis, usually by water jets, and a suitable ingress protection rating of IP68 is recommended. With zonal rated luminaires there is no cheap option, as they must be tested and certified as suitable for a particular zone. The responsibility for the correct choice of luminaire rests solely with the lighting designer and therefore every effort must be made to make the right choice. It is a good idea to seek the advice of a specialist manufacturer when choosing the best luminaire for the application.

With regard to the components of zonal rated luminaires, it should be sufficient to know that a certified version will contain the correct components, as any alterations to the body, connections or components, other than those contained in the installation instructions, will render the certification null and void. On this basis, any repairs to or modification of the luminaires must be made with the full approval of the manufacturer. Any cabling, switches or other components necessary for the correct installation and operation of the luminaires must also be rated in accordance with the required zonal rating.

Emergency lighting in dusty environments is usually undertaken with slave luminaires connected to a central battery outside the dusty area, as this avoids opening the luminaires to replace batteries. If the luminaire has the necessary protection, then the addition of emergency gear has no additional problems. Emergency signage can be achieved using sealed bulkheads with signage attached to the diffuser or cover. If the area is zonal rated there are options available for specialist standalone luminaires. A risk assessment will highlight any special requirements for a particular area, but generally speaking dust should not cause any variation from the requirements of current legislation.

As a final reminder, in any dusty environment it is necessary to ensure that all products used in the lighting installation are suitable for the task in hand. Cabling and electrical connection boxes, including switches, glands and seals should be chosen for suitability.

23.2.4 Chemicals and chemical vapours

Chemicals can have an adverse effect on all luminaires, the extent of which varies with the materials and chemicals involved. The types of areas involved with chemicals are large in quantity and must be looked at individually. An obvious application is any manufacturing process involving the use of chemicals either directly as in their creation or indirectly as part of another process. Such chemicals can be either acidic, alkaline or neutral. If neutral, then the main criterion will be the ingress protection. An IP rating of IP65 will reduce the possibility of foreign liquid penetration in most cases, although it may be necessary for various reasons to use luminaires with an increased rating of IP68. If the chemicals or chemical vapour are either acidic or alkaline then the first consideration when choosing a luminaire should be the possibility of a chemical reaction with the external components. The lighting industry tends to use various plastics for luminaire bodies, diffusers, clips and connections. This is for reasons of cost, ease of manufacture and aesthetics. However, there are many instances where the materials can be attacked by certain chemicals in everyday applications. Table 23.1 shows examples of types of material used in luminaire components and the effect that various chemicals have on them. Note however that the list is not exhaustive and it may be necessary to check with manufacturers as to the suitability of their products within a particular environment.

Table 23.1 Chemical resistance to some luminaire materials

Chemical	BC7	PMMA	PC	Polyester	Poly-styrene	Stainless steel
Acids (weak < 10%)	H	L	H	H	H	H
Acids:						
— accumulator acid	L	L	L	L	L	0
— acetic (max. 30%)	L	0	L	H	L	H
— hydrochloric (max. 20%)	L	H	L	H	L	0
— nitric (max. 20%)	L	L	L	L	L	L
— phosphoric (max. 30%)	L	0	L	L	L	L
— sulphuric (max. 50%)	L	L	L	L	L	0
Bases:						
— ammonia (max. 25%)	H	H	0	H	H	H
— ammonia (max. 50%)	H	L	0	L	H	L
— sodium hydroxide (max. 45%)	H	L	0	0	H	L
Salt solutions:						
— common salt	H	H	L	H	H	L
— metal salt	H	H	L	H	H	L
Hydrocarbons:						
— aliphatic	0	L	H	L	0	0
— aromatic	0	0	0	L	0	0
— paraffins	L	H	H	H	L	H
— carbon dioxide/carbon monoxide	L	H	H	H	L	H
— ethyl acetate	0	0	0	0	0	L

Table continues

Table 23.1 Chemical resistance to some luminaire materials — *continued*

Chemical	BC7	PMMA	PC	Polyester	Poly-styrene	Stainless steel
Aromatic hydrocarbons:						
— aniline	0	L	0	L	0	L
— benzene and derivatives	0	0	0	0	0	H
— hydrogen peroxide	0	L	L	0	0	L
— xylene	0	0	0	0	0	H
Chloride hydrocarbons:						
— carbon tetrachloride	0	0	0	L	0	L
— trichlorethylene	0	0	0	0	0	0
— methylene chloride	0	0	0	0	0	L
Alcohols:						
— up to 30%	H	L	L	H	H	H
— methanol/ethanol	0	0	0	L	0	H
— phenol	0	0	0	0	0	L
Ethers:						
— ether	L	L	0	L	L	H
— petroleum ether	0	L	0	L	0	H
Unsaturated chloride hydrocarbons:						
— chloroform	0	0	0	0	0	L
Oils and fats:						
— petrol/kerosene	0	L	L	H	0	H
— mineral oil	L	0	L	H	L	H
— vegetable oils (hot)	H	H	0	H	H	H
— cooking fats (hot)	H	H	0	H	H	H

Key: H = resistant to attack; L = limited resistance to attack; 0 = no resistance to attack

Bear in mind that the chemical composition of plastic materials can be different between alternative manufacturers and that stainless steel is supplied in different grades for different applications, therefore the list is only for general reference. In the case of the limited resistance to corrosion effect on polycarbonate it is suggested that this material is not used for clips that hold diffusers or panels in place. The limited resistance is just that and the chemical will have some effect over time, which could eventually endanger life. It should also be borne in mind that some chemicals that come into contact with luminaires are not obvious. For example, using aggressive detergents and disinfectants for cleaning luminaires can have an effect on luminaire components. Likewise, placing luminaires in areas such as car washes, swimming pools, industrial kitchens, laundries, slaughterhouses, stables and cultivation farms will require careful consideration.

Even exterior luminaires can be susceptible to corrosion in normal use and regular maintenance is recommended. Try to use luminaires with stainless steel screws and clips where possible, and if they are placed in exposed positions at or near to seaside locations where salt water can be ferocious to many materials, consider units with 306 marine grade stainless steel.

Luminaire manufacturers should be approached if there is any doubt whatsoever as to the suitability of their products in these hostile environments, as it will be they who have to answer for warranty claims if luminaires fail.

Figure 23.4 Tereos, Lillebonne (© Tereos; courtesy of Sammode Lighting)

In addition to the possibility of chemical attack there is also the problem of ingress of unwanted substances. All seals must therefore be considered for their vulnerability. Ingress protection cannot be limited to IP65 rating and consideration should be given to whether IP68 rating would be more appropriate. If chemical ingress is prevented, then the possibility of degradation of internal components is reduced.

LED luminaires are suitable for use in many areas of industry and, as long as the external components are not prone to attack, then LED sources can be used. However, it must be mentioned that there are several chemicals and gases that are known to affect LED chips and their components. Table 23.2 is again not exhaustive, but serves to highlight the delicacy of these products when used in certain areas.

Table 23.2 Chemicals known to affect LED sources and components

Chemicals known to affect LED sources and components	
Acetic acid	Lard
Acetone	Linseed oil
Acrylic tape	Loctite® adhesives, activators
Ammonia	Loctite® thread lockers
Benzene	Methyl acetate
Butadiene	Methyl ethyl ketone (MEK)
Castor oil	Methyl isobutyl ketone (MIBK)
Clorox® bleach and cleaner spray	Mineral spirits (turpentine)
Cyanoacrylate	Nitric acid
Dichloromethane	Petroleum
Dymax 984-LVUF	Potassium hydroxide
Ethyl acetate	Rosin flux
Formaldehyde	Silicone oil
Gasoline	Sulphuric acid
Glycol ethers	Tetrachloromethane
Gorilla Glue®	Toluene
Halogenated hydrocarbons containing F, Cl, Br elements	Xylene
Hydrochloric acid	

Note: the information in this table has kindly been provided by Philips, Tridonic and the Lighting Industry Association.

Many medium power LEDs are constructed with silver finished lead frames and a silicone compound based encapsulant. Both of these are prone to being damaged when subjected to certain pollutants in the presence of oxygen. Particular volatile organic components (VOCs), which contain sulphur or chlorine, are high in this category. The effects of this contamination can cause a serious deterioration in light output and colour appearance. In a similar manner, cleaning of LED luminaires should avoid using organic solvents such as acetone or other agents that contain sulphur or chlorine based compounds. For further information of this subject advice must be sought from the luminaire manufacturer or supplier.

Emergency lighting of areas where there is a risk of chemical attack can be considered as being the same as for normal environments except that the emergency luminaires need to be treated the same as for the standard luminaires.

As mentioned in previous sections, it is necessary to ensure that all products used in the lighting installation are suitable for the task in hand. Cabling and electrical connection boxes, including switches, glands and seals, should be chosen for suitability.

23.2.5   Submersion: pools, ponds and water features

There are many instances where the lighting designer can enhance the ambience of a particular area or activity by placing specialist luminaires in water. In doing so, the luminaire is subjected to varying amounts of pressure depending on the depth of the installation for an indefinite length of time. The ingress protection for these types of installation will almost certainly be a rating of IP68. The method of testing for IP68 involves submersion of the product under test and allows for certification at a certain depth for a certain time duration. It is important that the lighting designer understands this point as a rating of IP68 on its own does not mean anything unless the depth and duration are specified.

One such area is swimming pools, either indoor or outdoor, where underwater lighting can be used to create colour effects or assist lifeguards to detect swimmers who are in difficulty. These luminaires can be recessed into the wall fabric of the pool, usually at a depth of around 1 m. Only fixed luminaires complying with BS EN 60598-2-18 (BSI, 1994/2010) can be used if they are in contact with the water. In addition, the luminaires must meet the requirements of the current edition of BS 7671: *Requirements for Electrical Installations. IET Wiring Regulations* (BSI, 2018). This will involve separate extra low voltage (SELV) luminaires, having a separate circuit to other equipment and having an operating voltage no greater than 12 V dc. When underwater lighting is located behind watertight portholes, and the luminaires are serviced from behind, they need to comply with the relevant parts of BS EN 60598 (BSI, 1998–2015). Careful installation is required to ensure that there is no conductive connection between any exposed conductive part of the luminaire and conductive parts of the porthole.

Figure 23.5 Swimming pool shower area (© Jonathan Letoublon; courtesy of Sammode Lighting)

The IP rating is set down in BS EN 60529 (BSI, 1992/2013) and consists of the letters IP followed by two digits. The Standard (amended by Amendment A2) provides detailed information about the IP tests, amending the text of BS EN 60529. The first digit gives an indication of the amount of protection a luminaire (or other item) has to the ingress of solid objects.

The second digit signifies the amount of protection the luminaire has against the possible harmful ingress of water. It must be noted that a luminaire that is compliant with IPX7, covering immersion in water, may not be compliant with IPX5 or IPX6, covering exposure to water jets. A device which meets both tests is indicated by listing both tests separated by a slash, e.g. IPX5/IPX7.

The levels of protection are described in Tables 23.3 and 23.4.

Table 23.3 Description of the first IP digit

First digit	Limit	Description
0	—	No protection against contact and ingress of objects
1	> 50 mm	Any large object such as the back of a hand, but no protection against deliberate contact with a body part
2	> 12.5 mm	Fingers or similar objects
3	> 2.5 mm	Screwdrivers or thick wires
4	> 1 mm	Some flies or insects, small wires
5	Dust-protected	Ingress of dust is not entirely prevented, but it must not enter in sufficient quantity so as to interfere with the satisfactory operation of the luminaire
6	Dust-tight	No dust ingress and complete protection against contact; a test duration of up to 8 hours based on air flow

Table 23.4 Description of the second IP digit

Second digit	Protection against	Description
0	—	No protection against water ingress
1	Dripping water	Dripping water (vertically falling drops) shall have no harmful effect on the specimen when mounted in an upright position onto a turntable and rotated at 1 rpm. Test duration: 10 minutes. Water equivalent to 1 mm rainfall per minute.
2	Dripping water when tilted at 15°	Vertically dripping water shall have no harmful effect when the luminaire is tilted at an angle of 15° from its normal position. A total of four positions are tested within two axes. Test duration: 2.5 minutes for every direction of tilt (10 minutes total). Water equivalent to 3 mm rainfall per minute.
3	Spraying water	Water falling as a spray at any angle up to 60° from the vertical shall have no harmful effect, utilizing either: (a) an oscillating fixture, or (b) a spray nozzle with a counterbalanced shield. Test (a) is conducted for 5 minutes, then repeated with the specimen rotated horizontally by 90° for the second 5-minute test. Test (b) is conducted (with shield in place) for 5 minutes minimum. For a spray nozzle, test duration: 1 minute per square meter for at least 5 minutes; water volume: 10 litres per minute; pressure: 50–150 kPa. For an oscillating tube, test duration: 10 minutes; water volume: 0.07 l/min per hole.
4	Splashing of water	Water splashing against the luminaire from any direction shall have no harmful effect, utilizing either: (a) an oscillating fixture, or (b) a spray nozzle with no shield. Test (a) is conducted for 10 minutes. Test (b) is conducted (without shield) for 5 minutes minimum. Oscillating tube: test duration: 10 minutes; spray nozzle: same as IPx3 spray nozzle with the shield removed.
5	Water jets	Water projected by a nozzle (6.3 mm) against the luminaire from any direction shall have no harmful effects. Test duration: 1 minute per square meter for at least 15 minutes. Water volume: 12.5 litres per minute; Pressure: 30 kPa at distance of 3 m.
6	Powerful water jets	Water projected in powerful jets (12.5 mm nozzle) against the luminaire from any direction shall have no harmful effects. Test duration: 1 minute per square meter for at least 3 minutes. Water volume: 100 litres per minute; pressure: 100 kPa at distance of 3 m.
7	Immersion up to 1 m depth	Ingress of water in harmful quantity shall not be possible when the luminaire is immersed in water under defined conditions of pressure and time (up to 1 m of submersion). Test duration: 30 minutes (reference: IEC 60529, Table 8 (IEC, 1989/1999/2013)). Tested with the lowest point of the luminaire 1000 mm below the surface of the water, or the highest point 150 mm below the surface, whichever is deeper.

Table continues

Table 23.4 Description of the second IP digit — *continued*

Second digit	Protection against	Description
8	Immersion over 1 m depth	The equipment is suitable for continuous immersion in water under conditions that shall be specified by the manufacturer. However, with certain types of equipment, it can mean that water can enter but only in such a manner that it produces no harmful effects. The test depth and duration is expected to be greater than the requirements for IPx7, and other environmental effects may be added, such as temperature cycling before immersion. Test duration: by agreement with manufacturer. Depth specified by manufacturer, generally up to 3 m.
9K	Powerful high temperature water jets	This is a protection provision for high temperature and pressurized water which is prescribed by German standard DIN 40050, Part 9 (DIN, 1993). The test specifies a spray nozzle that is fed with 80 °C water at 80 to 100 bar and a flow rate of 14 to 16 litres/min. The nozzle is held 10 to 15 cm from the tested device at angles of 0°, 40°, 60° and 90° for 30 seconds each. The test device sits on a turntable that rotates. Test duration: 30 seconds in each of 4 angles (2 minutes total).

Fountains and water features are areas where decorative lighting is becoming more popular. Sealed SELV luminaires with colour changing LED sources can make a big difference to the aesthetic experience of these structures. In fountains, it is advantageous to place the luminaires recessed into the ground near to the jet nozzles so that the water spray is illuminated well. In ponds and water features, strategically placed lighting can enable the most stagnant arrangement to come to life.

The construction of luminaires will of course depend on the application. Specialised luminaires are required that meet any regulatory restrictions and these should be manufactured and tested together with all necessary certification. These luminaires will be capable of withstanding the arduous environment in which they are placed. Chlorine and ether in swimming pools are usually of concern to the designer and the bodies, seals, diffusers and fastenings must be able to resist attack from these chemicals. Marine grade stainless steel is used extensively for these types of luminaire. Ponds and water features are less arduous in one respect, but these areas can pose an additional problem with vandalism and theft. Therefore, luminaires fixed into the structure rather than loosely placed should be considered. In addition, heat can be a problem if any part of the luminaire can be touched by enquiring fingers. In this respect HID lamps should be avoided if possible. LED light sources have the advantages of running far cooler, are economical to run and have a much longer life.

Emergency lighting for underwater applications should be via slave luminaires connected to a central battery outside the damp area, as this avoids opening the luminaires to replace batteries. If the luminaire has the necessary protection, then the addition of emergency gear has no additional problems.

As mentioned in previous sections, it is necessary to ensure that all products used in the lighting installation are suitable for the task in hand. Cabling and electrical connection boxes, including switches, glands and seals, should be chosen for suitability.

23.2.6   Wash-down/clean rooms

Clean rooms can be found in many commercial and industrial buildings. Such applications can include pharmaceutical companies, hospitals and electronics manufacturers. The extent to which a room is 'clean' is defined by BS EN ISO 14644-1 (BSI, 2015b) and ISO 14644-1 (ISO, 2015).

The size and number of particles per cubic metre is considered according to Table 23.5, which is from ISO 14644-1.

Table 23.5 Size and number of particles per cubic metre

ISO number (N)	Maximum concentration limits (particles/m³ of air) for particles equal to and larger than the stated sizes					
	0.1 mm	0.2 mm	0.3 mm	0.5 mm	1 mm	5 mm
ISO 1	10	2	—	—	—	—
ISO 2	100	24	10	4	—	—
ISO 3	1000	237	102	35	8	—
ISO 4	10 000	2370	1020	352	83	—
ISO 5	100 000	23 700	10 200	3520	832	29
ISO 6	1 000 000	237 000	102 000	35 200	8320	293
ISO 7	—	—	—	352 000	83 200	2930
ISO 8	—	—	—	3 520 000	832 000	29 300
ISO 9	—	—	—	35 200 000	8 320 000	293 000

The luminaire construction is therefore critical to ensure that no contamination of the clean room area takes place. The ingress protection rating alone is not suitable for this type of specialised use and separate certification is necessary to ensure conformity. An accepted method of lighting these areas is to have a certified sealed ceiling with portholes within it and a remote method of lighting; see section 23.4, 'Remote lighting techniques'. Where recessed luminaires are used it is paramount that the integrity of the ceiling is maintained where it meets the luminaires.

Figure 23.6 Malt processing room in Poland (courtesy of ATM Lighting, Poland)

Many industrial processes involve arduous atmospheres and it may be necessary to wash down the area on a regular basis. If the washing down uses water jets only then luminaires with an ingress protection rating of IP65 may be acceptable. It is important, however, that the pressure of the jets is below that used in the test procedure, namely a test duration of one minute per square metre of luminaire area for at least 15 minutes with a water volume of 12.5 litres per minute and a pressure of 30 kPa at a distance of 3 m. If the parameters of the wash-down are different to this, it may be necessary to use luminaires with a higher IP rating.

The construction of luminaires involving clean rooms is very specialised and advice must be sought from manufacturers as to their suitability for a particular area. If the luminaires are mounted using remote techniques, then no special requirements are necessary other than the possibility of high operating temperatures in a sealed enclosure. However, some clean rooms operate in a sealed environment under pressure and may be thermally controlled. An inlet of pressurised cool air next to a luminaire could cause the light sources to run cooler than the rest and a difference in both light output and colour appearance may be noticed. Access to light sources and control gear in remote mounted luminaires will need to be checked and adequate provision must be made. Access to specialised clean room luminaires will need to be verified with the manufacturer as in some cases unauthorised access could nullify the warranty. Any cleaning of luminaires, whether they are in a car wash, factory or clean room, must be carried out to the manufacturer's instructions and care taken to avoid using detergents or other chemicals that could be detrimental to the component parts.

For emergency lighting, it is generally better to use slave luminaires connected to a central battery outside the clean area, as this avoids opening the luminaires to replace batteries. If the luminaire has the necessary protection, then the addition of emergency gear causes no additional problems.

Again, it is necessary to ensure that all products used in the lighting installation are suitable for the task in hand. Cabling and electrical connection boxes, including switches, glands and seals, should be chosen for suitability.

22.2.7 Marine (onshore, offshore and submersion)

Care must be taken when the lighting designer is proposing luminaires for use in a marine environment, due to the hostile conditions which can be prevalent. Such uses can be floodlighting of dockyards, container and cargo terminals, jetties and quaysides. In addition, any lighting involved with offshore oil rigs, mobile platforms and wind farm structures will also need special consideration.

The construction of the luminaires will depend on the application itself. Any luminaires that are near to the sea and open to the elements will be subjected to salt water in the form of water droplets or mist. The external materials of the luminaire must therefore be able to withstand frequent attack from salt. Any luminaires mounted in a position that will enable waves to hit them must have an ingress protection rating of at least IP66, although many products designed for this application are rated at IP68. The materials used on these luminaires invariably include toughened glass and marine grade stainless steel although some success has been seen with other materials. Oscillation and vibration can be seen on luminaires mounted on high masts, which bend in high winds. This is also true when luminaires are mounted on cranes, gantries or offshore oil rigs and wind farms. Care must be taken when specifying the light source, as discharge lamps are prone to vibration and subsequent failure.

Figure 23.7 Congorep oil platform, Republic of Congo
(Jean Ber, © Perenco; courtesy of Sammode Lighting)

Once again, it is necessary to ensure that all products used in the lighting installation are suitable for the task in hand. Cabling and electrical connection boxes, including switches, glands and seals, should be chosen for suitability.

23.2.8   Vibration, impact and vandalism

As mentioned in the previous section vibration can be a problem in certain circumstances. There are basically two types of vibration, which are different in cause, effect and remedy. The first type is known as primary vibration and is due to a luminaire being mounted onto a structure which is itself vibrating. Examples of primary vibration are:

- luminaires on moving cranes
- post-top mounted luminaires
- luminaires mounted on process machinery
- luminaires mounted on vehicles.

The effects of primary vibration are loosening of components, fixings and contacts, possible damage to the luminaire structure including any glassware, and physical disorientation due to brackets slipping. In extreme cases there could be risk to life if luminaires fall from their anchor points or fixing brackets. Another possible effect is where a lamp becomes loose from the lampholder and eventually disconnects itself from the electrical circuit. To remedy these possible causes, it is suggested that all nuts and bolts are secured in place using anti-slip washers and tightened to the correct torque as recommended by the luminaire manufacturer. Mounting brackets need to have safety cables or chains fitted so that in the event of bracketry failure the luminaire is not allowed to fall. Also, the use of rubber washers at mounting points can be beneficial. As the move towards LED light sources continues to grow, the problems of traditional lamps loosening from lampholders becomes less important, and LEDs tend to withstand vibration well. In cases where HID lamps with GES caps are used there are lamps and lampholders available that 'lock' together in situ and therefore prevent falling lamps. In all cases where there is a risk of falling lamps a cover needs to be in place. This cover could be polycarbonate, glass or wire mesh depending on the application.

The other type of vibration is known as secondary vibration, and this is due to an internal oscillation from the electrical circuit within the luminaire. The effect from this secondary vibration is usually a low pitched 'hum' and is particularly noticed in quiet surroundings such as churches, libraries and quiet offices. The noise is usually caused by wire wound ballasts in HID luminaires with a metal body acting as a sound box or amplifier. The ballast induction transmits electrical waves to metalwork in close contact with the ballast and a 'mains hum' of 50 Hz or a multiple thereof is heard. The remedy to this problem is unfortunately only achieved by trial and error. It is beneficial to place a plate of aluminium between the ballast and the metal mounting place, which will break down the electrical field transmission. In addition, the use of rubber washers at ballast mounting points will reduce the effects further.

Figure 23.8 Vandal resistant lighting at Gdansk Wrzeszcz railway station (courtesy of ATM Lighting, Poland)

Impact involves a collision between an object and a luminaire. The effect of that impact may be nothing at all, or catastrophic. Impact occurs in places such as warehouses and factories internally, and bollards and floodlights externally. There is a method of testing luminaires to see what sort of impact they can withstand. This is known as the 'IK' system and is detailed within BS EN 62262 (BSI, 2002) and IEC 62262 (IEC, 2002). Table 23.6 below gives details of each rating.

Table 23.5 Testing for IK rating

IK rating	Energy (joule)	Description
IK00	—	No protection against any mechanical impact
IK01	0.15	Protected against a 200 g object dropped from 7.5 cm height
IK02	0.2	Protected against a 200 g object dropped from 10 cm height
IK03	0.35	Protected against a 200 g object dropped from 17.5 cm height
IK04	0.5	Protected against a 200 g object dropped from 25 cm height
IK05	0.7	Protected against a 200 g object dropped from 35 cm height
IK06	1	Protected against a 500 g object dropped from 20 cm height
IK07	2	Protected against a 500 g object dropped from 40 cm height
IK08	5	Protected against a 1.7 kg object dropped from 29.5 cm height
IK09	10	Protected against a 5 kg object dropped from 20 cm height
IK10	20	Protected against a 5 kg object dropped from 40 cm height
IK10+	—	Not included in the standard

It is possible to represent the IK rating as a number following the two values of the IP rating. Therefore, a IP65 luminaire with a IK rating of 7 could be shown as IP657. However, this practice is not widespread.

Vandalism against luminaires is less easy to describe. It can range between a small amount of graffiti on a diffuser to complete disintegration of the entire unit. One of Newton's laws states that every action has an equal and opposite reaction. In a similar way everything that can be done can be undone. Therefore, it would appear that it is impossible to describe any luminaire as being 'vandal-proof'. The amount of 'vandal-resistance' will vary depending on the external construction of the luminaire and the amount of force or ingenuity used in the vandalism act. It is recommended that any luminaires and cabling mounted in an area prone to vandalism should be fitted out of arm's reach. That makes it more difficult for the perpetrator, but not impossible if they are determined. An air rifle can cause damage at reasonable heights, as can small rocks and pieces of wood. If a luminaire is mounted at a low level, it can be fitted with anti-tamper screws to avoid easy access. However, security screwdriver bits can be purchased quite easily in discount stores for those who are intent on causing vandalism. An IK rating in these circumstances is completely useless.

There are many options available for vandal resistant luminaires, some of which resemble miniature fortresses. Bodies can be made from 5 mm steel, diffusers from an 8 mm sandwich of polycarbonate and acrylic, and fastenings from security head stainless steel bolts, yet these units can be destroyed by determined vandals. If graffiti is known to be a problem in a particular area then bear in mind that the external parts of the luminaire must be able to withstand the chemicals involved in the removal of the graffiti. Chemicals are available to coat luminaires so that graffiti simply washes off. However, it would be wise to check with the luminaire manufacturer as to their warranty before applying such coatings. There are many options available from manufacturers for vandal resistant luminaires and there should be at least one suitable for most applications.

HM Prisons are places where vandal resistant luminaires are necessary. The Ministry of Justice is responsible for the specification of luminaires in prisons. It has an approval scheme for cells that involves testing and certification to ensure that the luminaires can withstand both tampering and attack. In addition, there are cells classed as 'safe cells' where prisoners who are prone to self-harm and potential suicide are kept. Luminaires in these cells are tested for suitability in a rigorous manner and are safe with regard to ligature points. Any gaps in the luminaire, such as between diffuser panel and body must be kept below 2 mm for this reason. For other areas within prisons it is the responsibility of an appointed electrical services consultant to ascertain the suitability of luminaires for use in accompanied or unaccompanied areas. In cells at police stations, courts and shopping centres the appointed consulting engineer will decide on the suitability of a particular luminaire although some authorities may require them to conform to the Ministry of Justice approval scheme. See also Chapter 21, 'Courts and custodial buildings'.

There is also the subject of anti-ligature luminaires. These luminaires will not allow persons to self-harm by attaching a ligature to the luminaire itself, or allow unauthorised access. Such areas will include unaccompanied rooms in mental institutions, care homes and mental health units in hospitals. Again, the luminaire construction will ensure that items such as paper clips cannot be inserted into gaps in the metalwork, which could with the aid of a shoelace become a ligature point. Any screws or bolts should be of the anti-tamper type to prevent access, as the possession of special tools is not expected in these areas.

Emergency lighting in secure vandal-prone environments can be via slave luminaires connected to a central battery outside of the secure environment. Otherwise, appropriate self-contained luminaires can be used. If the luminaire has the necessary protection then the addition of emergency gear causes no additional problems. Emergency signage can be achieved using vandal resistant bulkheads with signage attached to the diffuser or cover. A risk assessment will highlight any special requirements for a particular area, but generally speaking vandalism should not cause any variation from the requirements of current legislation.

As a final reminder, in any vandal-prone environment it is necessary to ensure that all products used in the lighting installation are suitable for the task in hand. Cabling and electrical connection boxes, including switches, glands and seals, should be chosen for suitability. The same applies in areas with vibration problems except that in this instance the designer should make all attempts to mount suitable luminaires away from the area involving vibration where possible.

23.2.9 Explosive environments

It is the duty of every company to protect their employees from explosion risk in areas with an explosive atmosphere. Such areas will include petrochemical factories and warehouses, filling stations, explosives manufacturing and storage facilities, paint manufacture and storage, oil refineries and certain chemical stores. In the EU there are two 'ATEX' directives (one for the manufacturer and one for the user of the equipment):

- 'ATEX 95': equipment directive 94/9/EC (EC, 1994) concerning equipment and protective systems intended for use in potentially explosive atmospheres

- 'ATEX 137': workplace directive 99/92/EC (EC, 1999) on minimum requirements for improving the safety and health protection of workers potentially at risk from explosive atmospheres.

While applicable up to 19 April 2016, ATEX 95, intended for manufacturers, has now been repealed and replaced by directive 2014/34/EU (EU, 2014). This more recent ATEX directive was published on Saturday 29 March 2014, and has been mandatory for manufacturers from 20 April 2016.

Figure 23.9 Boat maintenance, 'Kiss the Sky', Monaco
(courtesy of Alain Caste and Sammode Lighting)

The ATEX 99/92/EC directive required that employers classify areas where explosive atmospheres may occur into zones. The classification given to a particular zone depends on the likelihood of an explosive atmosphere occurring and its persistence if it does. Areas are classified into zones: Zone 0, Zone 1 and Zone 2 for gas, vapour and mist, and Zones 20, 21 and 22 for dust and must be protected from effective sources of ignition. Equipment and protective systems intended to be used in zoned areas must meet the requirements of the directive and this, of course, includes luminaires. Zones 0 and 20 require Category 1 marked equipment, Zones 1 and 21 require Category 2 marked equipment and Zones 2 and 22 require Category 3 marked equipment. Zones 0 and 20 are the zones with the highest risk of an explosive atmosphere being present as can be seen below:

- Gas, vapour and mist:

    — *Zone 0*: a place in which an explosive atmosphere consisting of a mixture with air of dangerous substances in the form of gas, vapour or mist is present continuously or for long periods or frequently.

    — *Zone 1*: a place in which an explosive atmosphere consisting of a mixture with air of dangerous substances in the form of gas, vapour or mist is likely to occur in normal operation occasionally.

    — *Zone 2*: a place in which an explosive atmosphere consisting of a mixture with air of dangerous substances in the form of gas, vapour or mist is not likely to occur in normal operation but, if it does occur, will persist for a short period only.

- Dusts:

    — *Zone 20*: a place in which an explosive atmosphere in the form of a cloud of combustible dust in air is present continuously, or for long periods or frequently.

    — *Zone 21*: a place in which an explosive atmosphere in the form of a cloud of combustible dust in air is likely to occur in normal operation occasionally.

    — *Zone 22*: a place in which an explosive atmosphere in the form or a cloud of combustible dust in air is not likely to occur in normal operation but, if it does occur, will persist for a short period only.

There is also a requirement that each luminaire has a maximum operating surface temperature to ensure that the atmosphere is not ignited by contact. Apparatus for use in hazardous areas is classified according to the maximum surface temperature produced under fault conditions at an ambient temperature of 40 °C, or as otherwise specified. The standard classifications are as shown The values are given as 'T-ratings' and are grouped as shown in Table 23.7.

Table 23.7 Surface temperature classifications

Mark	Maximum temperature (°C)
T1	450
T2	300
T3	200
T4	135
T5	100
T6	85

Manufacturers must ensure that their products are tested and certified by a 'Notified Body' such as BASEEFA (https://www.competency.baseefa.com) in the UK. In addition, the ATEX directive also requires products to be marked with the CE mark, the EX mark and the luminaire coding as described above.

23.3   Emergency lighting

Emergency lighting has been discussed in each of the relevant chapters and in detail in Chapter 3, 'Emergency lighting'. It is also appropriate to mention that emergency lighting is necessary in most extreme environments and it is the responsibility of the owner or user to carry out a risk assessment to highlight high-risk areas. It is the responsibility of the lighting designer to determine the most appropriate method to use and to select equipment that can be easily maintained in the extreme environment. A summary of points of particular interest are listed below.

Cold environments

This is potentially a difficult environment for non-maintained fluorescent luminaires as these are often used as external fixtures and at temperatures that go below zero. These luminaires are typically rated at 20 °C and regular checks must be performed to ensure that they start correctly in the cold environment. The batteries are likely to suffer a shorter life or reduced capacity, and it may be a better solution to use a central battery system using a 230 V ac supply. For both options it may be a better solution to use LED luminaires.

Hot and humid environments

The main problem with any environment with an ambient temperature above 25 °C is battery life. Prolonged operation in higher ambient temperatures will cause very short life from sealed batteries in self-contained luminaires. Special vented nickel cadmium batteries are available, which may help in certain applications. Also, when using a central battery system, it may be necessary to compensate the charge rate for the operating conditions. In all cases it will be necessary to check that the ambient temperature inside the luminaire does not exceed the maximum case temperature required on electronic control gear.

Dusty environments

The requirements for emergency lighting luminaires in areas where dust is prevalent are generally the same as for normal luminaires.

Corrosive environments

The requirements for emergency lighting luminaires in areas where chemicals or corrosive atmospheres exist are generally the same as for normal luminaires.

Explosive environments

The requirements for emergency lighting luminaires in explosive areas are generally the same as for normal luminaires. It must be remembered that emergency versions of zonally rated luminaires will contain special control gear, and this should never be replaced by standard gear. Any modifications to luminaires must be carried out only with the approval of the manufacturer.

Generators

In some applications in buildings there may be a back-up generator involved that provides mains power to certain luminaires upon failure of mains circuits. This solution is common in places such as hospitals where lighting levels must be maintained for safety reasons. In this case the nominated 'emergency' luminaires are standard luminaires operating on 230 V ac, the only difference being that they are marked externally to show what they are.

23.4   Remote lighting techniques

Remote lighting techniques can be used in many extreme environments that are detrimental to lighting fixtures. The advantage is that luminaires outside an extreme area may not need the same protection as those located within it. There are several ways in which this can be achieved.

23.4.1   Projector lighting

An example of this technique would be an external area on a petrochemical site where a piece of equipment has a Zone 2 classification up to 2 m above it. Any height above that is where normal unclassified luminaires can be mounted. In this situation, floodlights could be used mounted at 5 m on columns, which will project the necessary light onto the equipment where it is needed. Another example would be on a filling station forecourt where luminaires are mounted in a canopy above the zonally classified area. The result is a more economical installation due to the lower cost of standard types of luminaire.

24.4.2   Panel lighting

A room that contains an extreme environment may be modified to have sealed transparent panels in either the ceiling or walls. Luminaires can then be placed outside the area with light shining into the protected room. This can be especially advantageous when dealing with emergency lighting in freezers or very hot production rooms where the operation of electronics and batteries can be seriously affected. Some factories, in which large amounts of dust are created, have skylights or northlights built into the building structure. These transparent panels can be cleaned and used effectively with floodlights mounted to the outside to produce the required lighting levels. Care is needed to ensure that any heat from the light does not crack the glass. When doing the lighting calculations remember to factor-in loss of light due to spill around the rooflight and in transmission through the glass.

24.4.3   Light guides

Fibre-optics can be used to create low levels of lighting under certain circumstances, where the light source is situated outside the problem area. For larger rooms 'light tubes' are available which use LED and discharge light sources. They consist of a long tubular structure with highly reflective internal prisms along the length, and connected to a light projecting luminaire at one or both ends. This takes the electrical components outside the extreme environment and reduces the chances of premature failure.

There are many examples of successful installations using the methods mentioned above. With light guides, in particular, it will be necessary to contact the manufacturer as to the suitability of their products in a particular environment.

23.5   Lamp performance charts

It has been mentioned in previous sections that lamps behave differently when operating in extremes of ambient temperature. Colour appearance may vary, but also the light output on starting will differ to that stated in data sheets and computer files. In some extreme cases the circuit will not operate, and areas can be left with no light. In less extreme cases a cold start, for example, may give only a small percentage of the nominal light output. Therefore, it is imperative that the appropriate light source is chosen for the given environment.

Table 23.8 shows typical values of the relative lumen output, as a percentage of the nominal lumen output, at various starting ambient temperatures for a range of standard lamps. Specific figures should be obtained from the lamp manufacturers being considered for any given project. The table does not include specialist lamp types as the values will vary between different manufacturers. Specific advice should be obtained from the manufacturer when using specialist lamps.

Table 23.7 Luminous flux related to ambient temperature

Ambient air temperature (°C)	Relative luminous flux (%) for stated lamp type				
	Compact fluorescent 26 W T/E	Compact fluorescent 55 W L/E	Fluorescent 58 W T8	Fluorescent 49 W T5	LED* 23 W board
−20	—	—	—	—	113
−15	—	—	—	—	112
−10	14	35	22	9	111
−5	23	40	32	14	110
0	36	49	45	22	109
5	62	65	60	32	108
10	85	80	76	45	107
15	96	92	91	60	106
20	99	99	98	76	105
25	100	100	100	91	105
30	96	97	97	98	104
35	92	94	92	100	104
40	86	88	86	97	103
45	82	84	81	92	103
50	76	80	76	86	102
55	73	75	71	81	102
60	68	71	66	76	100

* The values given for the LED board are from temperature measurements taken at the test point on the driver, this particular example by courtesy of Tridonic UK. LEDs like to operate in cold ambient temperatures and good quality boards can operate down to −40 °C. However, it is essential to check that the electronic driver is capable of operating at low temperatures.

References

BSI (1992/2013) BS EN 60529: 1992 + A2: 2013: *Degrees of protection provided by enclosures (IP code)* (London: British Standards Institution)

BSI (1994/2010) BS EN 60598-2-18: 1994 + A1: 2012: *Luminaires. Particular requirements. Luminaires for swimming pools and similar applications* (London: British Standards Institution)

BSI (1998–2015) BS EN 60598: *Luminaires. Particular requirements* (various Parts) (London: British Standards Institution)

BSI (2002) BS EN 62262: 2002: *Degrees of protection provided by enclosures for electrical equipment against external mechanical impacts (IK code)* (London: British Standards Institution)

BSI (2018) BS 7671: 2018: *Requirements for Electrical Installations. IET Wiring Regulations* (London: British Standards Institution)

BSI (2015a) BS EN 60598-1: 2015: *Luminaires. General requirements and tests* (London: British Standards Institution)

BSI (2015b) BS EN ISO 14644-1: 2015: *Cleanrooms and associated controlled environments. Classification of air cleanliness by particle concentration* (London: British Standards Institution)

DIN (1993) DIN 40050-9: *Road vehicles; degrees of protection (IP-Code); protection against foreign objects; water and contact; electrical equipment* (Berlin: Deutsches Institut für Normung)

EC (1994) 'Directive 94/9/EC of the European Parliament and the Council of 23 March 1994 on the approximation of the laws of the Member States concerning equipment and protective systems intended for use in potentially explosive atmospheres' *Official Journal of the European Communities* **L100** (19.4.1994) 1–29 [no longer in force] (available at http://eur-lex.europa.eu/legal-content/EN/TXT/?uri=celex:31994L0009) (accessed September 2018)

EC (1999) 'Directive 1999/92/EC of the European Parliament and of the Council of 16 December 1999 on minimum requirements for improving the safety and health protection of workers potentially at risk from explosive atmospheres (15th individual Directive within the meaning of Article 16(1) of Directive 89/391/EEC)' *Official Journal of the European Communities* **L23** (28.1.2000) 57–64 (available at http://eur-lex.europa.eu/legal-content/EN/TXT/?uri=celex:31999L0092) (accessed September 2018)

EU (2014) 'Directive 2014/34/EU of the European Parliament and of the Council of 26 February 2014 on the harmonisation of the laws of the Member States relating to equipment and protective systems intended for use in potentially explosive atmospheres (recast) Text with EEA relevance' *Official Journal of the European Union* **L96** (29.3.2014) 309–356 (available at http://eur-lex.europa.eu/legal-content/EN/TXT/?uri=celex:32014L0034) (accessed September 2018)

IEC (1989/1999/2013) IEC 60529: 1989 + AMD1: 1999 + AMD2: 2013 CSV: *Degrees of protection provided by enclosures (IP Code)* (consolidated version) (Geneva: International Electrotechnical Commission)

IEC (2002) IEC 62262: 2002: *Degrees of protection provided by enclosures for electrical equipment against external mechanical impacts (IK code)* (Geneva: International Electrotechnical Commission)

Chapter 24: Exterior workplaces

24.1   Introduction

Exterior workplaces occur in many different forms. There are those that involve the movement of people, such as airports; those that involve the storage and movement of goods, such as container terminals; those that involve the operation of large plant, such as an oil refinery; and those that exist temporarily as happens during the construction of a building.

Regardless of the purpose of the site, the lighting systems of exterior workplaces have common aims. In all exterior workplaces, the lighting is designed to ensure the safety of people working on the site and to enable the work to be done quickly and easily, without discomfort.

This chapter gives an overview of lighting exterior workplaces. For an in-depth coverage of individual workplaces and their specific problems, refer to SLL Lighting Guides 1: *The industrial environment* (SLL, 2012a) and 6: *The exterior environment* (SLL, 2016).

24.2   Factors to be considered

When designing lighting for exterior workplaces, there are a number of factors that need to be considered.

24.2.1   Scale

The scale of the equipment to be used on the site is important in determining the lighting approach. Some industries, such as the chemical industry, have plant that is large and complex so there is no possibility of separating the lighting from the plant. As a result, the lighting has to be integrated into the plant (Figure 24.1). Others are large and simple and can be lit by area floodlighting. Yet others are small and have a limited number of lines of sight, e.g. loading bays.

Figure 24.1 Lighting of a chemical complex
(© FotoBug11/Shutterstock)

24.2.2   Nature of work

The nature of work in exterior workplaces can vary widely. All exterior workplaces require lighting for a safe working environment, but the location and requirement for fine visual discrimination may vary from day to day as work places move. In these circumstances, consideration should be given to using mobile localised lighting. Some lighting will also be required where working at night exposes the workers to danger (Figure 24.2).

Figure 24.2 A mobile luminaire used to provide lighting in a temporary work zone

24.2.3 Need for good colour vision

Where colour is used to convey information, lighting with good colour rendering properties is required. For example, control and power wiring is colour coded and in chemical plants it is common to use colour to identify the contents of pipes. For such applications, a light source with a CIE general colour rendering index of at least R_a60 is recommended.

24.2.4 Obstruction

Many exterior workplaces contain obstructions, e.g. stacked shipping containers. Obstructions tend to produce shadows. Shadows can be minimised by:

- using high mounted floodlights so that light can pass over some obstructions

- lighting all areas from more than one direction

- having high-reflectance surfaces for hardstands, such as concrete rather than dark tarmac

- providing localised lighting in the shadowed area.

24.2.5 Interference with complementary activities

Some common exterior workplaces are interfaces between one mode of transport and another, e.g. railway yards, airports and docks. Care should be taken to ensure that train drivers, aircraft pilots and ships' pilots approaching the facility can see and understand all the relevant signals. They may experience difficulty in doing this either because of low visibility caused by disability glare or because of confusion caused by similarity between signal lights and the workplace lighting.

24.2.6   Hours of operation

Not all exterior workplaces operate throughout the night. If this is the case, consideration should be given to switching to security lighting after the end of work (see Chapter 27). Even when the site is active throughout the night, it is often the case that the number of staff involved is small. If this is the situation, consideration should be given to a switching system that allows different parts of the site to be lit or unlit according to the needs of the work.

The use of movement detection can be considered in areas where no dangerous work is being carried out. Even then, the whole of the potentially occupied area needs to be covered so that there is no danger of anyone being plunged into darkness without the ability to reactivate the lighting from their location.

24.2.7   Impact on the surrounding area

Exterior workplace lighting should be limited to the site. Stray light from a site may be regarded as light trespass by neighbours and a source of sky glow by others (see Chapter 26, 'Roads and urban spaces'; SLL Lighting Guide 6: *The exterior environment* (SLL, 2016) and the *Guide to limiting obtrusive light* (SLL, 2012c)).

24.2.8   Atmospheric conditions

Some exterior workplaces are difficult environments for lighting equipment. Chemical plants may produce a corrosive atmosphere. Oil refineries have a flammable environment. Coastal container terminals will expose luminaires to a high level of salt. See Chapter 23, 'Extreme Environments'.

24.3   Lighting recommendations

24.3.1   Illuminance and illuminance uniformity

The recommendations for exterior workplace lighting given below are: minimum maintained mean illuminance on the relevant working plane, minimum uniformity of that illuminance, maximum glare rating and minimum colour rendering of the light source(s). The illuminance uniformity is measured over the relevant area, which can range from the whole site to a small part of the site. Exterior working activities are very diverse. Table 24.1 below gives some lighting recommendations for generic activities. Recommendations for specific industries can be found below and in the *SLL Code for lighting* (SLL, 2012b) and SLL Lighting Guide 1: *The industrial environment* (2018).

24.3.2   Glare control

Glare control for outdoor lighting workplaces is important as the background behind any spotlight or floodlight is often dark sky, dark buildings or machinery. This means that the glare from typical light sources is exacerbated as glare is the difference between size and brightness of the light source(s) compared to the background brightness. Thought must be given to siting lights so they are, as far as is practicable, above normal lines of sight and not beyond the normal line of sight from a workplace.

24.3.3   Light source colour properties

Light source colour rendering is important for discerning colours, which can be significant where colour coding is used for identification. The ability to identify colours accurately and confidently is determined by the light source spectral power distribution and the illuminance.

Table 24.1 Illuminance recommendations for exterior workplaces

Activity	Minimum maintained mean illuminance (lx)	Illuminance uniformity (minimum/average)	Typical applications
Safe pedestrian movement in low risk areas	5	0.25	Industrial storage areas with only occasional traffic
Safe movement of slow vehicles	10	0.4	Open storage areas served by forklift trucks
Safe movement in medium risk areas	20	0.4	Vehicle storage areas, container terminals with frequent traffic
Normal traffic	20	0.4	Road lighting in container terminals, marshalling yards
Very rough work	20	0.25	Excavation and site clearance
Rough work	50	0.25	Handling timber
Safe movement in high risk areas	50	0.4	Critical area within chemical plants, oil refineries etc.
Normal work	100	0.5	Brick laying, carpentry
Fine work	200	0.5	Painting, electrical work

Any light source with a CIE general colour rendering index of $R_a 80$ or above will allow accurate and confident colour naming at the illuminances recommended for workspaces at night. Light sources with a colour rendering index of around $R_a 60$, such as high-pressure sodium lamps, allow reasonable but less confident colour naming at the higher illuminances recommended for spaces, but both the accuracy and confidence decline at lower illuminances. Low pressure sodium lamps do not allow accurate colour naming under any illuminance and should not be used. LED light sources can pose a problem when it comes to colour specification. As there is now little cost or output differences between LEDs with moderate colour rendering or high colour rendering, it is generally better to use LEDs with a colour rendering of $R_a 80$ or higher.

24.3.4   Loading areas

Many industrial premises have a loading bay (Figure 24.3) where lorries and vans can back up to, or partly into, an opening in the building. These may have a weather canopy over the opening. External lighting is needed to illuminate the opening and any raised loading ramp within it so the driver can back up safely to them, watching for people or goods left in front of the opening. Any lighting above or around the opening must not cause disabling glare towards the driver of the reversing lorry or van. Luminaires on or just inside a loading bay are often exposed to the weather so they should have the appropriate IP rating (see section 23.2.5 for more information on IP ratings).

Inside the loading bay, lighting is needed to illuminate the area inside, where forklift trucks or trolleys manoeuvre to drive or lift loads into the lorries. This can be either at ground level or from a raised loading ramp. To enable workers to see inside a vehicle it can be helpful to place a low wattage floodlight above the loading bay platform aimed down and out through the opening. Lighting can also be provided either side of the opening to light the loading area and into the back of the lorry, using either protected linear fluorescent or linear LEDs.

Outdoor loading areas are usually lit by area floodlighting, either mounted on a building or on poles or masts. Such lighting should provide uniform illumination without glare to people working in the area, particularly forklift truck drivers whose viewing direction may frequently be upward.

Figure 24.3 Lighting of a simple loading bay

Table 24.2 Lighting recommendations for loading

Application	Horizontal illuminance (lx)	Horizontal illuminance uniformity	Maximum glare rating	Minimum colour rendering index
Loading bay	150	0.4	25	40
Outdoor loading area	100	0.5	45	20

24.3.5 Chemical and fuel industries

Some parts of these industries have large outdoor facilities. Some such facilities are open, e.g. a coal stockyard, while others are complex structures with platforms at many different levels, e.g. an oil refinery. For the former, lighting is usually done by conventional area floodlighting techniques. For the latter, lighting is done by integrating luminaires into the plant.

Luminaires in these facilities are often exposed to adverse conditions. These may range from a very dirty and potentially explosive atmosphere, as in a coal and ash handling area, through corrosive atmospheres, as in some chemical plants, to risks of fire and/or explosion, as in the oil and gas industries where whole plants are considered hazardous areas. Luminaires that are capable of dealing with the prevailing conditions need to be used (see Chapter 23).

Consideration also needs to be given to ensuring easy access to luminaires for maintenance. The lighting recommendations for the chemical and fuel industries are given in Table 24.3. The approach to designing lighting for the outdoor areas of these industries is discussed in section 24.4.

Table 24.3 Lighting recommendations for chemical and fuel industries

Activity	Horizontal illuminance (lx)	Horizontal illuminance uniformity	Maximum glare rating	Minimum colour rendering index
Handling servicing tools, adjusting manual valves, starting and stopping motors, lighting of burners, operating switch gear	20	0.4	50	20
Moving on walkways	50	0.25	50	20
Filling and emptying trucks and wagons with risk-free substances, inspection of pipes and packages	50	0.4	45	20
Fuel loading and unloading sites	100	0.4	45	20
Filling and emptying trucks and wagons with dangerous substances, replacement of pump packing, general service work, reading of instruments	100	0.4	45	40
Repairs of machines and electric devices	200	0.5	45	60

24.3.6 Sidings, marshalling yards and goods yards

These railway facilities can cover large areas. Lighting is usually done by conventional area floodlighting but there are two features that require special attention. The first is the level of obstruction caused by the closeness of wagons on adjacent lines. The second is the need to ensure good visibility of all signals. To avoid shadows between wagons, confusion with signals and glare to workers, a high mast lighting installation is commonly used. However, due to the increased use of automatic movement systems, low level lighting is becoming more popular (see Chapter 22, 'Transportation', and SLL Lighting Guide 16: *Transport buildings* (SLL, 2017) for fuller details and guidance).

The masts should be positioned near to those areas that require higher illuminances (see Table 24.4). The floodlights should be aimed along the tracks, but not aiming at such an angle as to cause glare to oncoming drivers. This aiming minimises shadows between adjacent lines of wagons and takes advantage of specular reflections to reveal the run of the rails. Where lighting has to be across tracks, reflections from wagon sides make an important contribution to the illumination between wagons. This contribution will only be important if the angle of incidence is more than 45 degrees (Figure 24.4). The lateral spacing of floodlights should not be more than twice the difference between the height of the floodlights and the height of the wagons.

Table 24.4 Lighting recommendations for sidings and railway yards

Activity	Horizontal illuminance (lx)	Horizontal illuminance uniformity	Maximum glare rating	Minimum colour rendering index
Railway yards, flat marshalling, retarder and classification yards	10	0.4	50	20
Hump areas	10	0.4	45	20
Freight track, short duration operations	10	0.25	50	20
Open platforms in freight areas	20	0.4	50	20
Servicing trains and locomotives	20	0.4	50	20
Railway yards, handling areas	30	0.4	50	20
Coupling area	30	0.4	45	20
Covered platforms in freight areas, short duration operations	50	0.4	45	40
Covered platforms in freight areas, continuous operations	100	0.5	45	40

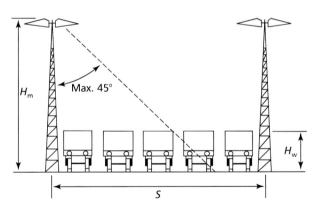

Figure 24.4 High mast lighting of a railway yard with reflections from wagons

24.4 Approaches to exterior workplace lighting

24.4.1 High mast floodlighting

Many large area sites, such as container terminals, railway marshalling yards and car storage areas use high mast floodlighting. A smaller number of high masts are preferred over a larger number of lower masts for reasons of economy and because they allow greater freedom of movement in the area illuminated.

The most economical mast height is usually between 20 and 30 m. At greater heights, the costs of the masts increase greatly while at lower heights, the numbers of masts, lamps and luminaires increase dramatically. A lower mast height can be justified where there is extensive obstruction.

The usual light sources for high mast lighting are either high pressure sodium or metal halide discharge lamps, although high output LEDs are being used more often now. The luminaires used are floodlights with the light distribution matched to the proposed spacing of the masts. The luminaires should be suitable for the atmospheric conditions. This means that, at the very least, the luminaire should have the necessary IP number and may require protection against corrosion and explosive atmospheres. See section 23.2.5 for more information on IP ratings. High mast columns need to be positioned such that they can be accessed without impacting on rail operations, and without the need for special measures to protect maintenance staff from moving trains. If the columns are of the folding type, their locations need to avoid fouling tracks and overhead electrification systems when lowered. Because stopping rail operations is very costly, extended maintenance intervals are desirable, but note that by using LED light sources, the intervention periods required for structural inspection of the columns are likely to be more frequent than for the lighting itself.

24.4.2   Integrated lighting

Oil refineries, cement plants and similar sites are usually lit by integrating the lighting into the plant (Figure 24.1). This is typically done by selecting a luminaire with a very wide light distribution, both upwards and downwards, and bolting it onto convenient parts of the structure so as to light all parts of the structure. The result is that too often the plant is lit up like a Christmas tree. Increased sensitivity to light pollution should mean that this approach is no longer acceptable. It is still necessary to integrate the lighting into the structure, but to reduce light pollution it is necessary to be more careful about the type of luminaire selected, more informed about suitable locations for those luminaires and more adventurous about the control of the lighting at night. The luminaire selected should provide a predominantly downward light distribution, ideally within 70 degrees of the downward vertical. This more restricted light distribution will require greater care in the positioning of adjacent luminaires to ensure they are close enough to provide uniform light for safe access and work, without leaving dark spots.

24.4.3   Localised lighting

In many exterior workplaces, the places where detailed visual work is carried out are limited. In this situation, there is little point in lighting the whole site to the level necessary for the detailed work. A better approach is to light the whole site to the level necessary for safe movement and to use localised lighting for the work areas. This localised lighting may be permanent, for a fixed working area, or temporary, for a construction site. In the latter case, lighting may be powered from a generator.

Any mobile lighting equipment and its supply system must be suitable for the environment it may be used in. Thus, in facilities where there are potentially explosive environments all mobile equipment must be suitably rated for that environment.

References

SLL (2012b) *SLL Code for lighting* (London: Society of Light and Lighting)

SLL (2012c) *Guide to limiting obtrusive light* (London: Society of Light and Lighting)

SLL (2016) *The exterior environment* SLL Lighting Guide 6 (London: Society of Light and Lighting)

SLL (2017) *Transport buildings* SLL Lighting Guide 16 (London: Society of Light and Lighting)

SLL (2018) *The industrial environment* SLL Lighting Guide 1 (London: Society of Light and Lighting)

Chapter 25: Exterior architectural lighting

25.1 Overview: key aspects

Outdoor architectural illumination allows people to see buildings in a different form — to reveal secrets, to provide intrigue. It enables people to see the form and character of a building that is not seen or maybe understood in the daytime.

The hours of darkness allow the designer to reveal the character, the scale, the size of a building; how it sits within its context; how it plays its part in the history and growth of an urban environment — all through the application of artificial lighting.

By lighting a building, we allow it to be seen in a very different way to how one may view a building in the daytime. During the day, the building is lit from above and will either be seen in a diffused light due to clouds, or there may be more contrast with direct sun, and this can help to provide a timepiece with shadows created by the sun defining the time of day. By lighting in the evening, we often look at lighting the building in the very opposite way, by maybe providing a very close graze of light, creating great contrast and play of light revealing texture that is not normally seen, or combining different beam angles that allow different features to be brought out.

Fundamentally lighting in the hours of darkness provides an opportunity to reveal the character and the identity of a building, an opportunity to bring people into an urban space in the hours of darkness, maybe to somewhere they wouldn't normally have come — it helps to provide a destination and a meeting place.

The following sections provide an overview of the key items a specifier should consider in the design and specification of outdoor architectural façade lighting.

25.2 Context

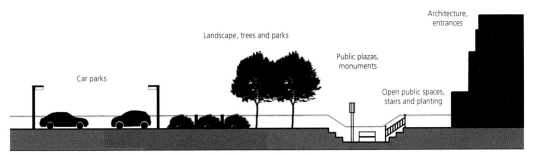

Figure 25.1 Context (courtesy of acdc)

Consider where the building is located, where it is in the world, what is around it and how those elements are lit. This is essential information which, if not taken into consideration, may impact the final design and therefore may not meet the needs of the end user or create the identity the building warrants within its context.

If the building is set within a rural environment, the specifier should bear in mind that a minimal amount of light is likely to have a huge impact upon the façade. If the building is in the middle of an urban environment, e.g. a hospitality space with cinemas, bars and restaurants, consideration must be given to how to illuminate a façade in order to make the right impression and define the brand and the use of the building through light, while avoiding over-lighting.

It may also be that the façade is part of a larger project, and other parts include the public realm in front, maybe side streets and landscape that includes steps, monuments, flagpoles etc. If this is the case then the designer should consider how the right balance might be created through different levels of light, possibly also colours of light (see section 25.3 for details). It is likely that the 'public realm' space will need to be lit in line with specific light levels and levels of uniformity; how will the façade provide the right focal point — the point of destination — for the space?

When establishing the context, the designer should also consider the viewpoints of the building. Is it a remote castle on a small island across a long expanse of water where, in the hours of darkness, the lit effect upon the verticals will be reflected in the calm waters below? Or is it within a dense urban environment where one is only really engulfed by the enormity of the façade having walked through the side streets? Or does one experience incredible views from far away as one approaches the town? If the latter, the lit effect should consider the highest points of the façade to increase the long views in the hours of darkness, defining the central position of the façade and its importance in the history of the urban space.

The scheme applied to the architecture is likely to depend upon its use and/or its architectural character. If the scheme is for a retail mall/shopping centre or a series of retail façades along a high street, the intention of the scheme is to bring attention to this environment in the hours of darkness — it is about steering our gaze, engaging with the customer, enticing us in. The designer should consider how lighting the perimeter of the space can be integrated with the architectural lighting so that they are working together as layers of light, not competing against each other.

The focus here is about making sure we look at where the building or buildings are, how will they be seen and from where. This should inform the design so that we look to reveal the building(s) through the application of light, bringing value to the external space and enabling the artificial light that is being applied to transform the architecture and the cityscape in the hours of darkness.

25.3   Colour and materials

Figure 25.2 (*a*) Oldham Town Hall (courtesy of BDP/Nick Caville), (*b*) Broadcasting Tower, Leeds (courtesy of acdc/Dan Hodgson), (*c*) The Regent Bridge, Edinburgh (courtesy of acdc/Stuart Armitt)

Consideration should be given to colour — this is not just the colour of the light, it is essential that we consider the architecture, the colour and finish of the building and how light and the luminaire can be applied or integrated.

The colour of the light being used and the colour and finish of the façade should be discussed very early in the design process. It may be that the façade has a highly polished or lacquered finish and therefore the light and points of light may reflect back into a space causing glare and visual discomfort — the façade materials may mean that the light is not grazing up the building and slowly fading away, as had been expected.

It is important that the colour of the light is discussed with a client very early on as it can sometimes be assumed that it may or may not be used. Applying coloured light to a façade or series of façades can enable the owners of the building to use it for corporate functions or enabling those hiring the building to have the colour of the light tuned to suit their branding needs, thereby promoting the brand, the colour and the venue. Some clients may be opposed to the use of coloured light on the façade and wish the character of the building to be defined simply through the contrast of white light using different optics, off-set distances etc. to define the façade(s).

Consideration should be given to the context of the building with regards to colour being applied. It should fit in with the brightness of the adjacent buildings to avoid competition and ensure that the correct colour is applied. A sophisticated control system allows for more subtle and appropriate colours suitable for the building material and the use of the building.

Historical buildings may include deep window reveals, pillars or a portico. The façades of such buildings are often a warm coloured stone with a matt finish and these elements can be emphasised and brought to life in the hours of darkness with a light having a warm colour temperature of 2700 K or 3000 K. Consideration may also be given to a dynamic white solution, thus enabling the specifier to pick the 'right' white. Dynamic white is usually provided by LED lamps/sources of both 2700–4200 K and 6000 K, and through the control of the light a specific white can be achieved that enhances the texture and form of the building. It may also be the case that the scheme itself is dynamic over the period of an evening, a week, or longer period, changing the way people perceive a building every time they visit through the different white colour tones applied.

Modern building design techniques mean that the colour of the light is very important whether being projected upon a building façade or lighting outwards through transparent or translucent façades (see section 25.9.5, 'Backlit façades'). As an example, if the finish of a building is CorTen™ steel (i.e. weathering steel, sometimes referred to as 'corten steel') with a rusting orange textured finish, in the hours of darkness it 'disappears' if not lit. If warm white light is projected upon the façade the colour and warmth begins to be defined and, if the contrast upon the façade is varied by 'picking out' architectural details using different beam angles, then the character of the CorTen™ can be further defined.

When specifying luminaires on any project, careful consideration should be given to the technical details of the luminaire and the 'binning' of the LEDs used — luminaires with narrow binning (i.e. good colour consistency) are usually available from higher quality suppliers. This is to ensure that when there is a regular array of luminaires, or a continuous run of linear luminaires installed end-to-end, that the colour of light source is consistent from one luminaire to the next. Where the colour is not consistent this can spoil the final lit effect.

If a façade is glazed, further investigation should be given to whether it is clear, opal or frosted in some way, as this can help to determine a suitable lit effect. Consider also how the internal lighting of a building can express its external appearance in the hours of darkness, thereby saving on installation costs, energy consumption and maintenance costs.

25.4   Contrast

Figure 25.3 (a) Knightsbridge Estate, London (courtesy of GIA Equation/©James Newton Photographs), (b) Stadkamer, Zwolle, Netherlands (courtesy of JHK Architects), (c) Old Town, Varaždin, Croatia (courtesy of acdc/Dan Hodgson)

	3:1		10:1	20:1		40:1	50:1
Barely perceptible	Just perceptible	Subtle	Moderate	Significant	Strong	Dramatic	Striking

Figure 25.4 Perceptions of contrast

When defining the lit effect at concept level, the designer should consider if the building will be bathed in a uniform level of light, a single colour or otherwise, carefully controlled and focussed, but still uniform. If so, this can be provided by offset or pole-mounted luminaires set back from the façade. Otherwise, if there are repetitive façade features such as window reveals, single low-output luminaires with carefully defined distribution can be used on the façade to define and capture window reveals, features or surfaces at night. These can be single colour or have dynamic colour changes.

It may be that there are other buildings that are already lit to the sides of a new scheme, or that there are roads that have a high ambient level of light or are of a specific colour temperature and the reflected light has an adverse effect upon the façade being designed. This may mean that the illuminance upon a building façade will need to be increased to have the desired impact, or a slightly different colour temperature may be used to create the necessary contrast within its context.

Section 25.7 below provides guidance on 'people' and it is the use of the building that will be key to any design. It may be that window reveals cannot be lit because the windows themselves are always in use and back-lit. In this instance using window reveals does not capture the character of the building as well as would an alternative method.

It may also be the case that the building has more than one façade that deserves to be lit but does not need the same treatment. A principal façade, seen and appreciated by the public from key viewing points, could have more contrast, interest and identity, whilst other façades, possibly facing side streets, could receive a slightly different treatment that may be more uniform but still helps to define the building, its role in the community and the view points from afar.

25.5   Control

Figure 25.5 Knightsbridge Estate, Brompton Road façades: (*a*) Summer, (*b*) Cool White (both courtesy of GIA Equation/©James Newton Photographs)

The control of external lighting is not just about dimming and dynamic lighting; it is also about controlling the luminaire light beam, using accessories to define the final lit effect, and ensuring that the light is focussed upon the building and not the dark sky.

The control of external architectural lighting is very often simply just on and off. If this is known early in the design stage then it is recommended that a small mock-up is constructed as it provides the specifier with an opportunity to consider the luminaire output, possibly any accessories that need to be used to control the light, and to ensure that any light pollution is minimised.

A mock-up is usually of one section of the design, so that all parties that have an interest in the final scheme can attend and sign it off; usually manufacturers are keen to help as it will assist in their products being specified. It should be stated that a mock-up is suitable for all external applications.

Accessories, such as a linear louvre, cowl or snoot, can help focus the light upon the vertical and the soffit of a building's frame and limit the view into the light source from adjacent buildings or those inside the building.

It may be that the contrast between one section of a design and another is too harsh; for example, if there are pillars and a flat vertical between. The contrast between the two should be considered and a balance made through control of the intensity. This should be considered early on in the specification of the luminaires, accessories and any wiring schematic.

A more sophisticated control method will need to be considered should the scheme need to be dynamic, either for dynamic white change or dynamic colour change. Very similar to interior schemes, 'scenes of light' can be created and these might be dynamic scenes or a series of static scenes that change from one to the next over the period of an evening, a day, a week or other period through the integration of astronomical clock. Such scenes are usually predefined early in the design process so that the specifier and the client are agreed on the final lit effect upon a space or façade, and also on the budget.

The control of a scheme may also consider how a space is used and that, as the hours of darkness grow into the early hours of the following day, not all of the scheme needs to remain on. Control of the light scheme may differ between weekdays and the weekend as the use of the external space differs. This can help to reduce the overall costs of the ongoing installation.

Local authorities may also have a curfew at which time all non-essential lighting (i.e. not required for safety and security) must be switched off. This saves energy during hours when few people are awake to appreciate the lighting of the buildings and spaces.

The specifier should consider the importance of the night sky and its protection from light pollution. Guidance is available in the *Guide to limiting obtrusive light* (SLL, 2012) and the ILP's *Guidance Notes for the Reduction of Obtrusive Light* (ILP, 2011).

The control system is often but not always linked to a central building control system as this can help the central control and maintenance of any new system employed. Detailed consideration of lighting controls is given in Chapter 10, 'Controls'.

25.6   Global applications

The specification of any product for any project should consider the location and thus the context and country it is being used in. The luminaires specified must be suitable for their environment. See Chapter 23, 'Extreme environments'.

The location of a project will determine the type of product including its IP rating, its IK rating and its suitability to be within a specific ambient temperature. See Chapter 23 for details on IP and IK ratings.

When mounted on a building, external luminaires may be in direct sunlight. The housing can become hotter through the thermal transference of heat from the building's material and so, in locations with high ambient temperatures, it is essential that the luminaire can withstand and operate in such temperatures. Whilst the luminaire should not be turned on during daylight hours, this may still happen due to on-site commissioning and it may also have some effect during dusk. The same consideration should be given to colder climates. The specifier should consider the extremes of the location of the scheme and ensure the luminaire specified has been tested and has the necessary independent certification to enable its use. Guidance on lighting in extreme climates may be found in CIBSE's *Buildings for extreme environments* publications (CIBSE, 2014, 2017a/b).

In specifying any luminaire, it may be desirable to consider a thermal cut-out option to ensure that the luminaire automatically cuts out if it gets too hot or cold, thereby reducing the risk of failure, disruption to the scheme at a later date or extending the time a contractor is on site.

Within any location there can be extremes of weather; this could be hurricanes, flooding, sandstorms etc. The luminaires specified should be suitable for such conditions, as appropriate to the location, otherwise it may result in the luminaire failing and disruption on site for maintenance. The ability of a particular luminaire to cope with extreme conditions can be determined by the IP rating and the stated ambient temperature range.

Should the luminaire need an externally mounted accessory, the location and any weather conditions should be reconsidered to ensure that dirt, dust, sand or leaves do not collect on the top of the luminaire or become trapped in the accessory, thereby reducing or eliminating the luminaire output in these conditions.

For ground-recessed luminaires, consideration should be given to whether 'walk-over' or 'drive-over' luminaires are required. This may only be in isolated instances, where access equipment is used for building maintenance, or for emergency services, but careful coordination is required to ensure the product's suitability for its location.

25.7   People

Any scheme designed is for the benefit of people: i.e. to make an impression, to invite people into a space, to encourage people to use, to live, to be proud, to love the city or the town in the hours of darkness.

It is these people that the light will have an impression upon, but it is also essential that the designer considers the impact of bad lighting design in terms of glare and light pollution.

The lit effect should enable someone to embrace and be engulfed in the urban space in the hours of darkness and so the control of the light upon the vertical, and not pouring light into windows or the night sky, is just as important. Careful consideration for the right optic delivering a close offset graze or narrow beam grazing up a pillar, picking out the architectural detail at the very top, is critical to the success of the scheme.

For those people that may live or work inside a building, e.g. a hotel, light should not have an adverse impact upon those that have paid to have a personal space to escape to, even for just a business trip. The light should be focussed between the windows, emphasising the solid elements or be heavily controlled through accessories to eliminate any disability glare. Likewise, for a commercial environment, consider the viewpoint from the internal spaces to ensure that the chosen luminaires will not produce disability glare for those in the working environment.

25.8   Type of luminaire

When specifying the type of luminaire for a given external architectural project, the specifier should bear in mind the following basic considerations.

25.8.1   Position

Where will the luminaire be installed? Will it be recessed, offset from the building or mounted upon the building? Will the scheme be a combination of more than one mounting position? (It is the combination of these layers of light that will define the scheme.)

Consideration should be given to the aesthetics of the luminaire in terms of its location and daytime visual appearance. External illumination should consider how the luminaire(s) can be integrated within the surroundings so that it is the lit effect that is seen and appreciated in the hours of darkness, bringing attention to the site, rather than the luminaire.

Within its defined location, the specifier should consider how the lit effect can be 'locked off' when commissioning is final and complete, this may determine the luminaire type and its 'adjustability' and therefore suitability for the project.

Position also affects contrast. By mounting the luminaire close to the façade and grazing up, the texture of a building will be accentuated but the further away one is from the building, the flatter the light will be on the façade and its ability to reveal texture will be reduced.

25.8.2 Shape

The concept scheme should consider whether it requires a spot, flood or linear source to create the desired lit effect, and whether the fitting will be recessed or surface-mounted. A spot or flood luminaire will often have a circular aesthetic for recessed applications whilst some manufacturers also provide a square mounting ring. Surface mount options vary greatly from one manufacturer to the next and the specifier should consider the differentiating features of the luminaires in relation to the demands of the scheme and how and if it can be integrated into the façade.

A linear solution would enable the scheme to provide a continuous linear graze, with no dark spots between, providing a vertical graze to the building and picking out any soffit framing its detail and context.

A floodlight approach, often associated with larger luminaires with a high output that can be mounted to the ground or pole offset from the building, will provide a wash of light or provide contrast and interest, but from a greater distance. These products can still have a narrow beam in order to pick out architectural detail.

25.8.3 Optic

Within the scheme that is being created the optic specified will help determine the contrast values from one surface to another, e.g. between pillars and a flat solid surface, where a narrow beam is used on one and a linear beam is used on another.

It may be that to ensure a building is lit on a 360 degree view, the verticals are lit from the floor with an asymmetric or linear beam, and the roof or clock tower lit from further away with a narrower or linear beam picking out the very highest point to accentuate the long view.

The specifier can establish what may be required by completing a simple section of the façade or elevation considering how the differing beam angles will work together or possibly clash creating harsh shadows due to prominent architectural details. A simple software model can also be used to help in this instance.

25.8.4 Output

There are many variants from one manufacturer to another, and little consistency between them. This again is where it may be suitable to consider a partial mock-up on site or within the designer's office to review the lit effect alongside some basic lighting software to compare the outputs and to ensure a building is neither overlit or underlit. It can reveal how the layers of light will work together, making sure for example that the output and optic specified for a ground-recessed luminaire will work alongside a building-mounted luminaire higher up, to create the right balance.

25.8.5 Controls

As detailed earlier in this overview, consider early in the design process how the scheme may be controlled, from simple on/off to a full dynamic scheme of light utilising a microprocessor-based lighting control system.

Within the design stages, ensure that a clear schematic is completed with zones for the control and that this is discussed with the electrical designer and controls supplier. Create scenes of light and consider how these could be visualised early on in the scheme to emphasise the importance of the final executed installation.

25.9 Type of application
25.9.1 Surface mount (building)

Figure 25.6 Knightsbridge Estate: (*a*) Summer, (*b*) Brompton Road façades, summer, (*c*) Brompton Road façades, winter (all courtesy of GIA Equation/James Newton Photographs)

The application of surface mounted luminaires creates lots of contrast upon a building façade. It is generally applied between the glazed sections of the facade, providing a very close graze up the building, or can be installed within the window reveals to accentuate the lighting scheme from both inside and out.

Depending upon the architectural style, a building-mounted application can include a high output surface-mount flood with a narrow beam grazing up a building façade over 20 metres and more. For a historic building, it is more likely that the façade will need a larger quantity of lower output luminaires mounted at regular intervals, possibly at each floor of the façade, to provide the desired lit effect.

When lighting close to the façade, consideration should be given to shadows and points of luminance that may be seen as too bright and not in keeping with the scheme. Long dramatic shadows can be created by ledges, or an architectural detail that may have previously been unseen. These can be reduced by using a lower output luminaire or by adding a lens that will soften the lit effect. It may be that changing from a very narrow beam to a narrow or medium beam will create an improved effect. Consideration should also be given to the roof. The sloping roof can be in a different finish or colour and a building-mounted luminaire may therefore miss this detail when installed upon the vertical. Therefore it may be suitable to incorporate layers of light to ensure key historical elements are captured as part of the scheme; this may be achieved by ground-mounted offset luminaires. For existing buildings, mock-ups can be used to confirm design intent and identify any unexpected lit effects caused by previously unseen architectural details.

A successful surface-mount application is often achieved by integrating the luminaires into the architecture such that the detail, e.g. architectural mouldings, can be used to hide the luminaires. Thus the architecture can be appreciated during the day without the visual intrusion of the luminaires but at night the artificial lighting brings the building to life.

If a linear solution is sought to provide a continuous linear graze up the building then careful consideration should be given to the specification of the luminaire to ensure there are no shadow gaps between one luminaire and the next when butted-up to each other — this is critical to a successful scheme.

A surface mount luminaire mounted within a deep reveal allows light to graze up the verticals and pick out the top horizontal. This enables an architectural façade with a repetitive architectural detail to come to life in the hours of darkness. Also, by incorporating colour allows what might be seen as an ordinary façade to be given a new personality and helps to define the space around it in the evening. With new optics and luminaire design this can usually be created by a single luminaire. Defining the use of the building and of the internal spaces (and therefore the windows) will establish if this is a viable solution (i.e. are the windows backlit and could this wash out any scheme designed?).

A window reveal within an atrium or historic building, e.g. a converted wharf or factory building, can help provide a scheme that is appreciated internally and externally and this therefore enables the scheme or the colour of light to be tuned for a specific corporate function, or to allow a dynamic scheme that evolves over an evening.

25.9.2   Recessed mount

Figure 25.7 Kings Cross railway station (courtesy of Studio Fractal/Will Scott)

Ground-recessed luminaires enable a building's façade to be 'grounded' in the hours of darkness. A scheme can allow for a tower to be lit or for a stained glass window to be backlit but, depending upon the context of the façade, those elements can appear to be hovering unless lit from the ground up.

A recessed luminaire can, like the other applications, be linear, spot or flood to provide the desired lit effect. To ensure the lit effect is focussed upon the building and not the night sky it is suggested that luminaires are specified that can be adjusted on site, or supplied on a set tilt, to ensure the desired lit effect is provided.

Consideration should be given to people and the use of the building or façade, so as to avoid looking into the light source thereby avoiding disability glare — particularly if the façade is near a road or pedestrian walkway. It may be that filters or accessories need to be used to reduce the impact but still maintain the lit effect. The same applies where the luminaire is lighting a public building such as a railway station or town hall; here people will stand and wait for friends and the scheme should enable them to do this without being affected by glare.

Recessed-mount luminaires are often used as one of the 'layers of light' within a scheme, integrating the luminaire at ground level to help frame the building from ground level and combining this with surface mount luminaires mounted at the next architectural soffit to pick out and frame the building at a higher level. This can often be the case to avoid long, dramatic shadows — by incorporating layers of light the character and identity of the building is defined.

25.9.3   Surface mount (ground)

Figure 25.8 Broadcasting Tower, Leeds
(courtesy of acdc/Stuart Armitt)

Surface ground-mount luminaires can help to provide either a uniform flood approach to a flat façade or, with different optics and outputs, can enable the designer to pick out specific architectural details. This allows the centre of the beam to provide a focus and the peripheral beam to graze other parts of the building so that, as discussed above (section 25.9.2), those parts are not 'hovering' within the scheme, while still capturing all of the building.

Surface ground-mount luminaires, if offset sufficiently from a building, allow the specifier to pick out the sloping angle of a roof that may be of a different colour or finish; capturing this defines the building, its context and its history, otherwise at night-time the viewer is simply seeing the vertical surfaces.

As with surface building-mount (section 25.9.1) the designer should consider shadows and cut-off angles. This can work with the building to bring out its character and form. The closer to the building the luminaires are, the longer the shadows will be — this can help to give the building its identity in the hours of darkness. Alternatively, it may mean the designer, through consultation with the client, needs to consider building-mounted luminaires to create a balance and reduce the contrast. If contrast is required the luminaires are not likely to be in a uniform layout and therefore careful coordination with the landscape architect will be required to identify mounting opportunities.

If a uniform floodlit effect is required the designer should consider a regular array of luminaires offset from the building with an asymmetric or flood optic (depending upon the distance) to provide a flood that gradually fades towards the top of the building. In modern architecture, some façades are flat and square and do not have a lintel such as might be found on historic buildings, so capturing the top of the façade and framing it can be difficult and some of the light may spill into the night sky. The designer should consider if other techniques may be more suitable in order to create a focus.

25.9.4 Pole mount

A pole-mounted solution is often sought when building- or recessed-mounting is not possible; it enables the luminaires to be offset from the building in what can be a more accessible location. Pole-mounted solutions can also allow existing poles to be used as mounting opportunities where there is already a power supply.

Depending upon the height of the pole in relation to the façade, this technique allows the specifier to provide a flatter and more uniform lit effect with minimum shadowing due to the luminaire being near to 90 degrees to the facade. Alternatively, if a more dramatic scene is desired, then choosing narrower beams of light can provide pools of light upon specific areas of the façade.

Consideration should always be given to the use of the building and the control of the luminaires. For example, where a luminaire is mounted on a 6 m pole and is focussed upon the façade, if the building is a residential or commercial property the luminaire should be fitted with a louvre or anti-glare cowl to limit the view into the light source. This may not be necessary for the theatrical lighting of a building, such as a stadium where it is the long view and focus of a person's journey that is key to the success of the lit effect, and there are minimal windows.

Depending upon the use of the building, coloured light is often used in this application. Pole-mounted solutions are generally used for large sports, retail or hospitality façades and colour brings focus and attention to the identity and use of the building. For example, for a football stadium, the colours used could be the colours of the team associated with the stadium.

As an alternative to pole mounting, it may be possible to mount lights on adjacent buildings. Obviously, this will need agreement with the owners of those buildings and the arrangement of internal or external surface electrical supplies to the lights, and ongoing arrangements for paying for the energy consumed and for access for maintenance of the lights.

25.9.5 Backlit façades

Figure 25.9 (*a*) Oldham Town Hall (courtesy of BDP/Nick Caville),
(*b*) Stadkamer, Zwolle, Netherlands (courtesy of JHK Architects)

Modern building techniques and materials can often present opportunities to provide a very different night-time appearance by creating a surface of light — a luminous façade, which can be a single colour or changing colours. It may also be the case that ambient levels of light around a building are very high and a different approach is required to create an identity. Therefore lighting the windows or backlighting the glazed sections creates a contrast in brightness between surfaces. With carefully positioned and focused luminaires, the lit effect can be striking from both the short and long views of the façade. This technique can use both interior and exterior luminaires depending upon the installation opportunities.

It will often be the case that the architect and end user have considered very early on that a façade will be backlit and the specification of the building façade material is key to the success of the night-time appearance. Careful planning and a thorough approach to the lighting design development with the architect and end user will be required to ensure the desired lit effect is provided. A small mock-up, or part full-scale mock-up is often considered to ensure all parties sign off the lit effect, which, whilst at some cost, ensures all parts are coordinated before being installed on site.

To achieve a consistent wash of light backlighting the façade, the designer should consider the height of façade as it may be that two types of optic are required. The design should consider the lit effect from the very top of the façade to the base, or from base to top, depending upon the mounting position. The array of luminaires should enable a constant wash along the length and depth of the façade and this can be achieved by a regular array of luminaires, equally spaced and with a sufficient offset to ensure there are no hotspots; again a small mock-up may help to finalise the set-up. Should the façade be of a greater depth it may be necessary to allow for an additional row of luminaires. It is likely that these fittings will need a narrower beam to reach the top or bottom third of a facade to continue the lit effect. Careful planning, coordination and modelling will be required to ensure the uniformity is maintained; it may be that the control and dimming of the luminaires will help with the layout and uniformity.

Should the façade design require backlit windows, then the specifier should consider how they can be converted into light-boxes and whether the light should be single colour or colour change, and how this might be controlled. A light-box will usually have an opal finish to the front with all matt white surfaces inside to assist in the inter-reflection of the light and create the homogenous lit effect required.

The backlit effect can be provided by one of two methods:

- Installing a luminaire at the top or bottom of the light box behind the diffuser flooding the space behind. It is recommended that the luminaire is directed towards the back surface and not towards the glass as this will risk the luminance at the top/bottom being too high.

- For a more homogenous lit effect consideration should be given to a regular array of LED panels with high colour binning and different dimensions to suit the application; a small mock-up with the final diffuser material will allow the depth of the light box to be determined to ensure the high luminance of each LED is not seen from the front.

Figure 25.10 (*a*) Kipco Tower, Kuwait (courtesy of Kevan Shaw Lighting Design), (*b*) Marketgait Apartments, Dundee (courtesy of RMJM)

The techniques discussed in this chapter are generally about how light is applied or projected upon a façade or series of façades — the final option is how light can be integrated into a façade. Delineation can include points of light, lines of light or integrated light, where people see the reflected light and not the light source itself.

Where this type of application is used, it is often associated with sophisticated control — of changing colour, of shimmering light, of light shows every hour or continually. It is about identity and bringing attention to the façade — because of its importance within its context, to frame the scale and height of the building, or to emphasise its use inside.

Large scale buildings that stand against a dark night sky may need only a minimal amount of light to have maximum impact. An integrated approach is often preferred as lighting the façade from the ground or rooftop can mean a high quantity of very high-powered luminaires that can result in light pollution and sky glow — an integrated solution can provide a high degree of identity and interest, resulting in a more individual approach to the scheme.

Integrating the light source can also mean easier maintenance; it may be that with careful architectural detailing the fittings can be accessible from inside the building and thereby reducing the need for external access using towers.

The layout and arrangement of luminaires can and will vary from one project to another. This type of application needs to be tailored to each project and often will require custom luminaires to suit the needs of the scheme. Careful and early coordination within the design team is essential regarding the mounting type, style, cabling and control.

Where linear lines of light are integrated, consideration should be given to whether a homogenous lit effect is required and, if colour change, whether the control applies to each individual LED or to the full or partial length of the luminaire. It is also essential to consider the viewpoint of the scheme, as what is viewed as essential from 5 m away will be very different on a tall building when viewed 50+ m away in terms of the level of control. That does not mean corners can be cut, but the viewpoint and what can actually be seen from a distance should be considered. It may be that a small or partial mock-up can assist in the evaluation.

If individual points of light are considered then the viewing angle should be one of the main considerations — a domed opal front will be more suitable to increase the viewing angle of the installation from street level or the long view from a distance.

Integrating a linear source into an architectural detail, similar to how a cove detail might be created for the perimeter of an internal space, should be coordinated very early with the architect. The detail should consider the viewing angles so that it is the lit effect and the reflected light that is seen and appreciated. By providing such a detail the viewer will not see the direct light source, which some may see as being too bright — diffusing the source so that it is the reflected light that is seen will result in a softer light but is likely to cover a larger surface area.

References

CIBSE (2014) *Buildings for extreme environments: Arid* (London: Chartered Institution of Building Services Engineers)

CIBSE (2017a) *Buildings for extreme environments: Tropical* (London: Chartered Institution of Building Services Engineers)

CIBSE (2017b) *Buildings for extreme environments: Cold climates* (London: Chartered Institution of Building Services Engineers)

ILP (2011) *Guidance Notes for the Reduction of Obtrusive Light* ILP GN01 (Rugby: The Institution of Lighting Professionals) (available at https://www.theilp.org.uk/documents/obtrusive-light) (accessed September 2018)

SLL (2012) *Guide to limiting obtrusive light* (London: Society of Light and Lighting)

Chapter 26: Roads and urban spaces

26.1   Introduction

The first electric street lighting in the UK was installed in the 1870s, almost 150 years ago. There are now approximately 7.5 million UK street lights and upwards of 300 million street lights installed worldwide. This chapter gives an overview of the lighting considerations for the lighting of a range of road types and pedestrian areas and points to the guidance for other associated spaces.

Lighting for roads and public amenity areas may be a complex design task with many technical and visual considerations from road users and pedestrians to think about before making design decisions. The lighting of roads can include all highway types and public areas, assisting in accident prevention, hazard perception, security and crime prevention, and may enhance the commercial night time economy of urban centres.

Good lighting design practice will take into consideration the health and safety of all road users including highways workers, maintenance considerations, electrical power consumption and the visual impact of their proposals. Choosing a lighting class for any road lighting design should be based on a risk assessment of the lighting requirements for that particular road. Choosing the appropriate lighting class for the road has a great influence on the running costs of the lighting system. Designing road lighting should only be undertaken by trained competent persons.

Road lighting classes are defined by the visual needs of different road users in a variety of environments:

- *M classes*: for drivers of motorised vehicles on traffic routes of medium to high speeds. Road luminance is the calculation parameter for these road types where the needs of the driver are dominant.

- *C classes*: for drivers of motorised vehicles, but are intended for use on conflict areas such as complex road junctions, shopping streets, roundabouts, queuing areas or similar where pedestrians and vehicular traffic may be brought into close proximity. Horizontal illuminance is the calculation parameter for these urban centres, where the lighting is designed to do what can be done for public safety and security, while also providing an attractive night time environment.

- *P classes*: intended for cyclists or pedestrians on footways, cycleways, emergency lanes or other areas adjacent a traffic route, or for residential roads or pedestrian streets. Horizontal illuminance is the calculation parameter for these spaces.

Advice on selection of lighting classes is given in PD CEN/TR 13201-1 (BSI, 2014).

The photometric recommendations for all types of road lighting in the UK are given in BS EN 13201-2 (BSI, 2015). Advice on the implementation of these recommendations is given in BS 5489-1: 2013 (BSI, 2013).

26.2   Traffic routes

The primary function of the lighting of traffic routes is to make other vehicles on the road visible. Road lighting does this by producing a difference between the luminance of the vehicle and the luminance of its immediate background — the road surface. This difference is achieved by increasing the luminance of the road surface above that of the vehicle so that the vehicle is seen in silhouette or negative contrast against the road surface with viewing distances from other drivers of between 60 m and 160 m.

The criteria used to define lighting for traffic routes are:

- *Average road surface luminance*: the luminance of the road surface averaged over the carriageway (cd/m^2) and there are recommendations for both predominantly dry and wet road surface conditions.

- *Overall luminance uniformity* (U_0): the ratio of the lowest luminance at any point on the carriageway to the average luminance of the carriageway.

- *Longitudinal luminance uniformity* (U_1): the ratio of the lowest to the highest luminance found along a line along the centre of each driving lane. For the whole carriageway, this is the lowest longitudinal luminance uniformity found for the driving lanes of the carriageway. This is only relevant to visual conditions on long uninterrupted sections of road and should be applied appropriately.

- *Threshold increment* (f_{TI}): a measure of the effect of disability glare, described as an equivalent veiling luminance caused by scattering of light in the human eye.

- *Edge illuminance ratio* (R_{EI}): The average illuminance just outside the edge of the carriageway in proportion to the average illuminance just inside the edge of the carriageway.

Traffic routes are divided into different classes. The different classes are based on the type of road, the average daily traffic flow (ADT), the speed of vehicles, the type of vehicles in the traffic and the frequency of conflict areas and pedestrians. Table 26.1 specifies the different classes and identifies the recommended lighting criteria. Details of the recommended lighting criteria for dry roads are given in Table 26.1. These are the lighting criteria usually adopted in the UK. However, where roads are likely to be damp or wet for a significant part of the hours of darkness, a stricter requirement for overall luminance uniformity can be used. The lighting criteria for this condition are also given in Table 26.1.

Table 26.1 Lighting recommendations for traffic routes

Lighting class	Minimum maintained average dry road surface luminance (cd/m^2)	Minimum overall luminance uniformity (dry road), U_o	Minimum longitudinal luminance uniformity for the carriageway (dry road), U_1	Minimum longitudinal luminance uniformity for the carriageway (wet road), U_1	Disability glare (dry conditions), f_{TI} (%)	Minimum surround/ edge illuminance ratio (dry road), R_{EI}
M1	2	0.4	0.7	0.15	10	0.35
M2	1.5	0.4	0.7	0.15	10	0.35
M3	1	0.4	0.6	0.15	15	0.3
M4	0.75	0.4	0.6	0.15	15	0.3
M5	0.5	0.35	0.4	0.15	15	0.3
M6	0.3	0.35	0.4	0.15	20	0.3

Note: edge illuminance ratio criterion should only be applied where there are no traffic areas with their own criteria adjacent to the carriageway

In some situations, it may not be possible to calculate the maximum threshold increment (f_{TI}). An alternative method to limit disability glare is to select a luminaire according to the classes given in Table 26.2 The different classes are defined by the luminous intensity of the luminaire, in candelas/1000 lumens of bare light source output, at 70, 80 and 90 degrees from the downward vertical, in any direction, and the luminous intensity above 95 degrees, in any direction. Classes G1, G2 and G3 correspond to a semi cut-off luminaire. Classes G4, G5 and G6 correspond to full cut-off luminaires.

Table 26.2 Luminaire classes for the control of disability glare (source: BS EN 13201-2 (BSI, 2015a))

Lighting class	Maximum luminous intensity/1000 lumens at 70° (cd/1000 lm)	Maximum luminous intensity/1000 lumens at 80° (cd/1000 lm)	Maximum luminous intensity/1000 lumens at 90° (cd/1000 lm)	Luminous intensity above 95° (cd)
G1		200	50	
G2		150	30	
G3		100	20	
G4	500	100	10	0
G5	350	100	10	0
G6	350	100	0	0

26.3   Conflict areas

A conflict area is one in which traffic flows merge or cross, e.g. at intersections or roundabouts, or where vehicles and other road users such as cyclists or pedestrians are in close proximity, e.g. on a shopping street or at a pedestrian crossing. Lighting for conflict areas is intended for drivers rather than pedestrians, although C classes can be applied to areas used by pedestrians and cyclists such as underpasses. The criteria used to define lighting for conflict areas are based on the illuminance on the road surface rather than road surface luminance. This is because driver's viewing distances may be less than the 60 m assumed for traffic routes and there are likely to be multiple directions of view. The criteria used for the lighting of conflict areas are:

- *Average road surface illuminance*: the illuminance of the road surface averaged over the carriageway (lx).

- *Overall illuminance uniformity* (U_0): the ratio of the lowest illuminance at any point on the carriageway to the average illuminance of the carriageway.

The recommendations for the different lighting classes for conflict areas are given in Table 26.3. These recommendations can be applied to all parts of the conflict area or only to the carriageway when separate recommendations are used for pedestrians or cyclists (see section 26.7). The choice of lighting class has to be matched to the lighting of the traffic routes approaching the conflict area. Guidance is given in Table 26.3.

Table 26.3 Lighting recommendations for conflict areas

Lighting class	Minimum maintained average road surface illuminance (lx)	Minimum overall illuminance uniformity
C0	50	0.4
C1	30	0.4
C2	20	0.4
C3	15	0.4
C4	10	0.4
C5	7.5	0.4

26.4   Pedestrian crossings

A specific form of conflict area is pedestrian crossings, which may require special consideration as areas around pedestrian crossings are known accident zone areas. If the road lighting class provides high surface luminance, the positioning of the normal columns/luminaires may provide good negative contrast (pedestrians visible as a dark silhouette against a bright background) and the crossing is lit to the lighting class of the road it is sited on, or lit to a higher lighting class.

It is also possible for additional local lighting to directly illuminate the crossing, making drivers aware of the crossing and pedestrians using it (positive contrast), where horizontal and vertical illuminance requirements (as well as the need to control direct glare to vehicle drivers) are paramount. Further guidance is available in Institution of Lighting Professionals Technical Report 12: *Lighting of Pedestrian Crossings* (ILP, 2007).

26.5   Coordination

It is obviously important that the lighting of conflict areas should be coordinated with that of the traffic routes. Table 26.4 indicates the compatible lighting classes for traffic routes and conflict areas. Where two traffic routes lit to different classes lead into a conflict area, the match should be made to the higher traffic route class.

Table 26.4 Compatible lighting classes for conflict areas on traffic routes

Traffic route lighting class	Conflict area lighting class
M1	C0
M2	C1
M3	C2
M4	C3
M5	C4
M6	C5

26.6   Areas adjacent to the carriageway, residential or minor roads or pedestrian streets

People and objects adjacent to the carriageway need to be seen by the driver. Such locations include unmade verges, footways and cycle paths and the emergency lanes of motorways. For all traffic routes other than heavily used footways and cycle tracks and the emergency lanes of motorways, lighting of the area adjacent to the carriageway should conform to the surround ratio/edge illuminance ratio shown in Table 26.1.

For traffic routes with heavily trafficked footways and cycle tracks an appropriate lighting criterion should be selected from Table 26.1. Which of the criteria is selected will depend on the lighting class used for the carriageway. Guidance on compatible criteria is given in Table 26.4. To ensure adequate illuminance uniformity, the actual maintained average horizontal illuminance should not be more than 1.5 times greater than the minimum maintained average horizontal illuminance.

Emergency lanes on motorways, often referred to as the hard shoulder, are lanes not normally used by road users except in an emergency situation or breakdown. Due to increase in traffic on some routes, emergency lanes have been converted to be used as a permanent or semi-permanent running lane for traffic and these are no longer designated as an emergency lane. These lanes should be lit to the appropriate lighting class.

For the lighting of subsidiary roads such as access roads, residential and minor roads and associated pedestrian areas, footpaths and cycle tracks, the appropriate P class of illuminance should be taken from Tables 26.5.

Table 26.5 Lighting recommendations for areas adjacent to the carriageway, residential or minor roads or pedestrian streets

Lighting class	Average maintained horiz. illuminance (min. lx)	Minimum maintained horiz. illuminance (min. lx)	Minimum maintained vertical illuminance, E_v (min. lx)	Minimum maintained semi-cylindrical illuminance, E_{sc} (min. lx)
P1	15	3	5	5
P2	10	2	3	2
P3	7.5	1.5	2.5	1.5
P4	5	1	1.5	1
P5	3	0.6	1	0.6
P6	2	0.4	0.6	0.2
P7	Performance not determined	—	—	—

26.7 Road lighting design

Road classification, which determines the illuminance or luminance requirements, are based on risk assessments by competent persons. The risk assessment will consider the type of user, speed, usage, complexity, environmental zone and other site-specific information for the road under consideration, as well as client specification to determine the road classification. Guidance on choosing a suitable classification is given in PD CEN/TR 13201-1 (BSI, 2014) and BS 5489-1 (BSI, 2013).

26.7.1 Fundamentals

The design process for traffic route lighting consists of the following stages:

- *Selection of the lighting class and definition of relevant area*: The lighting class of the carriageway is selected (Table 26.1). The nature and extent of adjacent areas and any conflict areas are identified and the lighting approach to be used chosen. The compatible lighting classes for adjacent areas and conflict areas are selected (Table 26.3).

- *Collection of preliminary data*: The following data are required before calculation can start: mounting height; luminaire type and optic setting or lens type; light source type; initial luminous flux of light source; IP rating of luminaire; cleaning interval planned for luminaire; pollution category for location; luminaire maintenance factor; light source replacement interval; light source maintenance factor at replacement interval; luminaire maintenance factor; luminaire tilt; width of carriageway; width of driving lane; width of adjacent areas; luminaire transverse position relative to the calculation grid; luminaire arrangement; road surface reflection properties (*r*-table) (see below).

The emphasis given to maintenance factors in this list arises from the fact that the lighting recommendations are made in terms of minimum maintained values. Table 26.6 sets out typical luminaire maintenance factors to be applied for different environmental zones, column/ mounting heights and cleaning intervals.

Table 26.6 Typical luminaire maintenance factors (IP65 rated)

Environmental zone	Mounting height (m)	Cleaning interval (months)					
		12	24	36	48	60	72
E1/E2	≤ 6	0.96	0.96	0.95	0.94	0.93	0.92
E1/E2	≥ 6	0.96	0.96	0.95	0.94	0.93	0.92
E3/E4	≤ 6	0.94	0.92	0.9	0.88	0.86	0.84
E3/E4	≥ 6	0.96	0.96	0.95	0.94	0.93	0.92

The reflection properties of a road surface are quantified by an 'r-table'. This consists of a matrix of values of $q \cos^3 \gamma$, where q is the luminance coefficient of the pavement material and γ is the angle of incidence of light from the upward vertical, in degrees (see Figure 26.1). This quantity is called the reduced luminance coefficient (r). The two dimensions of the r-table are the angle β (the angle between the vertical plane of incidence and the vertical plane of observation) and the tangent of the angle γ (the angle of incidence from the upward vertical), see Figure 26.1. Each cell in the r-table contains a value for the reduced luminance coefficient multiplied by 10 000.

Although different road materials have different reflection properties, and those properties change over time and with wear, there are only two r-tables commonly used in the UK, one for asphalt-based roads and one for concrete roads. The r-table for the asphalt-based roads is called the representative British road surface. r-tables are characterized by two parameters, one concerned with lightness and one concerned with specularity. The parameter for lightness is the average luminance coefficient, Q_0. This is highly correlated to the average luminance produced on the road surface. The parameter for specularity is:

$$S_1 = r(0, 2)/r(0, 0)$$

where $r(0, 2)$ is the reduced luminance coefficient for $\beta = 0$ degrees and tan $\gamma = 2$, $r(0, 0)$ is the reduced luminance coefficient for $\beta = 0$ degrees and tan $\gamma = 0$.

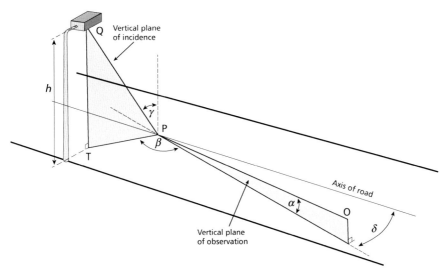

Figure 26.1 In principle, the relevant angles for characterizing the reflection properties of the road surface are α (angle of observation from the horizontal), β (angle between the vertical planes of incidence and observation), γ (angle of incidence from the upward vertical) and δ (angle between the vertical plane of observation and the road axis); in practice, for lighting of traffic routes, it is assumed that α has a fixed value of one degree corresponding to a viewing distance of about 60 m and δ is irrelevant because the reflection properties of road surfaces are isotropic.

The representative British road surface is characterized as $Q_0 = 0.07$ and $S_1 = 0.97$. For concrete road surfaces the corresponding values are $Q_0 = 0.10$ and $S_1 = 0.24$. There are other r-tables available for different pavement materials. Where it is required to design for a frequently wet road, the calculations described below should be made using r-tables for both dry and wet surfaces.

26.7.2 Calculation of design spacing

The design of road lighting for traffic routes to meet the selected criteria uses information on the luminous intensity distribution of the luminaire, the layout of the luminaires relative to the carriageway and the reflection properties of the road surface.

The luminous intensity distribution of the luminaire is supplied by the manufacturer.

The layout of the luminaires for two-way roads is usually single-sided, staggered or opposite. In a single sided installation, all the luminaires are located on one side of the carriageway. The single-sided layout is used when the width of the carriageway is equal to or less than the mounting height of the luminaires. The luminance of the lane on the far side of the carriageway is usually less than that on the near side. In a staggered layout, alternate luminaires are arranged on opposite sides of the carriageway. Staggered layouts are typically used where the width of the carriageway is between 1 to 1.5 times the mounting height of the luminaires. With this layout, care should be taken that the luminance uniformity criteria are met. In the opposite layout, pairs of luminaires are located opposite each other. This layout is typically used when the width of the carriageway is more than 1.5 times the mounting height of the luminaires. Sometime hybrid arrangements are needed to avoid trees on one side of the road or the other.

The layout of luminaires for dual carriageways and motorways can be opposite, central twin, central twin and opposite, high mast, or catenary. In a central twin layout, pairs of luminaires are located on a single column in the central reservation. Designers should take into account positioning of columns and any inconvenience and financial costs associated with closing traffic lanes for luminaire maintenance.

With an r-table matched to the pavement material, the luminous intensity distribution for the luminaire and the layout of the luminaires relative to the carriageway, the luminance produced by a single luminaire at any point P on the road surface can be calculated using the equation:

$$L = I q \cos^3 \gamma / h^2$$

where L is the luminance at the point P produced by the luminaire (cd/m²), I is the luminous intensity in the direction from the luminaire to the point P (cd), ($q \cos^3 \gamma$) is the reduced luminance coefficient at point P and h is the luminaire mounting height (m).

This process can then be repeated for adjacent luminaires and the contributions from all luminaires summed to obtain the luminance at that point for the whole lighting installation. This process can then be repeated over an array of points on the road to obtain the luminance metrics used to characterize the road lighting for traffic routes.

Although this process can be done manually, for all road types and shapes it is almost always done using software. Straight road column spacings can be quickly calculated using software that shows the road classification criteria can be met from the input parameters such as road width, pavement width, column set-back, bracket overhang distance, road reflectance and luminaire tilt angle. This allows the designer to access the photometric file for the selected luminaire and then to manipulate the variables to ascertain the optimum and maximum spacings to allow for positional variations on site.

Of these variables, clearance and set-back have limits. To avoid lighting columns becoming hazards to road users and to allow safe passage, the clearance of all parts of the lighting equipment above the carriageway should be at least 5.7 m. To reduce the risk of death or injury caused by collision with a lighting column, the minimum set-back of the lighting column from the edge of the carriageway is related to the design speed of the road, as shown in Table 26.7.

Table 26.7 Minimum set-back of lighting columns

Design speed for road (km/h)	Minimum horizontal set-back from the edge of the carriageway (m)
50	0.8
80	1.0
100	1.5
120	1.5

26.7.3   Bends in the road

It is common practice to reduce column spacing on bends by 10% for slight bends, compared to straight roads. On more severe bends (radius ≤ 500 m), illuminance criteria should be used for the design. A risk assessment may be required and the road and any potential objects or hazards should be lit using conflict area classification as the viewing distances are reduced and luminance criteria may not be appropriate. Overall uniformity is important and should not fall below recommended values.

Columns should not be located in vulnerable positions on bends. Risk assessments should determine the best column locations and if passive safety columns are required. The preferred location of columns is on the outside of a bend, but this may not always be appropriate and should be determined by the risk assessment.

Conflict areas have different shapes and use illuminance as a criterion rather than luminance. The illuminance produced at a point P from a single luminaire is given by the formula:

$$E = I \cos^3 \gamma / h^2$$

where E is the illuminance at point P from the luminaire (lx), I is the luminous intensity in the direction from the luminaire to the point P (cd), γ is the angle of the direction of I from the downward vertical (degrees) and h is the luminaire mounting height (m).

This process can be repeated for adjacent luminaires and the contributions from all luminaires summed to obtain the illuminance at that point for the whole lighting installation. This process can then be repeated over an array of points on the road to obtain the illuminance metrics used for the lighting of conflict areas. Manufacturers may provide a relative isolux diagram, this being the illuminance pattern provided on the road surface by single luminaire relative to the maximum illuminance and plotted in terms of mounting height. Given a layout of luminaires around a conflict area, the mounting height and information about the maximum illuminance, the overall illuminance pattern can be generated. Again, much of this work will now be done using software specifically designed for road lighting calculations.

Some suggested luminaire layouts for commonly occurring conflict areas, e.g. roundabouts, are given in BS 5489-1 (BSI, 2013), as is advice for the siting of lighting equipment around special locations, such as road or rail bridges, elevated roads and around aerodromes, railways, coastal waters, harbours, inland waterways, siting of columns around overhead power lines, as well as advice on guidance on covered shopping malls or canopied areas, subways, footbridges, external stairways, ramps and outdoor car parks. See also Chapter 22, 'Transport buildings', Chapter 23, 'Extreme environments', Chapter 24, 'Exterior workplaces' as appropriate.

Section 26.8 below and BS 5489-2 (BSI, 2016) provide guidance on the lighting of tunnels.

26.7.4   Plotting of luminaire positions

Having determined the ideal spacing, the luminaire positions are identified, starting with the conflict areas. After these are settled, the luminaire positions for the traffic routes and adjacent areas are identified. Finally, a check is made to determine if the luminaire positions are compatible with possible column positions.

Glare from luminaires should be controlled. To limit disability glare, where luminaires have lenses, clear bowls or reflectors, these should conform to at least class G1 of Table 26.2. For discomfort glare, the simplest approach is to select a luminaire where the light source is not visible, either directly or as an image, from any relevant direction. If a more quantitative approach is desired, glare index can be used. This is calculated from the equation:

$$\text{Glare index} = I\,A^{-0.5}$$

where I is the maximum luminous intensity at 85° from the downward vertical, in any direction (cd) and A is the apparent area of the luminous parts of the luminaire on a plane perpendicular to the direction of I (m^2).

Table 26.8 shows the glare index classes appropriate for subsidiary roads, footpaths and cycle tracks.

Table 26.8 Lighting classes based on glare index

Lighting class	Maximum glare index
D1	7000
D2	5500
D3	4000
D4	2000
D5	1000
D6	500

26.7.5   Lighting design for subsidiary roads

The design process for lighting of subsidiary roads and associated areas, footpaths and cycle tracks consists of the following stages:

- *Selection of the lighting class and definition of relevant area*: The lighting class is selected (Table 26.5) and the relevant areas defined.

- *Collection of preliminary data*: The following data are required before calculation can start: mounting height; luminaire type and lens or optic type or setting; light source type; initial luminous flux of light source; IP rating of luminaire; cleaning interval planned for luminaire; pollution category for location; luminaire maintenance factor; light source replacement interval; light source lumen maintenance factor; maintenance factor; luminaire tilt; width of relevant area; luminaire transverse position relative to the calculation grid; luminaire arrangement; glare index of luminaire.

26.7.6   Calculation of design spacing

The calculation procedure for subsidiary roads and associated areas, footpaths and cycle tracks is given in section 7 of BS EN 13201-3 (BSI, 2013).

26.7.7   Plotting of luminaire positions

Having determined the ideal spacing, the luminaire positions are identified, starting with T-junctions, areas of traffic calming measures, and severe bends. After these are settled, the luminaire positions for the straight sections of the roads, paths or tracks are fitted to match. Finally, a check is made to determine if the luminaire positions are compatible with possible column positions.

26.8   Lighting for urban centres and public amenity areas

Urban centres and public amenity areas are used after dark by pedestrians, cyclists and vehicular traffic and people and the surrounding environment need to be easily recognised. During times when businesses or commercial premises operate, high levels of lighting may be necessary. Architectural lighting of buildings, floodlighting of landmarks or other methods may be employed to assist all road users with visual orientation of their surroundings. Each site has to be considered on its own merits as uniform layouts for all sites are unlikely to occur. See Chapter 25, 'Exterior architectural lighting'.

In such places, the lighting of the road surface for traffic movement is not the only or even the main consideration. Rather, the functions of lighting in urban centres and public amenity areas are to do what can be done for public safety and security, while also providing an attractive night time environment and assist with stimulating commerce and trade. To fulfil these functions, a master plan should be produced to meet some or all of the following objectives:

- to provide safety for pedestrians from moving vehicles

- to deter anti-social behaviour

- to ensure the safe movement of vehicles and cyclists

- to match the lighting design and lighting equipment to the architecture and environment

- to control illuminated advertisements and integrate floodlighting or festive lighting, both permanent and temporary

- to illuminate road and directional signs

- to blend light from private and public sources

- to limit obtrusive light

- to maintain lighting installations and protect them from vandalism or accidental damage

- to facilitate CCTV surveillance.

This battery of objectives and the individual nature of each site ensure that there is no standard method of lighting urban centres and public amenity areas, nor any universally applicable recommendations. What can be given are some general recommendations for the illuminances to be used in city and town centres, although even these may need to be adjusted for a particular site, depending on the ambient environment, the level of crime, street parking etc. Table 26.5 lists the lighting classes recommended for city and town centres, based on the type of traffic, the traffic flow, and the environmental zone. The minimum maintained illuminances associated with each lighting class are given in Table 26.3.

Guidance on some of the techniques used to light urban centres and public amenity areas are given in SLL Lighting Guide 6: *The exterior environment* (SLL, 2016) and various Institution of Lighting Professionals (ILP) documents specifically related to all aspects of road lighting considerations (https://www.theilp.org.uk).

26.9   Tunnel lighting

A tunnel is defined as a structure over a road that restricts the normal daytime illumination of a road section such that the driver's capability to see is substantially diminished. Tunnels are typically divided into two types: long (in excess of, typically, 200 metres) and short (typically 200 metres or less); short tunnels can include underpasses (BS 5489-2 (BSI, 2016)). The lighting treatment of these is the same in principle but standards normally allow some relaxation for short tunnels to avoid unnecessarily large lighting installations.

The lighting of tunnels has to address two different problems. The first is the 'black hole' effect experienced by a driver approaching a tunnel. The second is the black-out effect caused by a lag in adaptation on entering the tunnel. Neither of these problems occurs at night, because then the average road surface luminance inside the tunnel is coordinated with the road surface luminance outside the tunnel (BS 5489-2 (BSI, 2016)). By day, this is not the case. By day, the luminances around the tunnel portal will be much higher than those inside the tunnel so both the black hole effect and the black-out effect will be experienced and therefore it is necessary to use artificial lighting in the tunnel to counter the reduction in safety that would otherwise occur.

The black hole effect refers to the perception that from the distance at which a driver needs to be able to see vehicles and obstructions in the entrance to the tunnel, that entrance is seen as a black hole. The major cause of the black hole effect is the reduction in luminance contrasts of the retinal images of vehicles and obstructions in the tunnel entrance caused by light scattered in the eye. There are two approaches that can be used to alleviate the black hole effect. The first is to reduce the luminance of the surroundings to the tunnel. This can be done by ensuring that the tunnel portal is of low reflectance by shading the tunnel portal and the road close to the tunnel entrance with louvres designed to exclude sunlight, by using low reflectance road surface materials outside the tunnel and by landscaping to shield the view of high-luminance sources, such as the sky. The second is to increase the luminance contrast of vehicles and obstacles inside the tunnel entrance. This is done by ensuring that there is a high road surface luminance level from the tunnel entrance for a sufficient distance into the tunnel (known as the 'threshold zone'), the luminance and distance being calculated as described in standards (BS 5489-2 (BSI,

2016)). These parameters are dependent on the design speed of the road, the actual applied speed limit, the average luminance in the driver's field of view when approaching the tunnel, the intensity of traffic and the mix of road users.

The black-out effect occurs because although the approach to the tunnel starts the process of visual adaptation, this adaption is comparatively slow and continues as the driver progresses through the tunnel. To avoid this, while minimising the amount of lighting to be installed in the tunnel, the lighting is continued from the end of the threshold zone through the tunnel in such a way that the road surface luminance gradually diminishes to a baseline level in the 'interior zone'. The profile of this reduction and the interior zone road surface luminance is defined in standards (BS 5489-2 (BSI, 2016)) and is dependent on the design speed of the road, the actual applied speed limit, the intensity of traffic and the mix of road users. Detailed guidance on the lighting of tunnels can be obtained from the BS 5489-2: *Code of practice for the design of road lighting. Lighting of tunnels* (BS 5489-2, 2016).

The type of lighting used to provide the luminances in the tunnel is most commonly linear LED luminaires specifically engineered for durability in the onerous environments that occur in road tunnels. These can be installed end-to-end to provide continuous lines of lighting, thus giving good visual guidance to drivers while also avoiding any distractive effects from flicker.

26.10 Lighting controls

Traditional lighting controls for street lighting were very simple. Most commonly, a photocell mounted to a luminaire would switch on or off the electrical supply to the lantern when ambient daylight levels reached a certain value at dusk and dawn. There are also smart photocells that can dim the lighting for given hours without the expense of a central control system.

Whilst simple photocell control is still widely used, modern road lighting installations can employ CMS (central management systems), also known as telemanagement or remote monitoring systems, providing local authorities with dynamic street lighting control systems. Using CMS, local authorities can precisely control switch on/off times, vary dimming outputs and have automatic failure notification of individual lanterns and control gear.

With the rising costs of electricity usage, the features and benefits of CMS in reducing local authority power consumption and energy bills, as well as the other associated advantages, has seen a steady and growing take-up of CMS systems.

Before specifying a CMS system, it is vital that potential users need to take guidance and evaluate what the various systems can offer in terms of operation, maintenance and running costs, to ensure that local needs are met before starting the procurement process. Specifying CMS systems should be done by competent persons with detailed consultation with suppliers so an evaluation of the features and benefits, as well as any limitations of various systems, can be analysed.

Key benefits include:

- Energy and operating cost reduction by the use of dimming, part night switching where lower illuminance levels can be automatically programmed when roads have less traffic, and automatic trimming of burning hours.

- Accurate recording of operational hours and energy use for unmetered supply (UMSUG) and settlement of energy payments.

- Reduced need for night scouting, where operatives patrol the streets looking for failed lanterns.

- Automatic reporting of failed lanterns means that repairs can be targeted more quickly.

- Variation in outputs to suit local communities.

- Changes to the operation of the lighting system can be made remotely and quickly from a central asset managers office.

CMS systems consist of nodes in each luminaire replacing the photocell. Nodes communicate using wireless technology or mains borne digital signals. Nodes both receive and transmit information to the collector.

Collectors interact between the nodes and the central system, sending commands to the nodes and receiving information from the nodes and passing this back to the central system.

The central system, consisting of a server, sends, receives, collates, processes and stores data from the local authority lighting asset. A user interface between the central system and the local authority asset management system allows for control of the system by authorised persons via a PC or similar using a web browser.

See also ILP PLG08: *Guidance on the application of adaptive lighting within the public realm* (ILP, 2016).

26.11 Smart cities

The possibilities and applications of smart city technology using a wireless network possibly using street lighting infrastructure are in the early days of trials and there is some way to go before common adoption across the country is possible. Concepts include giving the general public parking information, tourist information, inform of traffic diversions, local services, internet availability, advise when roads may need gritting, as well as other concepts and possibilities that may not yet have been considered.

References

BSI (2013) BS 5489-1: 2013: *Code of practice for the design of road lighting. Lighting of roads and public amenity areas* (London: British Standards Institution)

BSI (2016) BS 5489-2: 2016: *Code of practice for the design of road lighting. Lighting of tunnels* (London: British Standards Institution)

BSI (2014) PD CEN/TR 13201-1: 2014: *Road lighting. Guidelines on selection of lighting classes* (London: British Standards Institution)

BSI (2015a) BS EN 13201-2: 2015: *Road lighting. Performance requirements* (London: British Standards Institution)

BSI (2015b) BS EN 13201-3: 2015: *Road lighting. Calculation of performance* (London: British Standards Institution)

BSI (2015c) BS EN 13201-4: 2015: *Road lighting. Methods of measuring lighting performance* (London: British Standards Institution)

BSI (2015d) BS EN 13201-5: 2015: *Road lighting. Energy performance indicators* (London: British Standards Institution)

ILP (2007) *Lighting of pedestrian crossings* ILP TR12 (Rugby: Institution of Lighting Professionals) [under revision]

ILP (2016) *Guidance on the application of adaptive lighting within the public realm* ILP PLG08 (Rugby: Institution of Lighting Professionals)

SLL (2016) *The exterior environment* SLL Lighting Guide 6 (London: Society of Light and Lighting)

Chapter 27: Security lighting

Security lighting is installed to help protect people and property from criminal acts. Other forms of lighting, such as outdoor display lighting, decorative floodlighting, shop window lighting and park lighting, can contribute to this goal but they are designed with additional criteria in mind. (For detailed advice on lighting exterior areas see SLL Lighting Guide 6: *The exterior environment* (SLL, 2016)).

27.1   Functions of security lighting

In public spaces, good security lighting is designed to help everyone see clearly all around. This means that people approaching can be easily identified and that other people's activities can be seen from a distance. This has the effect of shifting the odds in favour of the law-abiding and against the criminal. The law-abiding are unlikely to be taken by surprise, while criminals are more uncertain about whether their activities have been witnessed or they have been recognized. In secure spaces to which the public does not have access, it is possible to use lighting to enhance the vision of guards while hindering the vision of potential intruders.

Lighting is only one part of a security system. The complete system usually includes a physical element such as fences, gates and locks; a detection element, involving guards patrolling or remote surveillance; and a response element, which determines what is to be done after detection occurs. Unless security lighting is integrated into the complete system, it is unlikely to be successful. For example, good lighting in a storage area that nobody is watching, and hence in which there is no possibility of a response, will simply help intruders do what they want to do, more quickly.

27.2   Factors to be considered

The characteristics of the lighting to be used as part of the security system will be determined by various features of the site. The factors that always need to be considered are the following.

27.2.1   Type of site

Sites can be conveniently classified by the extent to which people have access to the site and the presence or absence of physical defences such as fences. Broadly, there are three types of site:

- *Secure areas*: where there are physical defences and to which access is controlled, such as a fenced storage yard.

- *Private areas*: where there are no physical defences but where the general public is not expected to be present, such as a house.

- *Public areas*: where people may be present at any time and which have no physical defences, such as a shopping centre car park.

27.2.2   Site features

One feature of a site that can have a major influence on the type of security lighting adopted is the extent to which the site is obstructed. Where a single building occupies a significant part of the site and contains the only items of value, it may be more effective to floodlight the building rather than to light the whole site. Where there are multiple obstructions, as in a container terminal, the whole site should be lit in a way that minimizes shadows. Another important feature is the average reflectance of the surfaces within the site. High reflectance surfaces increase the amount of inter-reflected light and this diminishes both shadows and glare (Figure 27.1).

Figure 27.1 Typical area with deep shadows
(© Tumarkin Igor-ITPS/Shutterstock)

27.2.3   Ambient light levels

The illuminances produced by the security lighting need to at least match or preferably exceed the illuminances of the surrounding area. A general rule is to exceed the illuminance of the surrounding area by one step as detailed in the *SLL Code for Lighting* (SLL, 2012); e.g. 20 lux, 30 lux, 50 lux, 75 lux, 100 lux (see Figure 22.1). So, if the surrounding area is lit to an average of 30 lux, the secured feature/area being lit for security purposes needs to be lit to 50 lux. Unless, this is done, the area covered by the security lighting will look dimly lit.

27.2.4   Crime risk

The frequency and nature of crimes occurring in different locations can vary widely. The level of risk will already be built into the level of defences used on secure sites but this is not possible in public areas. In public areas, increasing risk of crime is associated with increasing illuminances used for security lighting. It is advisable to consult with other interested bodies such as the police, local authorities, Neighbourhood Watch schemes etc.

27.2.5   CCTV surveillance

CCTV cameras are widely used for remote surveillance of large areas. The amount of light required for effective operation of CCTV cameras can vary dramatically from one product to the next — from starlight to bright security lighting. Further, if moving objects are to be easily seen, illuminances above the minimum will be required to avoid ghosting of the image. For good colour reproduction, the camera manufacturer should be consulted before selecting the colour rendering of the light source and, if there is any doubt about the sensitivity of the camera, the light intensity needed.

The other aspect of cameras that needs care is their limited dynamic range. A high level of illuminance uniformity is necessary if dark areas in the CCTV image are to be avoided. Further, care should be taken to mount CCTV cameras in positions where they do not receive any light directly from the luminaires as such light will sometimes cause a 'white-out' of that part of the image. Information can be obtained from CCTV suppliers about the uniformity of lighting required for a clear and uniform image.

In some high security areas, infrared lights are used for the CCTV to allow a CCTV view of the area without inadvertently providing light for potential intruders. However, infrared images do not allow easy recognition of an intruder's features. Also, there are many applications where non-maintained security lights are used that are triggered to come on when the intruder is detected by the monitoring system (PIR, HF, laser etc). These are also sometimes linked to the monitor system to draw the attention of the security staff to the images of areas where the lights have been triggered.

27.2.6   Impact on the surrounding area

Security lighting should be limited to the protected area. Stray light from a security lighting installation may be considered to be light trespass by neighbours and a source of sky glow by others. Further, where signal lights are used to control traffic on roads and railways, care should be taken to avoid confusion caused by either disability glare to the observer, veiling reflections on the signals, or the identification of the security lighting itself as a signal.

27.3   Lighting recommendations

27.3.1   Illuminance and illuminance uniformity

The recommendations for security lighting involve maintained mean illuminance, illuminance uniformity, glare control and light source colour properties. The maintained mean illuminance and illuminance uniformity recommendations are given for secure areas and public areas separately. The recommendations for glare control and light source colour properties are applicable to both. The maintained mean illuminances listed in Tables 27.1 and 27.2 are derived from BS 12464-2 (BSI, 2014) and are minima. It may be necessary to increase these illuminances where the risks of crime are unusually high.

Table 27.1 Illuminance recommendations for security lighting of secure areas

Application	Minimum maintained mean illuminance (lx)	Illuminance uniformity (minimum/average)	Notes
Large open areas, e.g. storage yards	5	0.1	The illuminance is measured on the horizontal surface of the area, using the method given in BS 5489-1 (BSI, 2013) Higher illuminance may be required if work is being carried out
Building façades	5	0.1	The illuminance is measured on the building facade
Fences	5	0.1	The illuminance is measured on the ground on either side of the fence
Entrances/gatehouses	100	—	The illuminance is measured at ground level; in addition, a vertical illuminance of 25 lx should be provided at the level of the vehicle driver

Table 27.2 Illuminance recommendations for security lighting of public areas

Application	Minimum maintained mean illuminance (lx)	Illuminance uniformity (minimum/average)	Notes
Light traffic and low crime risk car parks	5	0.25	The illuminance is measured on the ground, using the method given in BS 5489-1 (BSI, 2013)
Medium traffic or medium crime risk car parks	10	0.25	The illuminance is measured on the ground, using the method given in BS 5489-1 (BSI, 2013)
Heavy traffic or high crime risk car parks	20	0.25	The illuminance is measured on the ground, using the method given in BS 5489-1 (BSI, 2013)
Paths in public parks where risk assessment shows the need	10	0.25	The illuminance is measured on the ground or pathways
Service station: pump area	50	0.33	The illuminance is measured on the ground
Service station: storefront	30	0.33	The illuminance is measured on the ground

27.3.2 Glare control

Glare control for outdoor lighting is quantified by the glare rating. The glare rating is calculated using the method set out in CIE Publication 112: 1994 (CIE, 1994) and in the *SLL Code for Lighting* (SLL, 2012). The glare rating will vary with viewing direction. For altitude, it is usually assumed that the observer is looking two degrees below the horizontal. For azimuth, calculations are done in 45-degree steps around the observation point.

It is important when designing security lighting to be clear about the value of glare. Where clear visibility at a distance is important to those guarding a secure area or those using a public area, glare needs to be carefully controlled. A glare rating of 30 or less is recommended. This can usually be achieved by eliminating any direct view of the light source for all luminaires mounted below 5 m. A different approach is where the security lighting is to be used to make it difficult for potential intruders to see into a site, glare is a positive so a direct view of the light source and a low mounting height are encouraged. For such applications, a glare rating of 70 or greater is recommended. However, this method should be used with caution, and consideration should be given to control systems, to reduce the effect of sky glow and nuisance light trespass.

27.3.3 Light source colour properties

Light source colour properties are important for naming colours, an element in many witness statements. The ability to name colours accurately and confidently is determined by the light source spectral power distribution and the illuminance. Any light source with a colour rendering index greater than 60 will allow accurate and confident colour naming at the illuminances used in public spaces at night. High pressure sodium lamps allow accurate but less confident colour naming at the higher illuminances used for public spaces but both the accuracy and confidence decline at lower illuminances. Low pressure sodium lamps do not allow accurate colour naming under any luminance and should not be used. Whilst a CRI of 60 may be sufficient, SLL Lighting Guide 6: *The exterior environment* (SLL, 2016) recommends a CRI of 80, or above, where criminal prosecution is likely.

27.4   Approaches to security lighting

27.4.1   Secure areas

The first question to consider is whether to light the space at all. It can be argued that lighting a secure area advertises the presence of something worth taking and hence attracts criminals, so keeping the area dark is a better approach. However, if the criminal already knows the area contains valuable materials, then the absence of lighting makes the secure area more difficult to defend. Thus, the choice of whether to light or not depends on the owner's assessment of risk. If the risk of criminal activity is high, lighting is desirable. If the risk of criminal activity is low, then providing lighting may be counterproductive.

27.4.1.1 Area lighting

Area lighting is commonly used in large open areas such as storage yards and container terminals. Typically, these sites are lit uniformly by floodlighting or roadway luminaires on poles 10 m or more in height. For typical roadway and floodlighting luminaires mounted singly on poles, the desired illuminance uniformity can be achieved by spacing the luminaires at up to six times their mounting height. The actual spacing will depend on the luminous intensity distribution of the luminaire and its light output.

If the area is unobstructed by trees, structures or topography, the most economic installation will be one very tall pole carrying many high-wattage lamps. However, this solution is a poor solution as it also produces the poorest illuminance uniformity, the harshest shadows, and the greatest amount of light trespass. If the area contains obstructions, such as lorries, vans or containers, a design utilizing multiple source locations will reduce shadowing. This is especially true if the luminaires are positioned within the site, between obstructions, and with overlapping light patterns. Reflectance of site materials can also be used to advantage. If the owner uses containers that are painted a highly reflective colour, or paves the area with concrete rather than asphalt, light diffusely reflected from these surfaces will diminish the depth of shadows. Bear in mind though that using reflectance of ground materials in this way will increase the possibility of sky glow.

27.4.1.2 Building façades

Security lighting for building exteriors is based on the principle that all points of entry to the building and the areas around them should be easily seen. Depending on the construction of the building, the points of entry can consist of walls and roof as well as doors and windows. The most comprehensive approach is to light the whole building. Security lighting for buildings is more effective if the building has a high-reflectance facade and the area adjacent to the building also has a high reflectance.

The building can be lit by luminaires set in the ground, mounted on the building or mounted on poles. Ground-mounted floodlights can provide uniform building lighting but they are very accessible and hence can easily be sabotaged. Luminaires mounted on the building are more economical than pole-mounted luminaires, since the expense of the pole is eliminated and wiring costs are reduced. However, for anything other than a simple rectangular building, it is difficult to adequately illuminate all of the building surfaces without using an excessive number of luminaires. Pole-mounted luminaires are usually the best option for uniformly lighting the surfaces of buildings and the surrounding area.

27.4.1.3 Perimeter fences

The purpose of lighting perimeter fences is to enable guards to detect holes or damage to the fence, and intruders loitering outside the fence or attempting to get over or through the fence. Fences come in many different forms, from masonry through steel palisades to chain link. The form of lighting used will depend on the possibility of seeing through the fence and whether one or both sides of the fence line are to be patrolled.

If the fence is solid, there is no possibility of seeing through it. Nonetheless, if both sides of the fence are to be guarded, lighting can be provided on both sides by positioning a luminaire directly above the top of the fence. The luminaire should be located well above the top of a wall to reduce the shadowed area at the base of the wall. It should also be vandal resistant to IK10, or better (see Table 23.5).

If a view through the fence is possible, and if the fence is patrolled from either inside or outside the secure area, it is useful to be able to see the area beside both sides of the fence from one side. For this to happen, light needs to be provided on both sides. This can be done from pole-mounted fixtures set back from the fence (Figure 27.2).

Figure 27.2 Lighting from secure side of fence lights area on both sides
(© Brendan Howard/Shutterstock)

In remote locations where there is no other site lighting, lighting designed to deliberately produce disability glare to people outside a fence can be used for perimeter fences enclosing large areas. In this system, a line of high-luminance luminaires is mounted at eye level and aimed outward from the secure area. For glare-lighting to be effective, the secure area should not be otherwise illuminated, any fence material should be of low reflectance and the luminaires should be closely spaced. Further, patrol roads or paths should be located within the perimeter fence, behind the line of the glare-lighting luminaires. This approach should be used with caution because of the likelihood of light trespass to nearby residents and visual discomfort to passers-by (Figure 27.3).

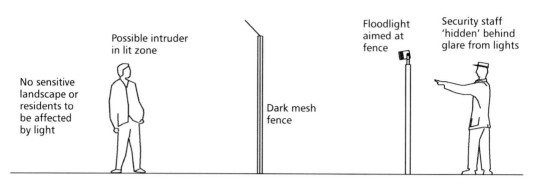

Figure 27.3 Floodlights between security patrol route and fence

27.4.1.4 Entrances and gatehouses

Access to a secure area is usually controlled by security personnel whose duty is to stop and inspect people and vehicles entering and leaving the site. At most exposed locations, a gatehouse will be provided. The entrance should be equipped with multiple luminaires so the loss of any one luminaire will not seriously degrade the lighting available to the guard on duty.

All vehicle entrances should have luminaires located so as to facilitate complete inspection of vehicles and their contents. Lights should be located to illuminate the vehicle license plate. Where on-coming vehicles approach the guardhouse, signs may be appropriate instructing drivers to turn off headlamps. In high security areas, some luminaires should be mounted at or near ground level to facilitate inspection of the underside of the vehicle.

These luminaires can be controlled with a manual switch or remote sensing device. Having a concrete road surface to increase the reflected light will help in the inspection of the underside of vehicles. Consideration should be given to providing back-up power supplies for use during electrical outages.

Care should be taken to provide good vertical illuminance so as to allow for facial identification, inspection of credentials, and packages without use of auxiliary hand-held devices such as flashlights.

Illumination inside the guardhouse should be limited to the minimum required for the completion of assigned tasks, such as report writing and equipment use. The ability to reduce the illuminance is necessary to allow the guard to see clearly through the windows at night and to limit the ability of someone approaching the gatehouse to see what the guard is doing inside. A ratio of 5:1 exterior/interior is recommended. Well-shielded task luminaires are essential to avoid reflections on any surveillance monitors and the windows of the gatehouse. Fitting the gatehouse with specular-reflecting, low-transmission glass at a tilted angle, painting the inside of the gatehouse in dark colours and ensuring that illumination can be dimmed will all help limit the view into the gatehouse.

27.4.2 Public spaces

The ultimate aim of the lighting of public spaces is to make the space look attractive and safe and hence encourage its use at night. Lighting can contribute to this perception by allowing action at a distance. What this means is that by enhancing the visibility of people and faces, suspicious or threatening behaviour may be detected early enough for an escape to be made. Similarly, greater visibility provided by lighting may enable people behaving in a suspicious manner to be recognized or at least described. Such observations at a distance are a benefit to the law-abiding and a disadvantage to the criminal.

Lighting designed to allow action at a distance requires that attention be paid to the illuminance provided, the uniformity of illuminance, the presence of disability glare and the spectral power distribution of the light source. For people to have a reasonable perception of safety at night in car parks and on business streets, the horizontal illuminance on the ground should lie somewhere between 10 and 50 lx depending on the ambient illuminance. Below 10 lx, perceptions of safety deteriorate rapidly. Above 50 lx, perceptions of safety are close to the maximum possible, so there is little more to gain from higher illuminances.

As for illuminance uniformity, if the principal of action at a distance is to be followed, it is essential that excessive variations in illuminance be avoided. Close spacing of luminaires is particularly important if excessive variation in the vertical illuminances on faces is to be avoided.

The most common sources of disability glare at night are luminaires in unsuitable locations, poor aiming of luminaires or poor luminaire design. This last problem is particularly common in 'historic' luminaires, which combine little shielding of the light source with low mounting heights. Care in the selection of luminaires, their aiming and mounting heights are essential if disability glare is to be avoided.

27.4.2.1 Car parks

The recommended minimum maintained mean illuminance for car parks depends on the level of traffic and the risk of crime (Table 27.2). Where traffic is light and the risk of crime is low, a minimum maintained mean illuminance of 5 lx is adequate; refer to BS 5489-1 (BSI, 2013). More traffic or greater crime risk implies higher illuminances for security lighting. Car parks are usually lit by pole-mounted luminaires arranged around and within the car park.

27.4.2.2 Parks

Parks and similar areas are intended for the pleasure and relaxation of the public but it is difficult to relax if one is worried about the possibility of assault. Lighting of such sites requires that people visiting the park should be able to see clearly all around them without destroying the ambience of the park. There are many different approaches that can be used, ranging from conventional path lighting to landscape lighting (see SLL Lighting Guide 6: *The Exterior Environment* (SLL, 2016)).

27.4.2.3 Service stations and mini-marts

These locations are often round-the-clock operations. A minimum maintained mean illuminance of 50 lx on the ground is recommended for all parking and customer use areas, including petrol pumps and islands, and air and water stations. Surrounding areas should be illuminated to a minimum maintained mean illuminance of 30 lx. A minimum vertical illuminance of 10 lx at 1.5 m above ground level should be provided for lighting faces. Where CCTV is in use these values may need to be increased, depending on advice from the camera suppliers.

27.4.3 Private areas

Security lighting for private houses differs from that provided for secure areas and public spaces because houses usually do not have the physical defences of secure spaces. The size of the house, the distance from neighbours, the nature of the terrain and whether the house is in a rural, suburban or urban area are all factors to be considered. Deterrence is usually the number one priority in residential security, followed by detection, recognition and, if all else fails, a signal for help.

Single-family houses

Illumination at the front entrance is mainly for the identification of callers. Luminaires on either side of the door aid recognition by lighting the face from two directions. Luminaires should not be located directly above or behind where a person at the door would be standing. The minimum vertical illuminance at head height should be 10 lx.

The front, back and sides of the house are best illuminated using luminaires mounted on the building itself. This method increases the illumination on the face if the correct luminaires are selected and should be controlled with a motion sensor. As a person approaches, the sensor will activate the luminaires, confronting an intruder with a well-lit environment.

The minimum maintained vertical illuminances for the surfaces of a private house should be in the range 5 to 20 lx, the actual illuminance being determined by the risk of crime and the ambient illuminance. The minimum recommended uniformity for all surfaces is 0.25.

27.5   Lighting equipment

27.5.1   Luminaires

The selection of the luminaire will be based on the light source to be used, the desired luminous intensity distribution, aesthetics and the degree to which the luminaire will be exposed to the environment. Environmental factors to be considered include exposure to wind, rain and salt; temperature extremes; luminaire mounting location; and the level of vulnerability of the luminaire to damage by attack (see Chapter 23, 'Extreme environments').

Any fixture mounted in an area that will be exposed to the weather should have an appropriate ingress protection (IP) rating (see Chapter 23, Tables 23.3 and 23.4).

Luminaires that are located in areas that are not temperature controlled may need special components depending on the light source used. Fluorescent light sources are most affected by ambient temperature extremes. Where the outside temperature is likely to drop below 5 °C, an LED or HID light source is recommended.

Any luminaire mounted on a ceiling or wall less than 3 m above the ground is likely to be the subject of vandalism or tampering with by intruders. Vandal resistant lighting should be considered in these applications. See Chapter 23, section 23.2.8, for information on impact (IK) ratings.

27.5.2   Lighting columns

The higher luminaires are mounted from the ground, the fewer columns and luminaires will be required to light a given area and the less likelihood of vandalism. As column heights are reduced, more columns with lower wattage luminaires are required to avoid glare and non-uniform lighting patterns. Steel and concrete columns are most resistant to attack. Aluminium and fibreglass columns can be damaged by forced oscillation. Columns made of these materials should be avoided in areas where vandalism is prevalent.

27.5.3   Lighting controls

Security lighting should always be controlled automatically; activation should never be made the responsibility of an individual. System design should consider the possibility of power outages and lamp failure. Redundancy should be considered when assigning luminaires to 'zones' of control so that the failure of one luminaire does not leave a large area unlit.

Types of automatic controls suitable for security lighting operation include time clocks, photocells, dimmers and motion detectors.

27.5.3.1 Time clocks

These are generally used to control large areas from one location, such as shopping centre car parks. Astronomical time clocks can be programmed to automatically adjust on-off times with the changes of season. All time clocks should include a battery back-up.

27.5.3.2 Photocell control

These daylight sensors are used to control individual or groups of luminaires. They can be designed to automatically energize luminaires during dark periods regardless of time of day. They have the added advantage of not needing to be re-set after power outages or at the changes to and from daylight saving time. Photocells should not be mounted where the light sensing area may be subject to flashlights, vehicle headlight beams or floodlights.

27.5.3.3 Dimmers

These can be used to reduce illumination and power demand by a set amount during low traffic periods in such applications as office car parks during working hours or shopping centre car parks late at night. By dimming all luminaires, the entire area remains uniformly illuminated.

27.5.3.4 Motion detectors

These are used to switch on specific luminaires when motion is detected. Motion detectors can employ infrared or ultrasonic technology. Passive infrared detectors (DIDs) are the predominant choice outdoors, due to the sensitivity of ultrasonic detectors to movement caused by wind. There are detectors with twin beams that are triggered by something tall, like a human being, but not by an animal such as a fox or domestic cat. Also, there are 'intelligent' versions that 'analyse' the movement and then only signal if the movement is suspicious. The designer should review the coverage pattern with the manufacturer's data to determine suitability for the application. Due to the run-up time of HID light sources, motion detectors should only be used with LED and fluorescent light sources.

Further detailed information on lighting controls is given in Chapter 10, 'Controls'.

27.5.4   Maintenance

No security lighting system can remain effective without regularly scheduled maintenance. A planned maintenance program should include: immediate replacement of failed lamps, repair or replacement of vandalized luminaires, regular cleaning and cutting back of any encroaching vegetation.

Further detailed information on lighting maintenance is given in Chapter 32, 'Maintenance'.

References

BSI (2013) BS 5489-1: 2013: *Code of practice for the design of road lighting. Lighting of roads and public amenity areas* (London: British Standards Institution)

BSI, 2014) BS 12464-2: 2014: *Light and lighting. Lighting of work places. Outdoor work places* (London: British Standards Institution)

CIE, 1994) CIE 112-1994: *Glare evaluation system for use within outdoor sport and area lighting* (Vienna: International Commission on Illumination)

SLL (2012) *SLL Code for Lighting* (London: Society of Light and Lighting)

SLL (2016) *The exterior environment* SLL Lighting Guide 6 (London: Society of Light and Lighting)

Chapter 28: Sports

28.1 Functions of lighting for sports

The function of lighting for sports is primarily to make what is going on highly visible to participants and spectators, without discomfort to either. Sports can be played both outdoors and indoors. Outdoor facilities range from large multi-use stadia to village tennis courts. Indoor facilities range from multi-use sports halls to single use swimming pools.

Some sports, such as football, rugby, cricket, tennis and golf, are big business while others, such as archery and curling, are specialist interests. Big businesses often depend on sales of television rights for a significant proportion of their income. In such circumstances, the lighting also has to serve the needs of television transmission so that the spectators watching via a screen can see what is going on. In many cases the lighting will be designed primarily for the needs of the broadcaster which take precedence over the needs of the player or spectator.

The guidance given here is for the most popular sports. Detailed guidance on lighting for a wider range of sports can be obtained from the SLL Lighting Guide 4: *Sports lighting* (SLL, 2006). The governing bodies of some sports make their own lighting recommendations. These recommendations may exceed those given here. The recommendations given here, and in SLL Lighting Guide 4, should be treated as minima.

28.2 Factors to be considered

Sports facilities come in many different forms: private and public, large and small. They can cater for thousands of spectators or for the players alone. The sports themselves can call for fine discrimination of rapidly moving targets or simply the ability to see a stationary target in a known position. The directions of view can vary widely from predominantly upward, as in badminton, to predominantly downward as in snooker, and anywhere in between, as in football. Despite the variability faced by the designer of sports lighting, the objectives are the same everywhere. They are:

- to facilitate a high level of performance by the players

- to enable spectators, both present and remote, to see clearly what is going on

- to enable the sport to be played after dark

- to create a safe environment for both players and spectators

- to create a comfortable visual environment for both players and spectators.

To meet these objectives it is necessary to consider many aspects of the situation. Those listed below are relevant to all sports lighting applications.

28.2.1 Standard of play and viewing distance

Any sport can be played at different levels, from the elite professional to the amateur. Providing lighting suitable for the amateur in a facility used by the completely professional is a disservice to the sport. Equally, providing the lighting necessary for the professional in a facility used by the amateur is a waste of money. Therefore, sports lighting recommendations are divided into three classes according the standard or level of competition.

Another factor that influences sports lighting recommendations are the distances from which spectators have to view the sport. The greater the distance from which spectators view the activity and the finer the detail that has to be seen, the higher the class of lighting recommended.

The three classes of lighting recommendations are:

(1) Lighting class 1:

- international and national competition
- large numbers of spectators with long viewing distances
- top level supervised training.

(2) Lighting class II:

- mid-level competition, principal local clubs and county regional competition
- medium numbers of spectators with medium viewing distances
- high level supervised training.

(3) Lighting class III:

- low-level competition; local or small club competition
- minimal or no spectator provision
- general training; school sports or recreational activities.

The nature of some sports, particularly the speed with which visual information needs to be processed, means there is some overlap in the lighting recommendations for different sports at different levels.

28.2.2 Playing area

The nominal playing area is the marked-out area of the court or pitch for the sport. However, for some sports, such as tennis, there is a larger area surrounding the nominal playing area within which play may occur. Further, even when play is confined to the nominal playing area, there is a surrounding area that a player may enter, e.g. the area around a football pitch. The total area to be lit includes the actual playing area and the safety zone around the actual playing area.

Unlike indoor lighting, such as in offices, where the lighting level is not calculated in a 0.5 m margin against walls, with sport, play takes place right up to the edge of the marked area. Indeed critical judgements often have to be made along the edge of the marked area. For this reason the lighting should meet the performance requirement up to the edge of the playing area. Advice on nominal playing areas and total areas for different sports can be obtained from the governing bodies of the sports and, for some sports, from SLL Lighting Guide 4: *Sports lighting* (SLL, 2006).

28.2.3 Luminaires

Luminaires used to light some sports facilities, such as sports halls, are at risk of damage from flying objects. To minimize this risk, where possible, luminaires should be located outside the main activity zone and should be adequately protected by nets, wire mesh etc. Further, luminaires and the associated protection should be designed so as not to contain any traps for balls, shuttlecocks etc.

Luminaires used in swimming pools may be subject to a corrosive atmosphere. Careful selection of luminaires is necessary to minimize this problem. Care needs to be taken in locating luminaires so that they can be accessed for maintenance/cleaning and not cause reflections on the water towards spectators and lifeguard positions. See also Chapter 23, section 23.2.5, for safety information for lighting within pools.

28.2.4   Television

Television cameras cannot match the human eye, neither for its sensitivity nor for its ability to adjust rapidly to sudden changes in luminance and colour. This means that where television cameras are regularly used at a sports facility, the lighting design needs to be more stringent. Lighting level, uniformity, glare and colour are critical factors in achieving good quality pictures. The depth of field of a camera will depend on the lighting level available in the direction of view of the camera. Consistency of light and colour over the playing area are important to avoid adjustments to the camera after the initial set-up. And lights directed towards the camera can cause picture flare. The correct location of floodlights is critical to achieving these objectives.

Broadcast technology is continually advancing with high definition (HD), 4 K and 8 K becoming standard. SLL Lighting Guide 4: *Sports lighting* (SLL, 2006) gives specific requirements for broadcasting, which is generally independent of the sport.

Metrics important for sports broadcasting:

- The minimum vertical illuminance at any point should be greater than 600 lux.

- The minimum/average vertical illuminance ratio should be greater than 0.6.

- The ratio of average vertical illuminances at any point on the four vertical orthogonal planes at 90° facing the four sides of the field of play should be greater than 0.6.

- The ratio of mean horizontal and mean vertical plane illuminances should be between 0.5 and 2.0, inclusive.

- The horizontal illuminance ratio (minimum/average) should be equal to or greater than 0.7.

- On large playing fields, such as football pitches, the maximum gradient in horizontal illuminance should not be greater than 20 percent every 4 m.

- The combined effect of flicker from all light sources at any point on the playing area should be less than 2%.

As for light source colour properties where television is used, for outdoor facilities the correlated colour temperature of the light should be in the range 5000 K to 6500 K. Where there is little contribution from daylight, the correlated colour temperature of the lighting can be within the range 3000 K to 6500 K. For both outdoor and indoor facilities, the general colour rendering index of the light source used should have a minimum value of $R_a 80$. ('Television Lighting Consistency Index' (EBU, 2012) is emerging as a preferred method for assessing the colour performance of lighting for cameras.) Further advice on the lighting of sports events for television broadcasting can be found in BS EN 12193: 2007: *Light and lighting. Sports lighting* (BSI, 2007).

28.2.5   Coping with power failures

Emergency lighting is required to cope with power failures. This can take two basic forms: emergency escape lighting and standby lighting. Emergency escape lighting is designed to help people exit a building quickly and safely, without panic. The requirements for emergency escape lighting are given in Chapter 3 and in SLL Lighting Guide 12: *Emergency lighting* (SLL, 2015).

Standby lighting for sports facilities can also take two forms. The first is safety lighting, which is designed to ensure that the event can be stopped without injury to the players, and the second is continuation lighting, which is designed to enable the event to continue.

Safety lighting is not necessary in all sports, only those where sudden loss of light could result in injury to the players, for example gymnastics, ice hockey, cycling, swimming and horse racing. The illuminance requirements for safety lighting are usually specified as a percentage of the normal illuminance recommendation for a set number of seconds.

Continuation lighting requires the provision of a secondary supply system powered from a generator or a central battery. A typical system would consist of a number of luminaires connected to both the mains supply and to a changeover switch that can detect the power failure and connect the luminaire to the generator or battery unit. If the light source being used is high-pressure discharge, it will also be necessary to use a hot-restrike system. If a generator is to power the secondary lighting system it may also be necessary to have a battery system to provide instant power to cover the run-up time of the generator, which can be as much as 20 seconds. For continuation lighting to be successful, it should provide illuminances at least to the level of those provided for Class III of the particular sport (see section 28.3).

28.2.6   Obtrusive light

Because of the high illuminances required, outdoor sports facilities are a common source of complaints about light pollution. Such complaints can take two forms: light trespass and sky glow.

Complaints about light trespass are usually made by the owners of adjacent properties. If the complaints are justified, the source of complaint can often be removed by careful aiming of the lighting or by bespoke shielding of the luminaires to prevent any direct light from the installation reaching the windows of the complainant (Figure 28.1). Light pollution in the form of light trespass is a recognized statutory nuisance under the Clean Neighbourhoods and Environment Act 2005 (HMSO, 2005).

Figure 28.1 Careful choice of light distribution and aiming
results in minimal spill beyond the playing area
(image courtesy of Paul Ruffles)

Complaints about sky glow are more likely to be made by pressure groups that object to the
use of the facilities at night. It is not the job of lighting designers to justify the use of sports
facilities at night but it is their job to minimize the amount of sky glow. This can be done by the
careful selection and aiming of luminaires and the advocacy of a curfew system for the use of
the lighting. Advice on designing outdoor lighting with minimum sky glow is given in the SLL's
Guide to limiting obtrusive light (SLL, 2012), CIE Publication 150: *Guide on the limitation of the effects
of obtrusive light from outdoor lighting installations* (2003) and ILP publication: *Guidance notes for the
reduction of obtrusive light* (ILP, 2005).

28.3 Lighting recommendations

The following tables summarize the recommendations for the lighting of sports facilities in
the different lighting classes. The recommendations are given for sports of majority interest.
Recommendations for lighting sports of minority interest are available in SLL Lighting
Guide 4: *Sports lighting* (SLL, 2006). The following notes are essential for interpreting the
recommendations.

The horizontal and vertical illuminances given are both minimum maintained average values.
Horizontal illuminance is for the playing surface. Vertical illuminance is usually on a specified
plane at a given height above the ground. Methods for measuring or calculating the mean
illuminance are given in SLL Lighting Guide 4.

Illuminance uniformity is the ratio of minimum illuminance to the mean illuminance over the
actual playing area. Methods for measuring or calculating the illuminance uniformity are given
in SLL Lighting Guide 4.

For indoor facilities, glare control is achieved by specifying a maximum unified glare rating
(UGR). For outdoor facilities, glare control is achieved by specifying a maximum glare rating.

28.3.1   Athletics

Athletics can take place outdoors in a stadium or indoors in an arena. The lighting in both sorts of facility should be adequate for both field and track events. Where sports involving flying missiles, such as the discus, javelin and hammer are to take place, the lighting should ensure the missile is visible throughout its flight. For the track, the vertical illuminance at the finishing line should be at least 1000 lx to enable the photo-finish equipment to operate. For class III outdoor tracks, the recommended horizontal illuminance can be reduced to 50 lx for jogging.

Table 28.1 Lighting recommendations for indoor athletics

Class	Horizontal illuminance (lx)	Illuminance uniformity	Colour rendering index
I	500	0.7	80
II	300	0.6	60
III	200	0.5	60

Table 28.2 Lighting recommendations for outdoor athletics

Class	Horizontal illuminance (lx)	Illuminance uniformity	Colour rendering index	Glare rating
I	500	0.7	70	50
II	200	0.7	60	50
III	100	0.5	60	55

28.3.2   Bowls

Bowls requires the players to be able to see the jack, the lie of the woods around the jack and the run of a live wood. To achieve this, a high level of illuminance uniformity is necessary and glare needs to controlled. An illuminance gradient of not more than 5 percent per metre is recommended.

For indoor bowls, the usual lighting approach is to use linear LED or fluorescent luminaires mounted at least 3 m above the floor, ideally on either side of the lanes (Figure 28.2). Glare is controlled by the choice of luminaire and ensuring that the reflectances of the walls and ceiling are at least 0.4 and 0.6 respectively.

Figure 28.2 Indoor bowling green showing luminaires parallel to the lines of play

For outdoor bowls, the usual lighting system is floodlights mounted at the corners of the green. Light should reach all parts of the green from at least two directions if good modelling is to be provided. Glare is controlled by careful selection of mounting height and aiming of floodlights.

Table 28.3 Lighting recommendations for indoor bowls

Class	Horizontal illuminance (lx)	Illuminance uniformity	Colour rendering index
I	500	0.8	80
II	500	0.8	60
III	300	0.5	60

Table 28.4 Lighting recommendations for outdoor bowls

Class	Horizontal illuminance (lx)	Illuminance uniformity	Colour rendering index	Glare rating
I	200	0.7	70	50
II	100	0.7	60	50
III	50	0.5	60	55

28.3.3 Cricket

Cricket is played with a hard ball delivered at high speed. The bowler needs to have a clear view of the pitch and wicket. The batsman needs to have a clear view of the bowler's action and run-up. The fielders need to be able to see the flight of the ball. To meet these objectives more light is usually provided more uniformly in the square near the wicket than in the outfield, and glare needs to be limited as far as possible.

For indoor cricket, which can take the forms of games and training nets, the usual lighting approach is to use linear LED or fluorescent luminaires mounted parallel with the line of bowling, with care taken to minimize glare. The luminaires are protected by nets hung at least 1 m below the luminaires, ideally on either side of the lanes (Figure 28.3).

Figure 28.3 Indoor cricket training facility showing luminaires parallel to the axis of play with the nets being used to reduce glare

For outdoor cricket, the usual lighting system uses high mounted floodlights. Light should reach all parts of the field from at least two directions. Glare is controlled by careful selection of mounting height and aiming of floodlights. A white ball is often used after dark to give a better contrast against the night sky.

Table 28.5 Lighting recommendations for indoor cricket

Class	Horizontal illuminance (lx)	Illuminance uniformity	Colour rendering index
I	750	0.7	80
II	500	0.7	60
III	300	0.7	60

Table 28.6 Lighting recommendations for indoor cricket training nets

Class	Horizontal illuminance (lx)	Illuminance uniformity	Colour rendering index
I	1500	0.8	80
II	1000	0.8	60
III	750	0.8	60

Table 28.7 Lighting recommendations for outdoor cricket

Class	Horizontal illuminance on wicket square (lx)	Illuminance uniformity on wicket square	Horizontal illuminance on outfield (lx)	Horizontal illuminance uniformity on outfield	Colour rendering index	Glare rating
I	750	0.7	500	0.5	60	50
II	500	0.7	300	0.5	60	50
III	300	0.5	200	0.3	60	55

28.3.4   Five-a-side football (indoor)

In this sport, players must be able to follow the movement of both the ball and other players. This sport usually takes place in multi-use sports halls (Figure 28.4). The lighting usually consists of a regular array of ceiling mounted luminaires spaced to provide the necessary illuminance uniformity. The luminaires need to be protected from the ball. Glare can be reduced by ensuring the ceiling has a reflectance in the range 0.6 to 0.9.

Figure 28.4 Good uniformity provided over all of playing area

Table 28.8 Lighting recommendations for indoor five-a-side football

Class	Horizontal illuminance (lx)	Illuminance uniformity	Colour rendering index
I	750	0.7	80
II	500	0.7	60
III	200	0.5	60

28.3.5   Fitness training

Fitness training involves the use of equipment such as weights, treadmills and rowing machines. The purpose of the lighting is to allow safe operation of the equipment and to provide a comfortable environment. Usually, the lighting consists of a regular array of ceiling mounted luminaires. The reflectance of the ceiling should be 0.6 or more so as to buffer the brightness of the luminaires viewed directly by someone looking upwards.

Table 28.9 Lighting recommendations for fitness training

Class	Horizontal illuminance (lx)	Illuminance uniformity	Colour rendering index
I, II, and III	500	0.8	60

28.3.6   Football

Football involves the rapid passage of a ball combined with physical contact between players. At high levels, these sports attract large numbers of spectators, which means that attention should be paid to emergency lighting and the lighting requirements may be specified by UEFA or FIFA. The purpose of the general lighting is to provide uniform illumination of the pitch, with good modelling of players and without shadows or glare to players or spectators. This purpose can be met by a number of different approaches, from pole-mounted floodlights to continuous lines of floodlights mounted on the roofs of grandstands. If the former approach is used, it is important to note that for association and Gaelic football, lighting masts should not be located within 10° of the goal line axis.

Table 28.10 Lighting recommendations for Association, Gaelic and American football

Class	Horizontal illuminance (lx)	Illuminance uniformity	Colour rendering index	Glare rating
I	500	0.7	70	55
II	200	0.6	60	55
III	75	0.5	60	55

28.3.7   Lawn tennis

The main visual requirements in tennis are for the players, match officials and spectators to see the ball, player and court clearly. The flight of the ball indoors will be seen easily if the ball is seen against a dark background. The reflectance of any vertical fabrics or surfaces surrounding the court should not be greater than 0.5. The ceiling above the court and extending 3 m behind the base lines should be kept free from luminaires. Typical lighting systems for indoor courts use luminaires that are mounted parallel to the sidelines, extend beyond the baselines and are outside the court area. For outdoor courts, sharp cut-off floodlights mounted on columns to the sides of the court are the usual choice. The choice of light source depends on the material forming the court. For both indoor and outdoor courts, the Lawn Tennis Association has specific illuminance requirements for the total area and the principal area (see section 28.2.2).

Table 28.11 Lighting recommendations for tennis (indoor)

Class	Horizontal illuminance on principal area (lx)	Illuminance uniformity on principal area	Colour rendering index
I	750	0.7	80
II	500	0.7	60
III	300	0.5	60

Table 28.12 Lighting recommendations for tennis (outdoor)

Class	Horizontal illuminance on principal area (lx)	Illuminance uniformity on principal area	Colour rendering index	Glare rating
I	500	0.7	70	50
II	300	0.7	60	50
III	200	0.6	60	55

28.3.8 Rugby (union and league)

Rugby involves the rapid passage of a ball combined with physical contact between players. At high levels, these sports attract large numbers of spectators, which means that attention should be paid to emergency lighting. The purpose of the general lighting is to provide uniform illumination of the whole pitch, with good modelling of players and without shadows or glare to players or spectators. This purpose can be met by a number of different approaches, from pole-mounted floodlights to continuous lines of floodlights mounted on the roofs of grandstands. If pole-mounted floodlights are used, they should be positioned so that they do not obstruct the view of spectators. If floodlights mounted on the roofs of stands are used care should be taken that shadows are not cast onto the pitch. For rugby, it is permissible to place floodlights in line with the try line.

Table 28.13 Lighting recommendations for rugby (union and league)

Class	Horizontal illuminance (lx)	Illuminance uniformity	Colour rendering index	Glare rating
I	500	0.7	70	55
II	200	0.6	60	55
III	75	0.5	60	55

28.3.9 Swimming

Swimming is not a sport that requires the participant to undertake difficult visual tasks. The purpose of the lighting of swimming pools is to ensure safety and to provide a pleasant ambience. The safety requirement will be met by lighting that provides sufficient illuminance with careful control of reflections from the water surface (see section 28.4.4). To ensure safety in the event of a power failure, safety lighting that produces 5% of the recommended illuminance for at least 30 seconds should be provided. Diving areas require special consideration with regard to glare and modelling.

Table 28.14 Lighting recommendations for swimming in indoor and outdoor pools

Class	Horizontal illuminance (lx)	Horizontal illuminance uniformity	Colour rendering index	Horizontal/vertical illuminance ratio for diving area
I	500	0.7	70	0.8
II	300	0.7	60	0.5
III	200	0.5	60	0.5

28.4 Lighting in large facilities

28.4.1 Multi-use sports halls

As its name implies, a multi-use sports hall is an indoor facility where many different sports are played, sometimes simultaneously, and where there is only limited provision for spectators. The essential characteristics of the lighting of multi-use sports halls are enough illuminance provided uniformly without glare. Given the multiple uses of the sports hall, this implies some flexibility in the lighting through switching (Figure 28.5).

Figure 28.5 High uniformity provided for various sports by switching different groups of luminaires

The usual design approach is to first identify the sports that will need to be accommodated and the potential for non-sporting uses. The lighting requirements for each sport need to be established and the relative importance of the sports listed. The lighting approach most commonly used is a ceiling-mounted regular array general lighting system with switching arrangements for different activities, levels of play or simultaneous use. With such a system, the illuminance on the walls and ceiling should be at least 50% and 30% respectively of the illuminance on the playing area. It is important for the layout of the playing areas and the type and layout of the lighting to be planned together. Where the different sports have been prioritized, the lighting should be designed to meet the requirements of the highest priority sport while ensuring that, as far as possible, all other activities are catered for. Where there is limited information on expected usage, or badminton is one of the sports to be catered for, the lighting should be designed to suit the layout of the badminton courts. Badminton has the most exacting visual requirements of the sports played in multi-use sports halls and a lighting scheme that satisfies the requirements for badminton and is matched to the court layouts will often cater adequately for a wide range of other sports.

Where there are activities such as gymnastics or trampolining, safety lighting should be provided to ensure safety in the event of a power failure. This should produce 5% of the recommended illuminance for at least 30 seconds.

28.4.2   Small sports stadia

A small sports stadium is an outdoor sports ground consisting of a central field area surrounded by an athletics track and sometimes a cycle track. The central area may be used for field athletics and other sports such as football, rugby and hockey. The spectator capacity is typically less then 5000, usually in a grandstand located on one side. The sports taking place in small sports stadia are usually at the level of lighting classes II and III. Floodlights mounted on masts either at the four corners of the stadium or located around the perimeter of the track, except in front of the grandstand, are the most common approaches. Floodlights can also be mounted on the grandstand provided care is taken to avoid casting shadows onto the track and central area. Figure 28.6 below shows the criteria for determining a suitable mounting height of floodlighting mounted around the track. Care should also be taken to avoid glare to participants in field events involving throwing and jumping.

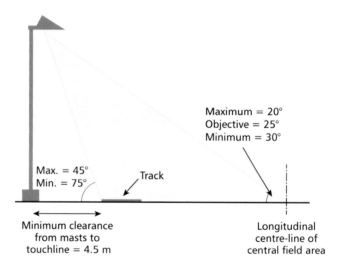

Figure 28.6 Section over half the playing area showing the criteria for the mounting height for side lighting

28.4.3   Indoor arenas

Indoor arenas are usually built to cater for a variety of events, some sporting and some not. Permanent spectator seating is arranged around the event floor with temporary seating being placed on the floor as required. Given the variety of uses, the temptation is to design the lighting to meet all possibilities but experience suggests that the best approach is to provide permanent lighting for the main sports event and for setting up, using temporary lighting for any specific event that calls for something different (Figure 28.7).

The usual approach for lighting the sports area of indoor arenas is to use floodlights similar to those used for outdoor stadia. The design is built up from overlapping beams until the whole area is covered. Higher illuminances are created by adding more layers. Some flexibility is needed to cover different sports that use different parts of the sport area. This can be achieved by switching different layers of light.

Figure 28.7 A large multi-functional indoor arena in use for ice sports

Given the different uses to which an arena may be put, there will be a need for frequent changes of the floor. This requires a separate lighting installation for setting up, a lighting installation that provides 100 lx on the floor. If the set-up lighting is also used as house lighting, a light source with a colour rendering index of 80 should be used. If the set-up lighting is not used as house lighting, a separate lighting installation will be needed over the permanent seating providing a similar illuminance to the set-up lighting. This lighting may need to be dimmed during the events.

28.4.4   Swimming pools

Swimming pools vary widely in design but they all share the problem of high luminance reflections from the water surface. This is important because such reflections tend to mask what is happening beneath the water. The reflectance of water increases rapidly as the angle of incidence exceeds 70°. In principle, it should be easy to eliminate high luminance reflections by ensuring that the angle of incidence is below 70°. However, movement of the water means that the angle of incidence can vary dramatically.

For indoor pools, a good approach is to use indirect lighting designed to ensure that there are no high luminances to be reflected, apart from any views of the sky and sun through windows or skylights (Figure 28.8).

Figure 28.8 Indoor 50 m swimming pool illuminated
by indirect lighting to reduce surface reflections

There are two factors that influence the location of indirect luminaires. The first is the need to maintain the luminaires. Luminaires should not be located over the pool unless they are accessible from catwalks or from behind the ceiling. The second is the need to avoid glare to spectators and pool attendants, both of whom may be sitting some height above the water. Luminaires in indoor pools should be constructed to withstand high temperatures, humidity and corrosion. A minimum IP rating of IP54 is recommended. See Chapter 23, section 23.2.5, for information on the IP rating system.

For outdoor pools, lighting is usually provided by floodlights mounted on masts around the pool. The mounting height should be such that the angle of incidence on the far side of the pool is more than 50° and preferably 60°.

Both indoor and outdoor pools may have underwater lighting. This reduces the effect on visibility of high luminance reflections from the water surface. Underwater lighting takes two forms, dry and wet. Dry underwater lighting has the luminaires behind watertight portholes. Wet underwater lighting has the luminaires in the water but with cables long enough so that they can be serviced from the poolside. Narrow beam floodlights are used for underwater lighting, with the beam axis aimed approximately 10° above the horizontal. Almost total internal reflection takes place at the surface of the water so there is no risk of glare to surface swimmers, judges or spectators. Underwater lighting should not be used for races or for water polo.

References

BSI (2007) BS EN 12193: 2007: *Light and lighting. Sports lighting* (London: British Standards Institution)

CIE (2003) *Guide on the limitation of the effects of obtrusive light from outdoor lighting installations* CIE Publication 150 (Vienna, Austria: Commission Internationale de l'Eclairage)

EBU (2012) *Television Lighting Consistency Index 2012* [online] (Geneva, Switzerland: European Broadcasting Union) (available at https://tech.ebu.ch/tlci-2012) (accessed August 2017)

HMSO (2005) Clean Neighbourhoods and Environment Act 2005 (London: HMSO) (available at http://www.legislation.gov.uk/ukpga/2005/16) (accessed August 2017)

ILP (2005) *Guidance notes for the reduction of obtrusive light* (Rugby: Institution of Lighting Professionals) (available at https://www.theilp.org.uk/documents/obtrusive-light) (accessed August 2017)

SLL (2006) *Sports lighting* SLL Lighting Guide 4 (London: Society for Light and Lighting)

SLL (2012) *Guide to limiting obtrusive light* (London: Society for Light and Lighting)

SLL (2015) *Emergency lighting* SLL Lighting Guide 12 (London: Society for Light and Lighting)

Chapter 29: Historic buildings and spaces

29.1 Introduction

Historic buildings can be divided into three types:

- old buildings, which have no legal protection due to the level of their architectural or historic interest, being converted to a new use, such as a disused factory becoming a wine bar

- listed historic buildings with a specific function, such as a Victorian art gallery or a working mill

- listed historic building preserved in their own right, such as a stately home or castle.

In addition, when lighting such buildings it is sometimes necessary to consider the spaces surrounding historic buildings especially where the space is partly or fully surrounded by historic buildings, such as many old city squares, some of which are designated World Heritage Sites in their entirety.

29.2 Historic building being converted to a new use

Many old buildings are put to new purposes that require appropriate lighting for the new functions whilst not completely distracting from the historic setting. The degree of exposure of the old fabric of the building does sometimes influence the types of lighting used. For instance, with an old industrial building being converted for start-up units, but where the old internal brickwork and ceilings are left exposed, it might be appropriate to consider luminaires that have an industrial feel about them whilst providing the right lighting levels and glare restrictions for the tasks being carried out in each area. If the interiors are being completely lined in new plaster walls and false ceilings, then it is essentially a new space that happens to be housed in an old shell.

If the building is not a listed building, then there is little limitation on where and how luminaires can be fixed or where cabling can be routed.

29.3 Re-use of historic buildings and interiors

Where the building is of itself a listed building or of historic interest, then the lighting needs more consideration, as it may not be allowed to be fixed to the historic fabric in ways that are permanently damaging to that fabric; equally, the lighting will need to provide the right type of light for the purposes the spaces within the building are being put to.

Thus, in a building being used to display historical artefacts or works of art, the design and provision of lighting shares much in common with other museums and galleries, see Chapter 16, 'Museums and art galleries'. There will be constraints, however, because the architectural and historical integrity of the building must be maintained and the fabric of the building respected. For example, it may be considered appropriate to use modern display techniques designed and installed in such a way that the integrity of the building is maintained. The Water Hall, Birmingham, which occupies part of the 19th-century city hall, is a good example (see Figure 29.1). Here the solution was to build the lighting, as well as other services, into a specially manufactured trunking system. This technique can provide a simple and elegant solution that, because it is not in direct contact with the building, is viewed as an independent element from the historic fabric beyond.

Figure 29.1 The Water Hall, Birmingham. The lighting system provides uplight and track lighting on flying booms that float below the historic fabric of the space (courtesy of Arup/Martine Hamilton Knight)

29.4   Historic buildings preserved 'as is'

Historic buildings, particularly those open to the public that are exhibits in their own right, form part of the national heritage in terms of both architecture and history, and are usually listed in a register of historic buildings. This means the options to change the lighting, wiring or structure are severely limited, which may require the designer to carry out research into the period and to seek advice from the recognised authorities on historic buildings before any changes are carried out.

It is impossible to make general recommendations for lighting historic buildings and structures; the best solution will be determined by what is available and possible in the particular space and, most importantly, the client's lighting requirements and the atmosphere of the space. The success of the building lighting will depend on the inventiveness and ingenuity of the designer.

For mainly daylit spaces, it is usually good to start by looking at what is not well lit when the room is lit only by daylight using the normal degree of control as discussed above. If areas remote from the windows appear under-lit then supplementary electric lighting should be provided and in such a way that it does not destroy the apparent daylit appearance of the space. Supplementary lighting will need to provide a soft enhancement of the daylight illumination without disturbing the natural pattern of light too much. This is best achieved by luminaires that provide a soft wash of light such as table lights or standard lights suitable for the era of the room.

Alternately, or in addition, lights that can be concealed behind or within furniture or other elements of the building can be used. The colour appearance of the light sources should also be considered to ensure that there is no visual clash between daylight and the electric light.

Figure 29.2 Osborne House: lighting provided by original
fittings with modern lamps and lighting controls
(courtesy of Kevan Shaw Lighting Design)

29.4.1 Daylight control

Most historic buildings were designed to be lit by daylight; it is only comparatively recently
that it has been possible to provide sufficient lighting by other means. While it is preferable to
maintain the daylit appearance of the building, this can create serious conservation problems if
the space also contains material likely to fade.

Figure 29.3 The Great Gallery at the Wallace Collection, London. The gallery
displays light-sensitive paintings and was originally lit by daylight (courtesy
of Sutton Vane Associates)

Figure 29.4 The Great Gallery at the Wallace Collection, London. The glass floor is above the gallery. When needed, the daylight from above is reduced by electric blinds or boosted by electric light that matches the colour of the daylight (courtesy of Sutton Vane Associates)

Whilst most rooms will have side windows some will have rooflights where control of sunlight and daylight will be a particular problem, both due to the more direct view of the sky vault and the practicality of control of any blinds or louvres at height.

Wherever the windows, a primary consideration will be whether daylight is to be used for task illumination, thereby reducing electric lighting use. It is usually important to restrict direct sunlight entry into the space to prevent the space becoming overheated and to avoid problems arising from glare. The introduction of blinds and louvres into historic window surrounds will need careful consideration and, in some cases, listed building consent.

See Chapter 2, 'Daylighting' for more details.

29.4.2 Lighting equipment

Any new lighting equipment is usually required to be in visual harmony with the historic interior. In most instances, any equipment that is visible will have to be of a design that matches the period of the building, or at least be sympathetic with it. It is unlikely that such equipment will be able to provide suitable lighting for both the building and the exhibits, so it will usually have to be complemented with concealed luminaires. Care should be taken that concealed luminaires do not create flashes or hotspots that betray their location, nor that the appearance of the light becomes unnatural, see Figure 29.5. There are occasions, however, when the best solution is not to provide an apparently period lighting design but to install a modern lighting system. This will usually apply only where a building is being used for a purpose for which it was not originally intended, e.g. an art gallery. In this case, historical exactness need not apply but due consideration of the proposed methods of display are required.

Where it is decided to use luminaires of the period, either during daytime or after dark, specialist manufacturers can provide electric replicas for this purpose. Consideration must be given to the light sources used in such replicas bearing in mind the amount and nature of the light that would have originally been emitted. Over-lighting a chandelier with inappropriate electric lamps can easily turn a beautiful sparkling piece into an object that cannot be viewed directly with any degree of visual comfort due to glare, thus defeating the reason for including it in the first place. The light provided by such luminaires will often need to be supplemented by background illumination, either to provide light levels expected by modern visitors to see the room or to balance the brightness of the luminaires if they have a high luminance. This applies particularly to luminaires with unscreened light sources, e.g. chandeliers. The techniques for providing supplementary lighting will depend on the room and its furnishings, but the suggestions above for supplementing daylight illumination may be appropriate. However, care should be taken to avoid destroying the apparent effect of the period lighting by obliterating its natural pattern.

Figure 29.5 York Minster is lit with hidden lighting equipment and no flares on the architecture (courtesy of Sutton Vane Associates)

For spaces where there are pictures hung on the walls the use of good quality picture lights could be considered. These not only light the paintings but also add some light back into the space and make the room appear better lit. These lights can be supplied via wall sockets or via wires down the suspension chains or ropes from a connection system at picture rail level. Care must be taken to select suitable picture lights to ensure that the light meets the requirements for conservation of the object. The majority of those currently available are unsuitable for use in a museum or gallery environment. See section 7.10 of SLL Lighting Guide 8 (SLL, 2015) for more information.

The other major constraint will be the limited number of options available for providing an electrical supply to lighting equipment and the installation of the equipment itself. In a few instances surface wiring, suitably disguised to blend with the building, has been successful, but alternative solutions should be sought if at all possible. Floor-standing luminaires are an attractive possibility, although this solution will often demand specially made, or at least specially disguised, equipment. Recent developments in infrared or radio controls allow remote switching and dimming of luminaires that avoids disturbing wall surfaces in order to install local switch drops. See Figure 29.6, where the cable at the base of the uplight has been fixed tightly around the stone mouldings at its base and then down to floor level, where it was run within the joints between flagstones, which were then refilled with mortar.

Figure 29.6 Freestanding uplight with spring-loaded arms locked into side mouldings meaning that there is no fixing into the historic fabric (courtesy of Paul Ruffles)

29.4.3 Emergency lighting in historic interiors

All the basic requirements discussed in Chapter 3, 'Emergency lighting', will apply to most historic interiors. The challenge will be providing functional emergency lighting in a visually acceptable way. This will stretch the ingenuity of the designer but every attempt must be made to reach an acceptable solution. Most enforcement authorities will allow some deviations from the standards in listed buildings. Negotiations with local authority building control, fire officers and appropriate local authority licensing officers should be undertaken at an early stage in the design process to determine appropriate emergency lighting strategies for the specific project.

Figure 29.7 Emergency light concealed in skirting board by exit door from room
(courtesy of Paul Ruffles)

29.5 Historic or sensitive exterior spaces

Many outdoor spaces have similar designation and form part of our heritage, be they the
gardens around a historic building, the streets in a world heritage city, bridges, ruins, or areas of
outstanding natural beauty. These all require extra care in lighting them well and appropriately.
The quality of light and its intensity and direction are important, but so are the daytime
appearance of the lighting infrastructure, see Chapter 25, 'Exterior architectural lighting'.

Although white light is normally recommended for heritage structures and spaces, the careful
use of coloured lighting can add to the atmosphere of some spaces. If you think it wrong to spray
paint the outside of a building or monument deep purple during the day, then is it acceptable to
colour it deep purple at night?

Care is also needed in and around buildings and monuments where bats and other wildlife,
sensitive to nocturnal lighting levels, fly or roost. Local planning departments may restrict
maximum lighting levels or operating times, especially along tree belts and rivers alongside sites.

29.5.1 Lighting equipment

Any new lighting equipment must be in visual harmony with the nature of the space and not
dominate the daytime scene. In most instances, any equipment that is visible will have to be of a
design that matches the period of its surroundings or has design quality if modern (Figure 29.8
below).

Where it is decided to use luminaires of the period, either during daytime or after dark, specialist
manufacturers can provide electric replicas for this purpose. Consideration must be given to
the light sources used in such replicas bearing in mind the amount and nature of the light that
would have originally been emitted.

Mounting luminaires can also prove tricky but, for façade lighting especially, paving stones can
be a useful tool. Luminaires can be fixed to the slab and the slabs laid, unfixed, onto ledges or
other parts of the building, eliminating any intrusion onto the fabric itself.

The routing of underground cabling needs care where there are historic flagstone surfaces or similar that may need to be lifted. In addition, there may be archaeological features directly below all or parts of the present surface. Special sensitivity is needed with buried cabling in or near known graveyards or ancient burial sites.

Figure 29.8 Lighting equipment in a space surrounded by historic buildings should not detract from them. The quality and spread of the lighting should enhance the use and appreciation of the space (courtesy of Paul Ruffles)

29.5.2   Emergency lighting in sensitive exterior spaces

Emergency lighting may be required around buildings to provide safe routes to places of safety if the main exterior lighting fails or there is an area power cut. In some cases, the main lighting can be used in whole or part for this if alternative power is supplied to them by separate protected cabling or they have local battery back-up. Otherwise, small LED floods can be incorporated into columns or bollards housing the main lighting or located separately — again either with an alternative emergency power supply or local battery back-up.

Reference

SLL (2015) *Lighting for museums and art galleries* SLL Lighting Guide 8 (London: Society of Light and Lighting)

Chapter 30: Commissioning of lighting installations

30.1 Context

Lighting installations are made up of equipment including, luminaires, drivers, emergency luminaires and lighting controls.

The installation works should have been completed in accordance with the project specification and certified to the local installation standard such as BS 7671: *Requirements for Electrical Installations. IET Wiring Regulations* (BSI, 2018) and BS 5266-1: *Emergency lighting. Code of practice for the emergency lighting of premises* (BSI, 2016).

Once the installation works are completed, commissioning appropriate to the installation complexity is needed to ensure that the lighting installation operates as intended.

Demonstration and training form part of the commissioning process to ensure that users can set and regulate the controls and settings of luminaires where adjustments are possible. Additionally, commissioning will enable those who will maintain the installation to understand and support it. Verification that the lighting energy consumption meets the design criteria once the building is complete and occupied is also a function of commissioning. Energy consumption should not exceed the requirements of the local Building Regulations.

Commissioning is applicable to new-build and refurbishment or retro-fit applications. If the works are an addition to, or constitute significant alterations to an existing lighting installation, then consideration should be given to conducting a condition survey of the existing lighting installation prior to any additional installation or commissioning works commencing. This will ensure that retained parts of the lighting installation are fit for purpose and sufficient spare capacity exists within the available building power supply and lighting control systems to accommodate the proposed additions.

Consideration should also be given to the possibility of phased commissioning and handover of project sections and the commissioning or part-commissioning of each phase in relation to the client's expectation for phased handover and occupation.

For more detailed information on commissioning lighting installations, refer to CIBSE Commissioning Code L: *Lighting* (CIBSE, 2018).

30.1.1 Luminaires

It should be verified that the specified luminaires have been installed at the correct locations and that the correct lamps, reflectors, diffusers and attachments have been fitted. Certain types of luminaires will also require aiming and/or focusing, and reflectors or filters may need to be correctly aligned to ensure that the light illuminates the intended area or item.

30.1.2 Emergency lighting

Guidance on the commissioning methods and requirements can be found in BS 5266-1: *Emergency lighting: Code of practice for the emergency lighting of premises* (BSI, 2016).

Emergency lighting commissioning includes verifying illumination levels under power failure conditions for compliance with BS 5266-1.

Standby battery duration and the operating and maintenance (O&M) media and training/handover must cover occupier periodic test methods and test documentation.

30.1.3 Lighting controls

Lighting controls often require commissioning by the manufacturer or their agent. This is to ensure that the controls work correctly as per the project specification.

30.1.4 Documentation, training and handover

The lighting installation should be fully documented to ensure an accurate record of the installation is available to enable future repairs, alterations, additions and maintenance to take place. All circuiting and control grouping of the circuiting must be clearly shown on plans located by the distribution boards and programmable management locations. The persons responsible for the lighting installation should be trained on the correct operation, use and maintenance of the installation, before the lighting installation is formally handed over to the users.

30.1.5 Energy efficiency

In respect of the conservation of fuel and power, there are statutory guidelines that refer to commissioning of building services. BS EN 15193-1: *Energy performance of buildings. Energy requirements for lighting. Specifications, Module M9* (BSI, 2017) contains information on the required energy performance for lighting installations for designers and the verification of installed and operational lighting installations. BS EN 15193-1 is a harmonised 'energy performance of buildings' (EPB) standard. The methodologies contained in this standard conform to international best practice and often inform national building regulations in respect of lighting energy.

In England and Wales, building regulations relating to energy usage are set down in Regulation L2A of the Building Regulations 2010 (amended 2017) (TSO, 2010, 2017). Specifically, Regulation L1 b (iii) requires that 'fixed building services' are:

> 'commissioned by testing and adjusting as necessary to ensure they use no more fuel and power than is reasonable in the circumstances.'

In Northern Ireland the requirement for commissioning fixed building services is given as Regulation 39(c) in Part F of the Building Regulations (Northern Ireland) 2012 (TSO, 2012).

In Scotland, Mandatory Standard 6.7 (Commissioning building services) in the domestic and non-domestic *Technical Handbooks* (Scottish Government, 2017a/b) states that:

> 'Every building must be designed and constructed in such a way that energy supply systems and building services which use fuel or power for heating, lighting, ventilating and cooling the internal environment and heating the water, are commissioned to achieve maximum energy efficiency.'

The regulations state that building control bodies need to be satisfied, as in other cases, as to the credentials of those who sign-off commissioning and confirmation of relevant compliances in respect of these regulations and standards.

Lighting energy data will need to be included in the building log book for the facility. An example of such a log book is available as CIBSE TM31: *Building log books* (CIBSE, 2006).

The CO_2 emissions (design and actual in respect of the lighting installation) will also be required to inform the whole building energy model to ensure compliance with the target emissions rate (TER), expressed as CO_2/m^2, and the actual building emissions rate (BER), also expressed as CO_2/m^2.

30.1.6   Competence

The competence of the commissioning team should be considered by the appointed commissioning management, as the team could be made up of several members, representing the installation contractor, the luminaire and controls manufacturers, the emergency lighting equipment manufacturers, the O&M media authors and the operator trainers.

30.1.7   Safety

The fixed electrical installation should be designed, constructed, inspected and tested in accordance with the current version of BS 7671: *Requirements for Electrical Installations. IET Wiring Regulations* (BSI, 2018), or an equivalent standard, and related standards or codes of practice if the project is outside of the UK.

The lighting electrical installation should therefore be complete, tested and certified as such with power available, and an agreed method of safety isolation available, before any intrusive pre-commissioning checks, functional commissioning work, witness testing or operator training commences.

In addition to electrical safety considerations, overall site safety for commissioning operatives is also required and managed through a process of risk assessment, plant operator competency training and site induction.

30.2   Forming a commissioning management team

For large installations a commissioning management team should be formed to coordinate and oversee the commissioning process. Further guidance is available in CIBSE Commissioning Code M: *Commissioning management* (CIBSE, 2003). The formation of a full commissioning management team may not be appropriate for projects with relatively simple lighting installations and small project teams, but an appropriate level of commissioning management should not be ignored just because the project is considered too small to warrant any form of commissioning and handover.

The following procedures should be followed:

- It is important to decide who will have overall responsibility for the lighting commissioning. This person should develop a commissioning checklist★ and a project-specific method statement. The method statement should be distributed to the lighting designer, the architect, the interior designer, the mechanical and electrical consultant, the main contractor, the electrical contractor and subcontractors and suppliers associated with commissioning luminaires and lighting controls supplied to a project.
- The individuals forming the commissioning team should meet on a regular basis to review project lighting installation progress and latterly, the commissioning and handover of the lighting installation.

★ Examples of commissioning checklists can be found in the appendices of CIBSE Commissioning Code L (2018)

- A name and contact details should be placed against each of the activities in the method statement. This will ensure that every aspect of the commissioning is considered.

- It is important to identify an overall designer of the lighting scheme. The lighting designer should represent the client's needs and overview the lighting design in its entirety. The lighting designer may be a separate lighting designer/consultant or may be the M&E consultant.

- Unless the installer is accredited to do so, installers should not commission the functional aspects of their own work as a separate and impartial commissioning engineer will be objective in their approach and thus maintain the quality of the lighting installation.

- At the start of the pre-commissioning phase the various parties should agree on a communication network and escalation matrix that will be used through to completion and handover. This network and matrix should include all relevant parties as it is common for specialist luminaires to be second fixed and/or set up by manufacturers, for lighting controls systems to be commissioned by the system manufacturer, and for the attendances of relevant commissioning engineers from other trades where interfacing takes place and cause and effect needs to be tested, commissioned and witnessed. Typical examples might be the incorporation of audio visual (AV) consoles in lecture theatres or sharing of lighting control occupancy data with a BMS or ensuring escape route luminaires operate at 100% output should there be a fire alarm condition. Such arrangements must take into account any contractual obligations and responsibilities.

30.2.1 Commissioning activities

An example of a general checklist of activities required for a successful commissioning process is included in Appendix LA2 of CIBSE Commissioning Code L (CIBSE, 2018). The person responsible for each activity will depend on the contractual arrangements but should be inserted as early as possible in the process. It is essential that responsibility for the completion of any task be assigned before the task is started.

30.2.2 Commissioning method statements

A commissioning method statement should be produced by the person with overall responsibility for commissioning activities (or their nominated deputy). In practice, responsibilities between parties will vary depending on the project contractual relationships.

30.2.3 Commissioning programme of works

The person designated with responsibility for managing the commissioning process should:

- Make sure that the main contractor includes lighting commissioning dates on the all trades programme of works issued to contractors and clients. Use a method such as critical path analysis to plan the pre-commissioning, commissioning and completion tasks, their duration and interdependencies with each other and other M&E services.

- Consider the critical points in the process by which time certain tasks must be completed for the next task to start; strategic co-ordination points (e.g. electrical power must be available and certified as complete and safe before luminaire function can be tested).

- Identify where tasks may be completed early (i.e. during the construction phase) or off-site. An example could be the pre-programming of lighting control equipment or graphical user interface (GUI) displays.

- Consider whether phased completion, if feasible, will help to reduce the overall commissioning timescale and plan accordingly.

- Continue to monitor progress against programme and advise project management if deviations in other trades programmes are likely to have a significant effect on the commissioning programme.

- Ensure that the client/client's representative is involved, particularly with regard to any lighting control programming requirements.

30.3 Pre-commissioning checks

Examples of commissioning checklists can be found in the appendices of CIBSE Commissioning Code L (CIBSE, 2018).

30.3.1 General considerations

Pre-commissioning should be carried out by using a project-specific commissioning method statement.

Intrusive lighting installation checks on site should not commence on site unless the installation has been electrically certified as safe as per the current edition of BS 7671 (BSI, 2018) and an agreed method of electrical isolation/electrical power being made available is in place. All involved with the preliminary checks will have had an appropriate site-specific health and safety induction before commencing any works that could compromise their health and safety.

Software applications such as graphical user interfaces and control panels can often be programmed off site at the manufacturer's or agent's premises before being brought to site. Graphical user interfaces (GUIs) normally require the addition of electronic 'as built' drawing files and, in some cases, an indication of any hard-addressing assigned to luminaires and/or lighting control devices to provide relevant and accurate graphical screen displays.

It is therefore important to ensure such electronic graphical files are truly 'as fitted' when working off site. This is in order to avoid delays should inaccuracies be noted at a later date on site during functional testing as re-programming may cause delays to the commissioning and handover programme.

It may therefore be appropriate to consider if the project warrants factory acceptance testing (FAT) of any pre-configured lighting equipment, where the programming can be reliably checked off site either to accelerate the commissioning process and/or reduce the likelihood of extensive programming changes that only become apparent on site and are considered likely to add significant time to the commissioning and cause the project handover to be delayed.

All pre-commissioning checks should be recorded on a pre-commissioning method statement checklist. As many as possible of these checks should be carried out off site.

30.3.2 Status of the lighting installation

All luminaires and lighting control system devices should be installed according to the system design drawings and an appropriate, stable power supply should be available. All luminaires and lighting control system devices should be those specified in the original design. Specification 'breaking' may have a serious adverse effect on total lighting efficacy, performance and the aesthetic quality of the design, and the amount of time required for commissioning.

Substitutions should only be made with the agreement of the lighting designer inclusive of an impact assessment on the commissioning programme and project completion.

If substitutions are accepted/agreed, a written change record should be made.

30.3.2.1 Mechanical checks

- All luminaire and lighting control device positioning that requires cooperation with other installers such as mechanical contractors and ceiling contractors should be co-ordinated early in the design phase and incorporated on to the reflected ceiling plans (RCPs).

- All luminaires should be in the correct position as defined by the construction issue drawings/RCPs and be in the correct orientation.

- All luminaires should be clean and undamaged with the correct lamps fitted (i.e. manufacturer, wattage or lumen output, correlated colour temperature (CCT), colour rendering index (R_a/CRI) and suitable for any dimming or regulation required.

- All luminaires and lighting control devices should be uniquely and clearly labelled and identifiable as same via the 'as fitted' drawings.

- All cover plates should be fitted and electrical segregation complete.

- All raise and lower gear should be checked and certified.

- All safety chains, safety cords and filter holders etc. on luminaires should be securely mounted; associated control gear should be fixed securely on lighting trusses, booms, barrels and bars, or placed in a secure position.

- Where the manufacturer publishes torque settings for the tightening of luminaire screws and bolts, it should be confirmed that the manufacturer's instructions have been followed and that the IP/EX d seal is intact and the relevant fixing bolts are not under- or over-tightened.

- For hazardous areas such as petrol stations and oil refineries there are many additional requirements outside of the scope of this *Handbook*. See Chapter 23, 'Extreme environments'.

30.3.2.2 Electrical checks

- All luminaires, switches and lighting control devices should be wired according to the wiring diagrams and as fitted drawings provided by the installation contractor.

- Screened cables and termination devices have been installed in systems where this is critical, i.e. ethernet and DMX systems.

- Confirm that appropriate power is available to the lighting installation to be commissioned. The voltage and frequency should be stable and within the limits laid down in the Electricity Safety, Quality and Continuity Regulations 2002 (TSO, 2002) and within the voltage drop limits specified in BS 7671 (BSI, 2018).

- All electrical test and measuring equipment should be fit for purpose and covered by a current calibration certificate. The current calibration certificate(s) should be attached to the pre-commissioning documentation/certification report.

- Fluorescent and HID lamps should be 'burned-in' according to the manufacturer's recommendations. The burn-in period is typically 100 hours, after which time the lamp may be stable in operation at full and reduced output.

- If powering-up wireless or Internet-controlled devices/luminaires, consider the security of the installation as it may be possible for unauthorised persons to remotely access the lighting installation and maliciously infect the lighting installation software/firmware to the detriment of the installation and the works programme. Therefore consideration should be given at equipment and device power-up to changing default passwords. The use of firewalls/security software where external/remote access to the network by unauthorised parties should also be considered.

- All luminaire and lighting control devices containing addressing and mode switches should be set and checks made to ensure that all luminaires and lighting control devices are communicating correctly at manufacturer's defaults.

- Checks should be made to ensure that all wireless communication paths are operating at a signal strength and quality to the manufacturer's specification.

- Check that all controller head-ends and GUIs have the correct versions of firmware and/or software installed.

- Check that all lighting energy sub-metering is operating and recording energy use.

30.3.3   Pre-commissioning certificate

It is recommended that the person responsible for commissioning management produces a pre-commissioning certificate.

This certificate can include a separate checklist of pre-commissioning tasks completed and copies of any manufacturer's individual certificates issued forming the works to be certified. Those responsible for the pre-commissioning should sign the completed certification to confirm that the pre-commissioning checks have been completed satisfactorily.

30.4   Functional commissioning

Examples of commissioning check lists can be found in the appendices of CIBSE Commissioning Code L (CIBSE, 2018).

30.4.1   Interior lighting

Carry out the functional commissioning works as defined by the commissioning method statement.

Method statements and risk assessments will be required for aiming and focusing luminaires and to ensure appropriate access plant is made available. If it is intended that the luminaires be adjusted by the end user after practical completion of the project, this must be indicated in the commissioning method statement and notified during operator training and handover.

30.4.2   Emergency lighting

Commissioning of emergency lighting should be carried out with reference to BS 5266-1: *Emergency lighting. Code of practice for the emergency lighting of premises* (BSI, 2016). Consideration should be given to how illuminances are measured or verified due to the relatively low light levels.

If measured with an illuminance meter, measurements are made whilst the luminaires are operating under mains power failure conditions at an agreed time within the battery discharge period. Illuminance meters will require the relevant scale and accuracy to provide accurate readings at lighting levels typically ranging from 0.5 to 15 lux and will have a valid calibration certificate (see also 30.4.4.3). For further information on illuminance meters, see SLL Factfile 13: *Illuminance meters*.

30.4.3   Exterior lighting

Lighting attached to a building providing access lighting or security lighting near the building and this part of the lighting installation should be commissioned according to the design specification. Carry out measurements of illuminance as defined in the commissioning method statement.

30.4.4   Lighting controls

30.4.4.1 Local networks

If the lighting control system is a networked system, check that the network connections allow communication with all luminaires and field devices to/from the relevant local controller(s) and to/from the point of commissioning.

Networks can be formed using cables, or by using radio frequency or infrared technology (generally referred to as 'wireless' based networks). If the lighting installation is being installed in an existing building, it is sometimes possible to use wireless survey equipment to determine if the chosen positions for wireless receiving and transmitting devices will be likely to achieve acceptable and stable signal strengths once installed and commissioned. Signal strength surveys are not possible on new buildings until the construction is complete and procurement of specified wireless devices has been made. It is therefore vital that some form of confirmation exists to ensure that the wireless signal paths are at the required signal strength, stable and interference-free as defined by the equipment manufacturer's product specification and by verification as part of the commissioning works.

30.4.4.2 Manual switches

Ensure that manual switches switch the correct zone of luminaires as labelled.

30.4.4.3 Daylight-linking and constant illuminance

Calibrate the light sensor(s) or control software to give the required light levels at the specified luminaire positions.

Where possible, the calibration of the light sensor(s) should take place at the lighting controller or operator workstation, via configuration software.

If field calibration of the light sensor is required, the calibration should be performed using a certified, calibrated portable light meter. A copy of a current calibration certificate should be attached to calibration results sheets.

BS 667: *Illuminance meters. Requirements and test methods* (BSI, 2005) provides guidance on the calibration and use of such light meters.

Direct manual calibration at the sensor itself may result in calibration being adversely affected as the person performing the calibration may block some of the light that would otherwise fall on the sensor. When local calibration cannot be avoided, care must be taken to minimise any adverse effects by the person commissioning, e.g. by the use of remote-head portable light meters and by wearing non-reflective clothing.

Calibration of the light sensors should take place when the building is fully furnished. Ensure appropriate time-delay settings are set to reduce nuisance dimming/regulation caused by transient conditions such as passing clouds.

30.4.4.4 Occupancy sensors

Ensure that the zone occupancy sensor is located and orientated correctly in relation to the occupants. Some occupancy sensors can be fitted with proprietary masks to define a particular field of coverage. Checks should be made to ensure masks are correctly fitted and allow the occupancy sensor to operate as per design intent.

Some occupancy sensors have variable sensitivity settings. It is important to ensure the sensitivity setting is adjusted to the optimal value to ensure correct operation.

The time delay setting is representative of the occupant work/movement patterns and requires agreement with the client prior to commissioning commencement.

30.4.4.5 Manual dimming/regulation

Ensure that the upper and lower limits of the dimming/regulation range are set as specified.

30.4.4.6 Sweep-off/cause and effect

Ensure that the lighting control start and stop times along with the override control (e.g. occupant or security staff override) are as specified. Ensure that the cause and effect relationships between luminaire zones and lighting control devices is documented and understood prior to commencement of commissioning.

30.4.4.7 End-user local operation

Occupants may have interaction with the lighting installation via light switches or localised/individual scene setting switches. These switching devices may be conventional hard-wired switches, hand-held infrared (IR) type remote switches or personal computing devices such as laptop computers, tablets or smartphones.

The following general procedures should be followed. Ensure that:

- the physical location of occupant control devices is correct
- each occupant control device is linked to the building control system communications network

- each occupant control device controls the correct lighting zone

- the default control settings for each occupant control device are correct

- any specified automatic override function operates correctly

- where Wi-Fi or Internet connectivity exists, the appropriate IT-security arrangements (firewalls, passwords etc.) are in place.

Ensure that the database containing occupant details can be easily accessed and amended by an authorised system administrator in order to reflect future changes in occupancy requirements.

30.4.4.8 Scene-set controllers

Ensure that:

- scenes operate according to specification

- scenes are labelled adequately to allow an untrained user to select the correct option.

30.4.4.9 Interfaces with other services

Ensure that any input/output (I/O) devices or software interfaces to other services such as AV, fire alarms, security systems, fenestration shading or BMS systems operate correctly at the final point of output or input from the perspective of the lighting installation.

Once the lighting installation is commissioned and set to work, it may be necessary to fully test interfaces to other services and with the commissioning engineers for the other systems/interested parties to ensure correct operation and that any maintenance inhibit, or isolation controls/procedures also work correctly.

30.4.4.10 Field, central control and head-end equipment

The following commissioning procedures should be taken in to account for field, central and head-end controllers or graphical user interface (GUI) controllers:

- The specified software release is installed.

- Passwords and associated access levels are set up correctly.

- All outstations and unitary control devices can be addressed, and data sent and retrieved. This should include any specified retrieval of point data and the ability to download configuration software and perform alterations to control points and strategies.

- Any specified building schematics are displayed correctly on request and that the monitored point data associated with each schematic are also correct, i.e. ensure that the 'binding' correlation of the graphics and monitored data is correct.

- Data logging functions operate correctly.

- Logged data can be displayed correctly.

- Archiving of logged data, system configuration details and control parameters operates correctly.

- Any specified automatic report generation software operates correctly.

- Any software scripts for feature lighting are installed and operate correctly.

- Any specified third-party management software, such as energy targeting and monitoring software, can retrieve the necessary data from the central controller. Check for the specified operation of the software (data analysis and display/ management reports etc).

30.4.4.11 Lighting installation energy

Checks should be made that the lighting installation electrical load is being continuously monitored via a sub-metering arrangement and that meter readings for specified time periods can be obtained.

Further information on energy metering can be found in CIBSE TM39: *Building energy metering* (CIBSE, 2009), section 4.9 and BS EN 15193-1: *Energy performance of buildings. Energy requirements for lighting. Specifications, Module M9* (BSI, 2017).

It may not be possible to obtain accurate lighting load readings over time to verify any design stage energy modelling at functional commissioning. It may be that the accuracy of the lighting energy modelling can only be verified against the actual energy used after client occupancy and in accordance with the building's post-occupancy evaluation plan.

30.4.4.12 Communication networks

It is important to ensure that any communication networks forming both the on-site lighting installation and any remote connections operate via a secure and stable communications network.

Before the lighting installation is connected to a remotely accessible network, it should be confirmed that the lighting installation has adequate security features to prevent unauthorised access. Consideration should be given to agreed passwords for end-users and engineering functions, remote access, firewalls and network security/encryption as specified.

- All local and head-end network control devices can be addressed over the communications network.

- The speed of communications is at least that specified. It is important that this is assessed when the network is under 'normal' operating conditions in order to reflect the in-use level of network traffic.

- Data communication is error free, i.e. there is no data corruption that is outside the project performance specification or manufacturers recommendations.

- No corruption of data occurs when the building control system shares a network with other IT-based systems.

- All network devices such as routers, servers and bridges operate correctly.

- Network resilience is satisfactory if dual or redundant networks are installed.

30.4.4.13 Emergency lighting

Emergency lighting will have a method of periodic testing specified. This can be self-testing luminaires, where the status LED changes colour and flashes, test key switch or automated monitoring and testing. The last of these will require test routines to be programmed to ensure emergency luminaires/standby batteries are tested at periodic intervals — never all at once but rather in defined groups at different times to ensure there is a satisfactory level of fully charged emergency lighting available at all times.

30.4.5   Relationship between lighting and automatic solar shading

For automatic shading systems (for example automated blinds), ensure that the system works as specified. The shading should be minimised before the lights are activated and the lights should be switched off before the shading is activated. Manual override may be required to avoid discomfort glare.

30.4.6   Measurement of illuminance

If illuminance measurements are required they should be detailed in the commissioning method statement and may be carried out in accordance with the methods set out in Chapter 31, 'Performance verification' and 30.4.4.3 above.

30.4.7   Proving interfacing to other services

Once the lighting installation including all lighting controls and interfaces are complete and working, arrangements should be made with other trades/services in attendance to ensure that interfacing works correctly and can be inhibited/overridden for maintenance purposes. Typical examples of interfacing may include:

- fire alarm systems
- AV systems/separate theatre lighting systems
- BMS systems
- security systems
- energy monitoring systems
- solenoid isolation fitted to water valves for WCs.

30.4.8   Visual inspection

Many luminaires and control devices have some form of communication to a controller or head-end. Such controllers allow remote communications with luminaires and control devices and will confirm that an electrical connection exists as part of the lighting installation.

Electronic verification cannot confirm that the luminaire or sensor has not been physically obscured by a protective covering that is reducing or inhibiting correct operation. It is therefore essential to complete a visual inspection of all relevant luminaires and sensors to ensure they are not obscured in any way.

30.4.9   Functional commissioning certification

It is recommended that the person responsible for commissioning management produces a functional commissioning certificate.

This certificate can include a separate checklist of functional commissioning tasks completed and copies of any manufacturer's individual certificates issued forming the works to be certified. Those responsible for the functional commissioning should sign the completed certification to confirm that the functional commissioning checks have been completed satisfactorily.

30.5 Lighting installation handover

30.5.1 O&M media

It may be a project requirement that relevant partially completed or completed and verified operation and maintenance media are complete and available for use by the client's representative during witness testing and occupant training.

The O&M media should be complete and available by project handover.

30.5.1.1 O&M media handover report

Completed O&M information may be specified as a deliverable in hard copy, electronic file or a combination thereof, or by using a BIM (building information model) process as defined by PAS 1192-3: *Specification for information management for the operational phase of assets using building information modelling* (BSI, 2014).

Responsibility for producing and checking the completed O&M media will have been assigned at an earlier stage. Responsibility for providing some of the information will almost certainly fall to the commissioning manager as defined by the terms of the specific contract. The following list is useful for compiling the O&M media:

- Check that an initial draft of the O&M media has been submitted to the lighting designer or equivalent party for approval prior to commissioning.

- O&M media should be produced as the work proceeds and updated when necessary. This work should commence at the start of the contract and be added to/updated as the contract progresses.

- Ensure that approved final copies of the O&M media are provided at handover.

- The O&M media should be properly indexed. Terminology and references used must be consistent with the physical identification of component lighting installation parts.

- Include the settings of each lighting scene in terms of luminaire and lighting control devices addresses, zones, scene reference fade time and any lighting channels that are assigned. (Note that different manufacturers of lighting control systems use the terms 'control channel', 'dimming channel', 'circuit', 'pre-set', 'state' and 'scene' in various, and sometimes inconsistent, ways that are not always clear to end users. The terms must be defined for each type of system.)

- Ensure that the O&M media includes the following and is included in the site health and safety file:
  - written description of system operation
  - control strategy/logic diagrams recording the version of configuration software installed at handover
  - details of system application software configuration and any licencing agreements
  - points list including hard and soft points (all points should have a unique mnemonic), unless this is clearly incorporated in the system software, in which case make appropriate reference to this element
  - description of user-adjustable points

— information on the operation of all interfaces to other services, the cause and effect operation and how to test/inhibit links to other services by maintenance staff

— commissioning record details: detailed data sheets for all control components and equipment wiring circuit details including origin, route and destination of each cable; comprehensive instructions for switching on, operation, switching off, isolation, fault finding and procedures for dealing with emergency conditions

— COSHH ('control of substances hazardous to health') and RoHS ('restriction of hazardous substances') information on supplied luminaires, devices and equipment and batteries

— instructions for any precautionary measures necessary

— instructions for the routine operation of the control system including simple day-to-day guidance for those operating the control system with limited technical skill

— instructions for servicing and system upkeep

— provision for update and modification

— recommendations, if appropriate, regarding: access for maintenance and lamp changing; cause and effect with other services and testing/isolation procedures; risk assessments for maintenance.

Note that other documentation requirements may be applicable depending on the sophistication of the system.

Ensure that the O&M media includes comprehensive system operation instructions.

30.5.2   Witness testing

When the lighting installation is offered for witness testing by the commissioning manager as being functionally commissioned, the witness tester should follow a witnessing procedure forming part of the commissioning plan method statement and have access to any O&M media that is required to complete an objective and thorough witness testing.

The requirements and scope for witness testing should be included in the lighting installation specification. It is recommended that as a minimum, witness testing should include the following:

- an audit of the lighting installation luminaires and attachments, emergency lighting, lighting control devices and head-end/GUI equipment

- confirm that all specified lighting installation spares and consumables as specified or provided for the project have been handed over to the client's representative

- verification of any lighting installation software, licencing agreements, back-up copies of system programming are available and the head-end/GUI(s) operate as specified.

- the operation of any critical parts of the lighting installation should be witnessed completely with a witnessing of a random sample of the remaining luminaires and lighting control devices

- the number of random points to be witnessed will depend on the size of the complete system; the following suggested method could be adopted:

  — if less than 300 luminaires and lighting control devices have been offered, then witness test to 100% of the lighting installation

  — if between 300 and 1000 luminaires and lighting control devices have been offered, then witness test 50% of the lighting installation

  — if more than 1000 luminaires and lighting control devices have been offered, then witness test 20% or a maximum of 500 luminaires and lighting control devices

- confirm all energy metering operational.

If the failure rate at witness testing is greater than 5% of the luminaires and lighting control devices offered for witness testing then the witness tester and/or lighting designer should consider, at their discretion, a request that the lighting installation is re-commissioned as specified and then return and either repeat the witness testing to the above percentages or decide if, in the interests of project quality, it would be appropriate to carry out witness testing to 100% of the offered lighting installation.

Accurate records of witness testing and comments should be made available to the commissioning manager.

Once the witness testing has been successfully completed, and the availability/status of relevant O&M media is deemed adequate then the lighting system should be confirmed as complete and functioning as per the project intent to the client, lighting designer and commissioning manager. If there are commissioning items that cannot be completed until later, these activities should be highlighted in a status report by the witness tester. Section 6, 'Post completion checks and adjustments', also refers to this eventuality.

The lighting installation should now be offered for operator training.

30.5.3   Operator training

Operator training is important, no matter how large or small the lighting installation. Domestic lighting installations frequently have remote controls via a dedicated handheld device or a tablet/smartphone application. Larger commercial and industrial lighting installations could comprise of interconnected luminaires, emergency luminaires and lighting controls, all operated from a head-end or GUI.

Therefore, the perception by the end user of either small or large installations is largely governed by how the operator understands and perceives the benefits of the lighting installation and how to work them.

The operator may be defined as:

- *the facilities manager*: for the lighting installation management, password protected changes, report generation and first line diagnostics, 3rd party support and maintenance arrangements

- *key end-user staff*: who may also be responsible for day-to-day monitoring of the lighting installation, aware/responsible for the outsourced facilities management and direct local actions such as lighting scene adjustments and/or automatic solar shading overrides via a lighting installation head-end or GUI

- *individual end users*: who have localised control of the lighting and solar shading at their location, such as a conference room or their desk.

Depending on the size and complexity of the lighting installation, it may be advantageous if the intended and relevant system operator(s) can be present during at least part of the commissioning stage if deemed advantageous. This will allow the operator to become familiar with the system and develop experience while commissioning staff are on site.

The operator(s) should be capable of understanding how the lighting operates as a complete installation and, in particular, any aspects of the lighting installation where they will have regular interactions and will benefit from local and detailed operation.

Typical tasks that operators may be required to perform are summarised below.

30.5.3.1 Facilities manager

At this level, system operators are expected to have a basic understanding of the control system architecture and performance criteria, O&M media access to locate luminaires and lighting system devices, and to have the ability to viewpoint data from lighting zones or, if appropriate, individual luminaires and control devices.

Typical abilities and handover training should cover:

- carrying out regular visual inspections to ensure the lighting installation/emergency lighting installation is in working condition, all as per the design intent

- maintaining and re-lamping luminaires

- calling-up and changing settings and/or parameters from schematics and/or address/zone lists

- acknowledging/investigating system alarms

- setting-up/viewing and interpreting trend logs

- changing time and occupancy programmes

- changing lighting scenes

- managing, collating and interpreting emergency lighting test and monitoring routines (automated and/or manual)

- lighting control system back-up and archiving of logged data

- awareness of escalation procedures should external support and attendance be required from the lighting installation installers/manufacturers

- awareness and management of any maintenance agreement with an off-site 3rd party such as a lighting controls/emergency lighting specialist company

- awareness of energy metering arrangements/locations and transfer of consumed energy data into the facility's energy log book; there should also be an agreed plan of action to investigate/correct any consumed energy above the installation design intent.

30.5.3.2 Key end-user staff

At this level, key end-user staff are expected to have a basic understanding of the control system architecture and performance criteria and a clear understanding of the facilities manager's duties for maintaining and supporting the lighting installation

Typical abilities and handover training should cover:

- carrying out regular visual inspections to ensure the lighting installation/emergency lighting installation is in working condition, all as per the design intent

- using scene-setting controls

- manually overriding automatic shading

- awareness of escalation procedures should the facilities manager require external support and attendance from the lighting installation installers/manufacturers

- awareness of any maintenance agreement via the facilities manager with an off-site 3rd party such as a lighting controls/emergency lighting specialist company

- awareness of energy metering arrangements/locations and transfer of consumed energy data into the facility's energy log book; there should also be an agreed plan of action to investigate/correct any consumed energy above the installation design intent.

30.5.3.3 Individual end users

Individual end users are expected to have a basic understanding of the control system architecture and performance criteria and a clear understanding of the facilities manager's duties for maintaining and supporting the lighting installation:

- using relevant/local scene setting controls

- using relevant/local manual override of automatic shading

- awareness of escalation procedures to the key end user, should support be required in respect of the lighting installation performance and operation in their place of work.

30.5.4 Commissioning completion certificate

Once the operator training has been successfully completed, it is recommended that the person responsible for commissioning management produces a commissioning completion certificate. The certificate may include a checklist of completed witness testing tasks and any comments. The commissioning certificate should be signed by the commissioning manager, the commissioning engineer and witnessed by the lighting designer and/or the client's representative who was present at the witness testing.

List any commissioning items that are not/could not be completed and to be completed at a later date; for example, final commissioning works once the building is furnished and occupied by the ultimate tenant (see section 30.6 below).
The lighting energy used during all commissioning activity may require meter reading and a record of energy used noted on the commissioning completion certificate.

On some projects, it may be necessary to perform a phased commissioning completion programme in which the lighting system is commissioned and certified in sections. However, if a certified section is altered in any way during the remainder of the construction programme, the affected section should be re-certified before handover.

30.6 Post-completion checks and adjustments

Some activities listed in sections 30.4 and 30.5 may not be possible to complete on a speculative project as the space may not be let and the facilities manager and end-user operators may not be in place or known.

Other project specification requirements, such as a soft landings period to evaluate the building performance once occupied and operational, will require post-completion checks and adjustments to the lighting installation.

30.6.1 Category A or B projects

Category A projects are defined as speculative buildings with no particular user known at the time of design, construction and completion. Post-completion alterations cause the category to change from category A to category B.

Category B projects are defined as buildings with a particular user known at the time of design, construction and completion.

A return visit to complete operator training may therefore be required sometime after Cat A completion if lighting installation changes at Cat B are planned.

- *Example 1*: illuminance cannot always be accurately checked until the space is completely fitted out and furnished. If required, provision should be made to return to site at an appropriate time to make and record illuminance values.

- *Example 2*: energy efficiency to BS EN 15193-1 (BSI, 2017) and/or metered energy consumption data may not be available until the facility has been in full use for a period of time and therefore the actual energy consumption against the design could not be accurately verified at practical completion.

30.6.2 Seasonal checks

It is important post-lighting installation completion that lighting installations are periodically checked for correct and optimised operation under representative operational conditions.

During the commissioning period, these conditions may not arise because the building is unoccupied. In addition, it is difficult to properly verify the performance of seasonal variations in lighting, lighting control set-up and actual lighting energy consumption against a predictive model.

For these reasons, the actual lighting installation performance against design intent should be checked/adjusted at periodic intervals once the building is occupied and during different seasons. Typical frequencies for post-occupancy checks should be listed in the lighting performance specification and ultimately in the building's post-occupancy evaluation plan.

References

BSI (2005) BS 667: *Illuminance meters. Requirements and test methods* (London: British Standards Institution)

BSI (2014) PAS 1192-3: *Specification for information management for the operational phase of assets using building information modelling* (London: British Standards Institution)

BSI (2016) BS 5266-1: *Emergency lighting. Code of practice for the emergency lighting of premises* (London: British Standards Institution)

BSI (2017) BS EN 15193-1: *Energy performance of buildings. Energy requirements for lighting. Specifications, Module M9* (London: British Standards Institution)

BSI (2018) BS 7671: *Requirements for Electrical Installations. IET Wiring Regulations* (London: British Standards Institution)

CIBSE (2003) *Commissioning management* CIBSE Commissioning Code M (London: Chartered Institution of Building Services Engineers)

CIBSE (2006) *Building log books* CIBSE TM31 (London: Chartered Institution of Building Services Engineers)

CIBSE (2009) *Building energy metering* CIBSE TM39 (London: Chartered Institution of Building Services Engineers)

CIBSE (2018) *Lighting* CIBSE Commissioning Code L (London: Chartered Institution of Building Services Engineers)

Scottish Government (2017a) *Technical Handbook 2017: Domestic* (Edinburgh: Scottish Government) (available at http://www.gov.scot/Topics/Built-Environment/Building/Building-standards/publications/pubtech) (accessed February 2018)

Scottish Government (2017b) *Technical Handbook 2017: Non-domestic* (Edinburgh: Scottish Government) (available at http://www.gov.scot/Topics/Built-Environment/Building/Building-standards/publications/pubtech) (accessed February 2018)

TSO (2002) The Electricity Safety, Quality and Continuity Regulations 2002 Statutory Instrument 2002 No. 2665 (London: TSO) (available at http://www.legislation.gov.uk/uksi/2002/2665) (accessed October 2017)

TSO (2010) The Building Regulations 2010 Statutory Instrument 2010 No. 2214 (London: TSO) (available at http://www.legislation.gov.uk/uksi/2010/2214) (accessed February 2018)

TSO (2012) The Building Regulations (Northern Ireland) 2012 Statutory Instrument 2012 No. 192 (as amended) (London: TSO) (available at http://www.legislation.gov.uk/nisr/2012/192) (accessed February 2018)

TSO (2017) The Building (Amendment) Regulations 2017 Statutory Instrument 2017 No. 856 (London: TSO) (available at http://www.legislation.gov.uk/uksi/2017/856) (accessed February 2018)

Chapter 31: Performance verification

31.1   The need for performance verification

Verifying the performance of a lighting installation is desirable for several reasons:

- Anyone who has paid for a new lighting installation may be interested to know, or have placed a contractual requirement to confirm, that they have got what they paid for.

- Anyone who has designed a lighting installation and has seen it installed should be concerned with how well the actual installation matches what was expected from the design. Discrepancies between the design and reality can indicate problems with the design process, the installation operation, commissioning or with the data used in the design.

- Lighting installations change as they age. Light sources tend to produce less light with increasing hours of use. Luminaires emit less light and can change their light distribution as they get dirty. The amount of inter-reflected light can change as the reflectance of surfaces change. For applications where minimum standards of lighting are specified, being able to measure the current performance of a lighting installation is desirable to either schedule maintenance correctly or to confirm that such maintenance has been undertaken on performance related management contracts which link to contractual payments/penalties.

- Potential tenants of a space may wish to check that the measured lighting level in the space meets that specified in the tenancy agreement.

- The duty of care imposed on employers, and others, means that the lighting conditions of the workplace must meet minimum standards. A failure to provide the minimum standard can have serious implications for the employer.

The levels specified in the *SLL Code for Lighting* (SLL, 2012) and in this *Handbook* are maintained illuminance values. This means that the average measured illuminance or luminance should never be lower than the average maintained illuminance specified, if the maintenance of the space has met the criteria used in the original calculations.

The verification of the performance of a lighting installation requires a field survey. Such a survey requires decisions about the relevant operating conditions, the use of photometric instruments and the selection of an appropriate measurement procedure.

31.2   Competency of those undertaking measurements

Measurement of photometric performance should only be undertaken by persons who are professionally qualified and competent in the discipline of lighting design. Such awareness should include:

- the type and requirements of the lighting installation being assessed

- measurement standards and guidance

- the correct operation of the test instruments concerned

- health and safety needs of the site.

31.3   Preparing for the survey

It is important to plan in advance all aspects of the survey. This involves liaison with the client or occupier of the space to ensure access, often in the evening. This will also aid the identification of any site specific health and safety requirements and enable a site visit risk assessment to be undertaken and any mitigation measures taken, such as safe access, personal protective equipment etc.

31.3.1   Equipment

The meters need to be checked to ensure they are within calibration and spare batteries obtained if necessary. If readings are to be taken at a certain height above floor level or at ground level, then a measuring stand or stick of the right length needs to be prepared. Other equipment to be considered includes a means of recording the survey results, tablet or clip-board, laser measure/ tape measure/measuring wheel, thermometer, camera, details of the installation to be assessed etc.

31.3.2   Site

Within buildings the management system may need to be overridden to ensure the thermal conditions in the evening match those for normal daytime use of the space and to ensure that thermal conditions in the test area are stable.

For exterior lighting, measurements need to be taken when it is fully dark and in good weather conditions. In mid-summer the sky may not get dark until midnight, or at all in high latitudes. Even light rain can affect light readings. Traffic routes are a potentially dangerous area and it might be worth considering traffic management planning. Risk assessments and training is needed before accessing any equipment (see ENA Engineering Recommendation G39: *Model code of practice covering electrical safety in the planning, installation, commissioning and maintenance of public lighting and other street furniture* (ENA, 2013)).

It is essential when making field measurements to keep a complete and accurate record of the state of the lighting installation and the environment in general at the time the measurements are made. Particular attention should be given to the light source type and age, the level and stability of the supply voltage, the state of maintenance of the light source and luminaires, the surface reflectances, the degree of obstruction and any other factors that could influence the measurement. Photographs of the space or area are a valuable supplement to a written record.

Before carrying out a field survey, it is necessary to decide on the lighting conditions that are of interest. For example:

- For an interior, how can daylight be excluded? If daylight levels are part of the survey, are there blinds? What are the weather conditions? Are the measurements to be concerned with average values over the whole interior or only over individual workplaces? Should the measurements around the workplace be taken with the people present etc? It is also necessary to identify the appropriate measurement plane: horizontal and/or vertical, and at what height and/or orientation.

- For exterior installations, the need to prevent shadows over the sensor, weather conditions, masking of other artificial light sources/spill light from other installations, shadowing created by other features such as vehicles, tress, buildings etc.

Before starting to take measurements, it is first necessary to ensure that any newly installed lamps/light sources have burnt for at least 100 hours to ensure they have reached their stable long-term output. If this has been done, then the first step in measurement is to stabilize the performance of the lamps, luminaires and instrumentation. The time required to stabilize the light output of an installation depends on the type of light source and luminaire. Installations using discharge lamps, including tubular fluorescent, require at least 20 minutes, and ideally one hour, to stabilize before measurements are made. Those involving LEDs require only a few minutes except if the LEDs are in a fitting with a large thermal mass and poor heat sink where it might take a long time for the body to get fully warm. It is always considered best practice to undertake a single point measurement after stabilisation and then check this periodically during the survey to ensure that stabilised conditions remain steady.

To stabilize the reading of some instruments the photocell should be exposed to the approximate illuminances to be measured for about five minutes before making the first measurement. Others may need the covers kept in place on the measuring cell whilst the instrument starts up to ensure it is zeroed correctly. Some instruments will do this without the need to cover the sensor.

Daylight is rarely stable and hence the illuminance and luminance it produces can rapidly vary over a very large range. For this reason when measurements of the electric lighting installation alone are required, daylight must be excluded from the interior or the measurements must be made after dark.

31.4   Instrumentation

Field measurements of lighting are usually undertaken with two basic instruments, an illuminance meter and a luminance meter.

31.4.1   Illuminance meters

Illuminance meters usually consist of a selenium or silicon photovoltaic cell connected directly, or indirectly via an amplifier, to an analogue or digital display (Figure 31.1).

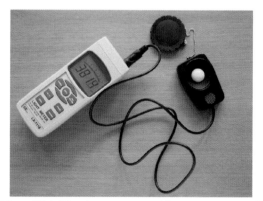

Figure 31.1 Illuminance meter with measurement cell on a long cord to allow reading the meter display without shadowing the remotely located cell (image courtesy of Paul Ruffles)

The quality of an illuminance meter is determined by a number of factors including calibration uncertainty, non-linearity, spectral correction error, cosine correction error, sensor detection angle, range change error and temperature change error. All these errors are discussed in detail in the *SLL Code for Lighting* (SLL, 2012) and BS 667: *Illuminance meters. Requirements and test methods* (BSI, 2005a). This standard defines two types of meter: type L, mainly designed for laboratory use, and type F designed for field use. The total uncertainty is ±4% for a type L meter and ±6% for a type F meter. These error limits assume the measurement of nominally white light, as meters are calibrated using illuminant A (tungsten 2850 K) and have a spectral correction to nominal $V(\lambda)$. The uncertainty in the match are allowed for in the overall uncertainty budget (F: ±6%, L: ±4%) so these figures are good for almost any source that can call itself white. Measurements of other light sources, such as light emitting diodes, fluorescent lighting etc. require the application of a colour correction factor (CCF) to the measurement, some instruments can adjust for this. Failure to consider this may show much greater errors because of the poor fit of the spectral sensitivity of the meter to the CIE Standard Photopic Observer at particular wavelengths.

Illuminance meters are available for measuring illuminance from 0.1 lux to 100 000 lux, i.e. from emergency lighting conditions to daylight conditions. It is important to use an illuminance meter with a range matched to the illuminances to be measured. See also Factfile 13: *Illuminance meters* (SLL, 2018) and *Choosing the right photometer/illuminance meter* (ILP, 2017).

31.4.2   Luminance meters

A luminance meter consists of an imaging system, a photoreceptor, and a display (Figure 31.2). The optical imaging system is used to form an image of the object of interest on the photoreceptor. The photoreceptor produces a signal that is dependent on the average luminance of the image it receives. The object of interest must be in focus and fill the photoreceptor aperture in order to obtain valid readings. This signal is amplified and displayed in either analogue or digital form. The photoreceptors used in luminance meters may be photovoltaic cells or photomultiplier tubes. The photovoltaic cells, as in illuminance meters, need to be colour corrected and used with associated circuitry to give a linear response and operate acceptably over a range of ambient temperatures.

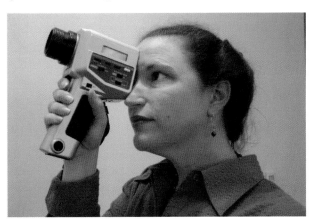

Figure 31.2 Luminance meter in use (image courtesy of the Lighting Research Center, Rensselaer Polytechnic Institute)

BS 7920: *Luminance meters. Requirements and test methods* (BSI, 2005b) discusses in detail the uncertainties that luminance meters may be subject to and specifies limits for the uncertainties for two classes of luminance meter. The two types of meter are: type L, laboratory meters, and type F, field meters. A meter that just meets the standard would have a best measurement capability of ± 5% (Type L) or ± 7% (Type F). The uncertainties for measurements of highly coloured light sources may be greater.

Luminance meters are available that provide measurements over a range of 10^{-4} to 10^8 cd/m² for areas varying from a few seconds of arc to several degrees. It is important to use a luminance meter with appropriate sensitivity and measurement area for the application.

31.5   Methods of measurement

The lighting recommendations given in this *Handbook*, the *SLL Code for Lighting* (SLL, 2012) and the SLL Lighting Guides usually involve some combination of:

● average illuminance

● some measure of illuminance variation, either illuminance diversity or illuminance uniformity

● some measure of glare limitation, which can be a maximum luminance, a unified glare rating (UGR) for interior lighting or a glare rating (GR) for exterior lighting, and

● a colour rendering index (CRI).

Of these, only the average illuminance, illuminance diversity, illuminance uniformity and surface luminance can be measured easily in a field survey. Because of the cost of luminance measuring equipment for use on site, both UGR and GR have to be calculated for given viewing positions and directions, and CRI is a property of the light source.

31.5.1   Open-plan areas

For areas such as open-plan offices, where there are no fixed desk locations, the measurement grid should be positioned to cover a representative area of the task plane. This should be where there are no obstructions above the working plane, which may reduce the measured levels, that were not included as part of the lighting design for that task area. Where the measurements cover a large task area in an open-plan office space, where standard calculations and illuminance prediction are based on the assumption that there are no obstructions above the working plane, ensure that there are no partitions, filing cabinets etc. above the level of the task plane in the measurement area.

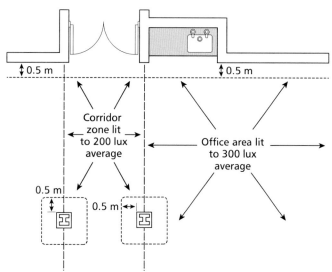

Figure 31.3 In open-plan areas where there are different lighting levels for different functions, such as corridor routes or filing areas, then these must be understood and the measurement grid determined for each area separately

Once the size of the area to be measured is known then the necessary number of points needed to obtain an accurate measured average illuminance can be calculated. The distance between the points (p) may be calculated using the formula:

$$p = 0.2 \times 5^{\log d}$$

where d is the length of the longer dimension of the area being measured.

For example, if it is required to calculate the illuminance on an area 6 m by 4 m, then applying the above formula:

$$p = 0.2 \times 5^{\log 6} = 0.6997$$

However, dividing the length of 6 m by 0.6997 gives 8.575, so rounding up to the nearest whole number, nine measurement points are needed. Dividing 6 by 9 gives a true spacing of 0.666 m. Then it is necessary to find the number of points in the width of the area that gives nearly the same spacing, in the case of the 6 m by 4 m area this is easy as a spacing of 0.666 means that six points are needed across the width. Once the number of points and the spacing has been calculated it is simple to arrange the points, with the first point starting a half spacing from the edge. If this half-spacing would put the first row or column within the 0.5 m perimeter zone outside the core area then the first row or column should be on the 0.5 m boundary (see Figure 31.4).

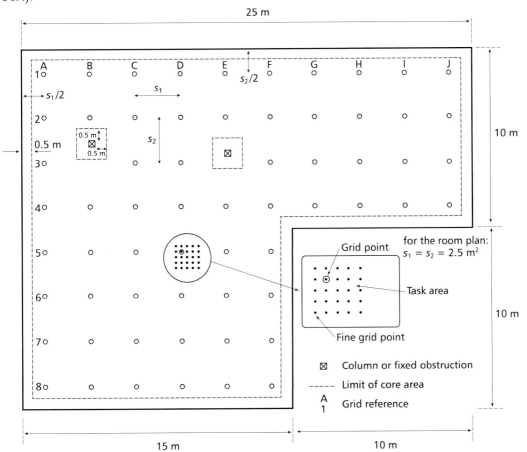

Figure 31.4 Measurement point layout in complex space

31.5.2   Defined task areas

Where the task area to be measured is an individual defined area, such as on a fixed control desk, an inclined plane of a piece of industrial equipment or on a vertical safety notice, then the first step is to define the size of task area clearly. Once the size is known, then the same calculation as given in 31.5.1 above can be carried out to determine the optimum number of rows and columns of measurement points. Where the task area is of a non-rectangular shape, such as on the control desk illustrated in Figure 31.5, then the area should be divided up into representative rectangular areas covering the main areas where tasks are performed.

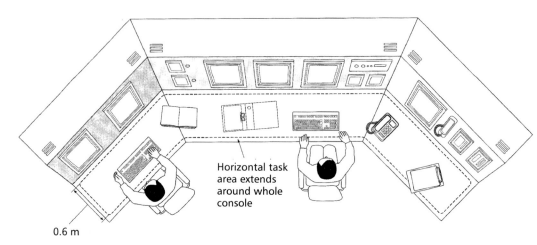

Horizontal task area extends around whole console

0.6 m

Figure 31.5 Task area across control desk

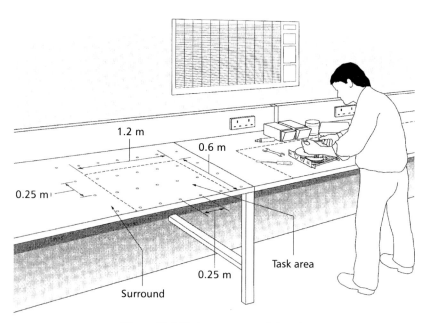

1.2 m

0.6 m

0.25 m

0.25 m

Task area

Surround

Figure 31.6 Task areas on work bench

31.5.3 Exterior lighting

For exterior lighting installations, careful attention must be paid to the temperature at the time of measurement, as it may not be the same as that typically encountered in use. In other words, measuring the lighting levels on a football pitch on a warm summer's night will not give the same lighting levels as typically encountered on a cold winter's evening during play. The measured results will need to have a factor added to allow for the performance of the lamps at the lowest or typical temperatures encountered in use.

For most exterior areas, a full grid of measurement cells should be used. The cells are usually rectangular and the cell size in each axis should be a whole number. The illuminance is measured at the centre of each cell. The maximum cell size may be determined from the equation:

$$p = 0.2 \times 5^{\log d}$$

where p is the grid interval and d is the size of the longer reference axis.

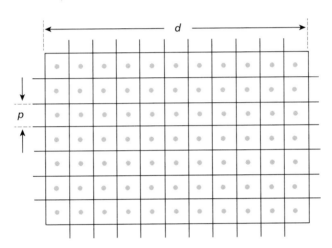

Figure 31.7 Calculation grid

The number of cells in the larger dimension is given by the nearest odd whole number to the quotient of the size of the longer reference axis (d) and the grid interval (p). This result is then used to calculate the nearest odd whole number of cells in the smaller dimension.

In a symmetrical but localized situation, as on an athletics track, the length l is one quarter of the distance of the overall inner track limit (Figure 31.8).

For the special case of road lighting, the verification method is covered in detail in BS EN 13201-4 (BSI, 2015) and further guidance on measurement procedures is given in the *SLL Code for Lighting* (SLL, 2012). The Institution of Lighting Professionals produces a guidance note, *Measurement of the photometric performance of LED lighting* (ILP, 2016), to advise on how the scotopic-to-photopic (S/P) ratio of the light source should be considered as well as the fact that a lot of road lighting is within the mesopic range.

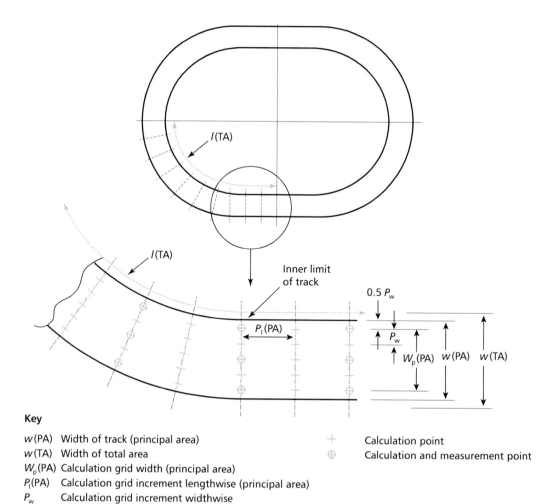

Key

w (PA) Width of track (principal area)
w (TA) Width of total area
W_p(PA) Calculation grid width (principal area)
P_l(PA) Calculation grid increment lengthwise (principal area)
P_w Calculation grid increment widthwise
l(TA) Length of inside edge of the total area

$+$ Calculation point
$\oplus$ Calculation and measurement point

The principal area (PA) is the actual track area; the total area (TA) is the principal area plus an additional safety area outside the prinicpal area. For circular or oval tracks, l(PA) = l(TA).

Figure 31.8 Track grid layout

31.6 Measurement of illuminance variation

To confirm compliance with the recommendations on illuminance variation, measurements of illuminances over the whole working plane are needed to calculate illuminance diversity and, over task areas and their immediate surrounds, to calculate illuminance uniformity.

31.6.1 Illuminance diversity

For a wide range of commercial and industrial interiors where the visual task may be adversely affected by excessive variations in illuminance, the full grid measurement method should be used. This will provide a coarse grid of points over the whole working plane. Additional measurements are then required, centred on selected points to check for local maximum and minimum illuminances. These additional measurements are made on a 3 × 3 grid of points at about 1 m centres. In this procedure any measurement locations within 0.5 m of room walls or large fixed obstructions are ignored.

31.6.2   Illuminance uniformity

To measure illuminance uniformity, a 0.25 m square grid of measurement points is established over the task area and its immediate surround at a number of representative positions. Task illuminance uniformity is assessed using the area-weighted arithmetic average of the measurement points within each task area and the minimum grid point illuminance value within that area. The lowest values of illuminance uniformity calculated from the measured values at the selected positions is taken as representative of the whole installation.

For measurement in an unfurnished area where there is no information on the task area and immediate surround dimensions, the grid should be applied to the whole working plane.

31.7   Luminance measurements

Luminance measurements are often made in response to complaints about glare from interior light. In these circumstances the conditions that are the subject of complaint should be established and luminance measurements made from the position of the people who are complaining. In this way, the source of the complaints may be identified. For further guidance on glare see the *SLL Code for Lighting* (SLL, 2012).

When measuring the luminance of light sources or luminaires, the meter should be mounted on a tripod and it is essential that the area of interest must fill the whole photoreceptor aperture of the meter. If a luminance meter is not available, an estimate of the luminance of matt room surfaces can be obtained indirectly by measuring the reflectance of the surface and the illuminance (lux) on it and then calculating the luminance (cd/m^2).

31.8   Measurement of reflectance

Sometimes it is necessary to measure the reflectance of a surface, e.g. to determine if the reflectance is outside the recommended range or to establish if the reflectance assumed in a calculation is reasonable. There are a number of ways to do this. One is to measure the illuminance falling on the surface and the luminance of the surface at the same point. The reflectance is then given by the expression:

$$R = (E\,\pi)/L$$

where R is the reflectance of the surface at the measurement point, E is the illuminance on the surface at the measurement point (lx) and L is the luminance of the surface at the measurement point (cd/m^2). See also Appendix 1, 'Reflectance and colour'.

Another method is to use a luminance meter and a standard reflectance surface made from pressed barium sulphate or magnesium oxide. The luminances of the surface of interest and the standard reflectance surface are measured from an appropriate position. Then the reflectance of the surface of interest is given by the expression:

$$R = R_s\,L_1/L_s$$

where R is the reflectance of the surface of interest, L_1 is the luminance of the surface of interest (cd/m^2), L_s is the luminance of the standard reflectance surface (cd/m^2) and R_s is the reflectance of the standard reflectance surface.

This method can also be used to obtain the luminance factor (or gloss factor) for non-matt surfaces where local values of luminance, from defined viewing positions, are of interest. This has little or no relevance to the average value of the inter-reflected illuminance received on the working plane or other room surfaces.

If a luminance meter is not available, then an approximate measure of the reflectance of a surface can be obtained by making a match between the surface of interest and a sample from a range of colour samples of known reflectance as described in SLL Lighting Guide 11: *Surface reflectance and colour* (SLL, 2001).

References

BSI (2005a) BS 667: *Illuminance meters. Requirements and test methods* (London: British Standards Institution)

BSI (2005b) BS 7920: *Luminance meters. Requirements and test methods* (London: British Standards Institution)

BSI (2015) BS EN 13201-4: 2003: *Road lighting. Methods of measuring lighting performance* (London: British Standards Institution)

ENA (2013) *Model code of practice covering electrical safety in the planning, installation, commissioning and maintenance of public lighting and other street furniture* Engineering Recommendation G39 (London: Energy Networks Association)

ILP (2017) *Choosing the right photometer/illuminance meter* (Rugby: Institution of Lighting Professionals)

ILP (2016) *Measurement of the photometric performance of LED lighting* (Rugby: Institution of Lighting Professionals)

SLL (2001) *Surface reflectance and colour* SLL Lighting Guide 11 (London: Society of Light and Lighting)

SLL (2012) *SLL Code for Lighting* (London: Society of Light and Lighting)

Chapter 32: Maintenance

32.1   The need for lighting maintenance for both traditional and LED light sources

A lighting installation starts to deteriorate from the moment it is first switched on. Maintenance keeps the performance of the system within the intended design limits to meet performance and safety levels and ensures the continuing efficient use of energy.

Maintenance activities include the replacement of failed or deteriorated light sources and control gear, the cleaning of luminaires, and the cleaning and redecoration of room surfaces. Detailed advice on lighting maintenance can be found in CIE Publications 97 and 154 (CIE, 2003, 2005) or the latest updates of these publications.

BS EN 12464-1: *Light and lighting. Lighting of work places. Indoor work places* (BSI, 2011) states that:

> 'The lighting scheme should be designed with an overall maintenance factor (MF) calculated for the selected lighting equipment, environment and the specified maintenance schedule.'

The recommended illuminance for each task in BS EN 12464-1 is the minimum maintained illuminance, which should be the minimum illuminance value achieved throughout the system lifetime.

The majority of light sources used now are LED, due to their low energy use and long lifetimes. The derivation of maintenance factors for LED light sources should be carried out in the same way as for other long-lived lamps. If the life of an LED product is quoted as 50 000 hours at the L70 point, then the maintenance factor calculation must start with a lumen maintenance factor of 0.7. Therefore the full maintenance factor will be less than this value once the degradation of the luminaire and room surfaces are taken into account.

32.2   Maintained illuminance

The illuminance recommendations in the *SLL Code for Lighting* (SLL, 2012) and in this *Handbook* are given in terms of maintained illuminance. Maintained illuminance is the minimum average illuminance of an installation. This is normally the average illuminance over the reference surface at the low point in the maintenance cycle of the installation. In other words, maintained illuminance is the minimum illuminance that the lighting installation will produce, on that surface, during its life.

Using maintained illuminance for recommendations requires the designer to adopt a series of maintenance policy decisions in order to determine the maintenance factor to be used in their calculations. To ensure that these decisions are appropriate the designer should either obtain a decision from the client on the maintenance policy to be implemented throughout the life of the installation or clearly state the assumed maintenance programme used in the design calculations.

32.3   Determination of maintenance factor for interior lighting

Characteristics of the lighting equipment and the degrading effects of the environment mean that the light level in a space decreases with time. Despite this, a lighting installation needs to ensure the specified light level is provided throughout the life of the installation. The anticipated decrease is quantified by the maintenance factor, and this factor is then used to increase the installed capacity of a lighting installation to offset the gradual decrease in light available over time.

The overall maintenance factor (MF) for an indoor lighting installation is the product of four factors:

$$MF = LLMF \times LSF \times LMF \times RSMF$$

where LLMF is the light source lumen maintenance factor (the decline in lumen output over time), LSF is the light source survival factor, LMF is the luminaire maintenance factor (which takes into account accumulated dirt on a luminaire) and RSMF is the room surface maintenance factor (which takes into account accumulated dirt and dust on all room surfaces).

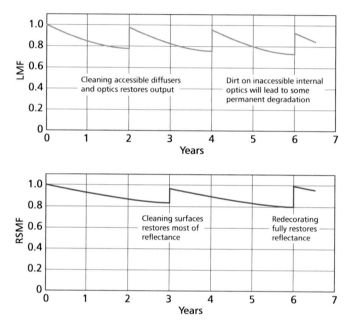

Figure 32.1 Indication of how available light is affected by a cleaning regime for a notional luminaire and room (the actual cleaning intervals to be chosen to suit luminaire, environment and room)

32.3.1 Designing for lighting maintenance

The maintenance factor is used in the calculation of the number of light sources and luminaires needed to provide the recommended maintained illuminance. Maintenance factor can be defined as the ratio of illumination on a given area after a period of time to the initial illumination on the same area, taking into account the depreciation of lamps, luminaires and room reflective surfaces. The closer the maintenance factor is to unity, the smaller the number of lamps and luminaires that will be needed to maintain the required lighting level through the life cycle of the installation.

The maintenance requirements for a lighting installation must be considered at the design stage. Three aspects are particularly important:

- *Assumptions about cleaning regimes*: the assumption about luminaire and room surface cleaning intervals must be realistic and accepted by the owner of the installation.

Unless this maintenance regime is fulfilled the installation will not meet the recommended minimum maintained illuminance during its life.

- *Practical access and handling*: good maintenance will only occur if access to the lighting installation is safe and easy. The location of lighting equipment and the potential methods of accessing it, should be considered at the design stage

- *Equipment selection*: the dirtier the operating environment, the more important it is to select equipment that is resistant to dirt deposition. For example, sealed luminaires avoid dust or contaminants getting onto internal reflectors and the inside surface of diffusers.

32.3.2   Maintenance factors for LEDs

LED light sources have become the main source of light for the majority of applications. This is because of their higher efficacy (and hence lower energy consumption) than many conventional light sources. Their longer life than many other light sources can reduce the need for maintenance, but leads to a risk that luminaires are left uncleaned for considerable periods as they are not 'visited' by necessity for lamp changing.

The factors used for RSMF and LSF do not change depending on the source of light. A common sense view should be taken on the selection of LMF when specifying any very long-lived lamp or light sources, such as LEDs. Room and luminaire cleaning regimes must not be used for calculation purposes that are unlikely to be implemented in the real world.

It is typical for LED manufacturers to state an LED life at a particular point in its depreciation; such as 50 000 hours at L70. This is the point at which the light output of the LED (or LED luminaire) has reached 70% of its initial light output. (Life figures can also be given for L90 or L80). These light output figures are only single points on a normally gradual fading of an LED product, see Figure 32.2 for an example. The actual curves will vary considerably between products. Obviously if a client or customer is assured that 'these LEDs will last 50 000 hours' (at the L70 point) the maintenance factor calculation must start with LLMF set to 0.7.

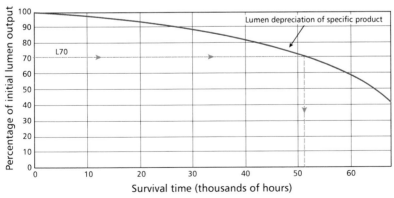

Figure 32.2 Typical depreciation curve showing predicted life at the L70 point

Rather than use this 0.7 default figure, it is better to calculate the likely service life of the installation and work out the LLMF from that figure. If a client can advise the operating times per annum of an installation and the proposed times before replacement or refurbishment of the luminaires, a more realistic LLMF can be applied.

For instance, a space operating at 24 hours per day, 7 days per week and 52 weeks per annum equates to 8736 hours per annum. Here an L70 life figure of 50 000 h corresponds to just 5.7 years. Whereas a space operating for 8 hours a day, 5 days a week, 52 weeks per annum equates to 2080 hours per annum. With an L70 figure of 50 000 h, this corresponds to over 24 years use. It is possible that the luminaires may be replaced within that period. If the installation were in a high-end retailer, and they anticipate the lighting and décor being upgraded every fifteen years at the most, then perhaps an L80 figure would be more appropriate, allowing the use of 0.8 as the LLMF rather than 0.7 — leading to fewer luminaires being needed to achieve the required task lighting levels throughout the life of the installation.

A proposed installation in a smart office reception is anticipated to operate for 10 hours a day, 6 days a week for 50 weeks per annum, a total of 3000 hours per annum. It is proposed that the design life is 10 years. The LLMF may be calculated using the life figure of 30 000 h. In the case shown in Figure 32.3 below, this would be about 0.92. Note that Figure 32.3 is an example curve — the curves for actual LEDs vary considerably from product to product and this will impact on the number of luminaires required and the overall energy use for the installation through its life. Any maintenance factor proposals and/or assumptions, should be stated by the designer and checked. Manufacturers should be asked for the LLMF of their LED products for the design life of the installation, not just 50 000 h.

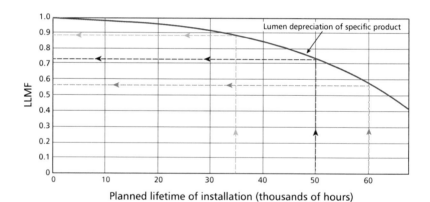

Figure 32.3 Knowing the planned lifetime of an installation allows the actual depreciation curve for the product to be used to establish the LLMF lifetime graph

Explanation of LED metrics

- Lxx: the light source lumen output depreciates over time; the Lxx value indicates the lumen output expected at a point in time, e.g. L70 @ 50 000 h indicates that at 50 000 hours, 70% of the initial lumen output will be still be achieved.

- B_y: the failure fraction value for the percentage of LEDs that have gradually fallen below the stated L value lumen output percentage, e.g. B10, B50.

- h: the service life in hours, e.g. 30 000 h, 50 000 h.

- C_y: abrupt failure value percentage, i.e. when a luminaire or individual chip catastrophically fails and emits no light.

- F_y: the sum of B (gradual) and C (catastrophic) failure values — the same as LSF.

Note that manufacturers' data are normally based on standard temperatures such as 25 °C. In very hot or very cold environments, the life and light output of the LEDs will vary from the standard figures. Therefore, request data from the manufacturers for the probable ambient temperature of the proposed installation. See Chapter 23, 'Extreme environments'.

Manufacturers should be consulted for the B_y and C_y figures for their products so that F_y can be calculated to determine lamp survival factor values.

Warranties and life guarantees offered by manufacturers or expected by clients have no relevance to the calculation of maintenance factors.

32.3.3 Lamp/light source replacement: traditional and LED light sources

There are two factors to be considered when determining the timing of lamp or LED module replacement: the decrease in light output and the probability of lamp failure. The relative weight given to these two factors depends on the type of light source. Tungsten–halogen lamps usually fail before the decline in light output becomes significant. Therefore the replacement time for these lamps is determined by the probability of lamp failure alone. All other electric light sources show a significant reduction in light output before a large proportion fail. For these lamps, both the decline in light output and the probability of lamp failure are important in determining the lamp replacement time. LED light sources will depreciate in output over time due to factors such as LED type, thermal management and luminaire construction, as well as the quality of the drivers.

For lighting installations with replaceable lamps, a common approach is to replace all the lamps at planned intervals. This procedure, known as group replacement, has visual, electrical and financial advantages over the alternative of spot replacement (replacing individual lamps as they fail). Visually, group replacement ensures that the installation maintains a uniform appearance. Electrically, group replacement reduces the risk of damage to the control gear caused by the faulty operation of lamps nearing the end of their life. Financially, by having the lamp replacement coincide with luminaire cleaning and doing both at a time when it will cause the minimum of disturbance, the cost of maintenance can be minimized. Group replacement is an appropriate procedure for routine maintenance and the frequency with which the procedure is carried out will have a direct bearing on the installed electrical load. However, in any large installation, a few lamps can be expected to fail prematurely. Where there is an overriding aesthetic or safety issue these lamps could still be replaced on an individual basis. When replacing fluorescent lamps operating on switch start circuit, it is advisable to also replace the starter switch to avoid stuck starter condition.

For many installations the most economic time for group replacement is when the light output of the lamps has fallen below a certain percentage of the initial value (commonly 80%) and the lamp failures are becoming significant to the loss of average illuminance. The latest time for group replacement is when the designed 'maintained illuminance' has been reached.

As light source development proceeds there is a temptation to replace one light source with another that is superficially similar but of higher luminous efficacy. However, it is essential to establish that the replacement light source and the existing control gear are compatible physically, electrically and photometrically. Before replacing any discharge light source with another of a different type or the same type but from a different manufacturer, advice on compatibility should be sought.

LED light sources that have fixed, or sealed LED modules need to be completely replaced at the end of their useful life. LED light sources that have replaceable LED modules may allow the luminaire housing to be cleaned and reused until the next planned maintenance schedule.

32.3.4   Lamp lumen maintenance factor (LLMF)

The luminous flux from all types of electric light sources reduces with time of operation. The rate of decline varies for different light sources so it is essential to consult manufacturers' data. From such data it is possible to obtain the lamp lumen maintenance factor for a specific number of hours of operation. Where the decline in light output is regular, LLMF may be quoted as a percentage reduction per thousand hours of operation.

Manufacturers' data will normally be based on test procedures that specify the ambient temperature in which the lamp will be tested, with a regulated voltage applied to the lamp and, if appropriate, a reference set of control gear. If any of the aspects of the proposed design are unusual, e.g. high ambient temperature, vibration, switching cycle, operating attitude etc., the manufacturer should be made aware of the conditions and will advise if they affect the life and/or light output of the lamp.

Typical values of LLMF for generic lamp types should not be used in calculations as the variation between wattage ranges and between manufacturers is too great. The actual LLMF for the intended light sources should be obtained from the manufacturers.

32.3.5   Lamp survival factor (LSF)

The lamp survival factor is the proportion of lamps that are expected to still be emitting light after a specified number of hours of operation, and varies with the type of lamp. It is used in the calculation of maintenance factor when group lamp replacement is to be adopted; LSF is not considered for spot replacement.

However, it may be appropriate to consult the client and write into the maintenance schedule that in the event of failure of an individual complete luminaire it should be repaired or changed at the earliest time when aesthetic or safety standards may be compromised.

As with lamp lumen maintenance factor it is essential to consult manufacturers' data for appropriate values of LSF. These data will be based on assumptions such as switching cycle, supply voltage and control gear. If the expected operating conditions depart from these assumptions, manufacturers should be informed and asked for advice on how the actual conditions might affect lamp/light source survival.

Typical values of LSF for generic lamp types should not be used in calculations as the variation between wattage ranges and between manufacturers is too great. Actual LSF for intended light sources should be obtained from the manufacturer.

32.3.6   Luminaire maintenance factor (LMF)

Dirt deposited on the reflective surfaces of a luminaire will cause a reduction in light output from the luminaire. The rate at which dirt is deposited depends on the construction of the luminaire, the nature of the dirt and the extent to which it is present in the atmosphere. The luminaire maintenance factor (LMF) is the ratio of the light output of a luminaire at a given time to the initial light output.

Tables are given in the *SLL Code for Lighting* (SLL, 2012) for typical values of LMF for six different types of luminaires and six different luminaire cleaning intervals in 'very clean', 'clean', 'normal' and 'dirty' environments. The actual cleanliness of any given space should be assessed, but typically very clean environments are often found in such locations as clean rooms and electronic assembly; clean environments are found in such locations as computer centres and hospitals; normal environments are found in offices, shops, schools, laboratories, restaurants, warehouses and so on. Dirty environments are common in steelworks, chemical works, foundries, woodwork areas and similar locations.

32.3.7   Room surface maintenance factor (RSMF)

Changes in room surface reflectance caused by dirt deposition will cause changes in the illuminance produced by the lighting installation. The magnitude of these changes is governed by the extent of dirt deposition and the importance of inter-reflection to the illuminance produced. Inter-reflection is closely related to the distribution of light from the luminaire and the room index. For luminaires that have a strongly downward distribution, i.e. direct luminaires, inter-reflection has little effect on the illuminance produced on the horizontal working plane. Conversely, indirect lighting is completely dependent on inter-reflections. As for room index, the smaller is the room index, the greater is the contribution of inter-reflected light.

Tables are given in the *SLL Code for Lighting* (SLL, 2012) for typical values of RSMF to show the typical changes in the illuminance from an installation that occur with time due to dirt deposition on the room surfaces for 'very clean', 'clean', 'normal' and 'dirty' environments, in small, medium or large rooms, lit by direct, direct/indirect and indirect luminaires. The actual cleanliness of any given space should be assessed; this will vary depending on whether the building is partly open to the environment (such as loading docks), naturally ventilated or sealed and air conditioned.

32.4   Cleaning luminaires

The rate at which dirt is deposited on and in a luminaire depends on the amount and composition of the dirt in the atmosphere and the type of luminaire.

For particularly dirty atmospheres or where access is difficult, the best choice would be dust-proof or dust-tight luminaires, ventilated luminaires that are designed to use air currents to keep them clean, or lamps with internal reflectors. Over the same period of time and in the same location, dust-proof (IP5X) and dust-tight (IP6X) luminaires and open reflectors with slots in the top will collect less dirt than louvred luminaires with closed tops, or luminaires with unsealed diffusers (see Chapter 8, 'Luminaires', for descriptions of luminaire types). Even the most protected luminaires, e.g. dust-tight luminaires, will collect dirt on their external surfaces. Therefore even these luminaires will need cleaning regularly (see Chapter 23, 'Extreme environments', for descriptions of protection categories).

The appropriate cleaning interval for luminaires and the lamps they contain is a basic design decision. The factors that need to be considered are the cost and convenience of cleaning at a particular time and the illuminance at that time in relation to the design maintained illuminance. As a general guide, luminaires should be cleaned at least once a year but for some locations this will not be sufficient.

A wide range of materials are used in luminaires. Table 32.1 suggests the most suitable cleaning methods for different materials, although the manufacturer of the equipment should always be consulted for advice on the best method of cleaning their products.

Table 32.1 Typical methods for cleaning materials used in luminaires

Material	Cleaning methods
Anodized aluminium	Surfaces should be cleaned with a non-abrasive cloth or sponge using a neutral detergent in warm water that does not leave a residue and then allowed to air dry. Ultrasonic cleaning techniques. Severe staining or contamination should be removed first by metal polish.
Stainless steel	Surfaces should be cleaned with a non-abrasive cloth or sponge using a neutral detergent in warm water and then the surface dried with a clean cloth, following the grain of brushed finishes where applicable. Surface lustre may be restored by applying an oil-based cleaning compound with a cloth and wiping off all surplus.
Galvanized steel, natural aluminium	Surfaces should be cleaned with a neutral-based detergent and wiped dry.
Enamel paint finish, polyester powder coat	Surfaces should be cleaned with a non-abrasive cloth or sponge using a neutral detergent in warm water and the surface dried with a clean cloth. Solvent-based cleaners should not be used.
Glass	Surfaces should be cleaned with a non-abrasive cloth or sponge using a neutral detergent in warm water that does not leave a residue, then wiped and allowed to air dry.
Acrylic, polycarbonate, glass-polyester, reinforced plastic	Remove loose dirt and dust with a vacuum cleaner. Surfaces should be cleaned with a non-abrasive cloth or sponge using a neutral-based detergent that does not leave any residue, then rinsed and wiped dry with warm water containing an anti-static solution. Solvent-based cleaners should not be used under any circumstances. Ultrasonic cleaning techniques.

32.5 Room surface cleaning

All room surfaces should be cleaned and redecorated regularly if a dirty appearance and light loss are to be avoided. Regular cleaning is particularly important where light reflected from the room surfaces makes an important contribution to the lighting of the interior, e.g. where daylight from the side windows is used or where the electric lighting installation has a high indirect component such as uplighting (see Appendix 1, 'Reflectance and colour').

32.6 Determination of maintenance factor for exterior lighting

The maintenance factor (MF) for an outdoor lighting installation is the product of three factors:

$$MF = LLMF \times LSF \times LMF$$

where LLMF is the lamp lumen maintenance factor, LSF is the lamp survival factor and LMF is the luminaire maintenance factor.

LLMF information should be made available by the manufacturer.

LSF information should be made available by the manufacturer, or a LSF value of 1.0 used where spot replacements of failed modules is agreed and written into the maintenance schedule.

LMF information is based on environmental zone, mounting height and cleaning frequency. Table 32.2, from Annex B of BS 5489-1: 2013: *Code of practice for the design of roadlighting. Lighting of roads and public amenity areas* (BSI, 2013), indicates typical luminaire maintenance factors.

Table 32.2 Luminaire maintenance factors (source: BSI, 2013)

Environmental zone	Mounting height	Maintenance factor for stated cleaning frequency					
		12 months	24 months	36 months	48 months	60 months	72 months
E1/E2	≤ 6 m	0.96	0.96	0.95	0.94	0.93	0.92
E1/E2	> 6 m	0.96	0.96	0.95	0.94	0.93	0.92
E3/E4	≤ 6 m	0.94	0.92	0.90	0.88	0.86	0.84
E3/E4	> 6 m	0.96	0.96	0.95	0.94	0.93	0.92

Notes: (1) the table gives typical luminaire maintenance factors for design calculations; (2) data are derived from *Review of luminaire maintenance factors* (Sanders and Scott, 2008) with interpolated values extending to 72 months and an upper limit of 0.96; (3) values may otherwise be obtained from site measurement or other researched data.

The maintenance factor is then given by the lumen maintenance of the LEDs at the end of their rated life (Lxx) times the failure fraction of the LEDs at the end of their rated life (F_y) times the reduced lumen output of the luminaire due to the accumulation of dirt on the luminaire luminous area.

For example, for an IP66 luminaire mounted at a height of 6 m in an E1 environmental zone, cleaned at 48 month intervals, with an LED rated useful life L90 at 50 000 hours:

$$F_y = 10\% \ (\text{i.e. } B_y \times C_y)$$

From Table 32.2:

$$LMF = 0.94$$

Hence the overall maintenance factor (MF):

$$MF = \left(\frac{90}{100}\right) \times \left(\frac{100 - 10}{100}\right) \times 0.94 = 0.76$$

References

BSI (2011) BS EN 12464-1: 2011: *Light and lighting. Lighting of work places. Indoor work places* (London: British Standards Institution)

BSI (2013) BS 5489-1: 2013: *Code of practice for the design of roadlighting. Lighting of roads and public amenity areas* (London: British Standards Institution)

CIE (2005) CIE 97: 2005: *Guide on the maintenance of indoor electric lighting systems* 2nd edn (Vienna: International Commission on Illumination)

CIE (2003) CIE 154: 2003: *The maintenance of outdoor lighting systems* (Vienna: International Commission on Illumination)

SLL (2012) *SLL Code for Lighting* (London: Society of Light and Lighting)

Sanders A and Scott A (2008) *Review of luminaire maintenance factors* (Wokingham: Transport Research Laboratory/County Surveyors Society) (available at http://www.trl.co.uk/reports/SL3)

Appendix 1: Reflectance and colour

A1.1   Introduction

We see the world around us due to physical processes such as light generation and reflection, and the physiological and psychological processes in our eyes and mind. Not all these processes can be specified or controlled by lighting designers and architects — and some are also beyond the scope of this *Handbook*. But it is good to be aware of these: you might not be able to specify them, but you might try to reduce or use their effects.

Although this appendix will focus on reflectance, the path from a ray of light from the source to our eyes can be a long one, and may involve many other different physical phenomena. Besides mostly travelling through space a ray: (*a*) can be scattered or absorbed by atoms, molecules and particles; (*b*) may be transmitted (refracted) or reflected at an interface of a surface; (*c*) may also be diffracted by an aperture, or an edge of an object; (*d*) may interfere with split parts of itself; (*e*) may undergo a fluorescence event, with a photon in a ray of light being absorbed by a molecule, and re-emitted as a photon with different wavelength. Some of these are quite rare, some very common. For example, fluorescence determines to a large extent the spectral composition of light generated by fluorescent lamps and light emitting diodes (LEDs), and is also used to make white appear brighter in paper and clothing.

Another complexity of light specification is that light levels and colours are typically not static, especially when natural light is used: the position of the sun changes with time of day and season. Also, the way light is scattered by the atmosphere depends on its particle composition (e.g. water droplets in clouds, pollutants) and the sun's orientation. Indoors, if electric lighting is used, light conditions might not be static: dynamic dimming and colour changing lights may be used to mimic or complement changing daylight conditions. Or lighting conditions may be changed to help to tell a story as in theatre lighting. Even if it is not intended to change a lit space, the lit effect might change due to degradation of the light source. Lights loose intensity over time, and might shift in colour due to degradation of components in the light, or get dirty.

Furthermore, objects are typically illuminated not only by direct light from one or more lighting fixtures, but also by light reflected from (potentially coloured) walls or other objects in its surroundings: reflectivity, position, and orientation of these need to be taken into account in lighting design. Also, these factors (i.e. reflectivity, position, and orientation) are not static and may change over time.

The visual appearance of a surface is dependent not only on its reflectivity but also on its surface texture, collimation and orientation of the illumination.

Last but not least, the way our eyes and our brain experience colour is not constant. Our eyes adapt to light level and colour: what we see is dependent on what we were looking at before. And the brightness and colour of a target object we see is also dependent on other objects in our field of view, even if they do not affect the illuminance and physical colour of the target object itself. Also, our memory and experiences can affect how we see things. For example: we will always know that a fried egg is white with yellow in the middle.

This appendix covers only the basic principles and concepts related to the reflectance and colour of, in particular, building materials and light sources. For a full exploration of surface reflectance and colour, refer to SLL Lighting Guide 11: *Surface reflectance and colour* (SLL, 2001). This also gives more information on how the colour and reflectance properties of existing surfaces can be assessed and it includes a printed chart of calibrated colour samples that can be used to assess, by comparison, the reflectance value of materials.

A1.2 Light reflecting properties

When light is incident on a surface, typically its main direction, distribution and spectral composition are altered by the surface's shape, texture and material composition. Reflection can be specular or diffuse, but most common building materials produce a combination of specular and diffuse reflection, known as glossy and semi-matte reflecting, which will be explained in the next sections.

A1.2.1 Specular reflection

Assuming a flat, smooth (polished) surface of a homogenous and non-absorbing material, light is either specular reflected or transmitted (and refracted). If the material is highly reflective, such as a silvered mirror, all light is reflected. In this case, reflected light is contained within a very small range of angles: all the light is reflected in the same plane, and at an equal and opposite angle to the surface normal as the incident light (see Figure A1.1). This is called specular reflection.

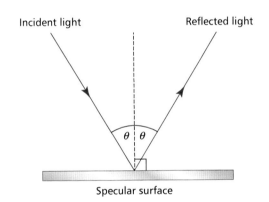

Figure A1.1 Reflection from a perfectly specular surface; the reflected beam is at the same angle to the surface as the incident beam and is also of the same intensity

If the material is not highly reflecting and partially absorbing (but not transmitting), the specular reflection might look coloured. This is for example the case with a gold surface. Gold reflects the green and red spectral components, but partially absorbs the blue parts of the spectrum (see Figure A1.2).

Silver has a high and fairly even reflectivity, and appears to us as having no colour. This is what we see in a regular mirror. A gold surface is less reflective in the blue parts of the spectrum, and has the colour we know as 'gold'.

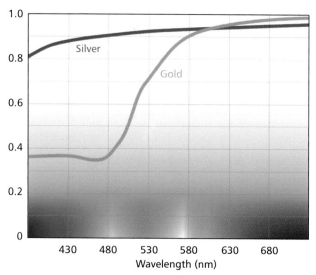

Figure A1.2 Spectral reflectivity of polished silver and gold for normal incidence (courtesy of Gerard Harbers)

If a smooth, homogenous surface is (partially) transparent, light is transmitted in addition to being reflected. Examples of these materials are window glass and transparent plastic.

A1.2.2 Diffuse reflection

With diffuse reflection, incident light on a surface is reflected in all directions (see Figure A1.3). It can be caused by light being scattered from a rough surface (brushed or sand blasted aluminium), by volume scattering of light by particles or fibres embedded in a surface (white emulsion paint), or a combination of both (white paper).

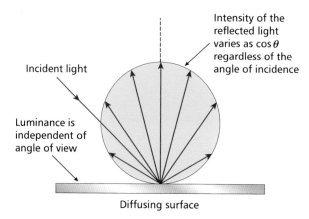

Figure A1.3 Reflection from a perfectly diffuse surface; the luminance of the surface is independent of the angle of view, i.e. the luminance is a constant and the intensity of the reflected light at an angle θ to the perpendicular to the surface varies as $\cos\theta$

Coloured diffuse reflecting surfaces are typically obtained by using coloured pigments. Pigments are organic and inorganic materials that change the colour of an incident beam of light by wavelength-selective absorption. Pigments are typically composed of very fine particles embedded (and insoluble) in a binder (also known as vehicle), which is a neutral or colourless material. Its purpose is to suspend the particles and to adhere the paint and ink to a carrier, such as a wall or a piece of paper. The pigment particles absorb spectral components and scatter the light[1].

A1.2.3 Glossy and semi-matte reflection

For most surfaces, the reflection is neither perfectly specular or perfectly diffuse — these surfaces may be termed 'glossy' (significant specular reflection) or 'semi-matte' (little specular reflection), as shown in Figure A1.4.

Consider the case of a coloured gloss paint layer in which coloured pigments are suspended in a clear gloss lacquer. Specular reflections occur from the surface of the lacquer but a reasonably high proportion of the light penetrates to the particle layer below, giving rise to coloured, diffuse, reflections. The overall effect is a coloured, high gloss finish.

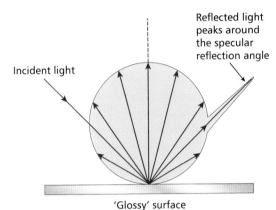

Figure A1.4 Most types of surface exhibit a combination of diffuse and specular reflection; the proportion of specular reflection determines how 'glossy' or 'shiny' the surface appears

A1.2.4 Transmission

With thin materials (for example paper), or low absorbing materials such as glass, light is typically also transmitted. This transmission can be clear, opalescent, or translucent.

Clear transmission occurs with, for example, clear glass and clear plastic materials (Figure A1.5a). If coloured, the material partially absorbs or transmits spectral components. Examples of this are colour filters for camera lenses or clear coloured plastic sheets. Wavelength-dependent absorption is obtained by adding a colorant in the form of a dye to a base material, with the dye being soluble in the base material.

With opalescent transmission light is transmitted diffusely, as with most paper-like materials (Figure A1.5b); no objects can be distinguished when viewed through the surface. This transmission can also be coloured such in advertising signs. As with coloured diffuse reflecting, this is achieved by adding pigments.

With translucent materials light is transmitted partially diffuse, similar to glossy or semi-matte reflection (see Figure A1.5c); objects behind the surface can be partially distinguished, especially when they are closer to the surface.

---

[1] As opposed to dyes, which exhibit only absorbance and no scattering, these maintain the specular appearance of the material.

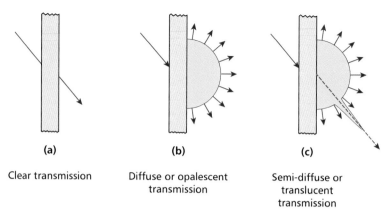

(a)	(b)	(c)
Clear transmission	Diffuse or opalescent transmission	Semi-diffuse or translucent transmission

Figure A1.5 Transmission of light through materials, such as stained or milk glass

A1.3   Illumination and colour

Without light, the world is dark and there is no colour. In the world of physics there is light, but no colour (Newton, 1704); there are only rays of light, having an intensity, and composed of spectral components. Our sensations of colour are only created when these rays of light enter our eyes, are converted into electrical signals by our cones, and analysed in our brain. To understand and specify colour and colour rendering performance, it is necessary to understand the physical aspects of illumination — typically characterised by its spectral distribution and derived colour rendering metrics — and the physiology and psychology of human colour vision, which will be briefly considered next.

A1.3.1   Colour constancy and chromatic adaptation

Human vision is very adaptable. We can see at very low light levels[2], under the light of a candle in the evening, for example, and we see well at very high light levels, as with the light from a bright sun in the middle of summer. Luminance of objects varies by five to six orders of magnitude under these different lighting conditions, but our vision system adapts so that on average objects appear to have the same brightness.

Our eyes and brain also adapt for colour vision. The spectral distribution of an incandescent filament lamp is very different to that of the sun on a clear day (see Figure A1.6 below). However, if we take an object, such as an apple, its colour appears the same independent of these large spectral differences[3]. This is called colour constancy, and is a result of chromatic adaptation processes in our retina and our visual cortex.

Colour constancy is a result of evolution. It is a psychological phenomenon and has no basis in physics. It enables us to distinguish between healthy and poisonous food, and recognise friend from foe, independent of the lighting conditions — lighting conditions which we as humans, and our primate ancestors, have been exposed to over millions of years. Daylight, in all its forms and shapes, and light from fire and oil lamps are examples of lighting that our visual system has learned to correct for in order to see colours correctly.

---

[2] Although we do not see much colour at such very low light levels.

[3] As long as the objects have sufficient luminance (brightness) to activate colour vision through our cones.

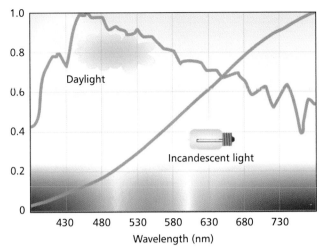

Figure A1.6 Spectral emission of daylight, at a correlated colour temperature (CCT) of 6500 K, and a halogen lamp, with a CCT of about 2700 K; they are very different, but due to colour constancy in human vision colour appearance of objects is similar when viewed under either of them (courtesy of Gerard Harbers)

Colour constancy can fail if spectral components in the light are missing. If only green light falls on a red surface it appears black; in that case there are no red spectral components present in the incident light to be reflected. Other lamps, such as some discharge lamps, emit most of their light at a relatively restricted range of wavelengths and can therefore 'distort' the colour appearance of a surface. Some poor-quality LED lamps have very little red radiation and make red surfaces look subdued. These 'distortions' can be measured and quantified. They determine the colour rendering performance of a lamp, which is quantified by a colour rendering index.

A1.3.2 Colour rendering

The effect of missing spectral components of the light produced by a lamp can be determined by looking at the colours of sample surfaces, and comparing these between the lamp under test and daylight or a tungsten filament halogen lamp with the same correlated colour temperature (CCT). This comparison can be done using actual samples but can also be done using the measured spectral distribution of the lamp, and using reference reflection spectra[4].

The International Commission on Illumination (CIE) has developed standardised calculation procedures and colour metrics for this purpose: CIE 13.3-1995: *Method of Measuring and Specifying Colour Rendering Properties of Light Sources* (CIE, 1995). In this standard, colour rendering is tested with up to 14 reference patches. In practice, the average of only the eight reference patches are used to obtain a single colour rendering index referred to as R_a. This standard, last updated in 1974[5], has some limitations, especially for solid state light sources. Fairly recently a new standard has been developed by the Illuminating Engineering Society (IES) of North America, which has been defined in report IES TM-30-15 (IES, 2015). This standard

---

[4] These do not have to be physical samples, and can just be a spectral power distribution in form of a set of wavelengths and relative intensities used in a spreadsheet, or computer program.

[5] The 1995 version concerned only minor editorial corrections and brought the standard up to date with modern spectro-radiometric and calculation practices, but did not change the technical recommendations.

defines a colour fidelity metric R_f, which is an average of colour differences of a sample set of 99 reference patches. This standard has been adopted by the CIE in the form of technical report CIE 224-2017: *CIE 2017 Colour Fidelity Index for accurate scientific use* (CIE, 2017).

A1.3.2.1 CIE 13.3-1995 Colour Rendering Index (CRI)

In this standard 14 test colour samples (TCS) are used to check colour differences between the light source under test and a reference source. The test colour samples are shown in Figure A1.7. Although not part of the standard, very often a 15th test colour sample is added (also shown in Figure A1.7). This 15th colour represents the colour of Asian skin. In the following description, this 15th value is not referenced, as it is not part of the CIE 13.3-1995 standard, but sometimes lighting manufacturers will report this value.

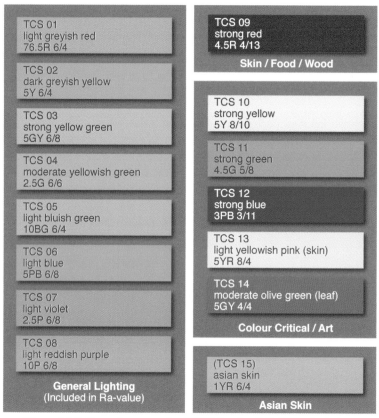

Figure A1.7 Test colour samples (TCS) for the CIE CRI calculation. The rendered colours are approximate, as well as the Munsell colour references. The exact spectral power distributions of the colours can be found in the standard, and these have to be used for the CRI calculation. TCS 15 is not part of the official CIE standard, but is sometimes added by lamp manufacturers when reporting CRI values (courtesy of Gerard Harbers)

As a reference source either daylight or light similar to an incandescent light is chosen. The standard uses a CIE 'D' standard source for daylight and a blackbody radiator to represent an incandescent source. Which one is chosen depends on the correlated colour temperature (CCT) of the source under test. If this is higher than 5000 K the CIE 'D' source is used and, if it is less, a blackbody radiator is used.

For each of the test colour samples the chromaticity coordinates are calculated when illuminated with the source under test and the reference lamp. This calculation requires only the spectral power distribution of the test source. The spectral power distributions of the test colour samples and reference light sources are available as mathematical formulae and tables, as defined in the standard. The chromaticity coordinates are corrected for chromatic adaptation using the Von Kries correction, and are further processed to yield colour difference values, which in turn are scaled to obtain colour rendering indices. In total fourteen colour rendering indices are obtained in this way. They are indicated by the symbol R_i where the index i can vary from 1 to 14. R_1 is the index associated with test colour sample 1, and similarly for the other index values.

The colour rendering indices in this standard have a highest value of 100. A value of 100 indicates that there is no colour difference of a test patch between the source under test and the reference source. The lower bound of the index could be lower than zero (i.e. negative). An index value higher than 95 is very good; most observers will see no colour difference between test and reference at this value. This limit should be used for very demanding colour applications such as museum lighting. A value higher than 90 is good; observers start to see colour differences but they are small enough to be acceptable for most applications. Values higher than 80 are acceptable but colour distortions are becoming noticeable. Lamps with these values can be used for general lighting in offices, hallways and indoor public spaces. Index values less than 80 have significant noticeable colour distortion. Typically, higher efficacies are obtained with lower colour rendering performance. For non-colour rendering sensitive applications, such as street lighting or security lighting, using lower colour rendering can be acceptable.

Instead of using all the fourteen indices, colour rendering performance is often summarised by reporting the average of the first eight. This value is referred to as the general colour rendering index R_a. The values R_9 through R_{14} are not used in the calculation of this number. The first eight colour test samples used in the R_a value calculation are pastel colours. They do not include strong and more saturated test colours (red, yellow, green and blue). They also do not include test colours representing skin tones (R_{13}, R_{15}), and the colour representing leaves (R_{14}).

Examples of R_a and individual R_i values for a selection of five types of light sources are shown in Figure A1.8. The first is an LED lamp for general lighting, with a specified R_a value of 80, but an actual R_a value of 81. The second, an LED with excellent colour rendering, is comparable to a halogen filament lamp. The third, a halogen dichroic lamp using an IR filter to achieve a higher efficacy. The last two are a compact metal halide and compact fluorescent lamps. All these lamps have an R_a value greater than 80. The individual R_i values are coloured red if they are less than 80, which means that these colours have significant colour distortion. Values greater than 95 are coloured green. These have no noticeable colour distortion. Although all these lamps have R_a values greater than 80, many values are less then 80, in particular in the R_9 column. Only the very high colour rendering lamps show good rendering performance for this test sample colour.

	Ra	R1	R2	R3	R4	R5	R6	R7	R8	R9	R10	R11	R12	R13	R14	R15
LED R_a80	81	80	85	89	81	78	80	86	66	16	64	79	58	81	93	75
LED Excellent Rendering	98	98	99	98	98	98	97	98	98	96	99	98	88	98	98	98
Halogen Dichromatic IR	98	98	99	99	99	98	98	99	97	92	97	98	97	98	99	97
Compact Metal Halide	82	90	94	69	82	81	81	87	71	27	59	62	55	93	78	88
Compact Fluorescent	87	91	93	86	91	89	90	88	70	17	76	91	81	93	92	88

Figure A1.8 Sample CRI values for five light sources. Index values less than 80 are indicated by red, and values greater or equal than 95 by green. These are measured values of real lamps, but not necessarily intended to be typical for the categories of lamps (courtesy of Gerard Harbers)

Test sample colour 9 is a strong red colour. It is an important colour for many reasons, the most important one being that red is the colour of blood, and a key part of skin colour. Skin has no single colour. It consists of a palette of different colours — it is not homogenous and light can penetrate skin deeply before it is scattered and reflected. Reddening of skin is caused by blood flow and can be associated with emotional states such as embarrassment, anger or romantic stimulation. Good strong red colour rendering performance of lamps is required in social environments to be able to detect these states. Also for medical lighting applications good red colour rendering performance is required to inspect general health[6]. Besides blood, red can be found frequently in nature (tannins). Red in a pure, strong form is found in fruits (e.g. raspberries, cherries, wine) but also in more subdued form as in most types of (stained) wood, which is an important building material. Even if the lamps have a R_a value greater than 80 (even close to 90), the R_9 value can be very low, as the R_9 value is not included in the R_a value (see Figure A1.8).

Depending on the lighting application, the other test sample colours R_{10} to R_{14} and R_{15} can be important to check too. Good colour rendering for strong yellow, green and blue (R_{10} through R_{12}) are, for example, important in museums and also for fashion. For skin tones, besides the very important R_9, R_{13} and R_{15} must also be considered. A good moderate green, R_{14}, is also required for outdoor lighting, but R_9 is also very important due to the many brown (dark red) colours in nature.

A1.3.2.2 IES TM-30-15 (CIE 224:2017) Colour Fidelity Index (R_f)

The CIE 13.3-1995 standard was first published in 1965, and was last improved in 1974 (by including the von Kries chromatic adaptation shift, see footnote [5] above). Since 1974, colour science has progressed. Many improvements have been suggested. Also, light source technology has evolved, in particular the rapid development of solid state lighting. For some of these light sources the CIE general colour rendering index (CRI), R_a, does not correlate well with the overall perceived colour rendering[7].

An improved colour rendering metric, which incorporates the improvements in colour science, and with much better correlation with colour rendering performance of LED lights, has been published by the Illumination Engineering Society of North America as IES TM-30-15 (IES, 2015). This publication presents two colour rendering metrics: the first is a colour fidelity metric, which can be used to replace the CIE 13.3-1995 CRI metric; the second concerns colour preference, and introduces a colour gamut metric. The first of these metrics, the colour fidelity metric (R_f) has also been adopted in slightly adapted form by the CIE through publication CIE 224: *CIE 2017 Colour fidelity index for accurate scientific use* (CIE, 2017).

The first improvement of this standard is that, instead of 14 colour test samples, the TM-30-15 standard uses 99 test samples. All the 99 samples are shown in Figure A1.9 below. These were carefully selected from an initial collection of over hundred thousand samples, and represent all possible colours of real objects. They cover the whole colour space uniformly. They were chosen from colours occurring in nature; colours used in textiles, printing and paints; colours

---

[6] As concerned to light and diagnosis of patients in hospitals, it also worth mentioning the Cyanosis Observation Index of a light, defined in standard AS/NZS1680.2.5: 1997: *Interior lighting*: Part 2.5: *Hospital and medical tasks*, Appendix G (AS/NZS, 1997). A bluish discoloration of skin indicates that the oxygen levels in blood are too low. This standard defines a metric for lighting that enables diagnosis of this condition by medical staff.

[7] See *CIE Position Statement on CRI and Colour Quality Metrics*, October 15, 1995 (CIE, 2015).

of plastics; and colours of various skin tones. The categories the different colours represent are indicated by the letters in the figure.

Figure A1.9 Colour evaluation samples (CES) as used by the IES TM-30-15 standard. The colours are only approximate representations, due to reproduction inaccuracies. This standard uses 99 samples, numbered from 1 to 99. The letters indicate the colour types: A (Nature), B (Skin), C (Textiles), D (Paints), E (Plastic), F (Printed), G (Colour Systems). The samples in this chart are ordered by hue angle. Colour samples 15 and 18 represent skin tones (courtesy of Gerard Harbers)

Other improvements in this standard include adoption of the CAM02-UCS (CIECAM02) colour space (CIE, 2004). It includes an improved chromaticity adaptation correction. It also represents perceived colour differences more accurately than the old CIE 1964 U★V★W★ space used in the CIE 13.3 CRI standard (CIE, 1995). And, instead of the CIE 1931 colour space (CIE, 1932), it uses the CIE 1964 10° colour matching functions, which better represent the average cone response of our eyes when looking at colours in lit spaces. Also, the discontinuous step at a correlated colour temperature of 5000 K switching between a CIE D daylight and a blackbody radiator source in the old standard has been removed. A smooth transition between 4500 K to 5500 K from a blackbody radiator to a daylight illuminant has been implemented in TM-30-15 (IES, 2015). In the CIE 224: 2017 standard (CIE, 2017), this smooth transition ranges from 4000 K to 5000 K.

The colour rendering performance of a light source is summarized by a single number, called the 'fidelity index', with the symbol R_f. It is scaled to have a minimum value of 0, and a maximum of 100, with 100 being perfect colour rendering, with no colour difference between the lamp under test and a reference source (daylight and/or blackbody radiator, depending on the correlated colour temperature). It is scaled such that the mean R_f (fidelity index) values of the CIE F standard illuminants are the same as the mean of their R_a (general colour rendering index (CRI)) values.

As with the CRI standard, also the individual fidelity indices can be reviewed. For a CIE standard fluorescent illuminant F3, the individual results are shown in Figure A1.10. This is an example of a source that does not perform very well from a colour rendering performance, with a colour fidelity index R_f of only 59. As another example, the individual fidelity indices for a high colour fidelity LED sources are shown in Figure A1.11.

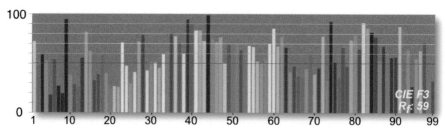

Figure A1.10 Individual $R_{f,i}$ fidelity index values for the standard CIE F3 illuminant. This light source does not have a very good colour rendering, and has a CIE colour fidelity index R_f of 59 and a CIE CRI R_a index of 57 (courtesy of Gerard Harbers)

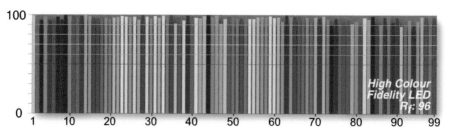

Figure A1.11 Individual $R_{f,i}$ fidelity index values for a high colour fidelity LED. This light source has excellent colour rendering, and has a CIE colour fidelity index R_f of 96, and a CIE CRI R_a index of 97 (courtesy of Gerard Harbers)

A1.3.3 Colour preference: IES TM-30-15 Colour Gamut Index (R_g)

Both the CIE 13.3 (CIE, 1995) and the CIE 224 (TM-30-15) (CIE, 2017) standards are colour fidelity tests: they measure colour 'distortions' compared to reference sources such as daylight and incandescent lights (more formally, blackbody radiators). When the source under test deviates from these references, the metric is negatively impacted. These colour 'distortions' are not always unwanted and can improve the lit effect of a space. Examples of this are theatre and architectural lighting with coloured lights — these lights have terrible colour fidelity performance but can help to create more dramatic effects.

Lamps considered to have a 'good' general colour rendering index R_a greater than 80, can still have significant deviations for the standard colour evaluation samples compared to the reference lamps, especially for the more saturated standard colour evaluation samples, which are not considered in R_a calculation. These deviations can make colours look less saturated (dull), or more saturated (vivid) compared to the reference lamp. The orientation of deviations can be calculated and plotted. An example of such a plot for the CIE F3 standard illuminant is shown in Figure A1.12.

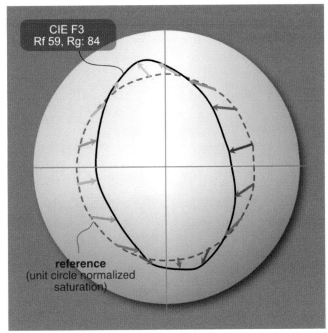

Figure A1.12 Normalised polar plot of sixteen average hue (angle) and saturation (amplitude) values for the TM-30-15 colour evaluation samples for the CIE F3 standard illuminant compared to its reference (a 3446 K blackbody radiator). The colour space used in this plot is CAM02-UCS. The background colour in this plot, and the colours of the arrows are approximate representations. Such a plot is called a 'colour vector graphic' in the IES TM-30-15 standard. The sixteen values are average values, averaged over the colour evaluation samples positioned within the polar segments (courtesy of Gerard Harbers)

This colour vector graphic shows sixteen arrows, connecting the chromaticity coordinates of an average of colour evaluation samples as observed with the reference (a 3446 K blackbody radiator) to those with the test source. The plot is in CAM02-UCS space, but is non-linearly scaled such that the chromaticity coordinates of the reference are on a unit circle. If an arrow is pointing inwards compared to the reference, the colours associated with that arrow appear less saturated (pale) than those of the reference. If the arrow is pointing outwards compared to the reference, they appear more saturated (vivid). In this particular case, the blue-purple and yellow-orange colours are more vivid, while all the other colours appear paler. In these type of plots, if the test lamp deviates from the reference, the lines connecting the test lamp coordinates very often form a somewhat distorted ellipse. The longer, or major axis of this ellipse indicates the opponent colours which appear more vivid, while the shorter, or minor, axis indicates the opponent colours which appear paler. For this lamp, there is a slight extension of the major axis beyond the reference circle, while the minor axis is heavily contracted.

An example of a colour vector graphic for an LED source is shown in Figure A1.13. This is an example where almost all the colours will appear more vivid than the reference source, which in this case is a blackbody radiator with a correlated colour temperature of 2997 K. The blue/green hues in this LED source have an equivalent saturation compared to a tungsten halogen lamp; all the other hues, especially the green/yellow and purple/red, appear more saturated. In this particular example, this colour rendering performance is achieved using a combination of red and blue LEDs, and green and yellow phosphors. This LED source has a colour fidelity index, R_f, of 79 (and a general colour rendering index, R_a, of 78). In colour preference tests, where colour samples illuminated with test and reference lamps are compared, these type of LED lamps, with low colour fidelity, can score higher than a high-fidelity reference (i.e. tungsten halogen filament) lamp. So, colour fidelity is certainly an important aspect of illumination, but provides a limited representation of the colour qualities of a lamp. Additional metrics are required to cover these better.

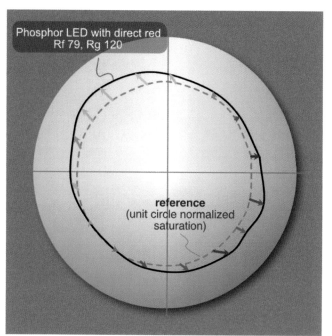

Figure A1.13 Normalized polar plot of 16 average hue (angle) and saturation (amplitude) values for the TM30-15 colour evaluation samples for an LED source. This source has a CCT of 2979 K, and uses blue and red LEDs, and phosphors to create the green and red colours. With the exception of the blue/greens, almost all the colours will appear more vivid than the reference lamp (courtesy of Gerard Harbers)

The TM-30-15 standard does provide a metric to represent a colour preference to complement the fidelity index, called the 'gamut index', and has the symbol R_g. It is the polygon area spanned by the sixteen average chromaticity coordinates within the sixteen hue angle bins (as defined by the standard) of the test source divided by those of the reference source, multiplied by 100:

$$R_g = \frac{A_t}{A_r} \times 100$$

A value larger than 100 indicates that it has a higher gamut (shows colours on average more vividly), and a lower number than 100 indicates a lower gamut (shows colours on average less saturated than the reference). The CIE F3 illuminant (Figure A1.12) has a gamut index R_g of 84, while the phosphor LED (Figure A1.13) has a gamut index R_g of 120.

The range of gamut index values is limited, and depends on the fidelity index values (Figure A1.14).

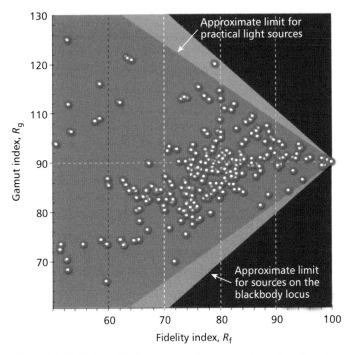

Figure A1.14 Colour fidelity index and gamut index values for a large collection of light sources. The range of possible gamut index values decreases with fidelity index, as indicated by the dark and light red areas (courtesy of Gerard Harbers)

For a source with fidelity index of 80, the gamut index ranges from approximately 70 to 120. For a source with fidelity index of 90, the gamut index ranges from approximately 80 to 110. The choice of colour fidelity and gamut index is dependent on the application. If perceived colour quality is not important, for example in security and street lighting, a low fidelity index and low gamut index can be chosen to achieve a high efficacy. For hospitality lighting, a fidelity index of 80 might be a good choice, with a relatively high value for gamut index of 110 or higher. In high-end retail applications, the appropriate choice might be to select a lamp with a fidelity index of 90, and a gamut index as high as possible, preferably in the range 105 to 110. For museum lighting, a lamp with fidelity index of 95 might be the best choice, with a gamut index about 100. However, it is recommended to carry out mock-ups to compare different light sources with colour samples to ensure that the most appropriate light source has been selected for the application. Typically, lighting manufacturers will provide the graphs shown in Figures A1.12 and A1.13 to assist with choosing the appropriate light source.

A1.4   Lighting properties of building materials

In assessing a building surface from a lighting design perspective, there are three main properties to consider: its reflectance, colour and surface finish. A further consideration is how these properties change over life. For example, a surface will get dirty, it may change colour (fade), or its finish may change (due to dirt and wear). These changes influence the lighting effect and need to be considered at the design stage.

Building surfaces come in a wide range of finishes: from a diffuse matte surface of a plastered wall, textured surfaces like brick or stone as well as carpets, and specular surfaces like glass and polished metal. The appearance of a surface can change depending on how it is lit. For example, if a textured surface is lit obliquely then its textured appearance will be enhanced but if it is lit from all angles then its texture will be suppressed.

From an indirect illumination aspect, it is normally the diffuse reflectance that is used. Diffuse reflection has been described in section A1.1.2. Its value can typically be obtained from the material datasheets, or requested from the manufacturer. Sometimes it is reported as a light reflectance value (LRV)[8], for example on paint swatches (see Figure A1.15). If it is not available it can be measured as described in section 5 of SLL Lighting Guide 11: *Surface reflectance and colour* (SLL, 2001). A further way of assessing diffuse reflectance is to use a reflectance sample card. This is provided with Lighting Guide 11, which also provides instructions for use, or may be purchased separately from the CIBSE website.

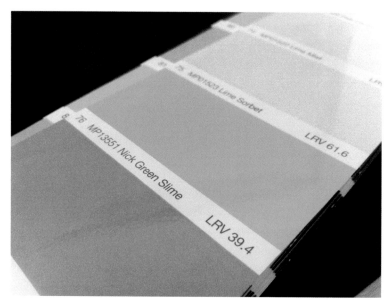

Figure A1.15 Light reflectance values as reported on a paint swatch.
The light reflectance value ranges from 0 to 100, with 0 representing pure black
(i.e. not light reflecting at all) to 100.0, pure white, with all the light being
reflected. Actual light reflectance values of black surfaces are higher than 0,
as often some light is reflected, and actual values of white are lower than 100,
as often some light is absorbed. (Image by Iroc8210 (own work) [CC BY-SA 3.0
(https://creativecommons.org/licenses/by-sa/3.0)], via Wikimedia Commons)

When assessing diffuse reflectance, the sample will need to be lit with diffuse light and preferably with the light source to be used in the final design. If a surface is all one material, such as a concrete or rendered wall, then the diffuse reflectance of only this material needs to be determined. However, if the surface is a combination of two materials then both will need to be taken into account. For example, a brick wall is a combination of the bricks and the mortar that holds them together and typically the mortar can be as much as 14% of the total area of the wall.

---

[8] BS 8300: *Design of buildings and their approaches to meet the needs of disabled people. Code of practice* (BSI, 2009/2010)

In this case, and any other combination of materials, the area weighted reflectance will need to be used. This is where the diffuse reflectance of the individual materials is weighted by the particular areas for a diffuse reflectance of the whole surface to be determined.

The area weighted reflectance of a brick wall is given by the equation:

$$\text{Area weighted reflectance} = \frac{(A_b \times R_b) + (A_c \times R_c)}{A_b + A_c}$$

where A_b is the area of brick (m^2), A_c is the area of cement (m^2), R_b is the reflectance of brick and R_c is the reflectance of cement.

This approach must be used wherever there is a combination of surface materials or features that have different reflectance and it is the combined diffuse reflectance that is required. The case of a brick wall has already been considered but it applies to other surfaces such as perforated panels, which are a combination of the main surface and the very low reflectance of the holes. It will also apply to whole room surfaces such as a wall that includes the wall surface, perhaps a door of different colour and windows — all of which will need to be taken into account.

The actual diffuse reflectances of building materials cover a wide range. For example, bricks, depending on the particular type, could vary anywhere between 0.2 and 0.7, and timber is likely to fall between 0.1 and 0.4. Reflection from clear glass is generally low, and does not vary much; it is typically around 0.15. Textured surfaces such as carpets will generally also have a relatively low reflectance unless they are very light in colour. Painted surfaces vary widely; a white emulsion painted plaster surface can have a reflectance as high as 0.8, while a dark painted surface can be as low as 0.1. Reflectance can be measured with a reflectometer.

A1.4.2   Colour of building materials

The colour of building materials varies widely. For painted surfaces the manufacturer's specification will usually include the colour specification as well as the diffuse reflectance. It is important that an accurate system of colour specification is used to ensure the desired effect as determined by the architect or interior designer — see Chapter 1, 'Lighting design process'.

There are several systems for colour specification. They typically consist of sets of colour patches (as in a colour fan or a colour book), each labelled with alphanumeric code. Some of these are national public standards (e.g. BS 4800 (BSI, 2011), BS 381C (BSI, 1988), RAL (https://www.ral-farben.de), and some of them are proprietary (NCS (Natural Colour System) (http://www.ncscolour.co.uk), Pantone® (https://www.pantone.com)). The colour of each of these patches is uniquely defined through its colorimetric and spectral reflectance data. These sample patches and associated colorimetric data can be used to check the actual colours of the building materials against the standard.

The colour of natural materials such as brick and stone are less precisely known. Actual samples are often required to judge their colour. Bricks, for example, range from dark reds through to pale yellows as well as the dark blue of engineering bricks. Stone also comes in many colours and shades but, like brick, it depends on the particular natural material. Cement can come in many colours depending on the desired effect required by the architect.

Table A1.1 gives the reflectance of some common materials found in buildings and some paint colours. Details of the reflectance of other materials can often be obtained from the manufacturers or by using the calibrated colour chart included in SLL LG 11: *Surface reflectance and colour* (SLL/NPL, 2001)

Table A1.1 Reflectances of common materials found in buildings and some paint colours (a reflectance value of 0.0 corresponds to black, and 1.0 to pure white)

Materials	Reflectance	Paint colours and BS 4800 code	Reflectance
White paper	0.8	White 00E55	0.85
Stainless steel	0.4	Pale cream 10C31	0.81
Cement screed	0.4	Light grey 00A01	0.68
Light carpet	0.3	Strong yellow 10E53	0.64
Light oak veneer	0.4	Mid grey 00A05	0.45
Teak veneer	0.2	Strong green 14E53	0.22
Dark oak veneer	0.1	Strong red 04E53	0.18
Quarry tiles	0.1	Strong blue 18E53	0.15
Window glass	0.1	Dark grey 10A11	0.14
Dark carpet	0.1	Dark brown 08C39	0.10
		Dark red-purple 02C39	0.10
		Black 00E53	0.05

A1.4.3 Surface finish of building materials

The nature of the surface finish will affect how light is reflected from it, but this will also be affected by the way the surface is lit. If a surface is matt then it will scatter light evenly in all directions. If, however, the surface is textured and the surface is lit obliquely then only the elements of the surface that receive light will reflect light, whereas those that do not will be in shadow and appear 'dark'. This combination of light and shade will be effective in enhancing the appearance of the surface texture, but it will reduce the average luminance, which can be interpreted as a reduction in its average reflectance. Similarly, if the surface is specular then it may be possible to see a reflected image of the light source but this will depend on the geometry between the surface, the illuminant and the viewing position. As has been mentioned earlier the designer will need to decide on the primary purpose of the material. If it is for effect, then the lighting should complement the surface material to enhance the effect and the light reflecting properties. If, however, the direction and intensity of the light reflected from the surface is important, then an appropriate reflection factor or factors will be required. As with the other lighting properties of materials much will be achieved by examining, experimenting and measuring actual material samples to determine the lighting effects.

There is a useful guide published by the British Coatings Federation, G024: *Colour tolerance for paints and coatings* (BCF, 2016).

A1.4.4 Surface deterioration and maintenance

Throughout the life of a building, surfaces will deteriorate through accumulation of dirt and wear. These typically reduce their reflectance. Degradation is governed by the extent of dirt deposition, which depends on the nature of the surface and the cleanliness of the atmosphere. It is hard to predict how much this will be, but it is an important aspect of lighting design, especially when surfaces are used for indirect lighting where illuminance levels depend on inter-reflected light. Cleaning or refurbishment, by building owners or their clients, should be encouraged to maintain the lit effect and stay within the design limits.

The accumulation of dust and dirt may also affect the performance of lamps and luminaires. For further guidance on the effect of dirt on and in luminaires, and the resultant loss of performance, refer to Chapter 32, 'Maintenance'.

A1.5 Colour contrast and adaptation

Effect of contrast between one surface and another: the apparent brightness and colour appearance of a surface will be influenced by the degree of contrast between the surface and adjacent or surrounding surfaces. For example, if an achromatic surface of a particular luminance is surrounded by a surface of a lower luminance the tendency will be for the surface to appear brighter and, conversely, if the surround is at a higher luminance then the surface will appear darker. The effect is known as brightness induction and has the effect of exaggerating a luminance difference between one surface and another.

A similar effect occurs between coloured surfaces and neutral surfaces, and between different coloured surfaces. A coloured surface will take on a hint of the complementary colour of the surrounding surface. This effect is known as colour induction. Therefore, a neutral grey surface if surrounded by a green surface will take on a red or pinkish tinge and the same grey surface if surrounded by a blue surface will take on a yellowish tinge and vice versa. This means that a greater contrast can be achieved by using this effect.

Visual adaptation (brightness and colour): an element of the human visual system includes an automatic process known as adaptation. In the case of brightness adaptation, it works rather like the automatic exposure control on a camera in that it adjusts the exposure value to the average luminance of the scene and the areas of higher luminance appear light whilst the areas of lower luminance appear dark. This means that a particular luminance will vary in brightness if the adaptation state changes. A similar process occurs for colour although this is usually less noticeable. If a person works for some time in a room lit with a particular coloured light source, for example in a photographic darkroom lit with red light, after some time the person will cease to be aware of the red source due to colour adaptation; but when switching to a normal 'white' source the scene will take on a greenish tinge for a short time until the eye re-adapts. The process of adaptation takes time to change from one level to another and designers need to be aware of this and to engineer the lighting to allow this to happen without loss of visual comfort or visibility. This will be required, for example, in a museum where adjacent galleries are lit to different levels for conservation purposes. To allow the transition to take place a linking corridor should be provided, which is lit at an intermediary luminance.

The above phenomena will all affect the appearance of surfaces, some more than others, but they all need to be borne in mind by designers when planning the appearance of a task and the appearance of a lit environment to achieve the most effective performance and visual quality.

References

AS/NZS (1997) AS/NZS 1680.2.5: 1997: *Interior lighting*: Part 2.5: *Hospital and medical tasks* (Sydney: Standards Australia/Wellington: Standards New Zealand)

BCF (2016) *Colour tolerance for paints and coatings* G024 (Leatherhead: British Coatings Federation) (available at http://www.coatings.org.uk/media/download.aspx?MediaId=7990)

BSI (1988) BS 381C: 1988: *Specification for colours for identification, coding and special purposes* (London: British Standards Institution)

BSI (2009/2010) BS 8300: 2009 + A1: 2010: *Design of buildings and their approaches to meet the needs of disabled people. Code of practice* (London: British Standards Institution)

BSI (2011) BS 4800: 2011: *Schedule of paint colours for building purposes* (London: British Standards Institution)

CIE (1995) *Method of Measuring and Specifying Colour Rendering Properties of Light Sources* CIE 013.3-1995 (Vienna: International Commission on Illumination)

CIE (1932) *Commission Internationale de l'Eclairage proceedings, 1931–1932* (Cambridge: Cambridge University Press)

CIE (2004) *A colour appearance model for colour management systems: CIECAM02* CIE 159 (Vienna: International Commission on Illumination)

CIE (2015) *CIE Position Statement on CRI and Colour Quality Metrics* [online] (Vienna: International Commission on Illumination) (available at http://www.cie.co.at/publications/position-statement-cri-and-colour-quality-metrics-october-15-2015) (accessed February 2018)

CIE (2017) *CIE 2017 Colour fidelity index for accurate scientific use* CIE 224 (Vienna: International Commission on Illumination)

IES (2015) *IES Method for Evaluating Light Source Color Rendition* IES TM-30-15 (New York: Illuminating Engineering Society)

Newton I (1704) *Opticks: or, a treatise of the reflexions, refractions, inflexions and colours of light* (Salt Lake City, UT: Project Gutenberg Literary Archive Foundation) (available at http://www.gutenberg.org/ebooks/33504) (accessed February 2018)

SLL (2012) *SLL Code for Lighting* (London: Society of Light and Lighting)

SLL/NPL (2001) *Surface reflectance and colour* SLL Lighting Guide 11 (London: Society of Light and Lighting/National Physical Laboratory)

Appendix 2: Circadian lighting

Lighting has a growing impact on the interior environment. Solutions have moved from the functional to the aspirational with a growing trend for spaces to be designed for people in order to enhance their health and wellbeing.

In lighting design there is a great deal of excitement about the potential impacts of natural and artificial lighting on the wellbeing of people. A greater scientific understanding of our circadian system and the impacts this can have on our health have driven an enthusiasm about the installation of dynamic lighting systems that mimic the variability of daylight.

To understand circadian lighting is to understand a mix of the biological, psychological and physiological, and lighting professionals have to rely on evidence from scientific research studies and interrogate the information given.

A2.1   Background

The term 'circadian lighting' refers to the 'non-image forming' functions of the human visual system. This understanding dates back to the 1990s and the discovery of the intrinsically photosensitive retinal ganglion cells (ipRGCs) in the retina. A small proportion of the retinal ganglion cells in the eye, receive light and use it to send messages about the external light/dark cycle to the rest of the body. If the ipRGCs do not receive sufficient light for a few hours they send a message to the hypothalamus, which contains the suprachiasmatic nucleus (SCN) and this, via the pineal gland, starts the secretion of melatonin, which triggers the sleep or circadian cycle alongside a number of other hormones, e.g. cortisol.

The SCN acts as the master circadian clock, overseeing a near perfect 24-hour cycle clock in each of the trillions of cells in the body.

The photopigment in the ipRGCs is called melanopsin and this, along with our rods, blue cones, red cones and green cones, make up our non-image forming system within the retina. Each element is more sensitive to different wavelengths of light and different values of irradiance or amount of light.

In circadian lighting terms the most sensitive wavelength appears to be in the blue spectrum — about 480 nm — the peak sensitivity of the ipRGCs.

The importance of blue spectrum lighting is not new; in the late 1990s many pieces of lighting manufacturer research suggested a punch of blue spectrum light to stimulate workers. It is also the dominant spectrum in daylight and perhaps this suggests the key to understanding the subject.

It is believed that the eyes and brain receive prompts from the external day/night cycle, which tell the body when to be awake and when to sleep. Historically people worked outside in daylight, but many of us now spend 90% of our time indoors in artificial light, in controlled internal environments. It is therefore felt the connection with the outside has been lost, and with it the spectrum of daylight which triggers a normal, healthy sleep cycle.

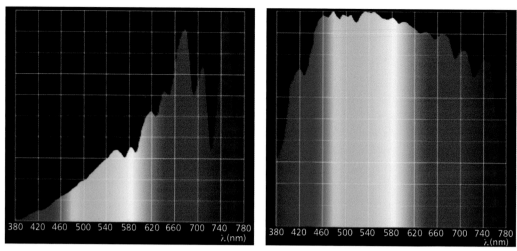

Figure A2.1 Typical spectral power distribution of sunrise and overcast daylight

Logically it is understandable that this may impact upon sleep patterns and there are bodies of evidence that suggest that upsetting the sleep cycle is bad for health, resulting in the higher rates of cancer, diabetes, ulcers and heart disease seen in shift or night workers. And, conversely, that exposure to daylight can encourage healing in medical environments — something for which more research is needed (Joarder et al., 2010; Joanna Briggs Institute, 2010; Stevens, 2006; Marqueze et al., 2015).

The human eye first truly developed through the Cambrian Explosion, about 542 million years ago. It is widely believed that most life forms as we know them developed within the sea in this period, and many developed the first photosensitive cells which form the building blocks of our eye. The function of these cells was limited to 'non-image forming' tasks, such as distinguishing light and dark. The ability to recognise night and day offered an advantage, allowing species to coordinate behaviour and mating patterns. In terms of image forming the cells did little, but eventually transformed into complex visual systems with greater image forming roles. It is quite believable that some non-image forming cells remain within our evolved eyes and still perform a function today.

But there is still debate as to whether we are sleeping less and if the 7–8 hours' sleep reflects our past patterns. Certainly some tribes sleep nearer six hours per night without external technological influences. Also, there is a belief that from the 15th to early 20th century people often had a 'first sleep' before waking, carrying out tasks and then settling for the 'second sleep' (Hegarty, 2012).

> 'He knew this, even in the horror with which he started from his first sleep, and threw up the window ...' *Barnaby Rudge*, Charles Dickens (1841)

A2.2 Circadian lighting solutions

With LED light sources comes the ability to dim and colour mix. This has run parallel with research in circadian rhythms, and so circadian lighting has been born. Many will have seen this concept — a lighting system, usually for offices, but sometimes schools or care environments, which carries out a colour temperature and lumen output change throughout the day. An artificial sunrise to sunset that travels from 2700 K to 6500 K and back again.

Figure A2.2 An example of a circadian lighting system in action at Astra Zenica
(courtesy of Redshift Photography/Hoare Lea)

The belief is that by providing appropriate intensity blue spectrum light during the main daylight hours, and a warmer spectrum when the body should be relaxing, a suitable environment can be created for melatonin suppression for alertness and cortisol release, which controls body temperature. Unfortunately, many early installations reported good results, but failed to have comparable spaces in which the lighting was changed but without the colour changing regimes, i.e. there was no control or 'double blind' regime established to give unambiguous and/or unbiased results.

Research is continuing to establish the impact of various regimes of colour and time profiles to establish what, if any, long-term benefit each provides to the users over and above similar modern adaptable lighting systems.

Figure A2.3 A typical fluorescent lighting system replaced by a circadian LED system in a Swedish school (LfP, undated) (courtesy of Malmö Stad, Department of Internal Services)

The other concern is that many studies rely on subjective answers from people asked directly about their response to new lighting — once the system and 'benefits' have been explained. Do such questions establish a basis of bias through suggestion?

One of the key questions is what level of exposure to blue spectrum light is required from artificial sources in order to have a valuable impact on the melanopsin cycle? If the reference basis is the spectral intensities of daylight then can, or indeed should, an artificial lighting system meet similar criteria?

Scientists from the University of Manchester (al Enezi et al., 2011) proposed the 'melanopic' illuminance curve of eye sensitivity knowing that the typical $V(\lambda)$ curve of 'photopic' (daylight vision) sensitivity was not a suitable device for measuring melanopic sensitivity. This new melanopic curve looks at wavelengths of light for melanopsin in the ipRGCs.

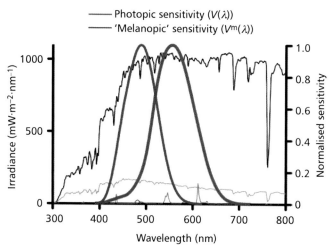

Figure A2.4 Comparison of photopic and melanopic sensitivity (courtesy of Robert Lucas, University of Manchester, after al Enezi et al., 2011)

In 2014 this was expanded by the same researchers to include all of the contributing cones and rods in the eye — each with their own sensitivity to light spectrum and each forming part of our visual and non-visual responses to light. This is called the α-opic illuminance sensitivity curve.

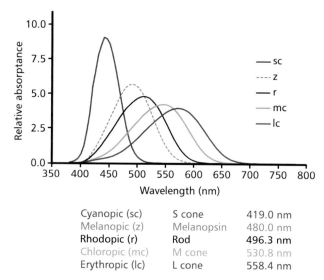

Cyanopic (sc)	S cone	419.0 nm
Melanopic (z)	Melanopsin	480.0 nm
Rhodopic (r)	Rod	496.3 nm
Chloropic (mc)	M cone	530.8 nm
Erythropic (lc)	L cone	558.4 nm

Figure A2.5 α-opic illuminance sensitivity curve (Lucas et al., 2013)

This curve represents a solid model for understanding the appropriate spectral wavelength for melanopsin and can be used to build the light spectrum appropriate for an internal luminaire. It is the closest the industry has to quantifying the exact spectrum required for melatonin suppression, but as the science community states:

> 'An important note of caution here is that it is not always clear whether lighting design should aim to maximize or minimize non-visual responses. In many ways, light can be considered a drug, having the potential for both beneficial and deleterious effects. These conflicting effects can occur concurrently, and in a single individual and context.'

> '…it is not yet possible to predict the non-image-forming impact of a given illuminant based on its intensity and spectral composition. However, some guidance is possible.'
>
> (Lucas et al., 2014)

The International Commission on Illumination (CIE) has released a statement regarding clarity on the latest thinking:

> '...concluded that non-visual responses are subject to complex signal processing in the central nervous system and influenced by as-yet-unresolved interactions of photoreceptive units. The missing understanding of the input–output characteristics between light stimulus and the resulting non-visual response seems to make tailored light application for a desired lighting effect impossible.' (CIE, 2015)

Other scientists and bodies are more supportive of the system. Mark Rea and his team at the Lighting Research Centre in New York are strong believers in the effectiveness of the circadian lighting. The WELL Building Standard (IWBI, 2017), see Appendix 3, introduces an alternative metric — the Equivalent Melanopic Lux (EML) — weighted to the spectral response of the ipRGCs; recommendations are given for EML values measured vertically at eye height as a key to creating healthy lighting. German standard DIN SPEC 67600 (DIN, 2013) also offers metrics for 'biologically effective' lighting by recommending minimum vertical illuminances (lux) at eye level for specific colour temperatures.

A2.3   Risks of early adoption

One major issue is the 'one size fits all' approach. People are different — from our chronotype (how we sleep), to our geography, work patterns, diet, age and subjective responses to light. We know the eye yellows and receives less blue spectrum light as we age, and a person of 50–60 years produces only about 35% of the melatonin of a 10-year old.

We also know that personal preference and light quality is important in a person's appreciation of their internal environment. Whilst science may favour cooler spectrum lighting it could be argued that preference and thus perception of illuminated quality may contradict this (Dangol et al., 2015).

One key question is illuminance. Modern building standards have consistently tried to lower illuminance levels and allow more creativity in interior environments but this runs counter to providing higher illuminances during parts of a circadian lighting cycle. This is a major concern for energy loads in a modern, low carbon world. However, illuminances may be lowered by using light with a higher blue content (around 480 nm). Even so, vertical illuminances recommended by both the WELL Building Standard (IBWL, 2017) and DIN SPEC 67600 (DIN, 2013) may be very difficult or even impossible to achieve from electric lighting alone in most internal spaces using common electric lighting practice. Lighting standards and codes generally recommend lower values of vertical illuminance to see visual tasks and avoid glare.

Public Health England has stated that the blue spectrum output of normal LEDs are not a risk to the human eye (Price et al., 2016), but a circadian system would be looking to increase the blue end of the spectrum and it has been seen in rats that this can cause retinal damage. The higher energy blue light has more of an effect on cells than the lower energy at the middle and red end of the spectrum, and research suggests this could cause oxidative stress in the retina tissue (Lougheed, 2014, Shang et al., 2013). This intensity of blue light has caused the American Medical Association (AMA, 2016) to express concern about 'potential harmful human and environmental effects'.

Colour mixing between colour sources requires dimming, which often causes flicker. Many electronic drivers for LEDs have high flicker modulation, similar to that of old fluorescent lighting that many said caused them headaches (Wilkins et al., 1989). Could a dimming or colour-mixing system cause detrimental flicker in the workplace?

A2.4   Conclusion

There are still many unanswered questions regarding circadian lighting and its adoption. Most scientific thinking agrees that in, terms of circadian impact on sleep, good quality daylight exposure is beneficial. Certainly, night shift workers and people in extreme environments with minimal daylight exposure can have sleep-related issues that can lead to health concerns. Conversely it is commonly agreed that exposure to intense blue light directly before sleep should be avoided.

Lighting design and engineering should consider some of the main themes of circadian lighting, weigh-up some of the 'unknowns' and some of the concerns before producing designs that claim to support a healthy circadian rhythm. For many of us the raison d'être of good 'human-centric' lighting design represents the normal practices of our roles — to design attractive and comfortable spaces to be used by people. To improve the built environment for people. Some of the concerns of human-centric lighting systems is that in trying to influence the physiology of people through light we could lose sight of this simple objective.

With many external influences to our daily lives logic suggests it would be surprising that a lighting system alone could provide the complete answer but it could be a part of the solution.

References

al Enezi J, Revell V, Brown T, Wynne J, Schlangen L and Lucas RA (2011) '"Melanopic" Spectral Efficiency Function Predicts the Sensitivity of Melanopsin Photoreceptors to Polychromatic Lights' *J. Biol. Rhythms* **26** 314–323

AMA (2016) *AMA Adopts Guidance to Reduce Harm from High Intensity Street Lights* [online] (Chicago, IL: American Medical Association) (https://www.ama-assn.org/ama-adopts-guidance-reduce-harm-high-intensity-street-lights) (accessed September 2018)

CIE (2015) *CIE Statement on Non-Visual Effects of Light: Recommending proper light at the proper time* [online] (Vienna: International Commission on Illumination) (http://www.cie.co.at/sites/default/files/783_CIE%20 Statement%20-%20Proper%20Light%20at%20the%20Proper%20Time.pdf) (accessed September 2018)

Dangol R, Islam MS, Hyvärinen M, Bhushal P, Puolakka M and Halonen L (2015) 'User acceptance studies for LED office lighting: Preference, naturalness and colourfulness' *Lighting Res. Technol.* **47**(1) 36–53

DIN (2013) DIN SPEC 67600: 2013: *Biologically effective illumination — Design guidelines* (Berlin: Deutsches Institut für Normung e.V.)

Hegarty S (2012) *The myth of the eight-hour sleep* [online] (London: BBC) (http://www.bbc.co.uk/news/magazine-16964783) (accessed March 2018)

IWBI (2017) *The WELL Building Standard* [online] (New York, NY: International WELL Building Institute) (https://www.wellcertified.com/en/explore-standard) (accessed September 2018)

Joanna Briggs Institute (2010) 'The effects of exposure to natural light in the workplace on the health and productivity of office workers: a systematic review protocol' *JBI Library of Systematic Reviews* **8**(16) 1–19

Joarder MAR, Price ADF and Mourshed M (2010) 'Access to daylight and outdoor views: a comparative study for therapeutic daylighting design' *World Health Design* **3**(1) 62–69

LfP (undated) *Case Study: Malmö school introduces Human Centric Lighting* [online] (Lyon: Lighting Urban Community International/Lighting for People) (http://lightingforpeople.eu/malmo-school-introduces-human-centric-lighting) (accessed September 2018)

Lougheed T (2014) 'Hidden blue hazard? LED lighting and retinal damage in rats' *Environmental Health Perspectives* **122** A81 (Durham NC: (US) National Institute of Environmental Health Sciences) (available at https://ehp.niehs.nih.gov/wp-content/uploads/122/3/ehp.122-A81.pdf) (accessed September 2018)

Lucas RJ, Peirson SN, Berson D, Brown TM, Cooper HM, Czeisler CA, Figueiro MG, Gamlin PD, Lockley SW, O'Hagan JB, Price LLA, Provencio I, Skene DJ, Brainard G (2013) *Irradiance Toolbox — User Guide* [online] (Manchester: Faculty of Life Sciences, University of Manchester) (http://personalpages. manchester.ac.uk/staff/robert.lucas/Lucas%20et%20al%202014%20suppl%20text.pdf) (accessed September 2018)

Lucas RJ, Peirson SN, Berson DM, Brown TM, Cooper HM, Czeisler CA, Figueiro MG, Gamlin PD, Lockley SW, O'Hagan JB, Price LA, Provencio I, Skene DJ, Brainard GC (2014) 'Measuring and using light in the melanopsin age' *Trends in Neurosciences* **37**(1) 1–9 (available at https://www.ncbi.nlm.nih.gov/pmc/articles/PMC4699304) (accessed September 2018)

Marqueze EC, Vasconcelos S, Garefelt J, Skene DJ, Moreno CR, Lowden A (2015) 'Natural Light Exposure, Sleep and Depression among Day Workers and Shiftworkers at Arctic and Equatorial Latitudes' *PLoS ONE* **10**(4) (available at http://journals.plos.org/plosone/article?id=10.1371/journal.pone.0122078) (accessed September 2018)

Price LLA, Khazova M and O'Hagan JB (2016) *Human responses to lighting based on LED lighting solutions* [online] (London: CIBSE/Public Health England) (http://www.lightmare.org/docs/PHE-CIBSE-SLL_LED_report_May2016HRLBL-b.pdf) (accessed September 2018)

Shang YM, Wang GS, Sliney D, Yang CH, Lee LL (2014) 'White light-emitting diodes (LEDs) at domestic lighting levels and retinal injury in a rat model' *Environmental Health Perspectives* **122**(3) 269–276 (available at https://ehp.niehs.nih.gov/wp-content/uploads/122/3/ehp.1307294.pdf) (accessed September 2018)

Stevens RG (2006) 'Artificial Lighting in the Industrialized World: Circadian Disruption and Breast Cancer' *Cancer Causes and Control* **17**(4) 501-507

Wilkins AJ, Nimmo-Smith I, and Slater A (1989) 'Fluorescent lighting, headaches and eye-strain' *Lighting Res. Technol.* **21**(1) 11–18.

Appendix 3: Building regulations and environmental labelling schemes

A3.1 Building Regulations

In England and Wales, Part L of the Building Regulations 2010 (as amended) (TSO, 2010, 2017) deals with the conservation of fuel and power. There are similar provisions in Scotland (the Building (Scotland) Regulations 2004 (as amended) (TSO, 2004)) and Northern Ireland (the Building Regulations (Northern Ireland) 2012 (TSO, 2012), Parts F1 and F2). This section describes the regulations and supporting documents for England. Similar regulations and guidance documents exist in the other countries that constitute the UK.

The requirements of the Building Regulations are brief, functional performance statements. For lighting, the relevant requirement is:

> 'providing fixed building services which (i) are energy efficient; (ii) have effective controls; and (iii) are commissioned by testing and adjusting as necessary so they use no more fuel and power than is reasonable in the circumstances.'

Approved Documents (ADs) give guidance on ways of complying with the requirements. In England there are separate documents for new dwellings (L1A) (NBS, 2016a), existing dwellings (L1B) (NBS, 2018a), new buildings other than dwellings (L2A) (NBS, 2016b) and existing buildings other than dwellings (L2B) (NBS, 2016c). They are supplemented by the *Domestic Building Services Compliance Guide* (NBS, 2018b) and the *Non-domestic Building Services Compliance Guide* (NBS, 2013). The recommendations in the Approved Documents and *Compliance Guides* do not have to be adopted, but if they are not then compliance must be demonstrated in another way. Note that, although the Building Regulations 2010 also apply in Wales, the Welsh Government has issued its own versions of the Approved Documents.

The Regulations apply to new buildings and extensions, and where there has been a material change of use (for example, a non-domestic building becoming a dwelling or vice versa). They also apply to replacement lighting installations in non-domestic buildings; if the new installation covers more than 100 m^2 of floor area, the relevant building control authority should be notified. Only fixed lighting is addressed; portable lighting is not covered.

For dwellings, the *Domestic Building Services Compliance Guide* (NBS, 2018b) recommends a proportion of internal lighting should be of low energy types (currently defined in terms of their lamp efficacy). There are also recommendations for the efficacy or wattage of external lighting and the way it is controlled. For example, external lighting should be controlled to switch off when there is daylight.

For other buildings the *Non-domestic Building Services Compliance Guide* (NBS, 2013) gives minimum recommendations for luminaire efficacy, depending on the way the lighting is controlled. As an alternative, the luminaires are deemed compliant if the calculated 'lighting energy numeric indicator' (LENI) is below a maximum value. The LENI is the notional energy consumed by the lighting installation per square metre in a year, and includes allowances for lighting control. The LENI is defined in detail in BS EN 15193-1 (BSI, 2017), although the *Non-domestic Building Services Compliance Guide* uses a simplified version.

For non-domestic buildings there are also recommendations for separate metering of lighting. Lighting controls should follow the guidance in BRE Digest 498: *Selecting lighting controls* (BRE, 2006), which gives recommendations based on the type of space and whether it is daylit or only occasionally occupied. See also Chapter 10, 'Controls'.

For new buildings the Approved Documents also give recommendations on the overall energy consumption of the building; in particular whether it is lower than a maximum target value that depends on the size of the building and the type of spaces within it. Compliance with the Building Regulations for non-domestic buildings can be assessed using the National Calculation Method (see http://www.uk-ncm.org.uk) by calculating the annual energy use for a proposed building and comparing it with the energy use of a comparable 'notional' building. Lighting is included in the calculation of energy consumption. For new non-domestic buildings this is particularly important, and the lighting system may have to be significantly more efficient than the minimum standards in the *Non-domestic Building Services Compliance Guide* (NBS, 2013) if the building as a whole is to meet its energy target.

The Approved Document includes recommendations about the commissioning of lighting systems (referring to CIBSE Commissioning Code M: *Commissioning management* (CIBSE, 2003)), and the provision of information to the users of the building (referring to CIBSE TM31: *Building log book toolkit* (CIBSE, 2006)). See also Chapter 30, 'Commissioning of lighting installations', and CIBSE Commissioning Code L: *Lighting* (CIBSE, 2018).

A3.2 BREEAM

BREEAM (Building Research Establishment Environmental Assessment Method) is an internationally recognised measure of sustainability for the procurement, design, construction and operation of a development, covering all stages of life, including new construction, in-use and refurbishment. Administered by BRE, BREEAM measures sustainable value in a series of categories, ranging from energy and health and wellbeing to energy efficiency and ecology, against performance benchmarks. Each of these categories addresses the most influential factors, including low impact design and carbon emissions reduction; design durability and resilience; adaption to climate change; and ecological value and biodiversity protection. Within every category, developments score points — called credits — for achieving targets, and their final total determines their rating. Detailed information on BREEAM is available online at the BREEAM website (http://www.breeam.com).

Light and lighting are covered by a number of categories including: visual comfort, external lighting and reduction of night time light pollution. The energy efficiency of interior lighting also helps determine whether the building achieves credits for reduction of energy use and carbon emissions. Independent BREEAM assessors verify design schemes against the credits. They are summarised below, although the BREEAM categories are currently under revision and may change in the future:

- *Visual comfort*: aims to ensure daylighting, electric lighting and occupant controls are considered and implemented appropriately to achieve visual performance and comfort for building occupants. Requirements include: adequate design of internal and external lighting; appropriate illuminance levels are achieved in accordance with relevant lighting standards; zoning of internal lighting to allow for occupant control; adequate view out to reduce eye strain and provide a link to the outside; good practice levels of daylight; and control of glare from the sun.

The current BREEAM criteria for daylighting are based around achieving a minimum average daylight factor in areas where daylight is required, and a minimum uniformity. The criteria also include an alternative method that gives daylight illuminance recommendations for different types of space. This is a type of daylight autonomy calculation and uses the number of hours per year for which given illuminances are exceeded.

- *External lighting*: promotes the specification and use of energy efficient luminaires and lighting controls for the external areas of the development. The average initial luminous efficacy of all the external luminaires within the construction zone is limited to a minimum value of luminaire lumens per circuit watt, and automatic controls are required to prevent operation during daylight hours and to detect presence in areas of intermittent pedestrian traffic.

- *Reduction of night time light pollution*: ensures that external lighting is concentrated in the appropriate areas and that upward lighting is minimised, reducing unnecessary obtrusive light pollution, energy consumption and nuisance to neighbouring properties. Requirements include automatic controls to switch off all external lighting (except for safety and security lighting) after a curfew hour and maximum luminances for illuminated advertisements. Additionally, the external lighting should be checked for compliance against national (e.g. Institution of Lighting Professionals (ILP) guidance notes (https://www.theilp.org.uk)) and international (CIE, 2017) guidance, which provide recommendations for the average upward light ratio of luminaires, vertical illuminances at windows of nearby properties, the intensity of each light source in potentially obtrusive directions beyond the site boundaries, and average luminances of floodlit buildings.

- *Reduction of energy use and carbon emissions*: promotes building energy efficiency. Credits are given depending on how much better the predicted building energy performance is, compared to a building that just meets Building Regulations requirements. The energy used for interior lighting contributes to the overall predicted building energy performance, so highly efficient interior lighting may result in extra credits being awarded.

A3.3 LEED

LEED (Leadership in Energy and Environmental Design) is an international rating system for the design, construction and operation of high performance, sustainable buildings. Run by the US Green Building Council (USGBC), LEED serves as an indicator of sustainability by incentivising savings in energy, water and building materials consumption, while at the same time improving occupant health and overall community connectivity.

LEED v4 is the newest version of LEED, which is available for all building, community and home project types at any stage in their life cycle. Light and lighting are covered by a number of credits, which are briefly described below. Points are given for the different credits depending on the level of compliance with the respective requirements. The credits can be accessed online at the LEED website (https://www.usgbc.org/credits).

The daylight credits encourage connection with the outdoors, reinforcement of circadian rhythms, and reduced use of electric lighting. Requirements include manual or automatic glare control in all regularly occupied spaces, as well as either a combination of minimum spatial daylight autonomy and maximum annual sunlight exposure, or illuminance levels falling within a given range during the day. Compliance can be demonstrated through computer modelling or, for the case of illuminance levels, site measurements.

Credits are given for quality views so that building occupants are offered a connection to the natural outdoor environment. To this purpose, a minimum percentage of all regularly occupied floor area should have a direct line of unobstructed sight to the outdoors that meets certain criteria.

The interior lighting credits promote occupants' productivity, comfort and wellbeing through provision of high quality lighting and lighting controls. For all regularly occupied spaces, luminaire luminance is limited to a maximum value — except for specific applications such as adjustable fittings, wall washers and uplights for which the light source cannot be viewed from a regularly occupied space — and direct lighting is limited to a maximum percentage of the total lighting load. A general colour rendering index (CRI) of at least 80 is required for the entire project, except for special lighting such as coloured feature lighting. Requirements also include a minimum rated life of light sources, as well as minimum area-weighted average reflectances for room surfaces and furniture finishes, and maximum ratios of average wall illuminance and average ceiling illuminance to work surface illuminance.

Exterior lighting is covered by the integrative process credits, which include requirements for assessment of site conditions, and by the light pollution reduction credits, which aim to increase night sky access, improve night time visibility and reduce impacts on wildlife and people. Light pollution reduction requirements include limitation of the amount of uplight and obtrusive light for all exterior luminaires located inside the project boundary.

Exterior lighting that is not used for safety, building entrances and circulation should be automatically switched off at night and have a maximum uplight rating depending on the lighting zone.

A3.4   WELL Building Standard

The WELL Building Standard (WELL) was introduced by the International WELL Building Institute (IWBI) as the first standard to focus exclusively on the health and wellbeing of building occupants, aiming to improve their nutrition, fitness, mood, sleep, comfort and performance. Version v1 of the standard (introduced in 2014) addresses seven wellness concepts (air, water, nourishment, light, fitness, comfort and mind). Version v2 (released in 2018) considers ten wellness concepts (air, water, nourishment, light, movement, thermal comfort, sound, materials, mind and community). Each concept is divided into features that are tailored to a specific type of building and incorporate requirements addressing specific aspects of occupant health, comfort or knowledge. Requirements are given as preconditions, all of which must be met for all levels of certification — and optimisations — which include optional technologies, strategies, protocols and designs.

At the time of writing, WELL v2 is a pilot version, and projects can aim for either WELL v1 or WELL v2. WELL v2 may help some projects overcome items they perceived as obstacles in WELL v1, such as design criteria and performance levels. Additionally, WELL v2 introduces more flexibility in how projects can pursue and achieve features on the whole.

In both versions, the 'Light' concept aims to provide a luminous environment that reduces disruption to the body's circadian system, improves sleep quality, and enhances mood and productivity.

A3.4.1 WELL version v1

In WELL v1, the 'Light' concept (http://standard.wellcertified.com/light) consists of eleven features, summarised in Figure A3.1 for office type applications.

Figure A3.1 WELL v1 features for Light; preconditions are shown in dark blue, whilst light blue shapes indicate optimisations

A number of WELL v1 features are similar to those in existing lighting standards such as BS EN 12464-1 (BSI, 2011), SLL Lighting Guide 7: *Offices* (SLL, 2015) and *SLL Code for Lighting* (SLL, 2012). This is the case for:

- *Feature 53*: which gives lighting requirements for basic visual performance, including minimum average illuminance on the horizontal working plane, zoning of lighting in control groups, and balancing of luminance distribution within a room and between adjacent spaces.

- *Feature 55*: which sets criteria for reducing glare from electric lighting by limiting lamp and luminaire luminances and imposing shielding angles for lamps of certain luminances.

- *Feature 57*: which provides specific recommendations for minimising glare and visual discomfort for the use of computer screens.

- *Feature 58*: requiring lighting with a general colour rendering index (CRI) of at least 80. Additionally, it also recommends a minimum value for the specific colour rendering index R_9 (for red colours).

- *Feature 59*: which sets requirements for minimum light reflectance values for room surfaces.

Feature 54 promotes luminous environments that minimise disruption to the human circadian system. It introduces an alternative metric, 'equivalent melanopic lux' (EML), weighted to the spectral response of the cells in the eye that help control the body's daily rhythms. Recommendations include minimum EML values for workplaces, measured vertically at 1.2 m above floor level, both in the presence of daylight and for electric lighting alone.

Dimming of electric lighting in response to daylight and in unoccupied areas is promoted by Feature 60. The other features (56 and 61 to 63) deal with solar shading and adequate levels of natural light within buildings. Requirements include controlled shading and glazing with variable transmission properties, maximum distances from windows to regularly occupied spaces, maximum annual sunlight exposure, and design parameters for windows to optimise daylight and minimise glare and heat gains. One of these parameters is minimum spatial daylight autonomy, a measure of the amount of daylight exceeded for a given proportion of the year.

In order to comply with any of the features, all the requirements of that feature should be met. Equivalences and alternative adherence paths are available for some features. The WELL standard is updated regularly with addenda being released quarterly, and the latest version is available online at http://standard.wellcertified.com/light, together with all amendments listed in a chronological order.

A3.4.2 WELL version v2

In WELL v2, the 'Light' concept (https://v2.wellcertified.com/v2.1/en/light) consists of eight features, which are graphically summarised in Figure A3.2.

Figure A3.2 WELL v2 features for Light; preconditions are shown in dark blue, whilst light blue shapes indicate optimisations with the maximum number of points applicable

Similar to WELL v1, some of the WELL v2 features for 'Light' resemble recommendations given in existing lighting standards such as BS EN 12464-1 (BSI, 2011), SLL Lighting Guide 7: *Offices* (SLL,2015) and *SLL Code for Lighting* (SLL, 2012). This is the case for:

- *Feature L02*: which requires project areas to comply with illuminance threshold requirements specified in one of various standards including BS EN 12464-1 (BSI, 2011).

- *Feature L04 Part 2*: which sets criteria for reducing glare from electric lighting by giving maximum UGR values, limiting luminaire luminances and imposing shielding angles for lamps of certain luminances.

- *Feature L06*: which gives requirements for balancing luminance distribution within a room and between adjacent spaces, but also over time in case of variable lighting.

- *Feature L07*: which sets criteria for minimum colour rendering quality and avoidance of flicker.

- *Feature L08*: which promotes occupants' ability to control the lighting in their immediate environment and the use of task lighting.

Feature L01, a precondition that should be met to receive certification, promotes adequate indoor exposure to daylight by setting criteria for minimum spatial daylight autonomy, maximum distances from glazed openings to regularly occupied spaces, and minimum glazing transmittance. It also promotes the use of educational resources throughout the project spaces to raise awareness of occupants on the importance of light exposure for circadian rhythms, sleep and overall health.

Feature L03 promotes luminous environments that minimise disruption to the human circadian system by giving recommendations for minimum 'equivalent melanopic lux' (EML) and 'melanopic daylight equivalent illuminance' (the daylight D65 illuminance needed to produce a similar stimulation to the light source considered); the recommendations apply to the electric lighting system and are less strict in the presence of adequate daylight.

Daylight is further addressed in Feature L04 Part 1, which promotes solar glare control through the use of window shading or a maximum limit to annual sunlight exposure in regularly occupied spaces and Feature L05, which promotes enhanced access to daylight by giving requirements on minimum glazing area and transmittance, higher spatial daylight autonomy than required in precondition L01, and adequate view out.

Overall, WELL v2 provides more flexibility in meeting the mandatory 'Light' criteria compared to WELL v1. Additional points that count towards the overall project score can be gained by optimising the daylighting and electric lighting solutions so that they also comply with the 'Light' optimisations. Of particular importance is the classification of circadian lighting criteria as an optimisation in WELL v2 rather than a precondition as is the case of WELL v1. Additionally, performance verification of these criteria has been simplified by making them applicable to electric lighting only, the measurement of which should be easier to undertake than in combination with daylight. Full details of WELL v2 features for 'Light' are freely available online (https://v2.wellcertified.com/v2.1/en/light).

A3.5　Enhanced Capital Allowances

The UK Enhanced Capital Allowances (ECA) scheme was introduced by Government to encourage businesses to invest in energy saving equipment. The scheme provides a tax incentive for making investments in energy saving equipment by allowing businesses to write off the whole cost of the equipment against taxable profits in the year of purchase. Similar schemes exist in other countries.

Energy saving technologies that are covered by the ECA scheme are specified in the Energy Technology List (ETL) which is managed by the Carbon Trust. Lighting technologies included in the scheme are categorised as follows:

- *High efficiency lighting units*: products specifically designed to provide efficient illumination. Four types of product are covered: amenity, accent and display lighting units; general interior lighting units; exterior area lighting units; and exterior floodlighting units. Performance criteria include minimum luminaire efficacy, minimum power factor, avoidance of glare, maximum wattage used by individual control gear, and minimum colour rendering index.

- *Lighting controls*: products specifically designed to switch electric lighting on or off, and/or to dim its output. Five types of product are covered: time controllers; presence detectors; daylight detectors associated with switching controllers; daylight detectors associated with dimming controllers; and central area and network control units. To comply with the scheme, products must incorporate one or more of the above lighting controls types and comply with the specific eligibility criteria given for each type.

- *White light emitting diode lighting units*: products specifically designed to provide white light by means of solid state lighting devices. Similar to high efficiency lighting units, four types of product are covered: amenity, accent and display lighting units; general interior lighting units; exterior area lighting units; and exterior floodlighting units. Performance criteria include minimum luminaire efficacy, minimum lumen output after certain numbers of hours of continuous operation, minimum colour rendering index, minimum power factor, avoidance of glare, and maximum wattage used by individual control gear.

Full details of the Enhanced Capital Allowances (ECA) scheme and the eligibility and performance criteria can be found online (https://www.gov.uk/government/publications/enhanced-capital-allowance-scheme-for-energy-saving-technologies).

References

BRE (2006) *Selecting lighting controls* BRE Digest 498 (Garston: BRE)

BSI (2011) BS EN 12464-1: 2011: *Light and lighting. Lighting of work places. Indoor work places* (London: British Standards Institution)

BSI (2017) BS EN 15193-1: 2017: *Energy performance of buildings. Energy requirements for lighting. Specifications, Module M9* (London: British Standards Institution)

CIBSE (2003) *Commissioning management* CIBSE Commissioning Code M (London: Chartered Institution of Building Services Engineers)

CIBSE (2006) *Building log book toolkit* CIBSE TM31 (London: Chartered Institution of Building Services Engineers)

CIBSE (2018) *Lighting* CIBSE Commissioning Code L (London: Chartered Institution of Building Services Engineers)

CIE (2017) *Guide on the limitation of the effects of obtrusive light from outdoor lighting installations* CIE 150 (2nd. edn) (Vienna: International Commission on Illumination)

NBS (2013) *Non-domestic Building Services Compliance Guide* (plus addendum) (Newcastle Upon Tyne: NBS) (available at https://www.gov.uk/government/publications/conservation-of-fuel-and-power-approved-document-l) (accessed September 2018)

NBS (2016a) *Conservation of fuel and power in new dwellings* Approved Document L1A (2013 edition with 2016 amendments) (Newcastle Upon Tyne: NBS) (available at https://www.gov.uk/government/publications/conservation-of-fuel-and-power-approved-document-l) (accessed February 2018)

NBS (2016b) *Conservation of fuel and power in new buildings other than dwellings* Approved Document L2A (2013 edition with 2016 amendments) (Newcastle Upon Tyne: NBS) (available at https://www.gov.uk/government/publications/conservation-of-fuel-and-power-approved-document-l) (accessed September 2018)

NBS (2016c) *Conservation of fuel and power in existing buildings other than dwellings* Approved Document L2B (2010 edition incorporating 2010, 2011, 2013 and 2016 amendments) (Newcastle Upon Tyne: NBS) (available at https://www.gov.uk/government/publications/conservation-of-fuel-and-power-approved-document-l) (accessed September 2018)

NBS (2018a) *Conservation of fuel and power in existing dwellings* Approved Document L1B (2010 edition incorporating 2010, 2011, 2013, 2016 and 2018 amendments) (Newcastle Upon Tyne: NBS) (available at https://www.gov.uk/government/publications/conservation-of-fuel-and-power-approved-document-l) (accessed September 2018)

NBS (2018b) *Domestic Building Services Compliance Guide* (2013 edition incorporating 2018 amendments) (Newcastle Upon Tyne: NBS) (available at https://www.gov.uk/government/publications/conservation-of-fuel-and-power-approved-document-l) (accessed September 2018)

SLL (2012) *SLL Code for Lighting* (London: Society of Light and Lighting)

SLL (2015) *Offices* SLL Lighting Guide 7 (London: Society of Light and Lighting)

TSO (2004) The Building (Scotland) Regulations 2004 Scottish Statutory Instruments 2004 No. 406 (as amended) (London: TSO) (available at http://www.legislation.gov.uk/ssi/2004/406) (accessed September 2018)

TSO (2010) The Building Regulations 2010 Statutory Instrument 2010 No. 2214 (London: TSO) (available at http://www.legislation.gov.uk/uksi/2010/2214) (accessed September 2018)

TSO (2012) The Building Regulations (Northern Ireland) 2012 Statutory Instrument 2012 No. 192 (as amended) (London: TSO) (available at http://www.legislation.gov.uk/nisr/2012/192) (accessed September 2018)

TSO (2017) The Building (Amendment) Regulations 2017 Statutory Instrument 2017 No. 856 (London: TSO) (available at http://www.legislation.gov.uk/uksi/2017/856) (accessed September 2018)

Appendix 4: Glossary of terms

A4.1   Introduction

The following definitions for lighting terms are given to assist the reader's understanding of the terms used throughout this Handbook. For the precise mathematical definitions of some of the terms, refer to the glossary in the *SLL Code for Lighting* (SLL, 2004) or in BS EN 12665: 2018: *Light and lighting. Basic terms and criteria for specifying lighting requirements* (BSI, 2018), and the IEC's *International Electrotechnical Vocabulary* (IEC, online).

The list includes definitions of some terms that are not used within the *Handbook* but are here for information.

A4.2   Glossary

absence detection

The verification of continued presence in a space after the luminaires have been manually switched on in order to maintain the 'on' state of the luminaires.

adaptation

Adaptation is the ability of the human eye to adjust to various levels of light and is a process which takes place as the visual system adjusts to the luminance and colour of the visual field or the final state of this process.

In a light-adapted eye the cones in the retina are fully active and detail can be seen easily. The rod pigments are bleached out from having been in a bright area. Moving from a well-lit area to a dark area means that initially little can be seen as the rods are initially not functional. Once in the dark, the sensitivity of the retina increases over time (this can take many minutes). At the start of the adaptation process the pupil dilates as a reflexive change.

Conversely, when going from a dark area into a bright area. The bright light momentarily dazzles us because the sensitivity of the receptors is set to dim light. Rods and cones are both stimulated and large amounts of the photopigment are broken down instantaneously, producing a flood of signals resulting in the glare.

Within about one minute the cones are sufficiently excited by the bright light to take over. Visual accuracy and colour vision continue to improve over the next ten minutes.

annual operating time (t_o)

Number of hours per annum for which the lamps are operating (unit: h).

astronomical time clock

A timing device or software function designed to switch lighting on at dusk and off at dawn in relation to the day of the year at a given geographical location.

average illuminance $(\bar{E})$

Illuminance averaged over the specified surface area (unit: lx).

Note: in practice this can be derived either from the total luminous flux falling on the surface divided by the total area of the surface or, alternatively, from an average of the illuminances at a representative number of points on the surface.

average luminance $(\bar{L})$

Luminance averaged over the specified surface (unit: cd·m^{-2})

Note: in practice, this may be approximated by an average of the luminances at a representative number of point on the surface.

automatic test system (ATS)

System consisting of various parts (such as timers, current detectors, changeover switches) that can automatically carry out the routine testing requirements of emergency lighting luminaires and indicate the test results.

Note: the system may be manually initiated.

background area

Area in the workplace adjacent to the immediate surrounding area.

ballast

Device connected between the supply and one or more discharge lamps that serves mainly to limit the current of the lamp(s) to the required value.

Note: a ballast may also include means for transforming the supply voltage, correcting the power factor and, either alone or in combination with a starting device, provide the necessary conditions for starting the lamp(s). A ballast may also contain an analogue or digital input to control the functionality of the luminaire.

ballast lumen factor ($F_{ballast}$)

Ratio of the luminous flux emitted by a reference lamp when operated with a particular production ballast to the luminous flux emitted by the same lamp when operated with its reference ballast.

Note: ballast lumen factor is sometimes signified by the abbreviation BLF.

brightness

Attribute of a visual perception according to which an area appears to emit (or reflect) more or less light.

brightness contrast

Subjective assessment of the difference in brightness between two or more surfaces seen simultaneously or successively.

built-in luminaire

Fixed luminaire installed into structure or equipment to provide illumination.

carriageway

Part of the road normally used by vehicular traffic.

centrally supplied emergency luminaire

Luminaire that is energised from a central emergency power system that is not contained within the luminaire.

changeover operation

Automatic connection of the lamp to the emergency lighting supply when failure of the normal lighting supply occurs, and connecting automatically back to the normal lighting supply when it is restored.

chromaticity

Property of a colour stimulus defined by its chromaticity coordinates, or by its dominant or complementary wavelength and purity taken together.

Note: see also CIE 15: 2004 (CIE, 2004).

colorimeter

Instrument for measuring colorimetric quantities, such as the tristimulus values of a colour stimulus.

colour contrast

Subjective assessment of the difference in colour between two or more surfaces seen simultaneously or successively.

colour rendering

Effect of an illuminant on the colour appearance of objects by conscious or subconscious comparison with their colour appearance under a reference illuminant.

For design purposes, colour rendering requirements shall be specified using the general colour rendering index and shall take one of the following values of R_a: 20, 40, 60, 80, 90.

colour rendering index (R_a)

Value intended to specify the degree to which objects illuminated by a light source have an expected colour relative to their colour under a reference light source.

Note: R_a is derived from the colour rendering indices for a specified set of eight test colour samples. R_a has a maximum of 100, which generally occurs when the spectral distributions of the light source and the reference light source are substantially identical.

colour stimulus

Visible radiation entering the eye and producing a sensation of colour, either chromatic or achromatic.

colour temperature (T_c)

Temperature of a Planckian radiator whose radiation has the same chromaticity as that of a given stimulus (unit: K).

Note: the reciprocal colour temperature is also used, unit: K^{-1}.

competent person

Person with the relevant current training and experience, and with access to the requisite tools, equipment and information, and capable of carrying out a defined task.

combined emergency luminaire

Luminaire containing two or more lamps at least one of which is operating from the emergency lighting supply and the other(s) from the normal lighting supply.

*Note: a combined emergency luminaire is either **maintained** or **non-maintained**.*

commissioning

The verification against design intent, setting to work and relevant operator training in respect of a lighting installation.

constant illumination

The measurement and regulation of excess illumination to the required level. Constant illumination is useful for saving energy during the early part of a lamp's operational life, before lamp depreciation becomes apparent.

contrast

(1)   In the perceptual sense: assessment of the difference in appearance of two or more parts of a field seen simultaneously or successively (hence: brightness contrast, lightness contrast, colour contrast, simultaneous contrast, successive contrast, etc).

(2)   In the physical sense: quantity intended to correlate with the perceived brightness contrast, usually defined by one of a number of formulae which involve the luminances of the stimuli considered, for example: $\Delta L/L$ near the luminance threshold, or L_1/L_2 for much higher luminances.

control gear

Components required to control the electrical operation of the lamp(s).

Note: control gear may also include means for transforming the supply voltage, correcting the power factor and, either alone or in combination with a starting device, provide the necessary conditions for starting the lamp(s).

correlated colour temperature (CCT) (T_{cp})

The temperature of the Planckian radiator whose perceived colour most closely resembles that of a given stimulus at the same brightness and under specified viewing conditions (unit: K).

cosine correction

Correction of a detector for the influence of the incident direction of the light.

Note: for the ideal detector, the measured illuminance is proportional to the cosine of the angle of incidence of the light. The angle of incidence is the angle between the direction of the light and the normal to the surface of the detector.

critical flicker frequency

See **fusion frequency.**

curfew

Time period during which stricter requirements (for the control of obtrusive light) will apply.

Note: it is often a condition of use of lighting applied by a government controlling authority, usually the local government.

cut-off

Technique used for concealing lamps and surfaces of high luminance from direct view in order to reduce glare.

Note: this term has been replaced by **luminous intensity classes**.

cut-off angle (of a luminaire)

Angle, measured up from nadir, between the vertical axis and the first line of sight at which the lamps and the surfaces of high luminance are not visible (unit: degree).

cylindrical illuminance (at a point, for a direction) (E_z)

Total luminous flux falling on the curved surface of a very small cylinder located at the specified point divided by the curved surface area of the cylinder (unit: lx).

daylight

Visible part of global solar radiation capable of causing a visual sensation.

daylight dependency factor (FD)

Level of efficiency that a control system or control strategy exploits the saving potential of daylight in a space.

daylight factor (D or DF)

Ratio of the illuminance at a point on a given plane due to the light received directly and indirectly from a sky of assumed or known luminance distribution, to the illuminance on a horizontal plane due to an unobstructed hemisphere of this sky, where the contribution of direct sunlight to both illuminances is excluded.

Note 1: glazing transmission losses, dirt effects, etc. are included.

Note 2: when calculating the lighting of interiors using this method, the contribution of direct sunlight needs to be considered separately.

daylight linking

Measurement of available natural light in real time at the working plane with automated control to electric lighting in order to 'blend' both sources to achieve the required illumination level.

daylight time usage (t_D)

Annual operating hours during the daylight time, measured in hours (unit: h).

design speed

Speed adopted for a particular stated purpose in designing a road (unit: km·h^{-1}).

diffuse sky radiation

That part of solar radiation which reaches the earth as a result of being scattered by the air molecules, aerosol particles, cloud particles or other particles.

diffused lighting

Lighting in which the light on the working plane or on an object is not incident predominantly from a particular direction.

direct lighting

Lighting by means of luminaires having a distribution of luminous intensity such that the fraction of the emitted luminous flux directly reaching the working plane, assumed to be of infinite extent, is 90% to 100%.

direct solar radiation

That part of the extraterrestrial solar radiation which as a collimated beam reaches the earth's surface after selective attenuation by the atmosphere.

directional lighting

Lighting in which the light on the working plane or on an object is incident predominantly from a particular direction.

disability glare

Glare that impairs the vision of objects without necessarily causing discomfort. Disability glare can be produced directly or by reflection.

discomfort glare

Glare that causes discomfort without necessarily impairing the vision of objects. Discomfort glare can be produced directly or by reflection.

display screen equipment

Alphanumeric or graphic display screen, regardless of the display process employed

Note: display screen equipment is sometimes signified by the abbreviation DSE.

(spatial) **distribution of luminous intensity** (of a source)

Display, by means of curves or tables, of the value of the luminous intensity of the source as a function of direction in space.

diversity (luminance, illuminance) (U_d)

Ratio of minimum illuminance (luminance) to maximum illuminance (luminance) on (of) a surface.

See also **uniformity**

downward light output ratio (DLOR) (of a luminaire: R_{DLO})

Ratio of the downward flux of the luminaire, measured under specified practical conditions with its own lamps and equipment, to the sum of the individual luminous fluxes of the same lamps when operated outside the luminaire with the same equipment, under specified conditions.

Note: the luminaire attitude should be declared so that appropriate corrections to the DLOR can be made if in application the installed attitude is different.

driver

Device connected between the supply and one or more LED lamps which serves mainly to limit the current and/or regulate the voltage to the lamp(s) to the required value.

Note: a driver may also include means for transforming the supply voltage and correcting the power factor. A driver may also contain an analogue or digital input to control the functionality of the luminaire.

Efficacy

See **luminous efficacy of a source**

emergency ballast lumen factor (EBLF)

Ratio of the emergency luminous flux of the lamp supplied by the emergency control gear to the luminous flux of the same lamp operated with the appropriate reference ballast at its rated voltage and frequency.

Note: the emergency ballast lumen factor is the minimum of the values measured at the appropriate time after failure of the normal supply and continuously to the end of the rated time duration.

emergency escape lighting

Part of emergency lighting that provides illumination for visibility for people leaving a location and attempting to terminate a potentially dangerous process before doing so. *See* **high risk task area lighting**.

emergency exit

Way out that is intended to be used during an emergency.

emergency lamp flux

See **practical emergency lamp flux**.

emergency lane (hard shoulder)

Lane parallel to the traffic lane(s) provided for emergency and/or broken-down vehicles only.

emergency lighting

Lighting provided automatically for use when the supply to the normal lighting fails.

emergency lighting charge time (t_{em})

Operating hours during which the emergency lighting batteries are being charged (unit: h).

emergency lighting charging power (P_{ei})

Input power to the charging circuit of emergency luminaires when the lamps are not operating (unit: W).

emergency lighting, total installed charging power

See **total installed charging power of the emergency lighting luminaires in the room or zone**.

emergency luminaire rated luminous flux

Lumen output in emergency operation as claimed by the luminaire manufacturer, 60 seconds (0.5 s for high-risk task-area luminaires) after failure of the normal supply, and continuously maintained to the end of rated duration of operation.

emergency safety lighting

Part of emergency lighting that provides illumination for the safety of people staying in a premise when the supply to the normal lighting fails.

energy consumption used for illumination ($W_{L,t}$)

Energy consumed in period t by the luminaires when the lamps are operating to fulfil the illumination function and purpose in the building (unit: kW·h).

equivalent veiling luminance (for disability glare or veiling reflections) (L_{ve})

Luminance that, when added by superposition to the luminance of both the adapting background and the object, makes the luminance threshold or the luminance difference threshold the same under the two following conditions: (1) glare present, but no additional luminance; (2) additional luminance present, but no glare (unit: $cd \cdot m^{-2}$).

escape route

Route designated for escape in the event of an emergency.

escape route lighting

Part of emergency escape lighting provided to ensure that the means of escape can be effectively identified and safely used when the location is occupied.

externally illuminated safety sign

Safety sign that is directly illuminated by both general and emergency light sources, when it is required, positioned within 2 m horizontally from the sign.

flicker

Impression of unsteadiness of visual sensation induced by a light stimulus whose luminance or spectral distribution fluctuates with time.

flicker frequency

See **fusion frequency**.

floodlighting

Lighting of a scene or object, usually by projectors, in order to increase considerably its illuminance relative to its surroundings.

flux

See **luminous flux**, **rated lamp luminous flux**.

fusion frequency

Critical flicker frequency (for a given set of conditions). Frequency of alternation of stimuli above which flicker is not perceptible (unit: Hz).

general colour rendering index

See **colour rendering index**.

general lighting

Substantially uniform lighting of an area without provision for special local requirements.

glare

Condition of vision in which there is discomfort or a reduction in the ability to see details or objects, caused by an unsuitable distribution or range of luminance, or to extreme contrasts.

See also **disability glare** and **discomfort glare**.

glare rating limit (R_{GL})

Maximum allowed value given by the CIE Glare Rating system.

global solar radiation

Combined direct solar radiation and diffuse sky radiation.

grid points for measurement and calculation

Arrangement of calculation and measurement points and their number in each dimension of the reference surface or plane.

hemispherical illuminance (at a point) (E_{hs})

Total luminous flux falling on the curved surface of a very small hemisphere located at the specified point divided by the curved surface area of the hemisphere (unit: lx).

high risk task area lighting

Part of emergency escape lighting that provides illumination for visibility for people involved in a potentially dangerous process or situation and facilitates safe termination of activities

Note: in sports lighting it is referred to as 'Safety lighting for participants'.

illuminance (at a point of a surface) (E)

Quotient of the luminous flux incident on an element of the surface containing the point, by the area of that element (unit: lx = lm·m^{-2}).

Note: the orientation of the surface may be defined, e.g. horizontal, vertical, hence horizontal illuminance, vertical illuminance.

illuminance meter

Instrument for measuring illuminance.

immediate surrounding area

See **surrounding area**.

indirect lighting

Lighting by means of luminaires having a distribution of luminous intensity such that the fraction of the emitted luminous flux directly reaching the working plane, assumed to be of infinite extent, is 0 to 10%.

inhibit mode

State of a self-contained emergency luminaire that is inhibited from operating by a remote device while the normal supply is on and in case of a normal supply failure the luminaire does not changeover to emergency mode.

Ingress Protection (IP) ratings

Numerical index used to define levels of sealing effectiveness of electrical enclosures, including luminaires, against intrusion from foreign bodies (tools, dirt etc) and moisture.

initial average luminance ($\bar{L}$)

Average luminance of the specified surface when the installation is new (unit: cd·m^{-2}).

initial illuminance (E_{av} or $\bar{E}$)

Average illuminance on the specified surface when the installation is new (unit: lx).

installed loading

Installed power of the lighting installation per unit area (for interior and exterior areas) or per unit length (for road lighting) (unit: W·m^{-2} for areas; kW·km^{-1} for road lighting).

integral lighting system (of a machine)

Lighting system consisting of lamp(s), luminaire(s) and associated mechanical and electrical control devices which forms a permanent part of the machine, designed to provide illumination in and/or at the machine.

intensity

See **luminous intensity**.

intensity distribution

See **luminous intensity distribution**.

internally illuminated safety sign

Safety sign that is illuminated, when it is required, by an internal source.

IK rating

Numerical index used to define the degrees of protection provided by electrical enclosures (including luminaires) against external mechanical impacts.

IP rating

Numerical index used to define levels of sealing effectiveness of electrical enclosures, including luminaires, against intrusion from foreign bodies (tools, dirt etc.) and moisture.

lamp

Source made in order to produce an optical radiation, usually visible.

Note: this term is also sometimes used for certain types of luminaires.

lamp code

Any combination of letters and numbers by which the lamp type is identified.

lamp dimensions

All dimensions of the lamp that are relevant for the luminaire design.

lamp lumen maintenance factor (F_{LLM})

Ratio of the luminous flux of a lamp at a given time in its life to the initial luminous flux.

Note: lamp lumen maintenance factor is sometimes signified by the abbreviation LLMF.

lamp luminous flux

See **rated luminous flux**.

lamp survival factor (F_{LS})

Fraction of the total number of lamps that continue to operate at a given time under defined conditions and switching frequency.

Note: lamp survival factor is sometimes signified by the abbreviation LSF.

lamp wattage

Wattage used by a lamp in operation (unit: W).

LED (light emitting diode)

Solid state device embodying a p–n junction, emitting optical radiation when excited by an electric current.

life of lighting installation

Period after which the installation cannot be restored to satisfy the required performance because of non-recoverable deteriorations.

light loss factor

See **maintenance factor**.

light output ratio (of a luminaire) (R_{LO})

Ratio of the total luminous flux of the luminaire, measured under specified practical conditions with its own lamps and equipment, to the sum of the individual luminous fluxes of the same lamps when operated outside the luminaire with the same equipment, under specified conditions.

Note 1: for luminaires using incandescent lamps only, the optical light output ratio and the light output ratio are the same in practice.

Note 2: light output ratio is sometimes signified by the abbreviation LOR.

See also **downward light output ratio** and **upward light output ratio**.

light source

See **source**.

light source colour

The colour of a light source can be expressed by its **correlated colour temperature**.

Lighting energy numeric indicator (LENI)

Numeric indicator of the total annual lighting energy required in the building (unit: $kW \cdot h \cdot m^{-2} \cdot year^{-1}$).

Note: the LENI can be used to make direct comparisons of the lighting energy used in buildings that have similar functions but are of different sizes and configurations.

loading

See **installed loading**.

local lighting

Lighting for a specific visual task, additional to and controlled separately from the general lighting.

localised lighting

Lighting designed to illuminate an area with a higher illuminance at certain specified positions, for instance those at which work is carried out.

longitudinal uniformity (of road surface luminance of a carriageway) (U_l)

Lowest of the ratios determined for each driving lane of the carriageway as the ratio of the lowest to the highest road surface luminance found in a line in the centre along the driving lane.

louvres

(1)   Daylight: fixed or adjustable blades or baffles on windows to restrict daylight and/or preclude sunlight.

(2)   Luminaires: fixed blades to restrict or reflect some portion of the light from the lamp or light source.

luminaire

Apparatus that distributes, filters or transforms the light transmitted from one or more lamps and which includes all the parts necessary for fixing and protecting the lamps (excepting the lamps themselves) and, where necessary, circuit auxiliaries together with the means for connecting them to the electrical supply.

luminaire code

Any combination of letters and numbers by which the luminaire type is identified.

luminaire maintenance factor (F_{LM})

Ratio of the light output ratio of a luminaire at a given time to the initial light output ratio.

Note: luminaire maintenance factor is sometimes signified by the abbreviation LMF.

luminaire luminous efficacy (η_1)

Quotient of the luminous flux emitted by the luminaire by the power absorbed by the lamp and associated circuits of the luminaire (unit: $lm \cdot W^{-1}$).

luminaire standby energy consumption ($W_{P,t}$)

Standby energy consumed in period t, by the luminaire emergency lighting charging circuit plus the standby control system controlling the luminaires when the lamps are not operating (unit: $kW \cdot h$).

luminaire parasitic power (P_{pi})

Input power consumed by the charging circuit of emergency lighting luminaires and the standby power for automatic controls in the luminaire when lamps are not operating (unit: W).

luminaire power (P_i)

Input power consumed by the lamp(s), control gear and control circuit in or associated with the luminaire, which includes any standby power when the luminaire is turned on (unit: W)

Note: the rated luminaire power (P_i) for a specific luminaire may be obtained from the luminaire manufacturer.

luminance (in a given direction, at a given point of a real or imaginary surface) (L)

The luminous intensity of the light emitted or reflected in a given direction from an element of the surface, divided by the area of the element projected in the same direction (unit: $cd \cdot m^{-2} = lm \cdot m^{-2} \cdot sr^{-1}$).

luminance contrast

Photometric quantity intended to correlate with brightness contrast, usually defined by one of a number of equations which involve the luminances of the stimuli considered.

luminance meter

Instrument for measuring luminance.

luminous efficacy of a source (η)

Quotient of the luminous flux emitted by the power absorbed by the source (unit: $lm \cdot W^{-1}$).

luminous environment

Lighting considered in relation to its physiological and psychological effects.

luminous flux (Φ)

Quantity derived from radiant flux (radiant power) by evaluating the radiation according to the spectral sensitivity of the human eye (as defined by the CIE standard photometric observer). It is the light power emitted by a source or received by a surface (unit: lumen (lm)).

Note: the values used for the spectral sensitivity of the CIE standard photometric observer are those of the spectral luminous efficiency function $V(\lambda)$.

See also **rated luminous flux** and **rated luminous flux**.

luminous intensity (of a source, in a given direction) (I_v)

Luminous flux per unit solid angle in the direction in question, i.e. the luminous flux on a small surface, divided by the solid angle that the surface subtends at the source.

Note: luminous intensity may also be denoted using the symbol I.

luminous intensity classes

Classes for external luminaires where the maximum luminous intensity is restricted above certain angles from the downward vertical. Needed to restrict disability glare from installations where the threshold increment (f_n) cannot be calculated. Also used to control obtrusive light.

Note: see BS EN 13201-2 (BSI, 2015).

maintained emergency luminaire

Luminaire in which emergency light sources are operating at all times when normal lighting or emergency lighting is required.

maintained illuminance ($\bar{E}_\mathrm{m}$)

Value below which the average illuminance on the specified area should not fall.

Note: it is the average illuminance at the time maintenance should be carried out.

maintained luminance ($\bar{L}_\mathrm{m}$)

Value below which the average luminance on the specified area should not (unit: cd·m^{-2})

Note: it is the average luminance at the time maintenance should be carried out.

maintenance cycle

Repetition of lamp replacement, lamp/luminaire cleaning and room surface cleaning intervals.

maintenance factor

Ratio of illuminance produced by the lighting installation after a certain period to the illuminance produced by the installation when new.

Note: the maintenance factor takes into account light losses caused by dirt accumulation on luminaires and room surfaces (in interiors) or other relevant surfaces (in exteriors, where appropriate), and the decrease of the luminous flux of lamps.

See also **lamp lumen maintenance factor, luminaire maintenance factor** and **room surface maintenance factor**.

mesopic vision

Vision intermediate between photopic and scotopic vision.

Note: in mesopic vision, both the cones and the rods are active.

maintenance schedule

Set of instructions specifying maintenance cycle and servicing procedures.

mixed traffic

Traffic that consists of motor vehicles, cyclists, pedestrians etc.

motor traffic (motorized traffic)

Traffic that consists of motorized vehicles only.

nominal lamp wattage (W_lamp)

Approximate wattage used to designate or identify the lamp (unit: W).

non-daylight time usage (t_N)

Annual operating hours during the non-daylight time (unit: h).

non-maintained emergency luminaire

Luminaire in which the emergency light sources are in operation only when the supply to the normal lighting fails.

obtrusive light

Spill light which because of quantitative, directional or spectral attributes in a given context gives rise to annoyance, discomfort, distraction or reduction in the ability to see essential information.

Note 1: in the case of outdoor sports lighting installations, obtrusive light is considered around the installation and not for spectators, referees or players within the sports area.

Note 2: in the case of large tertiary buildings with predominantly glazed facades, interior lighting may be considered as obtrusive light if it gives rise to annoyance, discomfort, distraction or a reduction in the ability to see essential information due to light spilling outside of the building structure.

occupancy dependency factor (F_o)

Factor indicating the proportion of time that a space is occupied, and lighting is required.

open area lighting (anti-panic lighting)

Part of emergency escape lighting provided to avoid panic and provide illumination allowing people to see their way to an escape route.

operating time (t)

Time period for energy consumption (unit: h).

See also **annual operating time**.

principal area ($A_{principle}$)

Actual playing area needed for the performance of a certain sport.

Note: usually this means the actual marked out 'field' area for that sport (for instance football), but in some cases this area comprises an extra playing area around the marked area (e.g. tennis, volleyball, table tennis). The dimensions of the particular area should be checked at the time when a lighting installation is being installed.

performance

See **visual performance**.

photoluminescence

Luminescence caused by absorption of optical radiation.

photometer

Instrument for measuring photometric quantities.

photometry

Measurement of quantities referring to radiation as evaluated according to a given spectral luminous efficiency function, e.g. $V(\lambda)$ or $V'(\lambda)$.

Note: photometry can also be defined as a measurement of quantities referring to radiation evaluated according to the spectral sensitivity of the human eye (as defined by the CIE standard photometric observer).

photopic vision

Vision by the normal eye when it is adapted to levels of luminance of at least several candelas per square metre.

Note: the cones are the principal active photoreceptors in photopic vision.

PIR (passive infrared)

Movement detector used as part of a presence or absence detection system.

Planckian radiator (blackbody)

Ideal thermal radiator that absorbs completely all incident radiation, whatever the wavelength, the direction of incidence or the polarization. This radiator has, for any wavelength and any direction, the maximum spectral concentration of radiance for a thermal radiator in thermal equilibrium at a given temperature.

practical emergency lamp flux (Φ_{PEL})

Lowest luminous flux of the lamp observed during the rated duration of the emergency mode (unit: lm).

$$\Phi_{PEL} = \Phi_D \times F_{Eballast}$$

where Φ_{PEL} is the practical emergency lamp flux (lm), Φ_D is the initial lighting design lumens at 100 h (lm) and $F_{Eballast}$ is the emergency ballast lumen factor.

presence detection

The automatic detection of presence in a space in order to switch the luminaires on during space occupancy.

radiant flux

See **luminous flux**.

rated luminous flux (of a type of lamp or luminaire)

Value of the initial luminous flux of a given type of lamp or luminaire declared by the manufacturer or the responsible vendor, the lamp or luminaire being operated under specified conditions (unit: lm).

Note 1: the initial luminous flux is the luminous flux of a lamp or luminaire after a short ageing period as specified in the relevant lamp standard.

Note 2: the rated luminous flux is sometimes marked on the lamp.

reference ballast

Special type ballast designed for the purpose of providing comparison standards for use in testing ballasts, for the selection of reference lamps and for testing regular production lamps under standardized conditions.

Note: it is essentially characterised by a stable voltage-to-current ratio, which is relatively uninfluenced by variations in current, temperature and magnetic surroundings.

reference surface

Surface on which illuminance is measured or specified.

reflectance (for incident radiation of given spectral composition, polarization and geometrical distribution) (ρ)

Ratio of the reflected radiant or luminous flux to the incident flux in the given conditions (unit: one).

Note 1: reflectance can also be defined as the ratio of the luminous flux reflected from a surface to the luminous flux incident on it.

Note 2: the reflectance generally depends on the direction and spectral distribution of the incident light and the surface finish.

reflections

See **veiling reflections**.

reflectometer

Instrument for measuring quantities pertaining to reflection.

Responsible Person

Delegated individual who is responsible for the provision and operation of appropriate emergency escape lighting.

rest mode

State of a self-contained emergency luminaire that has been intentionally extinguished while the normal supply is off and that, in the event of restoration of the normal supply, automatically reverts to normal mode.

rooflight

Daylight opening on the roof or on a horizontal surface of a building.

room surface maintenance factor (F_{RSM})

Ratio of the light reflected by the surfaces of a room after a certain period of use of the lighting installation to light reflected when the installation is considered conventionally as new.

Note: room surface maintenance factor is sometimes signified by the abbreviation RSMF.

safety sign

Sign that gives a general safety message, obtained by a combination of colour and geometric shape and which, by the addition of a graphic symbol or text, gives a particular safety message.

scene setting

A software function or manually via a scene setting switch in order to select the available lighting scenes in a space.

scene setting operation time (t_s)

Operating hours of the scene setting controls (unit: h).

scotopic observer

Vision by the normal eye when it is adapted to levels of luminance less than some hundredths of a candela per square metre.

Note: the rods are the principal active photoreceptors in scotopic vision.

self-contained emergency luminaire

Luminaire providing maintained or non-maintained emergency lighting in which the battery, lamp, control unit and the test and monitoring facilities, where provided, are contained within the luminaire or adjacent to it, within 1 m cable length.

semi-cylindrical illuminance (at a point) (E_{sz})

Total luminous flux falling on the curved surface of a very small semi-cylinder located at the specified point, divided by the curved surface area of the semi-cylinder (unit: lx).

Note: the axis of the semi-cylinder is taken to be vertical unless stated otherwise. The direction of the curved surface should be specified.

semi-direct lighting

Lighting by means of luminaires having a distribution of luminous intensity such that the fraction of the emitted luminous flux directly reaching the working plane, assumed to be of infinite extent, is 60% to 90%.

semi-indirect lighting

Lighting by means of luminaires having a distribution of luminous intensity such that the fraction of the emitted luminous flux directly reaching the working plane, assumed to be of infinite extent, is 10% to 40%.

shielding angle

The angle between the horizontal plane and the first line of sight at which the luminous parts of the lamps in the luminaire are directly visible (unit: degrees).

Note: the complementary angle to the shielding angle is the **cut-off angle**.

Skylight

Part of sky radiation capable of causing a visual sensation.

Note: when dealing with actinic effects of optical radiations, this term is commonly used for radiations extending beyond the visible region of the spectrum.

slave luminaire

See **centrally supplied emergency luminaire**.

source (light source)

Object that produces light or other radiant flux.

Note: the term light source indicates the source is essentially intended for illuminating and signalling purposes.

solar radiation

Electromagnetic radiation from the sun.

See also **direct solar radiation** and **global solar radiation**.

spacing (in an installation)

Distance between the light centres of adjacent luminaires of the installation.

spacing to height ratio

Ratio of spacing to the height of the geometric centres of the luminaires above the reference plane.

Note: for indoor lighting the reference plane is usually the horizontal working plane; for exterior lighting the reference plane is usually the ground.

spectral luminous efficiency

See **luminous flux**.

spherical illuminance (at a point) (E_o)

Total luminous flux falling on the whole surface of a very small sphere located at the specified point divided by the surface area of the sphere (unit: lx).

spill light (stray light)

Light emitted by a lighting installation which falls outside the boundaries of the area for which the lighting installation is designed.

spotlighting

Lighting designed to increase considerably the illuminance of a limited area or of an object relative to the surroundings, with minimum diffused lighting.

stroboscopic effect

Apparent change of motion and/or appearance of a moving object when the object is illuminated by a light of varying intensity.

Note: to obtain apparent immobilisation or constant change of movement, it is necessary that both the object movement and the light intensity variation are periodic, and some specific relation between the object movement and light variation frequencies exists. The effect is only observable if the amplitude of the light variation is above certain limits. The motion of the object can be rotational or translational.

standby lighting

That part of emergency lighting provided to enable normal activities to continue substantially unchanged.

standby energy consumption

See **luminaire standby energy consumption**.

standby power

See **luminaire standby power**.

standby power of the controls (with the lamps off) (P_{ci})

Standby input power to the control system in the luminaires during the period with the lamps not operating (unit: W).

stray light

See **spill light**.

sunlight

Part of direct solar radiation capable of causing a visual sensation.

Note: when dealing with actinic effects of optical radiations, this term is commonly used for radiations extending beyond the visible region of the spectrum.

surrounding area (immediate surrounding area)

Strip surrounding the task area within the field of vision.

Note: in exterior applications this strip should have a width of at least 2 m.

survival factor

See **lamp survival factor**.

task area

Partial are in the work place in which the visual task is carried out.

Note: for places where the size and/or location of the task area are unknown, the area where the task may occur is the task area.

total energy used for lighting (W_t)

Energy consumed in period t by the luminaires in a room or zone when the lamps are operating, plus the standby loads when the lamps are not operating (unit: kW·h).

total installed charging power of the emergency lighting luminaires in the room or zone (P_{em})

Input charging power of all emergency lighting luminaires (unit: W).

total installed lighting power in the room or zone (P_n)

Power of all luminaires (unit: W).

total installed parasitic power of the controls in the room or zone (P_{pc})

Input power of all control systems in luminaires when the lamps are not operating (unit: W).

traffic lane

Strip of carriageway intended to accommodate a single line of moving vehicles.

transmittance (for incident radiation of given spectral composition, polarization and geometrical distribution) (τ)

Ratio of the transmitted radiant or luminous flux to the incident flux in the given conditions.

unified glare rating limit (R_{UGL})

Upper limit of glare by the CIE Unified Glare Rating system.

uniformity (luminance, illuminance) (U_o)

Ratio of minimum illuminance (luminance) to average illuminance (luminance) on (of) a surface.

upward flux ratio

Ratio between the flux from all considered luminaires above the horizontal plane passing through the luminaires in their installed position on site plus their flux reflected by the ground and the minimal irreducible flux reflected towards the sky by the sole reference surface.

Note: upward flux ratio is sometimes signified by the abbreviation UFR.

upward light output ratio (of a luminaire) (R_{ULO})

Ratio of the upward flux of the luminaire, measured under specified practical conditions with its own lamps and equipment, to the sum of the individual luminous fluxes of the same lamps when operated outside the luminaire with the same equipment, under specified conditions.

Note 1: upward light output ratio is sometimes signified by the abbreviation ULOR.

Note 2: the luminaire attitude should be declared so that appropriate corrections to the ULOR can be made if in application the installed attitude is different.

upward light ratio (R_{UL})

Proportion of the total luminaire flux that is emitted above the horizontal by all luminaires to the total luminaire flux from all luminaires in an installation, when the luminaires are mounted in their installed attitudes.

useful data

Lamp and luminaire data beneficial to the designers and users in the planning and operation of lighting installations.

utilance (of an installation, for a reference surface) (U)

Ratio of the luminous flux received by the reference surface to the sum of the individual total fluxes of the luminaires of the installation.

utilization factor (of an installation, for a reference surface) (F_U)

Ratio of the luminous flux received by the reference surface to the sum of the individual luminous fluxes of the lamps of the installation.

$V(\lambda)$ correction

Correction of the spectral responsivity of a detector to match the photopic spectral sensitivity of the human eye.

veiling reflections

Specular reflections that appear on the object viewed and that partially or wholly obscure the details by reducing contrast.

visual acuity (visual resolution)

(1)   Qualitatively: capacity for seeing distinctly fine details that have very small angular separation.

(2)   Quantitatively: any of a number of measures of spatial discrimination such as the reciprocal of the value of the angular separation in minutes of arc of two neighbouring objects (points or lines or other specified stimuli) which the observer can just perceive to be separate.

visual comfort

Subjective condition of visual wellbeing induced by the visual environment.

visual field (field of vision)

Extent of space in which objects are visible to an eye at a given position and direction of view.

Note: in the horizontal plane meridian the field of vision extends to nearly 190° with both eyes open, the area seen binocularly is about 120°, and the area seen by one eye only is about 154°. The extent of the field of vision tends to diminish with age.

visual performance

Performance of the visual system as measured for instance by the speed and accuracy with which a visual task is performed.

visual task

Visual elements of the activity being undertaken.

Note: the main visual elements are the size of the structure, its luminance, its contrast against the background and its duration.

window

Daylight opening on a vertical or nearly vertical area of a room envelope.

workplace

Place intended to house workstations on the premises of the undertaking and/or establishment and any other place within the area of undertaking and/or establishment to which the worker has access in the course of his/her employment.

Work plane (working plane)

Reference surface defined as the plane at which work is normally done.

Workstation

Combination and spatial arrangement of work equipment, surrounded by the work environment under the conditions imposed by the work tasks.

References

BSI (2015) BS EN 13201-2: 2015: *Road lighting. Performance requirements* (London: British Standards Institution)

BSI (2018) BS EN 12665: 2018: *Light and lighting. Basic terms and criteria for specifying lighting requirements* (London: British Standards Institution)

CIE (2004) CIE 15: 2004: *Colorimetry* (Vienna: International Commission on Illumination)

IEC (online) IEC 60050: *International Electrotechnical Vocabulary* [online] (Geneva: International Electrotechnical Commission (http://www.electropedia.org) (accessed August 2018)

SLL (2004) *SLL Code for Lighting* (London: Society of Light and Lighting)

Index

Note: page numbers in *italics* refer to illustrations; page numbers in **bold** refer to tables.

1–10 volt interface 99–102
absence detection *see* occupancy detection
accent lighting 204, 206, *207*
access for maintenance 419
    industrial premises 181
    transport buildings 282–3
    wash-down/clean rooms 307
accessible design 4
    educational premises 190–1
    occupancy detection 234
    places of worship 233–4
    transport buildings 281–2
accreditation schemes 8, 61, 453–4
acidic environments 299–302
acrylic materials 297
adaptation *see* visual adaptation
aesthetics 16, 59, 141
air conditioning systems
    air handling luminaires 68
    coordination of services 66–70
air flow across luminaires 66, 68
air handling luminaires 68
airports 287–9
alternative products 58, 59
ambience (experience) 3
ambient temperature effects
    on control gear 99–100
    lamp performance charts 314–15, **315**
    on lamps 66, 69, 74, *82*, **315**, 330
    optimal operating temperatures **70**, 70
amenity (function) 2–3
amplitude dimming 99
amplitude modulation drivers 106
analysis (project) 9
annual operating time 461
anti-panic lighting 32, 473
Approved Documents (ADs) 452
architectural considerations
    listed buildings 234–5
    places of worship 239–40
    (*see also* historic buildings and spaces)
architectural lighting *see* exterior architectural lighting
archives (documents) **168**
area (anti-panic) lighting 32
area lighting (security) 358
arenas 376–7
art galleries *see* museums and art galleries
arts studios **193**, 197
assembly halls **193**, 198
astronomical time clock 461
ATEX directive 311–12
athletics 370
athletics tracks 376, 413, *414*
    (*see also* sports lighting)
atmosphere 3, 251–2
atria 26, 152–3, 198
autism 191
automated solar shading 20, 398
automatic lighting controls *see* daylight linking;
    occupancy detection
automatic test systems (ATS) 48, 111, 147–8, 397–8, 462

average illuminance 411, 461
average luminance 461
awnings 19

background area 462
backlit façades 336–7
back-up generators 38, 313–14, 368
ballast 462
    (*see also* control gear)
ballast lumen factor (BLF) 462
bars and pubs **256**, 257–9, 267
bathrooms 223, 243, **244**
batteries
    central battery systems 37–8
    cold and freezing environments 295
    maintenance and inspection 47
    self-contained emergency luminaires 37
    standby power supplies 368
bed-head luminaires 223
bedrooms/bed-sitting rooms 241–2, **244**, 246, 249
bicycle routes and structures 292
BIM (building information model) 399
bistros 262–3
blinds 18, 20, **166**
BMS (building management systems) 39, 131
board rooms **168**
bollards 121
boundary fences **356**, 359
bowls 370, **371**
break rooms **168**
BREEAM (Building Research Establishment
    Environmental Assessment Method) 61, 453–4
Bribery Act 2010 55–6
briefing 8–9
brightness 462
brightness contrast *see* contrast
buildability 4
building façades *see* exterior architectural lighting
building information model (BIM) 399
building management systems (BMS) 39, 131
building materials, lighting properties 439–43
building mounted luminaires 333–4
Building Regulations 6, 30, 142–3, 388–9, 452–3
built-in luminaire 462
buried cabling 386
burn risk 234, 243
'burning in' 393, 408
bus shelters 291
bus stations 291
bus stops 291
busbar systems 130

cable management systems (CMS) 283
cabling systems 39, 128, *129*
    (*see also* electrical wiring)
calculations 10–11
canteens **168**, 186
car parks **45**, **244**, **261**, 261–2, **357**, 361
carbon emissions 389, 454
Carbon Trust 459
care homes 249
carriageway 462
cathodoluminescence 97
CCTV surveillance 280, 355–6
CDM (Construction (Design and Management))
    Regulations 2015 7
CE marks 121–2
ceiling height
    hospital wards 224

ceiling height (*continued*)
    for indirect lighting 173
    offices 165–6
    places of entertainment 252
ceiling voids, coordination of services 63–5
ceilings
    luminous 175–6
    minimum illuminance *167*, 169
    surface reflectance **166**
    suspended or open 192
cellular offices **168**
centrally supplied emergency luminaires 37–8, 39, 40,
    49, 111, 283, 462
certification 8
    commissioning completion 403
    emergency lighting 49
    functional commissioning 398
    luminaires 121–2
    pre-commissioning certificate 393
chandeliers 382–3
change management 392
changing rooms 159, 223
chemical industries 321, **322**
    (*see also* exterior workplace lighting)
chemical resistance **299–300**, 299–301
chemicals and chemical vapours 299–302, 312
chemiluminescence 97
children's play areas **244**, 248
chilled beams 67–8, 68–9
chokes *see* control gear
chromatic adaptation 430–1, 443
chromaticity 462
churches *see* places of worship
CIBSE Code of Conduct. 54
cinemas 35–6
    (*see also* places of entertainment)
circadian lighting 2, 112, 142, 249, 445–51
circadian system 17
circuit protective devices (CPD) 127–8
circulation areas
    communal residential buildings 249
    courts 271
    industrial premises 186–7
    places of entertainment 267
    prisons 276
    (*see also* corridors)
classrooms 192, **193**, 193, 195–6
    (*see also* educational premises)
clean rooms 305–7
cleaners' rooms 161
cleaning 423–4
    avoiding corrosive chemicals 300, 302, 307
    cleaning interval 423
    design assumptions 418–19
    hospital luminaires 220
    light emitting diodes (LEDs) 302
    room surfaces 424, 442–3
    transport installations 282
    various materials used in luminaires **424**
    windows 28
clerestory windows 24–5
climate-based daylight modelling 24
closed circuit television (CCTV) surveillance 280, 355–6
clubs 264–5
CMS (cable management systems) 283
CMS (central management systems) 351
CO_2 emissions 389, 454
coach stations 291
Coanda effect 66

cold and freezing environments 294–6, 313
cold stores 185
colorimeter 462
colour 426
    in diffuse reflection 428–9
    various building materials 441
colour adaptation 430–1, 443
colour constancy 430–1
colour contrast 234, 443, 462
colour correction factor (CCF) 409
colour fidelity index 434–6
colour gamut index 436–9
colour induction 443
colour rendering 73, 431–6, 463
    communal residential buildings 242
    custodial buildings 277
    hospitals and healthcare buildings 218
    industrial premises 179
    metrics 431–2
    museums and art galleries 211–12
    office lighting 170
    retail premises 204
    school lighting 194
    security lighting 357
    sports lighting **370–5**
    for various lamp types **92**
colour rendering index (CRI) 73, **92**, 432–4, 463
colour specification 441
colour stimulus 463
colour temperature 73, 463
    communal residential buildings 242
    custodial buildings 277
    office lighting 170
    retail premises 204
    school lighting 194
    for various lamp types **92**
    (*see also* correlated colour temperature (CCT))
colour vision 430–1
combined emergency luminaire 40, 463
commissioning 387–405, 453
    certification 393, 398
    communication and escalation 390
    competence 389
    completion certificate 403
    documentation, training and handover 388
    electrical checks 392–3
    electrical safety 389
    emergency lighting 48–9, 387–8, 394
    energy performance verification 388–9
    exterior lighting 394
    interfaces with other services 396, 398
    interior lighting 394
    lighting controls 148–9, 388, 394–8
    luminaires 387
    management team 389–90
    mechanical checks 392
    method statements 389, 390
    post-completion checks and adjustments 404
    pre-commissioning certificate 393
    pre-commissioning checks 391–3
    programme of works 390–1
    witness testing 400–1
common building areas 151–62
    (*see also* circulation areas; corridors; entrance halls/
        lobbies)
communal residential buildings 241–50
    bathrooms 243, **244**
    circadian lighting 249
    circulation areas 249

communal residential buildings (*continued*)
    colour appearance 242
    corridors **244**, 245, 249
    daylighting 241–2
    emergency lighting **44**, 243
    energy efficiency 242
    entrance halls/lobbies **244**, 245
    exterior lighting 248
    gardens and terraces 260–1
    illuminance recommendations **244**
    kitchens **244**, 247
    lighting controls 248–9
    lounges **244**, 247–8
    nursing and care homes 249
    recreation areas **244**, 248
    safety considerations 242–3
    security 243–4
    study bedrooms and bed-sitting rooms **244**, 246, 247
communication networks *see* networked systems
community rooms 237
compact fluorescent lamps 83, **92**, **315**
competency 389, 406, 463
computer display screens *see* display screens
computer rooms **193**, 196–7
concept design 9–10
concert halls 265–7
concourses 284
conference rooms **168**
conservation of exhibits 211, 217
constant current drivers 106–7
constant illuminance *see* daylight linking
constant illuminance adjustment 137–8
constant illuminance factor 144–5
constant illumination 463
constant voltage drivers 107
construction 14
Construction (Design and Management) Regulations 2015 7
Construction Products Regulation (305/2011/EU) 30
construction sites *see* exterior workplace lighting
contamination *see* chemicals and chemical vapours; dusty environments
contrast 463, 471
    exterior architectural lighting 328–9, 332
    perceptions of *328*
    (*see also* colour contrast; glare control)
control gear 99–113, 463
    amplitude modulation drivers 106–7
    cable lengths 106
    circadian lighting luminaires 112
    cold and freezing environments 295
    constant voltage drivers 107
    discharge lamps 104–5
    DMX drivers (digital multiplexing) 108
    emergency lighting 110–11
    fluorescent lamps 81, 103–4
    galvanic insulated 'SELV' drivers 109
    for hot and humid environments 297
    light emitting diodes (LEDs/OLEDs) 105–10
    maximum operating temperature 178
    noise from 100
    non-insulated drivers 109
    outdoor drivers 110
    phase-cut dimmers 108, *109*
    terminology 99–102
    for various lamp types **92**
control rooms/desks 182–4, *184*, 412
control systems *see* lighting controls

converted historic buildings 379
cooling systems
    air handling luminaires 68
    coordination of services 66–70
coordination with other services 63–70
correlated colour temperature (CCT) 73, 464
    circadian lighting 142
    tuneable 112, 142
corridors 153–5
    communal residential buildings **244**, 245, 249
    hospitals 222
    industrial premises 186–7
    (*see also* circulation areas)
corrosion resistance **299–300**, 300
corrosive environments 299–302, 313
cosine correction 464
cost (value) 4
counters (desks) 152, 221, *222*, 285
courts 269–73
    (*see also* custodial buildings)
cove lighting 175
cricket 371, **372**
critical flicker frequency *see* fusion frequency
curfew 464
custodial buildings 273–8
    emergency lighting 278
    illuminance recommendations 276–7, **277**
    impact resistant luminaires 274–5, 310
    light source colour properties 277
    lighting control and energy efficiency 277
    prison standard cell and 'safer cell' 273–5
custom and immigration centres *see* custodial buildings
cut-off 464
cut-off angle 342, 464
cycle routes and structures 292
cycle tracks 343, 344, 348–9
cylindrical illuminance 231, 235, 269, **344**, 464

DALI (digital addressable lighting interface) 100, 139, 255
dark adaptation *see* visual adaptation
daylight 97
daylight autonomy (DA) 24
daylight availability 21, *22*, 22–4, 165, 178
daylight dependency factor (FD) 464
daylight de-rating factor 144–5
daylight factor 22–4, 464
daylight linking 137, 165, 195, 232–3, 255, 464
    commissioning 394–5
    light sensor calibration 394–5
daylight monitoring 5
daylight time usage 464
daylighting 16–29
    benefits 16–17
    courtrooms 270
    depth of penetration 24
    educational premises 191
    environmental assessment rating 454
    glare control 17–18, 20
    hospitals and healthcare buildings 218
    industrial premises 178
    museums and art galleries 210
    offices 165, 176
    overheating control 18, 21
    performance verification 407
    places of entertainment 253
    places of worship 231–2
    prisons 276
    privacy and security 18

daylighting (*continued*)
    retail premises 201–2
    shading 19–21
    transport buildings 288, 291
    uniformity 22, 22–3
    (*see also* windows)
DC (direct current) power supplies 131–2
dealing rooms **168**
decoration *see* interior design; surface finishes
design changes 14, 58
design constraints 6–8
design coordination 11
design ethos 53–62
design integration 11
design issues 2–6
design process 1–15, 8–14
design reports 13–14
design speed 465
designer role 390
diffuse reflectance 441, **442**
diffuse reflection 428–9, 440
diffuse sky radiation 465
diffused lighting 465
digital addressable lighting interface (DALI) 100, 139, 255
digital multiplexing (DMX) 100, 108, 139
dimming controls 74, 100, 138
    amplitude dimming 99
    commissioning 395
    constant illuminance adjustment 137–8
    light emitting diodes (LEDs) 99, 102, 106, 108, 255
    security lighting 363
    for various lamp types **92**
dining areas **244**, 247, 249
direct current (DC) power supplies 131–2
direct lighting 465
direct luminaires 114
direct solar radiation 465
direct/indirect luminaires 115
    minimum % of each component 174
    and surface finishes 167
directional lighting 465
disability glare 465
    (*see also* glare control)
disabled refuge areas 157, 219
disabled toilets 158, 234
discomfort glare 465
    (*see also* glare control)
display lighting 207–8, **208**, **209**
display screens 164–5, 465
    average luminaire luminance limit **170**
    control rooms 182–3
    horizontal 183–4
    maximum luminance 169–70, **183**
    visual aids 192
    (*see also* veiling reflections)
disposal of equipment 62, 74
distribution of luminous intensity 465
diversity 465
    (*see also* illuminance diversity)
DMX (digital multiplexing) 100, 108, 139
document stores **168**
documentation 12–14, 48, 388
domestic security lighting 361–2
downlights 115–16
    (*see also* recessed luminaires)
downward light output ratio (DLOR) 465
drainage systems 64
drama studios **193**, 199

drawings 12
drivers 466
    (*see also* control gear)
DSI protocol 139
dusty environments 297–9, 312, 419
    emergency lighting 313
    luminaires for 297–8, 423
dynamic (exterior) lighting 329

EBLF (emergency ballast lumen factor) 466
educational premises 190–9
    daylighting 191
    emergency lighting **44**
    glare control 194
    illuminance recommendations 192–3, **193**
    light source colour properties 194
    lighting control 195
    lighting for disability 190–1
    surface finishes 192
efficacy *see* luminous efficacy
electric discharges 94–6
electric shock protection 124
electrical checks 392–3
electrical connections 129–31
electrical fault protection 39, 124, 127–8
electrical interference *see* electromagnetic compatibility (EMC)
electrical risers 162
electrical safety verification 389
electrical test and measuring equipment 393
electrical testing 48–9, 392–3
electrical wiring 126–30
    cabling systems 39, 128, *129*
    connection methods 129–31
    coordination of services 66
    emergency lighting 39
    in historic buildings 383–4
electrochromic glazing 21
electroluminescence 96
electroluminescent (EL) light sources 91
electromagnetic compatibility (EMC) 39, 100–1, 121, 220
electronic control gear *see* control gear
embedded energy/carbon 5–6, 61–2
EMC (electromagnetic compatibility) 39, 100–1, 121, 220
emergency ballast lumen factor (EBLF) 466
emergency escape lighting 32–6, 466
    minimum duration 43, **44–5**, **46**
emergency exit 466
emergency lamp flux *see* practical emergency lamp flux
emergency lane (hard shoulder) 466
emergency lighting 30–52
    automated testing and monitoring 48, 111, 147–8, 397–8
    changeover operation 40, 462
    code of practice 6
    commissioning 48–9, 387–8, 394
    control gear 110–11
    corridors 154
    design approaches 36–7
    documentation 48
    electrical circuits 38–40
    installation 47
    legislation and standards 30–1
    light emitting diodes (LEDs) 110–11
    light sources 41–2
    maintenance and inspection 47–8
    monitoring 111

emergency lighting (*continued*)
  open area (anti-panic) lighting 32, 473
  planning 42–6
  power sources 37–8
  specific locations **44–5**, 45–6
    communal residential buildings 243
    courts 273
    custodial buildings 278
    for dusty environments 298
    entrance halls/lobbies 152
    escalators 158
    extreme environments 313–14
    historic and sensitive spaces 384, **385**, 386
    hospitals and healthcare buildings 219
    industrial premises 182, 184
    places of entertainment 262
    plant rooms, electrical risers and service spaces
      162
    sports lighting 368
    staircases 157–8
    transport buildings 283–4
    underwater applications 305
    wash-down/clean rooms 307
  system types 36–7, 37–8
  testing 48–9, 397–8
  types 31
  vandal resistance 311
  (*see also* emergency escape lighting; emergency
    luminaires; emergency safety lighting; standby
    lighting)
emergency lighting charge time 466
emergency lighting charging power 466
emergency luminaires 117
  centrally supplied systems 37–8, 39, 40, 49, 111, 283
  classification **41**
  cold and freezing environments 295
  combined 40, 463
  hospitals and healthcare buildings 220
  for hot and humid environments 297
  light sources 41–2
  maintained/non-maintained 40, 43
  maintenance and inspection 47
  photometric compliance 43
  photometric measurements 49
  rated luminous flux 466
  self-contained units 37, 40, 48, 110–11
  slave luminaires 40
  testing 48–9, 110–11
  total installed charging power 477
emergency safety lighting 31, 36, 43, 276, 368, 466
emergency signage
  escape routes 33–5
  exit signs 33–4, 152, 154, *155*
  for extreme environments 298, 311
enamel paint finish, cleaning **424**
end of life recycling 62
end-user training 403
ENEC marks 121–2
energy consumption 5–6, 71, 466
  alternative products 58–9
  compliance target 453
  effect of maintenance factor 61
  LENI calculation 143–7
  luminaire parasitic power 145, 471
  luminaire power 471
  monitoring 397
energy efficiency 454
  benchmarks 143
  Building Regulations 452

energy efficiency (*continued*)
  communal residential buildings 242
  courts 272–3
  custodial buildings 277
  lighting control for 142–7
  parasitic loads 145–6
  places of entertainment 254
  retail premises 203
  verification 388–9
energy metering 143, 397, 453
energy rating systems 61, 453–5
Enhanced Capital Allowances (ECA) 459–60
enquiry desks 152, 221, *222*, 285
entrance halls/lobbies 151–2
  communal residential buildings **244**, 245
  hospitals 221
  places of entertainment 257, 266
entrances
  bars and pubs 257
  communal residential buildings **244**
  light adaptation 212
  security lighting **356**, 360
  shops 205–6
  theatres and concert halls 266
environmental assessment tools 8, 61, 453–5
environmental impacts 6
  (*see also* spill light; sustainability)
Equalities Act 2014 233
equivalent veiling luminance 467
escalators 158, 285
escape route lighting 32, 467
  external exits 45
  hospitals and healthcare buildings 219, 220
  places of worship 234
escape route signs 33–5
escape routes, cable routes 128
escape stairs 157–8
estimating lighting requirements 24
ethernet *see* networked systems; Power over Ethernet
  (PoE)
evacuation lift cars 45
executive offices **168**
exhibition lighting 215
exit signs 33–4, 152, 154, *155*
  (*see also* emergency signage)
explosive environments 297–8, 311–13
exterior architectural lighting 325–39
  backlit façades 336–7
  colour and materials 326–8
  contrast 328–9
  delineation 338–9
  glare control 331, 334
  global applications 330–1
  historic and sensitive spaces 385–6
  integrated with architecture 338–9
  lighting control 329–30, 332–3
  luminaires 327, 330–1, 331–6, 385
exterior lighting
  car parks **244**, **261**, 261–2, **357**
  commissioning 394
  communal residential buildings **244**, 248
  environmental assessment rating 454, 455
  façade lighting 261, 358
  historic and sensitive spaces 385–6
  image making 3
  light spill 454, 455
  lighting control 260
  maintenance factors (MF) 424
  performance verification 407, 413

exterior lighting (*continued*)
  places of entertainment 259–62, 266
  safety and security 4
  (*see also* exterior architectural lighting; road lighting;
    security lighting; urban centres)
exterior luminaires 117–21, 300
  architectural lighting 327, 330–1, 331–6, 385
  ground mounted 234, 335–6
  ground-recessed luminaires 121, 331, 334–5
  luminous intensity classes 471
  places of entertainment 259–60
  pole-mounted 336
  surface (building) mounted 333–4
  surface (ground) mounted 335–6
exterior workplace lighting 317–24
  chemical and fuel industries 321, **322**
  glare control 319
  illuminance recommendations 319, **320**
  integrated lighting 324
  light source colour properties 318, 319–20
  light spill 319, 324
  loading areas 320–1
  localised lighting 324
  obstructions 318
  sidings, marshalling yards and goods yards 322, **323**
external lighting *see* exterior lighting
external shading 19
external smoking areas 261
externally illuminated safety sign 467
extra low voltage (SELV) luminaires 109, 220, 303, 305
extreme environments 294–316
  chemicals and chemical vapours 299–302
  cold and freezing 294–6
  dusty environments 297–9
  emergency lighting 313–14
  explosive environments 311–13
  hot and humid 296–7
  marine 307–8
  vibration, impact and vandalism 308–11
  wash-down/clean rooms 305–7
  water submersion 302–5

façade lighting 261, 358
  (*see also* exterior architectural lighting)
facial recognition *281*, 361
  (*see also* modelling)
facilities management 149, 402
factories *see* industrial premises
factory acceptance testing (FAT) 391
fan coil units (FCUs) 67, 68
fibre-optic lighting 217, 314
field surveys *see* performance verification
finishes *see* surface finishes
fire alarm equipment **46**, 65
fire protection 39, 297, 311–13
fire risk assessment 42–3, 283
first aid rooms **46**, 160
fitness training 373, **373**
five-a-side football 372, **373**
flammability 124
flicker 101, 181–2, 194–5, 233, 467
floodlighting 467
  area lighting 358
  exterior architectural lighting 332, 335
  exterior workplaces 322, 323–4
  high mast 322, 323–4
  projector lighting 314
  sports lighting 371, 373, 374, 376, 378
floodlights 119–20, 123

floors, surface reflectance **166**, 167, **442**
fluorescent lamps 80–3
  'burning in' 393
  characteristics **92**
  cold and freezing environments 295
  components 81–2
  control gear 81, 103–4
  emergency lighting 41
  lamp lumen maintenance factor (LLMF) **72**
  lamp replacement 421
  lamp survival factor (LSF) **73**
  luminous flux related to ambient temperature *82*,
    315
  mechanism 96
  optimal operating temperatures **70**
  (*see also* compact fluorescent lamps)
flux *see* luminous flux; rated luminous flux
football 373, **373**
footpaths 343–4, 344, 348–9
  communal residential buildings **244**
  places of entertainment 260
  public parks **357**
foyers 266–7
freezing environments 294–6
fuel industries 321, **322**
function rooms 263, *264*
furniture, surface reflectance **166**
fusion frequency 467
  (*see also* flicker)

galleries *see* art galleries
galvanic insulated 'SELV' drivers 109
galvanized steel, cleaning **424**
games rooms/areas **244**, 248, 258
gardens 260–1
gas discharge lamps
  cold and freezing environments 295
  lamp replacement 421
  restrike time 74
  (*see also* fluorescent lamps; high pressure discharge
    lamps; low pressure sodium lamps)
gas lighting 93
gatehouses **356**, 360
general lighting 467
general lighting service (GLS) lamps 78, **92**
generators 38, 313–14, 368
glare 467
glare control
  daylight 17–18, 20–1
  glazing-based solutions 21
  luminaire mounting height **33**, **187**
  performance verification 415
  security lighting 357, 361
  specific locations
    educational premises 193
    exterior architectural lighting 331, 334
    exterior lighting 260
    exterior workplaces 319
    high-risk task area lighting **33**
    hospital wards 225–7
    industrial premises 180, **184**, 185–6, **186**, 187
    museums and art galleries 213, *214*
    offices 170
    places of entertainment 253–4
    road lighting 123, 341–2, **342**
    transport buildings 287
  spotlights 213
  unified glare rating (UGR) 170
glare rating limit 467

glare-lighting (for security) 359, **360**
glass, cleaning **424**
glazing
  facade/glazing ratio 26
  glazed streets, courtyards and atria 26, *27*
  light pipes 27, *28*
  maintenance 28
  prismatic refractors 25
  'smart' 21
  tinted 21
global solar radiation 467
gloss factor 416
glossary 461–79
glossy and semi-matte reflection 429
graffiti damage 310
graphical user interfaces (GUIs) 391, 396
graphics workstations **168**
grid points *411*, 467
ground mounted luminaires 234, 335–6
ground recessed luminaires 121, 331, 334–5
group replacement 421
guardhouses **356**, 360
guest houses *see* places of entertainment
GUIs (graphical user interfaces) 391, 396

hand-held switches 220
handover 14, 148–9, 388, 399–404
harbours 289
hazardous environments *see* extreme environments; high
  risk task area lighting
Health and Safety (Safety Signs and Signals) Regulations
  1996 30
health benefits of daylight 16–17
  (*see also* wellbeing)
health clubs *see* places of entertainment
healthcare buildings *see* hospitals and healthcare buildings
hearing impairment 233
hemispherical illuminance 468
heritage buildings *see* historic buildings and spaces; listed
buildings
high intensity discharge (HID) lamps 393
high pressure discharge lamps
  control gear 104–5
  high pressure mercury lamps 83
  high pressure sodium lamps 87–90, **92**
  lamp lumen maintenance factor (LLMF) **72**
  lamp survival factor (LSF) **73**
  mercury discharge lamps 83
  metal halide lamps 83–6, **92**
high risk task area lighting 33, 273, 468
high temperatures 296–7, 312
historic buildings and spaces 379–86
  converted to a new use 379
  daylighting 380–2
  emergency lighting 384, **385**, 386
  exterior architectural lighting 327, 333, 334
  exterior spaces 385–6
  lighting equipment 382–4
  listed buildings 234–5, 379
  museums and art galleries 379, 382, 383
  preserved 'as is' 380
  re-use of 379
hospices *see* communal residential buildings
hospital streets 222
hospital wards 223–7
hospitals and healthcare buildings 218–29
  changing rooms and cubicles 223
  cleanliness 219–20

hospitals and healthcare buildings (*continued*)
  clinical areas and operating departments 227–8
  colour rendering requirements 218
  daylighting 218
  electrical safety 220
  emergency lighting **44**, 219
  entrance halls, waiting areas and lift halls 221
  hospital streets and general corridors 222
  illuminance recommendations 221–9
  lines of sight 218
  luminaire safety 219–20
  night lighting 219, *222*, 227
  operating theatres 228–9
  reception and enquiry desks 221, *222*
  toilets, bath, wash and shower rooms 223
hostels *see* communal residential buildings
hot and humid environments 296–7, 313
hot surfaces 234, 243
hotels *see* places of entertainment
'hum' 309
humid environments 296–7

illuminance 468
illuminance diversity 32, 34, 414, 465
illuminance measurement 49, 398
illuminance meters 49, 395, 408–9
illuminance uniformity 415, 478
image (identity) 3
immediate surrounding area *see* surrounding area
immigration centres *see* custodial buildings
impact protection (IK) rating 123, **309**, 309–10, 469
incandescence 93–4
incandescent lamps 92, 103
inclusive design *see* accessible design
indirect lighting 468
  average luminance of reflecting surface 170
  cove lighting 175
  luminaires 114–15
  minimum height above floor level 166
  minimum reflectance of reflecting surface 172
  and surface finishes 167
indoor arenas 376–7
indoor bowls 370, **371**
indoor cricket 371, **372**
indoor tennis 373, **374**
induction lamps 90, **92**
industrial premises 177–89
  ancillary areas 186–7
  control rooms 182–4
  daylight availability 178
  directions of view 180, *181*
  emergency lighting **45**, 184
  environmental considerations 178
  general lighting 187
  hazardous environments 178, 182
  legal requirements 177–8
  localized lighting 187
  machinery stroboscopic effects 181–2
  obstructions in 179–80
  safety and emergency egress 182
  speculative factory units 186–7
  storage 184–6
  supplementary task lighting 187
  visual inspection 188
infection control 220
information centres **168**
information desks 152, 221, *222*, 285
infrared lights 211, 356
ingress protection (IP) 243

ingress protection (IP) (*continued*)
    cold and freezing environments 294
    control gear 101
    dusty environments 297
    exterior lighting 260
    hospitals and healthcare buildings 220, 228
    hot and humid environments 297
ingress protection (IP) rating 303, **304–5**, 468, 469
    chemical resistance 299, 301
    water submersion 302–3
inhibit mode 468
initial average luminance 468
initial illuminance 468
inrush current 101, 112, *113*
inspection
    electrical checks 392–3
    emergency lighting 47–8
    mechanical checks 392
    visual 188, 398
    (*see also* performance verification)
installation 14, 47, 387
installed loading 468
integral lighting system 468
integrated chilled beams 68–9
integration with other services 63, 68–9
intensity *see* luminous intensity
interfaces with other services 396, 398
interior design 202–3, 252–3
    (*see also* surface finishes)
International Protection (IP) system *see* ingress protection
        (IP) rating
Internet-controlled devices/luminaires 393
    (*see also* networked systems)
IT rooms **193**, 196–7

kitchens **46**, 160, **244**, 247

laboratories *see* science laboratories
lamp code 469
lamp dimensions 469
lamp flicker *see* flicker
lamp life
    light emitting diodes (LEDs) 77, 420
    for various lamp types **92**
    (*see also* lamp survival factor (LSF))
lamp lumen depreciation factor 61
lamp lumen maintenance factor (LLMF) 72, 72, 418,
        419–20, 422, 469
lamp luminous flux *see* rated luminous flux
lamp performance charts 314–15, **315**
lamp replacement 4–5, 421–2
lamp survival factor (LSF) 42, 72–3, **73**, 418, 419, 422,
        469
lamps
    ambient temperature effects 66, 69, 74, *82*, **315**, 330
    'burning in' 393, 408
    characteristics 71–4, **92**
    disposal 74
    lumen maintenance factor (LLMF) **72**, 72, 418,
        419–20, 422, 469
    operating position 74
    optimal operating temperatures **70**
    output range **92**
    performance charts 314–15, **315**
    unpowered 42
    wattage 469
    (*see also* fluorescent lamps; gas discharge lamps; light
        emitting diodes (LEDs); metal halide lamps;
        tungsten halogen lamps)

landings 156–7
LCMs (lighting control modules) 131
lecture theatres 196
    lighting recommendations **193**
    lines of sight 191
    raked floors 192
LEDs *see* light emitting diodes (LEDs)
LEED (Leadership in Energy and Environmental Design)
        61, 454–5
legal requirements 6–7
    Building Regulations 6, 30, 142–3, 388–9, 452–3
    industrial premises 177–8
    procurement 53
legibility (understanding) 3
LENI (lighting energy numeric indicator) 6–7, 143–7
libraries **168**, **193**, 198
life of lighting installation 469
    (*see also* lamp life)
lift lobbies 156
lifts **46**
light adaptation *see* visual adaptation
light distribution *see* illuminance uniformity
light emitting diodes (LEDs) 469
    cable length 106
    changing to 205
    characteristics **92**
    chemical resistance 301–2, **302**
    cleaning 302
    cold and freezing environments 295
    colour of radiation **75**, 77
    dimming 99, 102, 106, 108, 255
    direct current (DC) power supplies 132
    drivers 105–10
    effect of operating temperature on output 74, 76
    emergency lighting 41, 110–11
    exterior architectural lighting 327
    flicker 182
    heat sinks **75**
    lamp life 77, 420
    lamp lumen maintenance factor (LLMF) **72**
    lamp replacement 421, 422
    low power and high power **75**
    lumen depreciation 72, 76–7
    luminous flux related to ambient temperature **70**,
        315
    maintenance factors (MF) 60–1, 417, 419–21
    manufacturer's data 420–1
    materials **75**
    technology 75–6
    time to abrupt failure 77
    tuneable 112, 194, 249
    useful life 77
    white 77, **92**, 108, 459
light exposure damage 211
light guides 314
light loss factor *see* maintenance factors (MF)
light nuisance *see* glare control; light spill
light output ratio 470
light pipes 27, *28*, 314
light pollution *see* spill light
light rail systems 290
light reflectance value (LRV) 440
light shelves 25
light sources *see* lamps
light spill *see* spill light
light transmission 429, *430*
light trespass *see* light spill
light tubes 27, *28*, 314
lighting calculations 10–11

lighting columns **347**, 347, 362
lighting control modules (LCMs) 131
lighting controls 5, 11–12, 134–50
    alternative products 59
    circadian lighting 142
    commissioning 148–9, 388, 391, 392, 393, 394–8
    dc-rating factors 144–5
    design basis 139–41
    distributed power and control systems 131
    documentation 13
    and emergency lighting 39–40
    and energy consumption 61, 143
    for energy efficiency 142–7
    Enhanced Capital Allowances (ECA) 459
    manual control 134–5
    photocells 136–7
    security lighting 356, 363
    specific locations
        communal residential buildings 248–9
        courts 272–3
        custodial buildings 277
        educational premises 195
        exterior architectural lighting 329–30, 332–3
        exterior lighting 260
        loading bays/docks 162
        places of entertainment 254–5
        road lighting 351–2
    standby energy within 145–6
    sweep-off/cause and effect 395
    total installed parasitic power 477
    for visual effects 141
    (*see also* control gear; daylight linking; dimming
        controls; networked systems; occupancy
        detection)
lighting energy numeric indicator (LENI) 6–7, 143–7,
    452, 470
lighting track 131
lines of sight 191–2
listed buildings 234–5, 379
lithium–ion batteries 37
LLMF (lamp lumen maintenance factor) 72, **72**, 418,
    419–20, 422, 469
LMF (luminaire maintenance factor) 418, 422–3, 470
loading *see* installed loading
loading bays/areas 161–2, 320–1, **321**
local control 102
local lighting 470
    (*see also* task lighting)
localized lighting 174–5, 187, 470
longitudinal uniformity 470
lounges **244**, 247–8, 249
louvres 19, 470
low pressure sodium lamps 86–7, *89*, **92**, 95
low temperatures 294–6
LRV (light reflectance value) 440
LSF (lamp survival factor) 42, 72–3, **73**, 418, 419, 422,
    469
luminaire code 470
luminaire maintenance factor (LMF) 418, 422–3, 470
luminaire mounting height
    glare control **33**, **187**
    hospital wards 223, 224, 225, *226*, 227
    outdoor pools 378
    road lighting 346
    sports lighting 376
luminaire parasitic power 145, 471
luminaire power 471
luminaire standby energy consumption 471
luminaires 114–25, 470

luminaires (*continued*)
    aesthetic appearance 59
    air flow across 66
    alternative products 58–9
    certification 121–2
    chemical resistance **299–300**, 299–301
    classification 122–4
    cleaning 423–4, **424**
    commissioning 387, 392, 393, 398
    coordination with other services 63–8
    electric shock protection 124
    emergency lighting 37–8, 40–1, 117
    ground-recessed 121, 331, 334–5
    impact protection (IK) rating 123, **309**, 309–10, 469
    ingress protection (IP) rating 101, 123, 178, 303,
        304–5, 468, 469
    integration with other services 63, 68
    interior types 114–17
    mounting height 165, **187**, 224, 227
    orientation 187
    period lighting 382–3
    road lighting 123
    safety 242–3
    security lighting 362
    selection 10
    specific locations
        for cold and freezing environments 294–5
        for dusty environments 297–8
        exterior architectural lighting 327, 330–1,
            331–3, 331–6, 385
        historic buildings 382
        hospitals and healthcare buildings 219–20
        for hot and humid environments 296–7
        marine environments 308
        road lighting **345**, 346–7
        sports lighting 366–7
        transport buildings 282–3
        wash-down/clean rooms 306
    standby energy within 145
    surface flammability restriction 124
    vandal resistance 310
    vibration effects 308–9
    water submersion 302–5, 306–7
    zonal rated 297–8
    (*see also* exterior luminaires; floodlights; lamps)
luminance 471
luminance contrast *see* contrast
luminance diversity 34, 465
luminance factor 416
luminance measurement 415
luminance meters 409–10
luminance uniformity 478
luminescence 42, 96–7
luminous ceilings 175–6
luminous efficacy 71–2, **92**, 471
luminous environment 471
    (*see also* wellbeing)
luminous façades 336–7
luminous flux 71, 471
luminous intensity 471
luminous intensity distribution 465

machinery
    integral lighting system 468
    stroboscopic effects 181–2
magnifiers 188
maintained emergency luminaire 472
maintained illuminance 417, 472
maintained luminance 472

maintenance 4–5, 28, 417–25
    alternative products 60
    designing for 418–19
    emergency lighting 47–8
    security lighting 363
    surface finishes 442–3
    transport installations 282–3
    (see also cleaning; lamp replacement)
maintenance cycle 423, 472
maintenance factors (MF) 60–1, 417–21, 472
    constant illuminance adjustment 137–8
    determination of 417–23
    exterior lighting 424
    light emitting diodes (LEDs) 60–1, 417, 419–21
    road lighting **345**
maintenance schedule 47, 417, 472
manual switches 134–5, 254–5, 394
manufacturer's data 420–1
marine environments 307–8
materials recycling 62
materials storage 184–6
mean cylindrical illuminance 231
measurement methods 410–14
mechanical checks 392
medical rooms **168**
meeting rooms **168**
mesopic vision 472
mess rooms 186
metal halide lamps 83–6, **92**
metering 143, 397, 453
mimic diagrams 184
mixed traffic 472
modelling
    in museums and art galleries 213
    in places of entertainment 253
    in places of worship 231
    (see also facial recognition)
modular cabling systems 128, 129
mosques see places of worship
motion detectors see occupancy detection; passive infrared
        (PIR) detectors
motor traffic (motorized traffic) 472
moving stairways and walkways 46, 285
museums and art galleries 210–17
    access for maintenance 215
    balance of lighting (exhibits/general lighting) 212
    colour rendering 211–12
    conservation of exhibits 211, 217
    daylight and windows 210
    emergency lighting **44**, 214
    flexibility in lighting 215, 217
    in historic buildings 379, 382, 383
    out of hours activities 214
    security and emergency 214
    shadows and modelling in 213, 216–17
    showcase lighting 216–17
    three-dimensional displays 215–16
    veiling reflections 214, 216
    visual adaptation in 212
    wall mounted displays 215
music rooms **193**, 199

National Calculation Method 453
natural light see daylighting
networked systems
    commissioning 394, 396–7
    emergency lighting 148
    security of the installation 393
    smart cities 352

networked systems (continued)
    (see also wireless control systems)
night working 319
nightclubs see clubs
no sky line 23
noise from control gear 100
nominal lamp wattage 472
non-daylight time usage 472
non-insulated drivers 109
non-maintained emergency luminaire 40, 43, 472
non-visual effects 16–17
Northern Ireland 388, 452
nursing homes 249
O&M (operations and maintenance) media 399–400
obtrusive light 473
    (see also spill light)
occupancy dependency factor 473
occupancy de-rating factor 144–5
occupancy detection 5, 135–6, 474
    commissioning 395
    in common building areas 155, 159, 161
    communal residential buildings 245, 248
    courts 273
    disability access 234
    places of entertainment 255
    security lighting 363
occupant controls see manual switches
occupant health and wellbeing 2, 16–17, 171, 455–8
occupant training 403
offices 163–76
    ceiling height 165–6
    cove lighting 175
    daylighting 165, 176
    direct lighting 171–2
    direct/indirect lighting 173–4
    display screens 164–5
    glare control 170
    illuminance recommendations 168–70
    indirect lighting 172–3
    light source colour properties 170
    localized lighting 174–5
    luminous ceilings 175–6
    obstructions 166
    obstructions in 166
    performance verification 410–11
    supplementary task lighting 175
    surface finishes 166–7
    wellness 171
oil refineries see chemicals and chemical vapours; exterior
        workplace lighting
OLED (organic light emitting diodes) 105–10
opalescent transmission 429, 430
open area lighting (anti-panic lighting) 32, 473
open plan offices **168**, 410–11
operating theatres 228–9
operating time 473
operations and maintenance (O&M) media 399–400
operator training 401–3
outdoor drivers 110
outdoor spaces see exterior architectural lighting; exterior
        lighting; exterior workplace lighting; urban
        centres
overheating control 18, 19
over-lighting 60

packaging materials 62
painted surfaces **442**
paintings
    conservation of exhibits 211

paintings (*continued*)
    lighting 215
panel lighting 314
parasitic load 145–6, 147
parks **357**, 361
particle size/concentration (dust) **306**
partitions 166, **166**
passenger/train interface (PTI) 287
passive infrared (PIR) detectors 135, 473
pathways/pavements *see* footpaths
pedestrian crossings 343
pedestrian streets 344
performance *see* energy efficiency; luminous efficacy;
        visual performance
performance verification 406–16
    competency 407
    equipment for 407
    exterior lighting 407, 413
    illuminance variation measurement 414–15
    instrumentation 408–10
    methods of measurement 410–14
    open plan areas 410–11
    preparing for the survey 407–8
    task areas 410–14
perimeter fences **356**, 359
period lighting 382–3
petrochemical plant *see* chemicals and chemical vapours;
        exterior workplace lighting
phase-cut dimmers 108, *109*
phosphor coatings 81
photocell control
    road lighting 351
    security lighting 363
    sensor calibration 394–5
    (*see also* daylight linking)
photocells 136, *137*
photoluminescence 96–7, 473
photo-luminescent signs 42
photometer/photometry 58, 473
photopic vision 473
picture lights 383
pigments 428–9
PIR (passive infrared) detectors 135, 473
places of entertainment 35–6, 251–68
    bars and pubs **256**, 257–9, 267
    character and atmosphere 251–2
    clubs 264–5
    colour appearance 253
    daylighting 253
    emergency lighting **44**, 262
    energy efficiency 254
    exterior lighting 259–62
    function rooms 263, *264*
    illuminance recommendations 256–62
    interior design 252–3
    lighting control 254–5
    modelling, glare and sparkle 253–4
    restaurants and eating areas 258, 262–3
    retail space in 267
    surface finishes 252–3
    theatres and concert halls 265–7
places of worship 230–40
    ancillary areas 236
    architectural considerations 239–40
    areas for prayer and service 235, **236**
    daylighting 231–2
    general lighting 237–8
    lighting for people with disabilities 233–4
    listed buildings 234–5

places of worship (*continued*)
    modelling 231
    multi-purpose rooms 236–7
    obstructions 239
    surface reflectance 238
    task lighting 230–1, 238–9
Planckian radiator (blackbody) 93–4, 474
plant rooms **46**, 162, **186**
plastic materials
    chemical resistance **299–300**, 300
    cleaning **424**
    high temperatures 297
platform edges 287
play areas **244**, 248
plug-in (electrical) connectors 129, *130*
pole-mounted (external) luminaires 336
police custody suites *see* custodial buildings
pollution *see* chemicals and chemical vapours; dusty
        environments; spill light
polycarbonate materials 297
polyester powder coat, cleaning **424**
portable luminaires 242
ports 289
post-completion checks and adjustments 404
post-occupancy evaluation 14
post-top luminaires 118, *119*
power demand *see* energy consumption
power distribution *see* electrical wiring
power factor 71
power factor correction 102
Power over Ethernet (PoE) 132–3
power range, for various lamp types **92**
power supply 126–33
cabling systems 39, 128, *129*
commissioning 392
direct current 131–2
distributed power and control systems 131
electrical connections 129–31
emergency lighting 37–8
Power over Ethernet (PoE) 132–3
    (*see also* standby power supplies)
practical emergency lamp flux 474
pre-commissioning certificate 393
presence detection *see* occupancy detection
principal area 473
prisons *see* custodial buildings
privacy and security 18
private houses *see* domestic security lighting
professional conduct/standards 53–7
project brief 8–9
project handover 14, 148–9, 388, 399–404
project reports 13–14
projector lighting 314
psychological effects 3
    (*see also* visual comfort; wellbeing)
public spaces
    parks **357**, 361
    public amenity areas 349–50
    security lighting **357**, 360–1
pubs and bars **256**, 257–9
pulse width modulation (PWM) 102

quaysides 286, 289

racking (storage) 185
radiant flux *see* luminous flux
radiation damage 211
radioluminescence 97

railway sidings, marshalling yards and goods yards 322, **323**
railways 287
raked floors 192
ramps 155–6
rated luminous flux 474
reading lighting 227
reception areas, emergency lighting **46**
reception desks 152, 221, 222
recessed luminaires
    thermal insulation restriction 124
    treated as direct lighting 173
    (*see also* ground-recessed luminaires)
reciprocating machinery 181–2
recreation areas **244**, 248
    (*see also* sports lighting)
recycling 62
reference ballast 474
reference surface 474
reflectance *see* surface reflectance
reflections *see* veiling reflections
reflectometer 474
refreshment areas 160
refuge areas 157, 219
refurbishment 379, 387
regulation 139
Regulatory Reform (Fire Safety) Order 2005 30
remote communication (control) 102
    (*see also* CMS (central management systems);
        networked systems)
remote lighting techniques 314
reprographics rooms **168**
residential homes *see* communal residential buildings
Responsible Person 30, 475
rest mode 475
restaurants 35–6, **168**, 258, 262–3
restrike time 74
retail premises 200–9
    accent lighting 204, 206, *207*
    daylighting 201–2
    display lighting 207–8, **208**, **209**
    emergency lighting **44**
    energy efficiency 203
    general lighting 204–5
    highlighting merchandise 203
    illuminance recommendations 203–4
    integration with the interior design 202–3
    light source colour properties 204
    nature of merchandise 202
    obstructions in 202
    self-pay terminals 203
    store entrances and shop fronts 205–6
retail space in places of entertainment 267
retractive switches 102, 136
RGB luminaires 108
RIBA Plan of Work 2013 14
risk assessments 13
    (*see also* fire risk assessment; high risk task area
        lighting)
road lighting 340–9
    areas adjacent to the carriageway 343–4, **344**
    bends in the road 347–8
    conflict areas **342**, 342, **343**
    design fundamentals 344–6
    glare control 123, 348
    lighting classes 340–4
    lighting control 351–2
    luminaire layout 346–7
    luminaires 117–18, 123, **345**

road lighting (*continued*)
    pedestrian crossings **343**
    pedestrian streets 343–4, 344
    performance verification 407, 413
    residential and minor roads 343–4, **344**, 348–9
    set-back of lighting columns **347**, 347
    traffic routes 340–2
    tunnel lighting 350–1
roller blinds 20
rooflights 26, 178, *179*, 475
room surface cleaning 424, 442–3
    (*see also* surface reflectance)
room surface maintenance factor (RSMF) 418, 419, 423,
    475
rotating machinery 181–2
rugby (union and league) 374, **374**
run-up time 73–4, **92**

safe disposal 62
safety 4
    communal residential buildings 242–3
    electrical 124, 389
    industrial premises 182
safety extra low voltage (SELV) 109, 220, 303, 305
safety lighting *see* emergency safety lighting; security
    lighting
safety signs 33–5, 475
    externally illuminated 467
    internally illuminated 469
    maintenance and inspection 47
    unpowered 42
    (*see also* emergency signage)
salt exposure 299–302
    (*see also* marine environments)
sanitary facilities *see* toilets
scene setting 135, 396, 475
school boarding houses *see* communal residential
    buildings
school dormitories **244**
school streets 198, *199*
science laboratories **193**, 197
Scotland 388, 452
scotopic observer 475
screen reflections *see* veiling reflections
sculpture 215–16
seasonal checks 404
secondary reflector luminaires 119
secure units *see* custodial buildings
security 4
    communal residential buildings 243–4
    custodial buildings 275, 280
    exterior lighting 259–60
    museums and art galleries 214
    and windows 18
security lighting 354–64
    ambient light levels 355
    area lighting 358
    building façades 358
    car parks 361
    CCTV surveillance 280, 355–6
    crime risk 355
    entrances and gatehouses 360
    glare control 357, 361
    glare-lighting 359, **360**
    illuminance recommendations **356**, 356, **357**, 361
    light source colour properties 357
    lighting columns 362
    lighting control 363
    luminaires 362

security lighting (*continued*)
    maintenance 363
    obstructions 354
    perimeter fences 359
    private houses 361–2
    public spaces **357**, 360–1
    secure areas 358
    service stations and mini-marts 361
self testing, emergency luminaires 48, 111
self-contained emergency luminaire 37, 40, 48, 110–11, 475
self-pay terminals 203
SELV (safety extra low voltage) 109, 220, 303, 305
semi-cylindrical illuminance **344**, 475
semi-direct lighting 475
semi-indirect lighting 475
seminar rooms 198
service spaces 162
service stations **357**, 361
services in ceiling voids 63–5
shading 19–21, 382, 398
shielding angle 476
shops *see* retail premises
showcase lighting 216–17
showers 160, 223, 243
shutters 19
sick bays 160
signage
    light emitting diodes (LEDs) 72
    safety signs 33–5, 475
    visual impairment 282
    (*see also* emergency signage)
Signs Directive (92/58/EEC) 30
sky glow *see* light spill
skylight 476
slave (emergency) luminaires *see* centrally supplied
        emergency luminaires
smart cities 352
smoke detectors 65
smoking areas 261
Society of Light and Lighting Code of Conduct. 54
solar gain
    glazing-based solutions 21
    overheating control 18, 19
    places of worship 232
solar glare 17–18
    (*see also* glare control)
solar radiation 476
solar shading 19
    automatic 20, 398
    historic buildings 382
source (light source) 476
    (*see also* lamps)
space classification **140**, 140–1
spacing to height ratio 476
SPD (suspended particle) glazing 21
specifications 12–13
spectral luminous efficiency *see* luminous flux
specular reflection 427–8
speculative factory units 186–7
spherical illuminance 476
spill light 6, 476
    environmental assessment rating 454
    exterior architectural lighting 330, 331
    exterior lighting 454, 455
    exterior workplace lighting 319, 324
    security lighting 356, 358
    sports lighting 368–9
    transport buildings 288–9

sports broadcasting 367
sports halls 375–6
sports lighting 365–78
    athletics 370
    classes of lighting 366
    colour rendering **370–5**
    cricket 371, **372**
    emergency lighting 368
    fitness training 373
    five-a-side football 372, **373**
    glare rating **370–5**
    illuminance recommendations **370–5**
    indoor arenas 376–7
    multi-use sports halls 375–6
    playing area 366
    stadia **45**, 376
    standard of play and viewing distance 365–6
    swimming pools *see* swimming pools
    for television 367
    tennis 373, **374**
sports stadia **45**, 376
spotlights 116, 476
    classification 122
    glare control 213
    showcase lighting 217
sprinkler systems 64
stadia 376
staff accommodation *see* communal residential buildings
staff changing rooms/showers 159, 160
stainless steel
    chemical resistance **299–300**, 300
    cleaning **424**
    surface reflectance **442**
stair lifts 157
staircases 156–8, **244**, 245, *246*, 259
    (*see also* steps)
stakeholders 9
standards 7–8, 121
standby energy consumption 145–6, 147, 471
standby generators 38, 313–14, 368
standby lighting 31, 36, 284, 477
    hospitals and healthcare buildings 219
    places of entertainment 262
    sports lighting 368
standby power supplies 38, 313–14, 368
steps 259, 260, 282
storage facilities 184–6
storage lockers 161
store rooms 161, **186**
stray light *see* light spill
street lighting 344
stroboscopic effects 181–2, 188, 233, 476
student residences 246
    (*see also* communal residential buildings)
study bedrooms 241–2, **244**, 246, *247*
substitutions 392
sunlight 477
supplementary task lighting *see* task lighting
surface (building) mounted luminaires 333–4
surface (ground) mounted luminaires 335–6
surface deterioration and maintenance 442–3
surface finishes 442
    educational premises 192
    in offices 166–7
    places of entertainment 252–3
    (*see also* cleaning)
surface reflectance 440–3, 474
    area weighted reflectance 441
    diffuse reflection 428–9, 440

surface reflectance (*continued*)
   glossy and semi-matte reflection 429
   hospitals and healthcare buildings 228
   for indirect lighting 172
   light reflecting properties 427–30
   measurement 415
   office surfaces **166**
   places of worship 238
   road lighting 345
   room surface maintenance factor (RSMF) 418, 419,
      423
   and security lighting 354, 358, 360
   specular reflection 427–8
   various building materials 441, *442*
surrounding area 477
survival factor *see* lamp survival factor (LSF)
suspended particle (SPD) glazing 21
sustainability 5–6, 53, 60–2
swimming pools 374, **375**, 377–8
   emergency lighting **46**
   luminaires 305, 367
   underwater lighting 303, 378
switch rooms 46
switches *see* manual switches
synagogues *see* places of worship

task area 477
task lighting 175
   background area 279
   high risk task areas 33, 273, 468
   industrial premises 187
   luminaires 117
   minimum height of luminaire above task 175
   performance verification 412
   places of worship 230–1, 238–9
   transport buildings 285
tea points 160
teaching spaces 191–2
technical design 10–14
technology 5
telemanagement *see* CMS (central management systems)
television 367
   (*see also* CCTV surveillance)
temperature *see* ambient temperature effects; cold
      and freezing environments; hot and humid
      environments
tendering procedures 56–7
tennis 373, **374**
terraces 260–1
testing
   electrical checks 392–3
   emergency lighting 48–9, 397–8
   (*see also* performance verification)
theatres 35–6, 265–7
thermoluminescence 97
tinted glazing 21
tinted solar control films 21
toilets 158–9, **186**
   communal residential buildings **244**
   emergency lighting 46
   hospitals 223
   places of entertainment 259
total energy used for lighting 477
total installed charging power 477
total installed parasitic power 477
track systems 131
traffic lane 477
traffic routes 340–2
training 388, 401–3

training rooms **168**
trams 290
transformers for LV incandescent lamps 103
transitions *see* visual adaptation
translucent materials 429, *430*
transmittance 477
transport buildings 279–93
   access, installation and maintenance 282–3
   accessible design 281–2
   bicycle routes and structures 292
   boarding and alighting points 286, 290
   bus and coach stations 291
   check-ins/counters/information desks 284–5
   concourses 284
   daylighting 291
   design priorities and strategies 280–1
   emergency lighting 283–4
   escalators and moving walkways 285, *286*
   hazardous environments 280
   lighting recommendations 284–92
   maintenance 282–3
   ports and harbours 289
   railways 287
   risk assessment 283
   trams and street running systems 290
T-ratings **312**
treatment rooms **46**
tritium powered signs 42
tungsten halogen lamps 79–80, **92**
   lamp replacement 421
   transformers for 103
tungsten lamps 78–9
tunnel lighting 350–1

underground cabling 386
underwater lighting 303, 378
   (*see also* water submersion)
unified glare rating (UGR) 477
uniformity (luminance, illuminance) 478
uninterruptible power supplies (UPS) 38
upward flux ratio 478
upward light output ratio 478
upward light ratio 478
urban centres 349–50
usable daylight index (UDI) 191
useful data 478
utilance (for a reference surface) 478
utility rooms **244**
utilization factor (for a reference surface) 478

vandal resistance 119, **309**, 310–11, 362
   (*see also* impact protection (IK) rating)
vehicle entrances 360
veiling reflections 164–5, 478
   control rooms 182
   maximum luminance 169–70
   museums and art galleries 214, 216
   wall mounted displays 215
   windowed control rooms 184
Venetian blinds 20
ventilation ducts and grills 64
vibration effects 308–9
view out 17, 210, 453, 455
visual acuity (visual resolution) 478
visual adaptation 2–3, 212, 253, 279, 281, 443, 461
visual aids 188, 192
visual comfort 453–4, 455, 478
visual communication 231
   (*see also* facial recognition)

visual contrast *see* contrast
visual effects 141
visual field (field of vision) 479
visual impairment 190, 233, 281–2
visual inspection 188, 398
visual perception 430–1, 443
visual performance 479
visual task 479
volatile organic compounds (VOCs) 302

waiting areas 155
wall mounted displays 215
wall mounted luminaires 114
    burn risk 234
    and ceiling height 165
    hospital ward lighting 225, *226*
    industrial premises 184
wall washers 116, *117*, 206
wallpacks 120
walls
    minimum illuminance *167*, 169
    surface reflectance **166**, **442**
warehouses **45**, 184–6
wash hand basins 158
wash-down/clean rooms 305–7
Waste Electrical and Electronic Equipment (WEEE)
        Regulations 2013 62, 74
water submersion 302–5, 306–7
    (*see also* marine environments; underwater lighting)
wattage 469
wayfinding 280
    (*see also* legibility (understanding); signage)

WELL Building Standard (WELL) 455–8
wellbeing 2, 16–17, 171, 455–8
wheelchair users 234
    (*see also* accessible design)
white light emitting diodes 77, **92**, 108, 459
whiteboards 196
wildlife conservation 385
window blinds *see* blinds
windowed control rooms 184
windows 24–6, 479
    blinds 18, 20, **166**
    daylight penetration depth 24
    glare control 17–18, 21
    light shelves 25
    light-boxes 337
    museums and art galleries 210
    places of worship 232
    privacy and security 18
    view out 17, 210, 453, 455
    (*see also* daylighting; glazing)
windy environments 308
wireless control systems 102, 255
    commissioning 393, 394
    signal strength surveys 394
witness testing 400–1
work plane (working plane) 479
workbenches 187, 412
workplace 479
Workplace (Health, Safety and Welfare) Regulations 1992
7, 176
Workplace Directive (89/654/EEC) 30
workstation 479